The Concept of Matter

CONTRIBUTORS

JOSEPH BOBIK

A. R. CAPONIGRI

V. C. CHAPPELL

LEONARD J. ESLICK

HERBERT FEIGL

MILTON FISK

JOHN J. FITZGERALD

MARIE BOAS HALL

N. R. HANSON

MARY B. HESSE

ROBERT O. JOHANN, S.J.

CZESLAW LEJEWSKI

N. LOBKOWICZ

NORBERT M. LUYTEN, O.P.

RICHARD P. MCKEON

ERNAN MC MULLIN

EDWARD MANIER

CECIL B. MAST

CHARLES W. MISNER

JOSEPH OWENS, C.SS.R.

HARRY A. NIELSEN

RICHARD RORTY

KENNETH SAYRE

WILFRID SELLARS

JOHN E. SMITH

JAMES A. WEISHEIPL, O.P.

ALLAN B. WOLTER, O.F.M.

A. E. WOODRUFF

$T\!b$

Concept of Matter

EDITED BY

ERNAN McMULLIN

UNIVERSITY OF NOTRE DAME PRESS

ACKNOWLEDGMENTS

This book is a record of a conference on "The concept of matter" held at the University of Notre Dame from September 5 to September 9, 1961. The papers for the conference were contributed in advance and circulated among those invited to participate. Written criticisms and suggestions were solicited, and several of the papers were modified by their authors in the light of these advance discussions. At the conference itself, the papers were presented only in summary and a formal comment on each was read by one of the participants. Each paper was then discussed in detail by the group as a whole (numbering thirty people), and the proceedings were audio-taped.

After the conference, most of the essayists rewrote their papers in the light of the points raised at the conference. The papers, as we have them here, are thus the final product of a long process of dialogue. Two extra papers (those by Drs. Hesse and Woodruff) were added subsequently, as well as the comment by Dr. Feigl, reprinted from *The Philosophy of Science*. In addition, some of the formal comments given at the conference have been included, though limitations of space unfortunately made it impossible to reproduce all of them.

Finally, sections of the conference discussion were transcribed from tape, and some edited excerpts are reproduced here in order to give the reader some idea of what went on. Choice of the excerpts was necessarily a very subjective matter on the part of the editor; almost any section could have been chosen. The aim was to find the pieces that would best illuminate the papers, or present some point not raised in the papers, or illustrate a fundamental disagreement between the participants. For, as the reader will soon note, there *were* disagreements of a deep-rooted philosophical sort, as well as differences on questions of historical, philosophical and scientific detail. But it was interesting to notice at the conference itself a consensus develop on many issues that at the outset seemed hopelessly controverted. We hope that the reader may, as he works through the book, come to share, at however many removes, in the excitement and tension of the original dialogue.

In addition to the essayists and commentators whose work is reproduced below, the following also took part in the conference discussions: Robert

Cohen (Physics, Boston University); Catesby Taliaferro (Mathematics, Notre Dame); Drs. John Oesterle and Ralph McInerny (Philosophy, University of Notre Dame); Father Edward O'Connor, C.S.C. (Theology, Notre Dame). Three of the essayists were unable to attend the conference: Drs. Lejewski and Hall, and Father Luyten, O.P.

Two points of editorial usage may be noted. The phrase, 'primary matter', was agreed upon as the best contemporary rendering of the Greek *proté hylé,* and this has been made uniform throughout the papers. Secondly, typography has been pressed into the service of semantics in a way to which readers of American philosophy are becoming accustomed. Single quotes are used for *mention* only, i.e. in order to *name* the expression they enclose. Double quotes are used not only for quoting material, but also (in the case of words or phrases) to indicate a *special* sense of the expression they enclose. Italics are used either for emphasis, or to indicate the foreign character of the expression italicized, or lastly, to warn that the italicized term is to be understood as referring to the *concept* associated with it, instead of to its normal concrete referent. (Thus, for example, one would use italics to say that *matter* underwent an evolution in the seventeenth century.)

Our thanks must go first and foremost to the National Science Foundation, without whose aid the publication of this book would have been impossible. Their grant of a substantial portion of the printing cost encouraged us to proceed. Secondly, to the University of Notre Dame which supported the original conference, and made its resources available for the preparation of this manuscript. Lastly, to the many who aided so generously along the way: Paul Schrantz, Janice Coffield, Ruth Hagerty, Mary Mast, Sr. M. Jeremiah, I.H.M., Sr. M. Petrus, R.S.M., who helped with the large task of typing and mimeographing; Joseph Bellina, who took charge of the audio-taping; Patricia Crosson who compiled the Index; and the staff of the University Press, especially Charles Mc Collester, for their patience, planning and perseverance.

E. Mc M.

CONTENTS

Contents

PART FIVE

MODERN SCIENCE: THE "DEMATERIALIZATION"
OF MATTER

It would be difficult to find a greater distance between any two terms than that which separates 'matter' in the Greek-medieval tradition and the technical signification, suitably expressed in mathematical symbols, that the word bears in science today.

John Dewey in "Antinaturalism in extremis", *Naturalism and the Human Spirit,* ed. Y. Krikorian, New York, 1944, p. 3.

This concept (matter) *has hardly changed from the times of Leucippus to the beginning of the twentieth century: an impenetrable* something, *which fills completely certain regions of space and which persists through time even when it changes its location.*

Milic Capek in *The Philosophical Impact of Modern Physics,* New York, 1961, p. 54.

INTRODUCTION:

THE CONCEPT OF MATTER

Ernan Mc Mullin

§1 *Foreword*

The notion of a "matter" that underlies can reasonably be said to be the oldest conceptual tool in the Western speculative tradition. Scarcely a single major philosopher in the short but incredibly fertile period that separates Thales from Whitehead has omitted it from the handful of basic ideas with which he set out to make Nature more intelligible to man. In many instances, ancient and modern, an initial judgement about the role to be attributed to matter has been decisive in orienting a philosophic system as a whole. So that to trace the story of the concept of matter is almost to trace the story of philosophy itself. In addition, this concept played a central part in the complex story of the dissociation of what we today call "natural science" from its parent, natural philosophy. The new physics (like the old) was concerned with motion, but its practitioners were less interested in definitions of motion than in the charting of the motions of different bodies and their reduction to a few abstract quantitative formulae of great predictive power. The optimistic belief that such a reduction could be brought about depended on the existence of an intrinsic "motion-factor" peculiar to each body, one that could somehow be operationally defined just as volume and velocity could. In the long search for this factor—a search which, as we shall see, is not yet at an end—one older concept played an indispensable role. Mass (as the motion-factor came to be called) was first grasped as "the quantity of matter". The subsequent history of this definition and of the gradual sundering of the concepts of matter and mass is enormously significant because of the light it can throw on the relationship between philosophic and scientific concepts generally.

For both of these reasons, an extensive analysis of the concept of matter may be expected to yield much fruit. In the essays, comments and discussions gathered together in this book, philosophers, physicists and historians of science have collaborated in presenting a complex and detailed picture. Their concern on the whole was not so much with the history of ideas as with substantive questions of present philosophic and scientific concern. To

1

attack these questions through analytic case-studies of historical examples seems by far the best approach in this instance. What we are interested in, then, is not so much what Plato, for instance, said about matter—though an exact knowledge of that will be indispensable to our quest—but rather whether the reasons he gives for invoking his particular sort of "material principle", in the attempt to relate the worlds of mind and sense, retain their validity for us today. Each philosophical essay in this collection is centered around the work of a particular philosopher or school; each attempts to find the sort of question to which the notion (or notions) of matter responded in this work, and to assess the meaningfulness of the question asked as well as the value of the answer given. The writers themselves represent very different schools of thought. Perhaps the most fascinating aspect of this book is the enormous variation it displays in the sheer *doing* of philosophy. The manifest differences in idiom and approach between the different philosophical articles mirror some fundamental disagreements as to what the task of philosophy itself is. The essays touching on modern science here, on the other hand, have a more negative and more easily-accomplished task: to show how and why the concept of matter faded out of science, leaving only its grin, so to speak, behind.

This raises a question about the over-all balance of the essays. A quick glance at the Table of Contents will show two things, both perhaps unexpected in a book under this title. The first is that among the essays as a whole the preponderance of the topics is philosophical, and second, that among the philosophical essays, the emphasis is upon Greek philosophy. The reason for the first of these is not just the well-known reluctance of scientists to write about science instead of doing science, nor even the fact that the career of the concept of matter in philosophy has been so much longer and so much more diverse. The reason is very simply that the concept of matter, as we shall see, plays no *direct* part in the doing of science today. It still plays a part, albeit a tenuous and difficult-to-define one, in *talking about* science and its implications. As for the emphasis on Greek origins, the reason here too is a simple one. One can distinguish more easily between the diverse themes associated with the notion of matter in modern philosophy if one sees how these themes came to be enunciated in the first place. And all of them—except one, perhaps—were first enunciated by the Greeks.

In this introductory essay, our task will be two-fold. First, we will try to gather together some of the threads of the philosophical discussions that follow to see what sort of pattern, if any, they make. Second, we shall review in somewhat more detail the relationship between the concepts of matter and of mass and the elimination from science of the concept of matter, thus bringing together in one place explicit conclusions and implicit suggestions scattered throughout the essays in the latter part of the book. But before we begin this, a couple of troublesome questions concerning the title of our enquiry: 'The concept of matter', must be cleared out of the way first.

"The" concept of matter: First, one might well ask about the propriety of the 'the' here. Surely there have been *many* concepts of matter, some of them scarcely connected with the others? What is the common bond to be? There is no *word* that we can trace etymologically through an evolution of senses, as we can in the case of 'mass'. Before Aristotle's time, there was not even an accepted word for the philosophical concept of matter, so what do we mean here by talking of "the concept of matter" in Thales or Plato? In the case of many other terms, like 'man', we can agree on the class of entities to which the term applies; what Thales meant by 'man' (in the sense of: what referents the term designated) is the same as what any other philosopher has meant. So that to trace the concept of man is much simpler, because one has only to ask how this *known* reference-class has been understood by different philosophers, i.e. what basic properties are the entities called 'man' said to have in common? But in the case of the concept of matter, there is no agreed reference-class of this sort; not only is there not agreement as to which entities ought to be called "material", but the term, 'matter', itself is frequently assumed not to be the name of a designatable entity.

In these circumstances, the criteria of continuity must needs be much looser. The continuity is one of *problem*, not of word nor of referent. The concept of matter responds in the first instance to a rather more sophisticated need than does the average non-philosophical concept. It has a descriptive or an explanatory role of a very general sort; it may be predicated of an entity not on the basis of some intrinsic property the entity possesses but rather because of the role the entity plays e.g. in a specific change. The matter-category appears first in the context of the discussions of change and the constitution of things, then in the related question of individuation, then in making a distinction between two orders of being, then in constructing a theory of knowledge connecting the two orders. . . . All of these are inter-related, and it is plausible to suppose that a similar ontological factor may play connected roles in each case. Yet this assumption, as we shall see, can be a mistaken one, and it is all too easy to assume that simply because one uses the same term, 'matter', in a myriad different philosophical contexts, the same factor is designated in each instance. The concept is defined by the problem to which it initially responds, by its specified interrelations with a large number of other very general concepts used in the context of the same problem. Thus it is a matter of no small difficulty to establish that the "same" concept of matter answers to two different philosophical needs, e.g. that a

3

"matter" which acts as a substratum of change could also be the "matter" which individuates. This is a problem underlying the whole enquiry of this book, and it is one of which the reader ought constantly be aware.

Matter and the concept of matter: The second preliminary question could be put this way: what is the difference between discussing matter and discussing the concept of matter? if the latter signifies the former, could it not be said that our study reduces to a study of matter? and if this is so, is it not a history of physics that is called for, since physics is, after all, the systematic study of matter, in at least one sense of that term? There is an important misunderstanding here. Even if one ignores the other senses of the term, assuming that 'matter' designates in some fashion the objects which scientists study, it is by no means true that the study of matter is equivalent to the study of the concept of matter, or that some new advance in the former will necessarily affect the latter. Matter is an autonomous concrete entity—we are prescinding for the moment from the various questions about its precise ontological status—whereas the concept of matter is relative to a specific conceptual-linguistic system. To discover more about matter, one finds out first what entities the term designates and then proceeds to analyze these entities by the appropriate empirical methods (e.g. physics and chemistry). To discover more about the concept of matter, one turns rather towards some particular language and perhaps towards some particular user of it, and asks: given the total context of this system and the concrete situations it was intended to describe or explain, what could he have meant by 'matter'? The term, 'meant', here has its usual ambiguity as between sense and reference. But the question is not: what entities did he designate by the term 'matter'? rather it is: what did the term convey to his mind? or more concretely: what minimal properties did he suppose anything qualifying as "matter" to have?

The two quests are connected in this way, and in this way only. A user of the term, 'matter', by an empirical study of the entities he calls "matter", might conceivably be led to *modify* his original nominal definition of the term in the light of his discoveries. For instance, if 'matter' has meant for him: something impenetrable and capable of affecting the senses, and he discovers that what he calls "matter" is not really impenetrable or that in certain circumstances it is not perceptible, he has an option. Either he will modify his original definition in order to retain the same referents under the term, by finding some other defining property for them, or else he will retain his original definition and concede that it does not apply to the class of entities to which he formerly supposed it to apply. In the former instance, the study of matter has affected the concept of matter, so to speak. But such instances are rarer than they might seem to be.

4

When Descartes discovered his law of refraction or when Boyle discovered his laws of chemical combination, do we assume that "the concept of matter" was altered thereby? By no means. Our understanding of matter (i.e. the material world) was substantially deepened by these discoveries. But this gives no reason to suppose that the criteria on the basis of which Descartes or Boyle recognized an object as "material" were affected too. If one could show, however, that on the basis of this and similar discoveries Descartes was led to postulate that "matter is extension", i.e. that the criterion for the "materiality" of an entity will simply be its extended character, then, of course, it would follow that Descartes' *concept* of matter, his idea of what it was that qualified an entity as a *material* entity, has been affected also. Or again, if one could show that recent results in field theory have led to a certain scepticism about the notion of a "material substratum", one is relating empirical results to implications for the general concept in a proper manner. But this mutual relevance cannot be assumed; it must be shown in each instance. If we were to take "the concept of matter" in the so-called "comprehensive" sense that would make every discovery about matter relevant to the concept of matter, our enquiry would become completely unmanageable.

To ask about the concept of matter, then, is to ask how the term is (or was) used in some specified context, either "ordinary-language" or technical. The uses of 'matter' in ordinary language are not very informative, because the term is a quasi-transcendental one in modern usage and is quite lacking in sharpness. We are interested here in the technical uses to which it has been put in various philosophies. It has long since ceased to have a technical use in science, and although it is still commonly availed of by scientists in talking about what they do (and especially what they do it *to*), their usage here is either an ordinary-language one or else a quasi-technical one borrowed from some philosophy.

The ambiguity we have just been discussing arises only when 'matter' is used as a cover-term for the objects studied by physics and chemistry. This is the commonest use of the term today, but it should be noted that the sense it gives is not equivalent to *any* of the senses of 'matter' in Greek philosophy. It is not an explanatory use; it is scarcely even a descriptive use, as a rule. The term, '*hylé*', was taken over by Aristotle from ordinary language (where it meant 'timber') and was made to serve as anchor in a complex conceptual analysis of change. In all of the many senses Aristotle gave it (except perhaps one), it was a "second-level" term, i.e. it did not designate a concrete entity in virtue of some intrinsic property, as, for example, 'man' or 'musical' would. It might designate a concrete entity relative to a specific change ("matter of this change"), or to a specific predication ("matter of this predication"), or to a specific explanation ("matter-cause of this particular explanation"). Or else, it might not designate a concrete entity as a "whole", so to speak, but rather, an intrinsic "principle" of that entity.

Such "second-level" terms are notoriously difficult to define; instead of seeking a simple definition in terms of intrinsic behaviorally-related properties like rationality and animality, one is forced to introduce the entire conceptual system of which the *definiendum* is a part. Aristotle's notion of "matter" as a substratum of change, for instance, can be understood only in terms of his ideas of substance, of predication, of form, and so forth. It cannot be "abstracted" from a few concrete instances of change in some absolute way, and then contrasted with form, "abstracted" in an equally absolute way. To know *precisely* what is meant by 'matter' here, one has to have recourse to the *total context* of Aristotle's philosophy, because to *state* what is meant will involve complex terms like 'real', 'distinct', 'substance', 'continuance', themselves incapable of any other than a systemic definition. If this fundamental point be ignored—as it often is—our quest in this book can easily be misconstrued.

It is not as though there is an absolute constituent or aspect of the world called 'matter', which different philosophers have described in ways more or less apposite. This would do if we were talking of hydrogen or nebulae. But for a "second-level" notion, a somewhat different account is required. The "matter" the philosopher singles out is constituted (not ontologically, of course, but epistemologically) by the conceptual system that defines it. Does this mean that there are as many "matters" as there are different systems? This would be the opposite error. It is possible for different philosophies to focus upon the "same" principle. But this identity is something to be carefully established, not casually assumed on the basis of an accidental similarity of term or of problem.

§2 *Matter in Greek Philosophy*

An underlying stuff?: From the beginning, the Greek cosmologists sought to find *permanent* physical factors that would give the human mind some sort of purchase in the slippery world of sense. One plausible assumption was that the multiplicity of things originated from a single simple stuff with familiar sense-properties, or from a few such stuffs. A further assumption might then be that this stuff is constitutive of things; changes could then be understood as being from one form or configuration of the stuff to another. The intelligibility here would reside primarily in the underlying material; so few changes (apart from seasonal ones and biological generation) were recognized as having structural similarities that the emphasis in physical

6

explanation would easily tend to be placed on the permanence and omni-presence of the stuff, in default of other aspects where the mind could take hold.

This may have been what Aristotle meant when he said that his early predecessors reduced things to their material cause. He must have been well aware that they invoked formal factors (like Anaximenes' rarefaction and condensation) and quasi-efficient causes (like Empedocles' Love and Strife or Anaxagoras' *Nous*). In addition, the Ionians could hardly have been said to exclude final causality, because *physis* for them still retained its connotation of a *living* principle. Nevertheless, the emphasis can fairly be said to have been on an underlying nature of some sort (stuff, seeds, atoms, elements . . .) as the primary source of intelligibility in natural things .

Now a world composed of water in its different forms is not impossible, it would seem. But to Aristotle's mind, it could not be *our* world, for one reason above all others: in such a world unqualified changes could not occur, since everything would then consist of the same sort of substance. And the existence of unqualified changes, and of a multiplicity of totally different sorts of substances, was for Aristotle a primary fact of our experience. If one is to explain *this* fact, the sort of "underlying nature" required will not be a substantial stuff with recognizable properties, but rather an indefinite substratum, the featureless correlate of substantial form.[1] The term, 'matter', might now seem to become descriptive, in a negative way, at least. To say of Anaximenes' air that it is "matter" merely means that it plays a certain role in explanation; this tells us nothing of its properties. But to say of Aristotle's underlying nature that it is "matter" appears to convey that it is lacking in substantial predicates. There is thus the tendency to assume that it is the "same" constituent that underlies all substantial changes, and, eventually, all corruptible being. The "sameness" here is of a very curious sort: to say that a constituent called primary matter plays a role in *all* substantial changes is not to say that the "same" stuff, in the normal sense of something sharing a common property, is found in each instance. Rather it seems to mean that there is an ontological constituent here which *plays a similar role* in each instance vis-à-vis substantial change.

In other words, the "sameness" of the primary matter in different concrete instances of change is not an ontological similarity of property (as of different instances of water), but rather a similarity of the roles played by the different instances of primary matter. It is still because of its role in explanation (i.e. as "material" cause) and not because of some properties it has or

---

[1] The legitimacy of taking Aristotle's primary matter to be in some sense a "constituent" of things is challenged in the essays by Sellars and Fisk below. It is defended (in three rather different ways) in the essays by Owens, Weisheipl, Mc Mullin.

lacks that it is called "matter" here. It is not a "stuff", therefore, despite its overtone of common constituent, any more than a man is said to be "stuff" in the light of his being the "matter" for a change from ill to well. In the last analysis, Aristotle's primary matter-substratum is a generalized matter-cause; to find a prolongation of the "stuff" analysis of the Ionians, one has to turn away from matter to the elements, which are kinds of stuff, identifiable in terms of definite properties. If these elements can change into one another, however, a more fundamental analysis of *their* substratum seems to be required. This analysis will not make use of the stuff-metaphor, though because of the inherent limitations of language in describing such an odd entity, it may seem at times as though it does.

In any instance of change, no matter how radical, there are obvious continuities, especially of quantity. The substratum of the change must in some sense be the bearer of these continuities, since there is a discontinuity between the initial and final forms. To call it "indeterminate", then, can be misleading because it may suggest that the substratum of one substantial change is ontologically equivalent (so to speak) to that of any other, which is manifestly not the case. If the notion of a "substratum" is going to be used at all, it must be admitted that it is the carrier of a certain determinateness. There are only certain things that a caterpillar can change into; an elephant for instance, is not one of them. If one can speak of a "substratum" at all here, these ontological restrictions on future becoming must somehow be transmitted through it.[2]

Total indefiniteness or indeterminacy can be predicated of the substratum of substantial changes in two senses only. First, the *notion* of primary matter abstracts from all the determinate elements that would occur in individual instances. Since it can be applied to the substratum of *any* substantial change, no matter what sorts of determinateness mark it off, and since it is not itself applied in virtue of any determinateness, it is indifferent to any such qualification; in a similar way, the notion, *animal*, is indeterminate relative to the kinds of determinateness that mark off the species to which it applies. *Animal* is, however, predicated on the basis of a certain formal property, whereas *primary matter* is not, so that the indefiniteness of the genus-concept is carried to a limit in the latter case. It will be noted that the "indeterminacy" here is the indeterminacy of the *concept* of primary matter, not of the concrete instance of primary matter.[3]

Secondly, a way of affirming the unity and primacy of substantial form is

---

[2] This point is discussed by Luyten and Mc Mullin below.

[3] See the essays by Weisheipl, Mc Mullin; this is rejected by Owens, Luyten.

to say that all the "actuality" and determinacy of the being resides in *it*. If it ceases to be and a new form begins to be, a plausible way of expressing this is to say that no actuality, no predicable determinacy, survives the change. To say of the substratum that it is "indeterminate" in this sense is simply a way of emphasizing that in a single substance there can be no actuality which is sufficiently independent of the central form to allow one to speak of its surviving the passing of this form unchanged. But this does *not* mean that the substratum is ontologically entirely indefinite. One may talk of the presence in it of "virtual" forms (as Aquinas did) or of "subsidiary" forms (as the medieval "pluralists" did); *some* way of introducing the determinacy requisite for the substratum of any actual substantial change is needed.

Aristotle's doctrine of "primary matter" rests on the principle that one cannot both defend the substantial unities of common experience *and* employ an analysis in terms of a universal "stuff". But the character of substratum-matter is not as clearly prescribed by this starting-point as is often supposed. Much will depend on the precise notion of *substance* employed. For Aristotle, this notion was derived from *living* unities, especially man; the criteria of its application to the inanimate world were much less definite. Primary matter would, then, be the substratum of the coming-to-be of such a living entity. A scientist could discuss this substratum in terms of the perseverance of chemical structures and physical properties, and would be tempted to regard this analysis as, in principle, exhaustive. The Aristotelian will answer that the relationship between these structures and the central form cannot be reduced in this way. The living form has a sort of "dominance" over the subsidiary structures, which means that it cannot be explained simply in terms of these structures.

If the primary matter-substratum is to retain its metaphysical flavor, if its existence and nature are to be regarded as questions for the philosopher rather than the empirical scientist, one seems forced to assign to the philosopher a special role in the discerning and defining of substantial unities in the physical world. The suggestion may even be that the way in which the living form directs the body is not fully open to the quantitative methods of the biologist. This is a dangerous tack, one that can readily make hylomorphism dependent upon vitalism. If the question of a matter-substratum is to be posed in contemporary terms, one will have to take account of alternative ways of describing living unities (e.g. those of Leibniz and Whitehead) which would not involve any correlative notion of a substratum-principle. And the transitions that are to qualify as "substantial" changes have to be decided upon: must they be from one "level" to another (e.g. from the living to the non-living) in order to give the philosopher a sufficient claim to a privileged form of analysis, quite different from that of the bio-chemist? It will not do to allege the "indeterminacy" of the substratum in support of this claim either, on the assumption that such a characteristic would render it inaccessible to science. The substratum is *not* indeterminate from the scientist's point of view, so that the primary-matter claim is likely to sound odd to him. In the final analysis, a very searching examination of the nature of living unities and their changes, and of the relations between them and inanimate bodies, is needed in order to re-evaluate the far-reaching ontological matter-form scheme that dominates Aristotle's philosophy of nature.

Multiplicity and defect: For Socrates and Plato, true knowledge resides in the immutable domain of idea, not in the myriad becomings of the world of sense. The mind rests in Unity and Good, but sense has to cope with images and multiplicities. To explain how this image-world falls short of the reality of the One and the Good, Plato must invoke something outside the realm of idea, something itself not an image, something permanent yet natureless, a Receptacle or container in which an image-mode of existence may be realized by means of negations which define and set off image-beings in a net of relations. The Receptacle is underived, so that multiplicity does not proceed from Unity; it has its own independent source, a source which is capable of "overcoming" Unity, so to speak, in order to produce the image-being.[4]

The material principle here is responsible first for the *multiplicity* of individuals, and hence also serves as a principle of individuation. It is in itself neither one nor many, but is the ground for many individuals, each of which simulates in a partial way the One. That which marks off each individual is unique to it, and is made possible by the negation-relations within the Receptacle. But this uniqueness cannot be grasped; it eludes the idea, so that the material principle is also a positive source of *irrationality,* not just of incompleteness or potency. Insofar as the world of sense falls away from the intelligibility of the Forms, the image-principle is responsible. This means that it is responsible for *defect* and for *evil* also. Falling away from the One is also a falling away from the Good. Matter itself is without finality; the images it contains manifest a finality, but a wavering one. This finality is the finality or dynamism proper to the image, the being which is separated from its own essence yet striving to be united in some fashion with it. So that matter is also the source of *becoming,* jointly with Form. There is a tight interconnection between all of these roles assigned to the material principle.

---

[4] See the essay by Eslick below.

10

Plato calls this principle a Receptacle or matrix, and thus relates it to space. Space is not regarded here as stuff or *plenum,* but rather as relative non-being, a ground for quantitative and ultimately all other sorts of relations. But now a question arises: from where does the multiplicity of the Forms themselves originate? Why do *they* depart from Unity? Are we to take *their* multiplicity as a sort of "given"? If we are not (and in the later dialogues, Plato strongly suggests that we are not), then either the Receptacle will in some way generate the multiplicity of the Forms also, or else a new source of multiplicity is required at a higher level. The former hypothesis will not do because the Receptacle seems capable of explaining only the multiplicities of individuals within species, and the imaging and becoming of the world of sense. A different source of negation is thus necessary at the level of the Forms, to keep them on the one hand from collapsing into the One, and on the other from becoming infinite in number and thus unknowable.

If multiplicity and materiality are to be linked, there will then be a temptation to see a certain "materiality" at the level of the Forms themselves, though of an "attenuated" sort, not involving the becoming which is characteristic of the Receptacle. This conclusion was to become more explicit in later neo-Platonism, where matter would appear as the principle of multiplicity, *tout court.* It led to the "universal hylemorphism" of the later Augustinian school: Gundissalinus, relying on Avicebron, suggested that a "spiritual matter", a "principle of receptivity" (R. Bacon), a "principle of possibility of being" (Bonaventure), is constitutive of all contingent being.[5] Aquinas disliked this broad use of 'matter' and was able to make his essence-existence composition explain multiplicity at the level of the angels, thus enabling him to restrict the terms 'matter' and 'material' to the order of physical becoming, i.e. of *corruptible* (not merely changeable) being.

Aristotle's handling of the fact of multiplicity is somewhat different to Plato's. The *differentiae* of individuals within a species escape knowledge, since knowledge is in terms of universals. In arriving at the universal, one "abstracts from" the singular, from the individual "matter", Aristotle says. Matter is thus what is left out of account in abstraction. The material factor enters into the essence of sensible bodies, while the formal or intelligible factor is not just imaged but is actually present in the body. The relationship between the material factor and quantity is not quite clear; the former is certainly not a kind of container; it cannot be specified simply in terms of quantitative relations. Aristotle attempts to distinguish between physics and mathematics on the grounds of the types of "matter" ("sensible" and "intel-

[5] See O. Lottin, "La composition des substances spirituelles", *Rev. Néoscholas. Philos.,* 34, 1932, 21–41.

ligible", respectively) that they study.[6] Leaving aside the many difficulties this mode of distinction raises,[7] it may be noted that "matter" here is no longer the concrete individualizing factor but a sort of surrogate in terms of quality or quantity. The place of a science in the hierarchy of knowledge is estimated in Platonic fashion by the degree of its "removal from matter", matter here being taken to be the mutable, rather than the individual, surprisingly enough. The assumption is the Platonic one that mutability is *per se* a barrier to intelligibility.

But Aristotle associates matter with potency rather than with privation, so that it is a principle of *defect* in a different way for him. When formal causality fails, when, for instance, an animal gives rise to a monstrous offspring, both Plato and Aristotle will attribute this to the material factor. But whereas Plato will make of this factor an autonomous source of indeterminacy, and will see the image-being as a product of the tensions between it and Form (so that a true science of such beings is impossible), Aristotle sees in it a source of potency, i.e. of capacity to be acted upon by causes outside the normal run. The monstrosity is not in his eyes an uncaused event, or an event lacking in formality; it is rather the rare instance where the potential of the seed to be interfered with by outside agencies is actualized. It is *finality* which has broken down here, due to the passive potential aspect of the material factor, not to the efficient nor the formal factors.

A crucial question must be asked at this point. How do we know that the "matter" of individuation is the same as the "matter" of substantial change?[8] Aristotle never discusses this; he uses the same word for each, and apparently assumes that their identity is obvious. But is it? It might seem that the relation of each to *time*, for instance, is rather different. Matter-substratum is a principle of continuity through time; matter-individuation is a principle of differentiation in space (or in space-time). But these are not far apart, especially if more recent views on the relations between space and time be taken into account. Again, the matter-substratum of any given body contains all sorts of determinate virtualities, as we have seen. But individuation seems to be just a question of space-time location. A factor that could serve as sub-

---

[6] "Intelligible matter" corresponds roughly with geometrical space; "sensible matter" is the perceptual aspect of a concrete individual (the *materia individualis* of Aquinas) or else the perceptual aspect of an individual considered abstractly as a member of a species (*materia communis*). Neither of these is related directly to matter as substratum or to matter as individuating. See the essay by FitzGerald below, and C. deKoninck, "Abstraction from matter", (*Laval Théologique et Philosophique*, 13, 1957, 133–96; 16, 1960, 53–69; 169–88).

[7] See A. Mansion, *Introduction à la physique aristolélicienne,* Louvain, 1945, chap. 5.

[8] Whether one takes the "matter" here as a constituent or simply as some sort of distinguishing aspect.

stratum of a concrete body could also (it would seem) serve to individuate it, but the opposite does not seem to be the case.

That which sets the body off from all other bodies *could* very well serve as a principle of continuity (or individuality) through change too; if the analysis of change simply says: there must be some basis for calling this the "same" being before and after the change, the individuating factor could account for it. But if this principle of continuity be understood as a *substratum*, this is not true. To function as a substratum of this particular body, it must have a sort of "ontological density" that goes far beyond the simple provision of a location. This can easily be overlooked if the "indeterminate" and "non-formal" aspect of the substratum be stressed; it can seem that the non-intelligible factor or aspect of the singular being that marks it off as an individual could also tag it in a nonpredicable way through a change. What marks off X from Y are, first, their intrinsic properties (but they might be indiscernible from one another on that score), second, their relative location, and third, their belonging to a particular existentially-designated universe. No hint here of substratum or stuff. Whereas what constitutes a permanent base in X for the acquisition of new substantial forms is something intrinsic to X and definite, though not possessing of itself any predicable properties.

If one is to speak in terms of *substratum*, then, there is some reason to question whether such a concrete matter-factor can be simply identified with an individuating-factor. The role of quantity on both sides of this alleged equivalence needs much further scrutiny. The medievals associated quantity and matter with individuation.[9] The potency and the dynamism of the matter-substratum seem, however, to involve quantity in a rather different way. The two "material" factors are clearly connected; it is a matter of some importance and some difficulty, however, to trace their connections more clearly.

Matter and spirit: Was Parmenides a materialist, as Burnet once argued?[10] He described Being as a sphere, extended, limited, corporeal, and said that Being is all there is. Does this amount to a denial of Spirit? The answer, of course, is: no. Parmenides' argument is based on an analysis—incorrect, as it happens—of the notion of *What-Is*, not of the notion of *matter*. Even though What-Is, as he describes it, possesses some of the characteristics we would associate with matter, these characteristics occur in a purely descriptive way in the argument; the argument in no way rests on, or terminates in,

---

[9] See Bobik's essay below, and the comments on it by Fisk and Weisheipl.
[10] *Early Greek Philosophy*, 4th ed., London, 1930, pp. 178–82.

the sphericity of Being, for instance. One could deny any one of these characteristics and the main point of Parmenides' contrast between What-Is and What-Is-Not would be unaffected. As for the other pre-Socratics, though they analyzed in terms of a "material", they frequently attributed life or initiative to it, so that it would be misleading to attach the materialist label to their thought. The *Nous* of Anaxagoras is material in character but there is here a first attempt to separate off an activity proper to man alone. The Atomists could in a sense be described as materialists, because their system implicitly excludes the category of Spirit by its very logical structure. The split between the ways of Truth and Opinion in Parmenides presages a more fundamental dualism, not only between reason and sense, but between the objects of reason and the objects of sense. Plato's ontology rests not so much on Matter and Spirit as on Matter and the Forms. The status of the human mind, the faculty for raising man out of the images into the truth, is becoming clearer: it is held to be a separable entity whose nature and destiny raises it above the sensible world.

In the Platonic tradition, therefore, spirit comes to be contrasted with "matter". Here, for the first time, the term, 'matter', is being used as a descriptive noun for a class of things, and 'material' can connote certain properties. Since the soul is incorruptible and imperceptible, matter will come to be regarded as the *corruptible* or the *perceptible*, indifferently. One can now speak of the "material world", a "piece of matter", and so forth, although these usages would not come in until after the Greek period.[11] (It is this sense of 'matter', incidentally, that seems to dominate ordinary English usage today.)

In Aristotle, the contrast between 'immaterial' and 'material' would not be quite so sharp, in fact, would at times be somewhat ambiguous. There is a trivial sense in which *every* form is "non-material"; there is also a sense in which a concept can be called "immaterial" because it prescinds from the singularities of matter. But to call a substance "immaterial" ought to mean something much stronger than this. The human soul, according to Aristotle, can abstract from matter and is thus "immaterial"; it is separable, even though not a substance, properly speaking. Man, though material, thus has an immaterial principle guiding him; it informs him as the form does matter. But the relation of soul to body is not the same as that of form to primary matter, because the body is already a highly determinate material

---

11 "The word 'matter' . . . designates (in modern usage) bodies, objects of our immediate experience, with the determinations that make them perceptible. But this sense is foreign to all the usages of '*hylé*' found in Aristotle; this term for him never corresponds to a total "datum", but always signifies a part, a constitutive element of a whole in which the correlative element is always form." Mansion, *op. cit.*, p. 155.

entity. Soul is the total form; mind is one of its faculties. The contrast here is between the immateriality of the separable human soul and the corruptibility of matter, not simply between mind and matter.

A contrast of this sort had been implicit in religious beliefs and practices long before this time. The human spirit was regarded as somehow different from the body it inhabits; belief in survival after death often involved some sort of dualism of the kind. But categories for describing this contrast were lacking; the spirit was taken to be a sort of finer material, no more. The Platonic and Aristotelian separations of soul and matter furnished basic insights for later theology, especially Christian theology. Consequently, the concept of matter has played an important role in practically all theologies since the Greek period. 'Material' is taken as a substantial predicate, denoting an order of being which is sharply contrasted with the immaterial, spiritual, incorruptible order. The latter order is assumed to be the one of ultimate concern, that towards which man's eyes should be turned.

The attitude towards the non-spiritual order ('material 'comes to take on an almost negative meaning when the positive term, 'spiritual', is substituted for 'immaterial') varied greatly from one theology to another. In the neo-Platonic tradition, it was seen as the imperfect, the diffracted image of the One-Good though in some sense the product of its superabundance too. For the Manichaeans, matter became a positive autonomous principle of evil and corruption; the material world was not only a prison of the soul but a positive source of spiritual decay. In Augustine, the doctrine of original sin linked the material order with the fall of man; in Adam's sin, even matter is somehow disoriented and turned away from God. In the Augustinian tradition which dominated early medieval and much early modern theology, man's life was pictured as a warfare between the spiritual and the material, with the "material" connoting passion, unreason, inertia, man's "lower" nature generally. In the Thomist tradition, the dualism was much less sharp; the soul is no longer an immaterial substance only extrinsically related with body by the "accident" of Divine infusion. It is the proper form of the body, and this body is man's indispensable instrument in attaining salvation. Matter is not regarded as corrupt; the source of human depravity is seen to be in spirit as much as (or more than) in matter. In describing the work of redemption and grace, the categories of *natural* and *supernatural* will be preferred to those of *material* and *spiritual*.

It was, perhaps, in Oriental theologies that the category of the "material" (i.e. the perceptible, the temporal, the corruptible) came most fully into its own. The dualism here is even more prominent than in Augustine, and the temporal is now something to be entirely transcended, escaped from, obliterated, rather than something to be put to use, transformed, raised up. The bond that links together these myriad theological uses of the terms, 'material', and 'matter' is discovered in a basic contrast between two orders of being. The *spiritual* is discovered either by looking within man for what is most properly man, or by looking above man for a higher order of being whose norms will be creativity, love and intelligence, instead of the physical norms of the corruptible sensible order. Then the *"material"* is understood as in some way the negation of the spiritual (Plotinus to Hegel), or, at least, as a falling-away in *some* sense from the perfections of the spiritual order. Much of the tension in Western theology has come from the effort to see the material order in its *own* terms and not as a broken mirror, to achieve a theology of the temporal in which the human transformation of the material order takes on sense and urgency.

Predication and explanation: So far, 'matter' has denoted either an absolutely constitutive factor or aspect (as substratum or as individuating), or else a certain sort of entity. But Aristotle introduced a wide range of meta-theoretic uses for the term too in the contexts of predication and explanation. For instance, he will call the subject of predication the "matter" of the predication. 'Matter' here does not connote some property of the referent but rather the semantic role played by the referent relative to some specific predication. Thus the sun is the "matter" of the predication: "the sun is shining". (The metaphor underlying this usage is that of predicate being applied to subject as form to matter; this metaphor can lead to the notorious difficulties of the "bare-substratum" theory of predication if pressed too hard.) Closely connected with this is 'matter' as a name for any subject of change, that-to-which-the-change-happens. Thus if a non-musical man becomes musical, the "matter" of the change is the man, i.e. the referent of that subject-term which is predicable both before and after the change. This "matter" is discovered in any given instance, not so much by an analysis of the change as by looking at a *specific predication about* the change. That in a qualified change there should be a matter-subject follows simply from the fact that any such change can be described symbolically by: 'X is non-Y and is later Y'. X is the matter-subject, non-Y and Y the privation and the form respectively. But if the change is "unqualified", it cannot be so described. There is no X-term for the subject of the change, dog-becomes-corpse. So that this analysis of *predication about* change will not suffice to produce a subject in such cases.[12] Aristotle calls upon a conceptual analysis of the general notion of change here; if an event is to be change and not just re-

---

12 Fisk argues below that *no* analysis will suffice for this purpose. All of the Aristotle essays in the first and second parts of the book touch on this question from different points of view.

placement, there must be something in common between before and after, a substratum. This substratum can by extension (he argues) be regarded as the "subject" of unqualified changes, even though the use of the term, 'subject', is now justified in a rather different way. It is called "primary matter" here to distinguish it from an ordinary matter-subject of a qualified change.

Lastly, there is the so-called "material cause". Aristotle analyzes different types of explanation of physical change, and claims that there are four necessary and sufficient factors in all such explanations. The "material" factor is "that out of which a thing comes to be and which persists, e.g. the bronze of the statue". From this it might seem that matter-cause and matter-subject (or substratum) are the same. But this is an error, induced by Aristotle's reliance on examples from art (instead of nature) in discussing causality. Suppose we take instead of the statue the example of a dark-haired man who becomes grey. The formal cause of this change cannot plausibly be said to be grey-hairedness (the form which a simple subject-form-privation type of analysis would point to). The formal cause will have to invoke the reasons in the essence of man himself (the substratum here) why such a change should take place. In general, then, the *formal* cause of most changes will involve features from what would ordinarily be called the substratum (or subject) of the change. So that the material factor is pushed further back, so to speak. The formal factor is what must be called upon *formally* in order to explain the sort of change that occurs. (Thus if the grain of the wood be alluded to in explaining the statue's lines, the wood is being introduced as *formal* not as material factor.)

What, then, is the *material* factor? In making 'matter' relative to *explanation* here, and to a specific explanation of a specific change at that, its whole conceptual base has been subtly altered. Two possibilities are open. If the formal factor be defined as that which gives intelligibility to the change (or to the substance, considered as a product of some specific change), then the material factor appears as the irreducible, the simple, the qualityless, etc., depending on what notion of form is being stressed. It almost inevitably comes out, then, either as primary matter or individuating matter, or else as that which is omitted, or prescinded from, in the explanation. In this event, the material factor would be both a sort of "constant" and a sort of "zero" in all physical explanations: it would be invoked in the same way in all and would contribute nothing special to any. For this reason, it seems preferable to say first that the formal factor is that which is taken as the source of intelligibility *in this particular explanation of change*. It is relative thus to a specific explanation which may be profound or superficial. In this case, the "material cause" in a particular explanation will be that which is "bracketed" or left out of *explicit* account in it, that whose nature is not up for discussion but is only mentioned, that factor whose own nature leaves problems for future exploration. We shall return to this in the context of contemporary science in §4.

§3 *From Matter to Mass*

The development of the notion of *mass* is the development of the science of mechanics itself, since mass ultimately appears as an intrinsic and invariant measure of the response of any given body to moving causes. Without such a notion, dynamics is impossible and kinematics is very restricted. Aristotle had much to say about mechanics, and even cast some of it into quasi-mathematical form. But he was blocked in a number of ways from developing an exact science of mechanics.[13] He could not fully admit the notion of *velocity,* for instance, on the score that it was a ratio of unlike magnitudes. Nevertheless, he formulated a number of laws in which velocity implicitly appears as a ratio of distance to time. In "violent" motion, he equivalently made the velocity of the moving body proportional to the motive power (*dunamis*) of the extrinsic cause and inversely proportional to the resistance of the medium and the weight of the body.[14] For the same motive power, a body of double the weight will travel only half the distance in the same time. The notion of "motive power" was, however, left very vague, and no indication was given of a quantitative operational way of defining it, even though phrases like 'twice the motive power' are common in the text.[15] In natural motion (free fall), the velocity was *directly* proportional to the weight. So that in both types of motion, weight was recognized as a decisive factor in establishing a particular velocity. Nevertheless, the connection between weight and motion was not pursued in later Aristotelian physics; modifications in the Aristotelian laws came through the study of the relationship between resistance, power and velocity, without explicit attention to the factor of weight. Weight seemed a

---

[13] See M. Clagett, *The Science of Mechanics in the Middle Ages*, Madison, 1959, chap. 7.

[14] *Physics*, VII, chap. 5. The *dunamis* here is a cause of velocity, so to speak, not of acceleration (a concept he does not analyze, though he does talk of the increasing speed of free fall), and it is a constant factor throughout the motion.

[15] To say that according to Aristotelian principles, "motive power was measured by the product of the weight of the body moved multiplied by the velocity impressed on it" (A. C. Crombie, *Medieval and Early Modern Science,* New York, 1959, vol. 1, p. 116) seems too explicit. It would not have occurred to Aristotle to measure the extrinsic power by looking at its effect, nor would he have given it as a product had he done so.

18

much more "accidental" feature than density did, especially in a *"plenum"* universe.

Quantity of matter: If physicists needed a quantitative mass-factor for their mechanics, none of the concepts of matter so far studied seemed to give much assistance. Matter as the individuating or as the non-spiritual was no help at all. Nor was matter as substratum much better. We have seen that the substratum-analysis ended with a primary matter itself unquantified. So that though Aristotle could talk of its being eternal and the "same" through changes, the notion of *quantitative conservation* simply could not be applied to it. He had already rejected the Ionian idea of an underlying stuff; the conservation of some sort of quantified material through all changes would run into precisely the same difficulties. So that despite the commonsense appeal of a qualityless quantified material that remains invariant through change, it must be said that Aristotle's authority was solidly against it.

Nevertheless, the metaphor conveyed by the word, *'materia',* exerted a constant pressure in the direction of quantification. In the thirteenth century, discussion of two very different problems led to the formulation of the notion of a "quantity of matter" which was conserved in change.[16] The first of these was the question of the Eucharist: how can the accidents of bread and wine remain in the Eucharist since the substance does not? Many answers were given. Aquinas suggested that the quantity here could act as a sort of pseudo-subject in lieu of substance, since it is the "first accident". A disciple of his, Giles of Rome, pointed out an ambiguity in this solution: if quantity be taken as volume here, the volume is not the "first" accident since it is not an invariant (when water changes into vapor, the quantity increases). So he proposed "quantity of matter" instead. The motive inspiring this was to find an invariant that would be ontologically "firm" enough to act as subject in Transubstantiation. Giles' suggestion attracted no followers at the time.

The other problem that focussed attention on "quantity of matter" was that of condensation and rarefaction, two phenomena which held a deep interest for the Aristotelian physicists, partly because they were so prominent in changes of one "element" to another. It seemed clear that in such changes *some* sort of quantity remained constant. Roger Swineshead spoke of this quantity rather vaguely as a constant *"massa elementaris"*. Richard Swines-

---

[16] See the essay by Weisheipl below. Max Jammer's recently published *Concepts of Mass* (Cambridge, Mass., 1961) documents the origins of the varied mass-concepts. We have found it very helpful.

head later clarified this suggestion, saying that the "quantity of matter" that was conserved in a process of condensation depends on the density and the volume of the body. This was the definition Newton was later to use, but the trouble then (as later) was: how could density be estimated? Swineshead, like all the others who were to discuss this question up to the time of Galileo, took density to be an irreducible quality, like color, not in need of further analysis.

But density could *not* be known through sense-experience in the way that color or volume is, although it might seem at first sight that it could. The density of a body could be estimated in two ways only: either by weighing it or by observing its resistance to motion through it. The first of these would make quantity of matter directly proportional to weight; the second was intuitively appealing but operationally impractical. What Swineshead may have had in mind (besides a vague idea of a compressed or less compressed "stuff") were the notions of specific gravity and specific weight.[17] The specific gravity of a body measured hydrostatically, gave its density in terms of water as a comparison factor. But, of course, this brings us back to weight again; quantity of matter would, then, still be equivalent to weight, or at least have to be estimated in proportion to weight. It would seem, then, that Swineshead's attempt to define *quantitas materiae* as a product of density and volume, if it were to be made operational, would have to rely on a weight measurement. Yet, significantly, such was the separation between the notions of *materia* (according to Aristotle, part of the essence) and of weight (a purely contingent factor depending on position) that no one seems to have thought of suggesting comparative weight measurements as a direct way of estimating comparative "quantities of matter". Density is still regarded here as an irreducible given; neither weight nor resistance to impressed motion are explicitly called on to explain it.

A very different use of the notion of "quantity of matter" can be noted in the area of dynamics. (Swineshead's analysis seemed to prescind from problems of *motion* entirely.) The problem of projectile motion had preoccupied Aristotelian physicists from the beginning, since Aristotle's postulation of continuing extrinsic causes for such motion led to so many difficulties. As early as Philoponus (sixth century), it was suggested that some intrinsic *"energeia"* is communicated by the moving cause to such bodies. Avicenna made this impulse (*"mail"*) proportional to the weight of the moving body. Buridan suggested that an "impetus" is communicated

---

[17] Implicitly defined by Archimedes in his *On floating bodies*; much discussed by Arab writers and analyzed in detail in a popular thirteenth-century treatise, *De insidentibus in humidum* (author unknown).

which is proportional to the "quantity of matter" of the body, and which stays with the body indefinitely unless it be dissipated by a contrary resistance. A large mill-wheel is harder to start than a small one, and also harder to stop. The impetus is here considered as a form which is proportionate to its matter. Buridan will speak of the latter as the "primary matter" of the body, even though it is quantified, thus breaking a basic Aristotelian rule. His "impetus" here has clear analogies with the momentum of seventeenth-century physics, and the conservation of this impetus in the absence of resistance strongly suggests the later idea of inertia.[18] But once again, no hint is given as to how "quantity of matter" is to be measured, other than a passing suggestion that it is related to density and volume. The overwhelming importance of Buridan's idea is that it makes *materia* for the first time something that *resists change of state* (whether of motion or of rest). In the Aristotelian tradition, *materia* had been linked with motion only in a very general way (as the source of potency). But here it is given a specific role in resisting change of motion. And this role now suggests, again for the first time, that through the concept of inertial mass a way of quantifying matter that does not depend on weight measurement may be found.

Jammer suggests that the neo-Platonic tradition encouraged the view of matter as inert and passive.[19] (For Aristotle, matter was just as much part of the nature of a thing as form was, and so could not be characterized as inert.) Of course, the "inertia" here is that of passivity, not of resistance. The idea of matter's playing an active negative role in motion is in the last analysis foreign to Plotinus just as much as to Aristotle. Nevertheless, Kepler was undoubtedly influenced by neo-Platonism in his formulation of the notion of inertia. The *anima motrix,* or form, which moves the planets, has to overcome not only an "impotence" of their matter but also an "inertia" which "works against" the impressed force. If the planets had no such "inertia", the smallest force would make them move infinitely fast. His key point is that this inertia is proportional to "quantity of matter" (understood as the product of volume and density), thus bringing the two notions together, as Buridan had done. Kepler's mass is specifically an inertial one, then, since it is a measure of resistance, whether of the planet to the *potentia* of the sun or of the ball to the push that sets it in

---

[18] The old debate about the closeness of *impetus* to later ideas (Duhem, Clagett, *pro*; Maier, Jammer, *contra*) still goes on. It is clear that *impetus* was still a basically Aristotelian notion, and had to be modified ontologically, so to speak, to fit into the later context. But that it provided a key to inertial motion for Galileo and Descartes can hardly be denied.

[19] *Op. cit.*, chap. 3.

motion. Until there is some sort of law of gravitation, there cannot be any explicit *notion* of gravitational mass. But, of course, Kepler does not specify how his "quantity of matter" is to be measured, and this leaves the suspicion that a weight-measurement might be required, in which case there would be recourse to a *measure* (even though not an explicit idea) of gravitational mass.[20]

Descartes: The identification of matter with extension by Descartes constituted a sharp break with all previous philosophic tradition as well as with nascent scientific views. There is no longer anything opposed to *idea* here: only thought and extension exist, and extension can be fully grasped by thought. To achieve this confident rationalism, matter in both the Platonic and the Aristotelian senses had to be eliminated as the principal obstacle to a total intelligible analysis of the world; and since the model for this analysis was geometry, matter not surprisingly was replaced by space. This, he hoped, would allow the deduction of the laws of motion in a geometrical fashion from a few simple axioms about figure, motion and rest. He managed to formulate a clear principle of inertia that went beyond Kepler by assigning inertia as a sufficient cause for the uniform continuance of unresisted motion, and this led him to a basic law of conservation of "motion", where the quantity was given by the product of volume and velocity.

But the difficulties in the way of this geometrical reduction were plain. His universe had to be a *plenum*, filled with a "matter" that is perceptible in some places and not in others. Variations in density of this "matter" (as between a stone and a corresponding volume of "empty space", for instance) could not be explained, in fact in a sense had to be explained away. All motion had to take place by percussion, but the laws of percussion he formulated (utilizing volume instead of an independent "quantity of matter") were quite obviously inadequate, giving in many instances exactly the opposite results to those perceived even at common-sense level. Indeed, Descartes knew quite well that, in general, geometrically similar bodies do *not* act in the same way under impressed forces. To get around this, he invoked "hidden percussions" of the medium upon the body, percussions that were not observable nor amenable to mathematical treatment. Further-

---

[20] In the early chapters of his book, Jammer assumes that the masses spoken of must be inertial as long as no *explicit* law of gravitation is invoked (p. 122). This leads to considerable ambiguity. The earliest treatments of "quantity of matter" took it to be a measure of "stuff" and later of inertia, it is true, but to the extent that they implicitly relied on weight-measurement, their mass-concept was *operationally* gravitational, even though by its *intent*, so to speak, inertial.

more, the whole phenomenon of weight entirely defied analysis in his categories; in his earlier work, he had suggested that gravity is an extra "dimension" of bodies, but with his later exclusion of all but geometry and motion, this idea had to be abandoned. The vortices that he so readily postulated in discussing problems of free fall were, indeed, as "occult" from the physicist's point of view as any of the forms that had preceded them.

Descartes' system is interesting in that it illustrates an extreme position vis-à-vis matter and mass. Essentially, it denies the existence of a non-geometric mass-factor; volume is the only intrinsic physical index of a body. All other quantitative features must be derived from it, while qualitative features will be relegated to the domain of mind. Philosophic problems of individuation and change (other than local change) go unresolved, while the basic scientific question of a factor that would measure differential response to motion is not faced. In a sense, he could just as easily have dropped the matter-category entirely, and said that his reduction of physics to mathematics constituted a physics without matter (as later exponents of his ideal would put it). In another way, his attempt illustrates a weakness in the Greek notion of quantity. For what he has done is to take the "first accident" of the scholastics and not only push it back into essence, but even make it equivalent to essence. This, of course, the scholastics would reject (although they always had been prepared to admit that quantity stood closer to essence than other accidents did), but its *scientific* weakness comes from the classical Greek and scholastic identification of quantity with extension. Had his scholastic mentors treated density, weight, etc. as quantitative factors instead of as irreducible qualities, he might have been more prepared to take account of them in his system.

Concepts of mass: It may be helpful from the beginning to separate off three operationally different notions of mass that were latent in seventeenth-century physics; though they were not distinguished from one another until much later, the distinction will allow us to understand the Newtonian development much better.[21] *Inertial mass* (*IM*) is a measure of the resistance of a body to change of motion. *Passive gravitational mass* (*PGM*) is a measure of the response of a body to a gravitational force. *Active gravitational mass* (*AGM*) is a measure of the ability of a body to cause a gravitational response in other bodies. The first two of these are hard to separate, because it would seem that *PGM* is simply a kind of *IM,* if the "response" be regarded as a sort of "resistance". But the two are not the same, as can be seen in the case of an ordinary weight measurement. There

---

[21] See the paper by Mast below.

the net force is zero, there is no motion, and the mass given by an application of Newton's Second Law (where the acceleration due to gravity in the locality is already known) is *PGM* not *IM*. No question of resistance to change of motion arises. On the other hand, gravitational motion (if fully treated) involves *IM* as well as *GM;* whether the body be in free fall or in projectile motion, it exhibits a resistance to change of motion *as well as* a characteristic response to the gravitational field. Thus in calculating planetary orbits we set the centrifugal force (mv^2/r) equal to the gravitational force (Gmm'/r^2), where the first '*m*' is *IM* and the second is *PGM*. In Newton's equations of motion generally, where '*m*' occurs on both sides of an equation, it will usually be *IM* on one side and *PGM* on the other. In Newtonian physics, *AGM* is rarely of direct concern (except in the two-body problem); ordinarily the motion of the "actively" gravitating body is left out of account.

The seventeenth-century development of the concept of mass with Beeckman, Baliani, Huygens, centered round the notion of inertia mainly. Newton fused inertial and gravitational ideas in his three "Laws", the first defining the notion of inertial motion, the second equating force (gravitational or other) with the product of (inertial) mass and the acceleration produced (or more exactly, with the rate of change of momentum, where momentum has already been defined as the product of velocity and the inertial "quantity of matter"), and the third equating action and reaction. The "quantity of matter" is defined in the traditional fashion as the product of volume and density. Newton notes that it is also "known by the weight of each body, for it is proportional to the weight, as I have found by experiments on pendulums" (Def. 1).

This raises the famous question as to whether Newton really *did* have a non-circular way of defining mass. There are really two questions. Is it possible to define mass in terms of density and volume? If it be defined in terms of specific *weight* instead of density, what happens to the "Laws"? On the first, it seems clear that Newton thought either that he had an autonomous way of defining density, or else that density was an intensive irreducible quality as the scholastics supposed. One way of defining density that did not *seem* to involve weight-measurement might well have occurred to him, because it involved the corpuscularian model of matter he himself frequently utilized in other contexts. Condensation could be thought of as a packing closer together of particles. Then one might think of estimating density in terms of the number of homogeneous equal-sized particles per unit volume. But, of course, this does not really avoid circularity, since some way of knowing the particles to be of equal masses would have to be given in advance. So that one seems ultimately forced to reject a density-definition of mass on the grounds that a knowledge of density presupposes a knowledge of mass.

Yet Newton's system obviously had an operational "hold" on mass *somewhere.* The Second Law related a hypothetical law of force (an inverse-square law, for example) with the behavior of a moving body. A measurement of specific weight plus a knowledge of g for the locality gave *PGM,* and Newton's pendulum experiments showed the proportionality of *PGM* and *IM.* In discussing planetary motion (the heart of Newton's system), the mass of the planet occurred on both sides of the equation of motion (*PGM* on one side, *IM* on the other) and thus cancelled out, so that no operational problem about its definition or measure arose in this context. Nevertheless, it must be admitted that the *quantitas materiae* and *vis inertiae* which Newton saw as numerically proportional are far from clearly defined in the *Principia.* Both labels were open to criticism: the first, because there was no operational way of defining the *"materia"* whose quantity was sought, and the second (as Kant was to emphasize), because the inertia cannot, strictly speaking, be regarded as a *"vis"* (or force).

Newtonian physics encouraged the transfer, both at the common-sense and at the philosophic levels, of the attributes of matter to mass. Just as the term, 'matter', had come, after a long evolution, to name the substratum of things, as well as to be a general name for physical objects, so 'mass', which originally denoted a single measurable characteristic of things, was "substantialized" as a sort of scientific synonym for the older term. The world was taken to consist of "point masses", since it sufficed to characterize bodies in terms of their mass and motion in order to make all possible deductions about their behavior (i.e. their local motions). Mass is no longer regarded merely as a property; it is the *substance,* conserved through all changes, underlying all other variable (and thus "accidental") properties. *Mass* could, thus, be regarded as a more scientifically adequate version of the older concept of matter; Newton's idea of mass as a numerical measure for matter (where 'matter' is regarded as the more basic term) gradually lost ground as new ways of defining 'mass', within the broad limits of the Newtonian system, came to be elaborated. Euler transformed the Second Law into an operational definition of *IM.* (It was possible to take it at the same time to be an empirical law, if some hypothetical mass-dependent function—such as the inverse-square law—were substituted for the 'F', so that the masses on either side of the equation cancelled.) Saint Venant showed that *IM* could be measured directly by impact experiments; Maxwell measured it in terms of a constant force (as of a "standard" coiled spring); Mach, who disliked the "metaphysical" concept of force, preferred to define *GM* in terms of mutually induced gravitational accelerations.

These are different ways of making the Newtonian system operational; it will be noted that by rejecting the definition of mass as "quantity of matter", they tend to remove the concept of matter from the realm of quantitative operational science. But before leaving the concept of mass, it will be worth noting that it (like its conceptual ancestor) has only a precarious operational foothold in some parts of science today.

The problem of mass: What we allude to here as "the problem" of mass is not one with which physics has as yet had to concern itself very much. It is not the question of whether inertial mass is entirely of electromagnetic origin, as Max Abraham once claimed. Nor does the variability of inertial mass with velocity, demonstrated in the Special Theory of Relativity, concern us.[22] Our problem is a more fundamental one. Its first manifestation was in Newton's own work. Since the measure of acceleration will vary with the reference-frame chosen, it seems that the value of the mass will depend on the acceleration of the observer measuring it. Newton was forced to introduce all sorts of postulated "absolutes" into his system; even at best, we have some trouble finding the "inertial system" relative to which his laws are supposed to hold. The second puzzle was adumbrated in Mach's claim that inertial mass depends upon the distribution of bodies in the universe as a whole. This claim appears to be empirically testable, but so far, the required level of experimental accuracy has not been reached.

But far more serious are the conceptual difficulties raised by the General Theory of Relativity.[23] To jump at once to the most serious of these, if one considers bodies of finite volume (and not just point-idealizations), it becomes impossible even to *define* mass exactly, let alone measure it. Take *AGM*, for instance, which is the most favorable case. Suppose a very small test-body, *B*, be introduced, one which is too small to alter the field appreciably. The gravitational effect at *B* will be calculated by an integral over the effects caused by different regions of the body, *A*, whose *AGM* is being measured. But how is this sum to be made? and will it not vary with the direction of *B* from *A*? We do not have a unique space-time frame, and the space-time itself (other than in idealized cases) may have non-uniform curvature. So that *AGM* will depend on the choice of reference-frame, and even then will be variable, depending on the direction and distance of the test-body used. If *A* is in motion, there will be no satisfactory

---

[22] Jammer, *op. cit.*, chap. 12, shows very elegantly that the relativistic "variability of mass" is due to the redefinition of space-time relations in the Lorentz-Minkowski system and to the consequent shift in the factor expressing the relation of momentum and velocity (i.e. mass). "It is not a new property of matter that has been discovered" (p. 165).

[23] I am indebted to the discussions I have had with Dr. C. Mast on this point.

way of defining "rigidity" for it, and there will also be other problems about the effect of A upon the metric. With PGM, things are even worse, because here we cannot make the initial ideal assumption of an indefinitely small test-body. The two-body problem has not even been solved relativistically for *point*-bodies; the mutual accelerations and consequent variations of the metric make the way towards a solution very difficult. *IM* involves forces other than gravitational ones, and so far no satisfactory relativistic treatment of these is in sight; it would quite certainly be even more difficult here than in the case of GM to define a unique value for the mass.

There seems to be good reason to suppose, then, that the notion of mass itself (i.e. of an intrinsic measure of response or resistance to motion) is a "classical" one, useful in the Newtonian approximation, but no longer even definable in a full relativity theory. The classical view depended on instantaneous propagation of light, on the making of unique time-"cuts", on the insertion of observers and test-bodies without disturbing the metric, on the reduction of bodies to point centers of gravity. Where none of these can be assumed, it seems dubious whether the quest for a unique invariant intrinsic motion-parameter has any hope of succeeding. In a way, this ought not surprise us: it was optimistic to suppose that a body could be isolated from the rest of the universe and its mass determined in absolute fashion. If mass is to be the measure of the response of the body to outside influences, it is scarcely to be wondered at that it should depend on the rest of the universe, on its space-time relations with other bodies here and now. And if these bodies are in constant motion and if the space and time factors cannot be neatly separated in Newtonian fashion, the "mass" is not likely to be either invariant or unique.

If one were to be imaginative at this point, one might see in this the interaction between two different traditions of matter: the substratum (with its implicit attributes of conservation; intrinsic absolute measure; close relation with motion) and the Receptacle (involving spatial relations with all other sensible beings; in its singularity incapable of being made intelligible). It is fortunate for the history of physics that at the level of Newtonian approximation, the former prevailed. But it may be that there is a "Platonic" period ahead for science in this regard. That the scientist will seek out new invariances to guide his grasp of beings in motion is sure; but that these invariances will be such that they can be "substantialized" as mass was, is most unlikely.

§4 *Seven Ways to "Dematerialization"*

In the previous section, we have seen one reason why the notion of matter has faded out of physical science after playing an important role as a sort of catalyst in the early days of mechanics. It may be instructive to conclude this introduction by indicating a number of other ways in which physical science has been claimed to "dematerialize" older views. Each of the six listed below seems to correspond to a somewhat different notion of matter. It would seem, then, that even if the category of 'matter' is not used in the actual work of science today, it may well be indispensable in talking *about* that work, and in particular in estimating its effect on everyday ways of thinking as well as on philosophic reflection.

Matter as objective: The first two of the strands that we propose to disentangle can be conveniently related to the classical distinction between primary and secondary qualities, if it be assumed (as it often has been in modern philosophy) that "matter" is to be *defined* by whichever properties are agreed upon as "primary". The term, 'material', will then be predicated on the basis of the referent's possessing these properties. And the concept of matter will be determined by the "primary" end of the primary-secondary distinction between properties. There are, however, two rather different ways of drawing this distinction, depending on whether *ontological* or *epistemic* primacy be the more stressed. In this section, we shall treat of the former. An "O-primary" property may be defined as one which does not depend in itself on the observer or on the interaction between apparatus and object; it is "objectifiable", absolutely intrinsic to the thing itself.

In his essay below, Dr. Hanson argues that Berkeley showed that an ontological primary-secondary distinction would not work in philosophy, because the "primaries" of Newtonian physics (extension, impenetrability, etc.) were observer-dependent in the same way as the alleged "secondaries" were. He then points to quantum theory where the influence of the observer-detector is shown to enter, in a complex and indissociable way, into every statement about the microscopic realm. And (he assumes), it is in this realm that one would ordinarily hope to anchor the predicate, 'material'. He concludes that the Berkleyan denial of the validity of the primary-secondary distinction is now extended to science also, and on the basis of a *scientific* discovery, not a philosophic theory. There are no "primary" or intrinsic absolute properties then, and the import of the 'de-' in our term, 'dematerialization', is that "matter" (no matter which properties be chosen to characterize it) is, in its description, detector-dependent; it is not the simple separately describable thing it was thought to be.

It should be noted that this notion of *"de*-materialization" would be quite metaphorical, if Dr. Hanson's paper did not go on to make a further point, i.e. that not only is the *description* of the properties dependent upon the means used to obtain it, but the properties *themselves* attributed to the object on the basis of the observation have been shown to be somehow dependent upon the means of observation; the detector is asserted to *impose* (in some fashion) these properties, at least partially. If quantum theory had merely shown that an accurate *description* of microscopic properties cannot, even in principle, be given, leaving open the possibility that the object still *possesses* sharp "classical" properties (only that we could never describe, or rather measure, them accurately), it would be misleading to label this a break-down of "objectifiability" or a "dematerialization". It would be a limitation on *describability,* but this is (from the point of view of classical physics) much less dramatic.

In particular, since such a limitation would in no way challenge the primary-secondary distinction (the "O-primary" properties would be just as objective as before, but would not be fully knowable or measurable by us), it is clear that the dematerialization thesis (insofar as it depends upon *this* strand) stands or falls on whether the "second-level" or interpretative claim about quantum theory's showing a basic independence of the properties *themselves* upon the action of the detector, can be substantiated. There is some question, then, about Dr. Hanson's final contention that this second-level claim does not *need* to be substantiated for his general point about the collapse of the primary-secondary distinction to be validated. Without the demonstration of this claim that he leaves to the future in the last sentence of the paper, his thesis remains incomplete, and the "objector" he creates in his §3 makes a telling point.

As to whether the objector's point is unanswerable: there is still much controversy as to how quantum theory is to be interpreted in this matter; the issue is a philosophic one that does not bear on the predictive structure of the theory itself, but one that has already proved to be of central importance in the controversies about the direction in which the theory should now be developed. Dr. Hanson's position would probably be supported by a majority of physicists, especially by those (although not by any means *only* by those) who adopt the so-called "Copenhagen interpretation" of quantum theory generally. The opposition would come from those who, like Bohm and de Broglie and a majority, perhaps, of Soviet physicists, believe that the possibility of a complete "separation" between detector and object has not been altogether excluded by any finding of quantum theory so far.

It is a mistake, then, to suppose that it would be *generally* agreed that "dematerialization" in this sense has actually occurred. One can make a good case for it, but the issue is likely to remain an open one for some time to come until the trend of development within quantum field theory excludes one or other of the two views above. It ought to be emphasized that even if one were to hold that "dematerialization" of this sort *has* occurred in physics, the smoothing-out of the primary-secondary distinction that it involves is a very modest non-Berkleyan one. The measured properties of the object are shown to depend, not upon the observer as such, but upon the *apparatus* he uses. The point made is not at all, therefore, the same as Berkeley's.

In the first years of the quantum theory of matter, some of the pioneers, notably Bohr, thought that they had shown a dependence of measurement upon the observer as such, and they used this in support of a Kantian-type philosophy. It would be generally agreed today that this is a mistake. Yet when people speak of "dematerialization" in the context of recent science, it is very often this that they have vaguely at the back of their minds. In this case the 'de-' would derive not from the primary-secondary distinction so much as from the older matter-spirit distinction; the idea would be that even apparently "material" properties have been shown somehow to depend upon mind or spirit. It must be emphasized that this inference cannot be legitimately drawn from quantum theory.

Matter and reduction: Instead of taking 'primary' as equivalent roughly to 'independent of the observer', it is possible to take it also as 'irreducible', i.e. not capable of being explained in terms of simpler properties. In the seventeenth century, an atomistic-type ideal of explanation began to be adopted; macroscopic properties, like density and temperature, were "explained" in terms of microscopic entities lacking in these properties. The macroscopic properties are thus "reduced", or eliminated, from the basic list of epistemic primaries needed by science. Instead of discrete irreducible "forms", there are complex physical structures whose total behavior is explained by appealing to the simpler elements of which they are postulated to be built up. It is assumed that every structure is capable of being broken down in this way; the "elements" of the explanation—the atoms, continuous fluids, etc.—are assumed to be unstructured, and their behavior is postulated in advance.

With the Democritean reduction, there entered also a Democritean notion of matter: a permanent stuff of which the universe is made, whose properties (hardness, inertia, bulk . . .) maintain themselves throughout changes. Some (like Descartes) made it co-extensive with space, others (like Boyle) made it move in space, but they agreed in using 'matter' in an absolutist sense: that which is characterized by certain basic properties which mark it off as the proper object of experimental science.[24] There is

------

[24] See the article by Hall below.

clearly a tension between this notion of matter and the reductionist mode of explanation that went with it; there seems to be no inherent reason why any given property or element should be taken to be basic in any other than a temporary sense. The atoms of today are the reducible structures of tomorrow, structures which still more basic elements will serve to explain. On this view, there need be no barrier to reduction, no *irreducible* properties or elements. In that case, how could "matter" be specified in terms of a set of permanent common properties? Properties that are epistemically (or E-) primary at one stage of physical theory may later cease to be so. If "matter" could properly be characterized only by E-primary properties—and this had been the constant (early modern) tradition—it now seemed that its definition had to be relativized.

This realization was slow in coming. It was helped along by the course of events in nineteenth-century science, which indicated that the attempt to define a world-stuff in terms of some irreducible property was not likely to succeed. The gradual disappearance of the earlier "stuff" view can be regarded as a sort of "dematerialization", in the sense that the abandoning of the familiar stuff-analogue leaves the mind groping for a way of representing the world. The cause of the disappearance is no longer the Aristotelian argument that change cannot be accounted for by a basic unchanging stuff which would just take on different forms, if the elements are to be completely interconvertible and if a substance is to be truly one. On the contrary, it is a very non-Aristotelian view of explanation that is primarily responsible. But this alone would not have sufficed—after all, it seems possible that the atoms of nineteenth century physics *might* have proved to be true "atoms", unstructured, incapable of further physical analysis. If that had been so, they would have made a world-stuff after Democritus' own heart. But the fact is that the atoms *were* reduced, and the process continues.

The recent history of science thus supports a more flexible use of the term 'matter', one that will approximate to Aristotle's "material cause", as noted in §2. One can plausibly equate "matter" with the "given" elements in a particular physical theory, the hypothetical entities in terms of whose combinations and interactions the theory will be constructed, the "materials" the theoretician (or "artist") has at his disposal. Since the notion of "material cause" arose in the first instance in the analysis of different facets of explanation, it is appropriate that the "matter" here should be the matter of *theory;* it is the *theoretical* electron, the construct whose properties are fully defined, that serves as the "material" for explaining light-emission, not that still-mysterious cause of cloud-tracks and point scintillations which is the real referent of that construct. When Aristotle made bronze the "material cause" in analyzing the customary description of the molding of a statue, he assumed that the concept, *bronze,* accurately and exhaustively described the real matter of the statue. Hence he could take this latter without remainder to be the "matter" of his "explanation" of the change. Today this would be called a *description* rather than an *explanation,* precisely because of this assumption. In an explanation of the hypothetico-deductive sort that characterizes science today, the "material" element of the explanation is necessarily postulatory and constructed.

"Matter" in this sense is, then, the as-yet unreduced element of theory, specified in terms of E-primaries that are primary relative to *this* theory. If the theory is the broadest possible physical one of its day, like Newtonian mechanics or general relativity theory, the "given" elements of it, whether mass-points or energy-momentum tensors, constitute the basic "matter" with which the science of the day has to deal. These "matter"-elements being fully specified, further reduction can come only by turning back to the "real" matter, and finding some new depths in it. The fact that further reduction, so far, at least, always seems to be possible, opens up a sort of endless horizon, with "matter" always receding before us. The dream of the first reductionists: that there would be a limit to their reduction, an "atom" or irreducible at which science would terminate, has not been realized. The 'de-' of our title is the reminder that their "limit" has long since been passed. It would be interesting to speculate as to whether an absolute limit still awaits the physicist, a limit dictated by the energies available for continuing to penetrate into the interior of the nucleus, perhaps, or by the uncertainty principle, or by the non-individual character of the sub-atomic "particles" that are the "matter" of today's quantum theory, or by the dwindling resources of imaging in a physical (and not just mathematical) way.[25] But this is a topic for another occasion.

Matter and substratum:[26] It is frequently said that the progress of physical science, especially of field theories, makes the notion of an underlying substratum seem unnecessary. The "substratum" here may be taken as a non-describable underlying something, and then the critic will say there is no sign of such an entity in his theory. To which the answer is: of course not, since explicit mention in the theory would preclude its being a non-describable factor. The fact that science continues to push back the "horizon" mentioned in the last paragraph tells us nothing about what lies beyond the horizon. More significant is the suggestion that the notion of an un-

---

[25] See the essay by Woodruff below.
[26] See the paper by Hesse further on.

derlying substantial substratum in which properties inhere, has been eliminated. One does not ask: in what does electromagnetic field strength inhere? what is the carrier of light-waves in "empty space"? Russell in this context speaks of "the disappearance of matter", suggesting that it has been "replaced by emanations from a locality" while "tables and chairs . . . have become pale abstractions, mere laws exhibited in the succession of events which radiate from certain regions".[27]

There is a misunderstanding here. It is true that the apparently continuous objects of sense-experience have been shown to be made up of a myriad of relatively discrete entities with large tracts of relatively empty space between them. But this does not mean that predicates like 'solid', 'impenetrable', cease to be applicable in their normal sense at the macroscopic level. Again, atoms are seen to consist of further separated entities, themselves no longer individuals. But if any matter is "vanishing" here at all, it is the massy particles of seventeenth-century physics. Finally, the ether, originally introduced as a substratum for the transmission of various types of energy, seems to have been eliminated by Relativity Theory.

One over-all comment can be made on this. The constructs of the average physical theory today cannot be classified in Aristotelian terms of substance and property. These latter categories are drawn from, and are applicable to, the objects of sense-experience. But a physical theory is an extremely complex indirect way of conceptualizing reality, and we must not look for one-to-one correspondences between it and the structures and categories of the world the theory represents. If it is wrong to substantialize energy and mass, it is equally wrong to make of the E and H of Maxwell's theory constructs corresponding to *properties,* about which we can ask: in what do they inhere? To say that they do not "inhere in" anything in Maxwell's theory, or that an ether-construct need not be invoked, as was once thought necessary, does *not* commit us to the view that there are real properties "floating" without a concrete substratum. This kind of illegitimate categorial transfer—one might call it the "Pythagorean" fallacy—rests on a faulty grasp of the relation between the constructs and models of physics and the experienced objects whose behavior the former are intended to "explain", in a quite precise, but not simple, sense of the term, 'explain'.

A quite different source for this sort of rejection of an "underlying matter" is to be seen in the philosophical tradition of phenomenalism which goes back to Berkeley. We noted earlier that there is only a single major use of 'matter' in modern philosophy that has not got a direct Greek correlate. The phenomenalists' concern with matter is a negative one: they

---

[27] *An Outline of Philosophy*, London, 1927, p. 106.

33

want to deny its existence. The "matter" they reject is "an incomprehensible somewhat", as Berkeley calls it, an inert substratum of qualities that itself neither perceives nor is perceived. In short, their enemy is Locke's notion of substance, or more generally, any dualistic view which supposes in perceptual objects an unperceivable reality behind the appearances.[28]

Berkeley's immaterialism is no sceptical questioning of the *reality* of the objects of perception; far from it. What he claims, rather, is that the objects of perception are "ideas" which find their support not in an unperceived substratum (for which there cannot be, in the nature of the case, any real—i.e. perceptual—evidence) but rather in a perceiving mind. The matter-substratum against which this polemic is directed is not the Aristotelian one (which is "given" in perception, just as much as form is, though in a different way) but rather a substratum to which one must *infer* (as many of the later scholastics made it appear one had to do), or one which is a passive ground, an inert mass whose motions must come from outside. Kant later argued that *some* sort of "matter" was necessary as a guarantor of empiricism against the rationalism of Descartes and Leibniz. In his system, matter appears in a great many different roles, some of them difficult to reconcile with one another,[29] but the basic one is that of the non-constructed, encountered element in sensation, the correlate of the *a priori* forms of sensibility and the source of singularity and contingency. The epistemological setting is new, but the notion of matter here has obvious Platonic overtones.

Returning to the phenomenalist critique, we may summarize: the phenomenalist position is basically an epistemological one, and 'matter' occurs here only as related in a certain sort of way to perception; the position is itself open to major criticism; it is effective, however, against some seventeenth-century variations on the notion of substratum; it is often vague (especially in its most recent "sense-datum" forms) about just what sort of "matter" it is rejecting, and about who has held for such "matter"; it does not seem to exclude a substratum-subject in the Aristotelian sense.

Matter and space:[30] The Greeks found the relationship between matter and space a very difficult problem. If they did not hold a *plenum* view, they had to assign *some* reality to the "void" (since it is a ground for possible motion), yet it had no predicates whereby it could be regarded as "material". The Atomists and Plato called it "Non-Being", yet a "Non-Being" which had some reality, a near-fatal thesis for *any* metaphysics to sustain.

[28] See the essay by Sayre below.
[29] See Smith's article below for this point.
[30] See the paper by Misner below.

A different problem was posed by the identification of matter and space in seventeenth-century rationalism. Could an adequate account of the universe be given in such terms? We have seen that the lack of a mass-factor doomed this approach to sterility in the domain of mechanics.

In recent times, there has been a major effort to revivify it, using the much more powerful methods of modern geometry. So confident do its exponents feel about their effort that they speak of matter as "evaporating into nothingness", of "building mass out of pure geometry", of "a universe of pure geometry", of seeing "the physical world in which we live" as "a purely mathematical construct".[31] These are strong words to the philosopher. The substance behind them is that attempts are being made to formulate a "geometry" of space-time in which particles would appear as geometrical singularities, electric charges as "worm-holes". They would be specified by the metric itself, and would thus not have to be added as "foreign entities". Their equations of motion would not have to be imposed *ab extra,* but would follow from the geometrical structure of the space. These attempts have not as yet been successful (though Rainich and Misner have succeeded in finding a purely geometrical representation of electromagnetic fields).[32] The advantage of this approach (if successful) would presumably lie in a simpler and more homogeneous mathematical treatment.

To say that such a model only "simulates" the presence of matter, that it is really "empty space", and that thus we have succeeded in doing away with matter, is another form of the "Pythagorean" fallacy, already mentioned. If the geometrical model gives an adequate theoretical representation of the motion of perceived physical objects, then it is acceptable as a *physical theory;* there will be no need to postulate a model in which the masses and the geometry have to be separately specified. There is no question of one model "simulating" matter in a way that the other does not. The geometrical model, by hypothesis, does not omit any feature of matter that the other model includes, for if it did, it would fail as a model. So nothing is "left out", there is no "abolition" of matter.

The mistake here arises from several sources. First, there is the classical ambiguity about whether to call space "material" or not. If it be taken as "non-material", then to formulate a physical theory in terms of a "pure

---

[31] Misner, §1, for the first quotation; the rest in J. A. Wheeler, "Curved empty space-time as the building material of the physical world", in *Logic, Methodology and Philosophy of Science,* ed. by E. Nagel *et al.,* Stanford, 1962, 361–73.

[32] G. Y. Rainich, "Electrodynamics in the General Relativity Theory", *Proc. Nat. Acad. Sc. U.S.A.,* 27, 1925, 106–36; C. Misner and J. A. Wheeler, "Classical physics as geometry", *Ann. Phys.,* 2, 1957, 525–603.

geometry" might seem to make its referent "non-material", or to imply that "there is no matter there". There is a confusion here between *physical* space, the container of, or set of relationships between, the concrete objects of perception, and *mathematical* space, which is a mental construct. The latter is called a "space" only because of certain definite *mathematical* properties it possesses. But the mathematical space-concept can be applied to many things besides physical space. To say, then, that physical space is "non-material", tells us nothing whatever about the "materiality" or otherwise of physical systems to which a mathematical space can be applied via a physical theory.

The second source of the difficulty is that the notion of 'geometry' has been broadened here to include, for example, time as well as space. Thus, the claim that the behavior of matter can be described in terms of "geometry" alone is ambiguous. Were this to mean *Euclidean* geometry, it *would* imply the Cartesian denial of an intrinsic Euclidean non-geometric mass-factor to physical bodies. The term is so broad here, however, that to say that something is exhaustively describable in terms of a "geometry" tells us nothing whatever about its "materiality" or "non-materiality".

Lastly, the notion of *matter* implicit in the claims made for geometro-dynamics is not coherent. Obviously the pure geometric model makes no difference to *physical* "matter", understood as perceptible objects; it would make no sense to say that physical matter has been shown not to exist in consequence of a geometrical discovery. The "matter" which "vanishes" in consequence of the new hypothesis must be a construct-matter within the model itself, or rather one that occurs in the classical theoretical model but not in the new purely geometrical one. But what could this construct-matter be? There are no theoretical predicates that could label it as "matter". To talk of it as a sort of jelly or an inert dot is simply metaphorical. The only difference between the two models lies, not at the level of their referents ("physical matter"), not in a "construct-matter" which occurs in one and not in the other (since there is no way of specifying "matter" that does not apply to both—or neither—equally), but in the methods of mathematical construction used. In one, the mass (not matter) is introduced as a separate non-geometrical factor; in the other, it is deduced from the geometry. Since the mass-measure will be the same in both cases, if matter is "that which mass measures", both models will bear *exactly* the same relation to it.

Matter and energy:[33] The mass-energy equivalence of Special Relativity Theory is often assumed to show that matter and energy are identical and

---

[33] See both Mast papers below.

that in consequence, matter must be less "substantial" than was supposed, a sort of "frozen" energy ready to be released in the form of "immaterial" radiation at any time. This is incorrect. The relation is between *mass* and energy, not matter and energy. Furthermore, it does not identify mass and energy either. They are operationally different measures, and have different dimensionality in an *MLT* system. They are not even numerically equal, unless the velocity of light is put as one unit. Energy is a particular sort of measure of a system; inertial mass is another. Einstein's law, $E = mc^2$, asserts an important relationship between the two measures which allows us to derive one from the other. To say that "mass can be transformed into energy" indicates that the two are in some way *not* identical, or else the notion of "transformation" would make no sense here. What it means is that the sort of entity that lends itself most easily to mass-measurement can change into the sort of entity that lends itself to energy-measurement, in such a way that the combined measures obey a law of conservation.

It is commonly said that once energy was found to be capable of transmission through space, it could then be regarded as a sort of entity.[34] But what was discovered, strictly speaking, was not that "energy" (an entity) was transmitted, but rather that a certain measure in one place was related by a conservation law to a certain measure in another place at a later time. Within the conceptual system itself, this could conveniently be represented as though a construct-entity whose measure was energy passed from one point of space to another. But to go from that to a statement about a moving real entity called "energy" is illegitimate—the Pythagorean "leap" once more. It is this reification of energy, combined with the earlier one of mass, that allows people to say that "mass and energy are identical, they are synonyms for the same physical substratum".[35] We may, if we wish, formulate a more fundamental concept (*massergy* ?) which relates mass- and energy-measures in a conservation law. But it is clear that the mode of existence of a nucleon and that of a nucleon which has been "transformed into energy" are not the same. And we have two terms ready at hand to signify that distinction.

The "dematerialization" here comes not so much from the mass-energy equivalence itself as from the evidence of certain sorts of physical interconvertibility, the measures of which are specified by the Einstein equivalence. It is a "dematerialization" in the sense that a material entity can transform

---

[34] "Energy, thus disjoined from matter (in transport through space), raised its ontological status from a mere accident of a mechanical or physical system to the autonomous rank of independent existence." Jammer, *op. cit.*, p. 173.

[35] Jammer, *op. cit.*, p. 188. For an extreme example of such reification, see Viscount Samuel's contribution to the chapter, "Energy and ether", in H. Samuel and H. Dingle, *A Threefold Cord*, London, 1961.

into something lacking in many of the notes of the seventeenth-century concept of matter: impenetrability, inertial (rest-) mass, and the like. According to earlier ideas on the conservation of mass, this would have been impossible.

The disappearance of the term 'matter' from science: If someone asks a scientist today: "what is *your* concept of matter?", the response may well be: "ought I have one?" Theories of matter, yes, but a characteristic way of using the term, 'matter'? When a physicist talks about "matter" nowadays, is he just using common-sense pre-scientific language? What is there about the referent of this term that marks it off as "material" in a scientist's mind? This is, perhaps, one of the most practical questions that faces us at the end of our enquiry into the concept of matter. We have already seen part of the answer: the term 'matter' has a great many different uses in the context of scientific inquiry, and these uses have been changing in the common direction symbolized by the prefix, 'de-'. But an equally important point remains to be seen, one that introduces a new sense of 'dematerialization': 'matter' in most of its standard uses is coming to be recognized as part of the *meta*-language of science, not a part of the working vocabulary or object-language of the scientist. It is a meta-theoretic term, one which serves to illuminate many facets of the scientific effort in the ways we have noted above, as well as allowing us to talk about the work of science in everyday language. But in its meta-theoretic senses, it has no direct function in scientific theory.

This can best be seen by examining the meta-theoretic character of one of these senses carefully. Let us take "matter" as "material cause", in the sense discussed above. To call something "matter" in this sense will not tell us anything of the properties the thing has: it may be bronze, electric charge . . . depending on the theory. 'Matter' here only serves to indicate the role that the elements so designated will play in setting up the theory; they are the "given", and every theory has its "given". There is no predicate attached to matter, as such, that could function within the theory itself. If we knew matter to be hard or elastic, the term 'material' could be usefully put to work in the theory, for from hardness or elasticity certain verifiable consequences would follow. But we do not, for 'material' in this sense is to be attached to an element (whatever the properties it may happen to possess) which plays a certain sort of part in the explanation in which it occurs. The playing of this part does not, as such, add any physically differentiable properties to the element.

'Matter' in this sense is thus a meta-theoretic term, like 'cause' or 'structure', one that is to be used in talking *about* a theory, or *about* theory in general. But it need not, indeed may not, be used as a functional term within the theory itself. There is nothing it could do there in its own right. It could designate, or refer to, certain elements that continually have to be referred to. But to justify the use of a term, it is not enough that it should designate the referents about which we wish to speak; it must also designate them under an aspect which is relevant to the sort of statement made. Even though the terms 'matter' or 'material' single out the referents we wish to speak of in a particular scientific theory, they do so for the wrong reason, that is, for a reason which is unhelpful in *this* context, though quite appropriate if one were to be doing philosophy of science instead. These terms will not be of direct service in empirical science, unless one can provide a sense for them which would allow them to function *in their own right* within the object-language of empirical theory. Few of the many traditional senses of 'matter' will suffice for this. Most of these are clearly meta-theoretic in character.

For instance, if 'material' serves to denote in a vague way anything that is accessible to empirical investigation, it becomes a sort of scientific "transcendental" term. It can then be used only in talking about science or its object in a general way; it could not serve within a first-level theory, where the predicates are expected to be of the kind which could *conceivably* be absent, because otherwise "verifying" their presence would constitute no warrant for the theory. (This has always constituted a major problem for scientific cosmologies of the Cartesian *plenum* type: if the universe is full of something, how could this something possibly be specified in terms that could be of use in the cosmology itself, since these terms are going to be applicable at all places and all times?) Or again, if 'matter' designates the *substratum* of the various properties treated in the scientific theory, then it does not itself occur among the working predicates of the theory. It is "that which underlies" and is never verbally captured; 'matter' in this sense is central to the philosophical analysis of change, but not to that empirical differentiation between changes which constitutes the basis of natural science. Or again, if 'matter' refers to the individuating principle of "material" objects, it does not fall within the competence of empirical science to treat of it, since science cannot reach the individual, as individual, in its explanations.

In all of these instances, 'matter' is an indispensable meta-theoretic term, but one that scientific theory itself seems able to dispense with. The only senses in which 'matter' could properly be used *within* the object-language would be, first, as a stuff-term connoting the possession of certain non-universal physical properties (e.g. impenetrability) from which consequences could be theoretically deduced (as in early atomic theory), and second, as a term used simply to mark off some of the elements studied in a physical theory from others (as "matter" was distinguished from "space" in Newtonian mechanics). We have already seen that the first of these senses is not of much service in science today; the second one still has some value, however, especially in theories of motion, but a gravitational field is not as easy to mark off from matter as "empty space" used to be.

It would appear, then, that the term 'matter' in most of its uses belongs to the meta-language of science, not to the scientific object-language itself. The realization of this has led to a gradual elimination of the term from technical scientific contexts; the scientist, unlike the philosopher, can do very well without it, although he will need it right away, and in several of its senses, if he is to talk *about* his science or try to make it intelligible in a larger context. Since scientists like to do this, they may sometimes be unaware that the terms 'matter' and 'material' they keep using have become a mark of philosophic, rather than scientific, discourse. This dismissal from science of 'matter' in most of its senses is perhaps the most striking way in which "dematerialization" has come about. This sense of 'dematerialization' differs entirely from the others discussed above; in them, the 'de-' was relative to a particular concept of matter and the "dematerialization" was brought about by advances in science. Whereas this last 'de-' concerns all, or almost all, the many concepts of matter we have reviewed; it does not say that they apply less, or differently, than was formerly supposed. It simply indicates that they do not, for the most part, pertain directly to *empirical science,* despite past belief to the contrary. In fact, it would not be too incorrect to say (within the restrictions noted above) that the scientist no longer needs the concept of matter in the routine practice of his science. He will call upon it at most only at those critical moments of philosophical shift and swing that accompany and condition major theoretical discoveries.

The point here is a philosophical one, not directly dependent upon scientific discovery, as were the other "dematerializations" above. Yet it had to await the development of science, for an obvious reason. There was no clear distinction in Greek physics between the philosophical and the scientific components, between meta-language and object-language, between philosophy of science (or of nature) and science. It is usually not too difficult to decide after reading a passage in Aristotle's works on Nature to what genre of explanation (in modern terms) the passage belongs. But since the need to distinguish the two had not yet been felt, no question arose about where the key-term, 'matter', properly belonged.

This was still to a great extent true in seventeenth century "natural philosophy". Its exponents, though well aware of the novelty of what they were doing, tended at first to regard it as a new form of philosophy, not as a discipline quite different in its methodology, basis and import. Thus, Newton, as we have seen, will define mass in terms of "matter" in his mechanics, relying on a pre-scientific and unexplicitated notion of "matter". Outside of the systematic philosophical context in which this notion had originated, it could not really have *been* defined; it originally responded to a far less specific need than Newton's. It had no operational physical definition, nor anything to harness it to one. It appeared here as a sort of "stuff", and the (unanswerable) question of what predicates are to identify it was shelved, since a numerical measure has now replaced it in the actual workings of science. 'Matter' is thus no more than a general name for any entity which produces the inertial or gravitational effects that are measurable as "mass". It will be useful to the scientist, not directly in his theories, but only as a label to mark off entities which "have mass" from those which do not. And as we have seen, even this dichotomy, almost from Newton's time onwards, became less and less clear-cut.

Today, then, the Newtonian concept of matter (*that which has mass*) is clearly understood to have been an entirely derivative one. As a means to theoretical insight, the concept of matter is entirely the property of the philosopher and the "meta-scientist". Their insights concerning it affect the course of science undoubtedly, though they lie at a level of conceptual analysis where the sharp tools of the hypothetico-predictive method are not directly effective. The advance, in turn, that these latter tools render possible, may well furnish vital material for the philosopher. But although interaction in both these directions between science and philosophy is important, this does not blur our final conclusion that the concept of matter can of its nature be of *direct* concern only to the philosopher, and especially to the philosopher of science, even though it is, for all the reasons we have seen above, of continuing though indirect concern to the scientist also.

PART ONE

Matter in Greek and Medieval Philosophy

THE CONCEPT OF MATTER
IN PRESOCRATIC PHILOSOPHY

Czesław Lejewski

The first systematic examination of the concept of matter in early Greek philosophy appears to have been attempted by Aristotle in Bk. I of his *Metaphysics*. Of course Aristotle approaches his subject from the point of view of his own theory of nature but this need not prevent us from adapting to our present purpose the pattern of his enquiry. Thus in what follows we propose to examine, in their historical order, the relevant doctrines of the older "physiologists", Thales, Anaximander, Anaximenes, and Heraclitus; then the concept of the void, which most probably was introduced into philosophical discussion by the pre-Parmenidean Pythagoreans, will be given attention. In particular we shall be interested in the doctrines of the Eleatics, whose rejection of the existence of the void appears to have influenced the theories of matter worked out by the younger philosophers of nature, Empedocles, Anaxagoras, Leucippus, and Democritus. The Pythagorean speculations on the nature and function of number are omitted as they are related rather to the concept of form than to that of matter.

In Bk. II, Ch. 3, of his *Physics,* Aristotle discusses his famous theory of the four kinds of cause: material, formal, efficient, and final. He gives it great prominence in his system because for him knowledge in general consists in knowing the causes of things. When he remarks in Bk. I, Ch. 3, of the *Metaphysics* that for the first philosophers the material cause was the only cause of all things, he refers to his theory of causality:

> That of which all things that are consist, the first from which they come to be, the last into which they are resolved (the substance remaining, but changing in its modifications), this they say is the element and this the principle of things, and therefore they think nothing is either generated or destroyed, since this sort of entity is always conserved, as we say Socrates neither comes to be absolutely when he comes to be beautiful or musical, nor ceases to be when he loses these characteristics, because the substratum, Socrates himself, remains.[1]

Admittedly this is nothing other than Aristotle's own formulation of what he thought was the concept of matter in the early stage of philosophizing.

---

[1] *Met.* 983b 8, Oxford trans.

Thus, for instance, the notion of substratum (as illustrated by the example of Socrates in the quotation) characterizes Aristotle's own conceptual scheme, and seems to be entirely foreign to the Presocratics from Thales to Democritus. Yet Aristotle is in substantial accord with the preserved fragments of the early Greek doctrines when he says that by material cause the first philosophers understood *that of which* all things that are consist, *the first from which* they come to be, and *the last into which* they are resolved. We tentatively accept this general characterization of the concept of matter although in the light of the views attributable to individual Presocratics we may wish to amplify it in a way which differs from the Aristotelian paraphrase.

It is rather disconcerting that our sources tell us so little about the doctrines of Thales. According to Aristotle, this founder of philosophy maintained that water was the "principle". The theory might have been suggested to him by the fact that food was moist and that so were the seeds of all things. The belief that heat itself was generated from the moist and kept alive by it, might also have influenced Thales.[2] If Aristotle's explanation (which is repeated by the doxographical tradition) is correct, it only implies that in Thales' view water was a necessary condition of life. Since for Thales the whole universe was probably alive, a position which he expressed by saying that everything was full of gods, it is not surprising that water suggested itself to him as *that from which* the world and everything in it had originated. For after all, this would only be a rationalization of certain mythological conceptions which in the time of Thales had currency not only in Greece but also in the neighbouring countries of the Near East. But can we go further and attribute to Thales the belief that *that of which* all things consisted was water in one form or another? Aristotle and the doxographical tradition appear to be somewhat ambiguous on this point. Since, however, the doctrine that everything not only had originated from water but in fact consisted of water, would call at once for some explanation of how the various modifications of the original matter could come about, and since, further, this problem according to our evidence was first approached by Anaximenes, we may be justified in suggesting that Thales did not go beyond asserting that water was the original "stuff" from which everything came to be. Nor do we have sufficient evidence for attributing to Thales the view that in the last resort everything would resolve into water. The isolated statement by Servius seems to suggest such a view but is not supported by any parallel testimony.[3]

---

[2] *Met.* 983b 18 ff.

[3] H. Diels, *Fragmente der Vorsokratiker*, 11A 13.

We know a little more about the doctrine of Anaximander, the compatriot and younger contemporary of Thales. He identified the primary matter with the indeterminate, or *to apeiron* as he called it, which he conceived as *that from which* everything came to be and *that into which* everything would finally be resolved. It is very unlikely, however, that Anaximander went so far as to assert that the *apeiron* was *that of which* all existing things consisted. The term 'apeiron', which according to the doxographical tradition he was the first to introduce into the philosophical vocabulary, appears to have had a double meaning. On the one hand it is synonymous with 'spatially infinite' or 'boundless' or 'inexhaustible'. On the other hand our sources imply that Anaximander used the term with reference to something that could be contrasted with qualitatively determined substances such as air, water, or earth. In Anaximander's view the original matter had to be boundless so that the coming to be might not cease. And it had to be qualitatively undetermined because otherwise it might destroy all other kinds of matter opposed to it.[4] From the only sentence preserved out of Anaximander's book, we learn that existing things are eventually resolved into that from which they came to be, "as is meet; for they make reparation and satisfaction to one another for their injustice according to the ordering of time".[5] Here the *apeiron* is both *that from which* and *that into which*; and it would appear that what "make reparation and satisfaction to one another" are existing things on the one hand and the *apeiron* on the other. To put it in terms reminiscent of what Heraclitus was to have to say about half a century later, all things are an exchange for the *apeiron* and the *apeiron* for all things.[6] According to Anaximander, the *apeiron* was eternal, un-aging, and indestructible. It was in eternal motion, and as a result, opposites such as hot and cold could separate off from it. This separating off of determinate opposites would lead eventually to the generation of the heavens and the worlds. However, the mechanics of the separating off of opposites is by no means clear to us, and possibly enough was not quite clear to Anaximander himself. It is tempting to assume that he conceived his original matter, the *apeiron,* as a sort of indeterminate mixture of determinate ingredients. And this is how Aristotle seems inclined to interpret the Milesian philosopher. Such an interpretation, however, probably reads doctrines into Anaximander that are more likely to have originated later with Empedocles and Anaxagoras.

A further step in formulating the concept of matter was made by Anaximander's pupil, Anaximenes. He identified matter with air. Air for him was

4 Aristotle, *Phys.* 203b 15, and 204b 24 ff.
5 Diels, 12B 1; the Burnet translation is used here and in what follows.
6 Diels, 22B 90.

not only *that from which* everything came to be and *that into which* everything would resolve, but also *that of which* everything consisted. He believed that the various kinds of substance known in experience were nothing other than different modifications of air due to rarefaction or condensation. Air in its usual state was most even and hence invisible, but it made its presence perceptible when it became cold or hot or damp or when it was in motion. Rarefied air would assume, he thought, the form of fire. When condensed a little, it would have the form of wind and then the form of cloud. Further condensed it would become water, then earth, and finally stones. All existing things consisted of these and similar materials.[7] The theory of rarefaction and condensation of air was much simpler and more intuitively acceptable than Anaximander's "separating off" from the indeterminate. It "divided the critics", being accepted by some and rejected by others, but it had far-reaching implications which seem to have been worked out only by the atomists. Like Anaximander's *apeiron*, the *air* of Anaximenes was boundless or inexhaustible as regards its volume, and it was in eternal motion, which accounted for its modifications. It encompassed the whole universe and was, as it were, the soul of the universe; which perhaps simply meant the principle and condition of life, just as water had been for Thales. It is not surprising that the philosopher regarded air as divine, as according to our sources he did.

Judging from what we find in the doxographic tradition, the concept of matter in Heraclitus was not unlike that in Anaximenes except that Heraclitus identified it with fire. It has to be admitted, however, that the evidence for his view (as derived from such fragments of Heraclitus' book as have been preserved) is not as conclusive as we would have wished. Heraclitus usually expressed himself in metaphorical language, whose meaning may easily have become lost through rationalization by the doxographers. Moreover, we must not forget that, generally speaking, Heraclitus' main problem was change, rather than primary matter. If the doxographers are to be trusted, Heraclitus had conceived of matter as *that from which* everything came to be, *that of which* everything consisted, and *that into which* everything would ultimately resolve; for him this primary matter was fire. Every other kind of substance was a modification of, or an exchange for, fire due to condensation. For when fire was condensed it became first moist and then water; with further condensation it became earth. Concurrently with this condensation the opposite process of rarefaction was supposed to take place. Thus rarefied earth would become liquid, turn to water, and so give rise to everything else.

---

[7] Diels, 13A 5, 6, and 7.

Such seems to be the way in which following Theophrastus the doxographers interpreted what Heraclitus had described as the upward and downward path.[8] In the fragments genuinely attributable to himself we do not find any explicit reference to condensation or rarefaction. One can hardly resist the suspicion that this sober theory of Milesian origin has been read into some obscure aphorisms of Heraclitus by Theophrastus. From the authentic fragments we only learn that the present world "was ever, is now, and ever shall be an ever-living Fire, with measures of it kindling, and measures going out". "All things are an exchange for Fire, and Fire for all things, even as wares for gold and gold for wares." According to Heraclitus "the transformations of Fire are, first of all sea; and half of the sea is earth, half whirlwind". On the other hand earth "becomes liquid sea, and is measured by the same tale as before it became earth".[9] Some testimonies about Heraclitus imply that he described the transformations or modifications of fire as living the death of one another. Thus in his view apparently air lived the death of fire, water the death of air, and earth the death of water; but in turn to become water meant the death of earth, and to become air or fire meant respectively the death of water or air.[10] In this idea we easily recognize Anaximander's theory of "reparation" and "satisfaction".

The predecessors of Heraclitus used to attribute to matter properties which, to our way of thinking, appear incompatible with it. Thus Anaximander described the *apeiron* in terms equally applicable to gods. For him the *apeiron* was un-aging, immortal, and divine, encompassing and steering all things.[11] Anaximenes similarly regarded as divine the air-principle. This line of thought, which eventually led to the distinguishing of a non-material principle in the origin and development of the universe, was also followed by Heraclitus. He taught that fire steered all things.[12] Moreover, in some of the fragments and testimonies we come across the concept of *logos*, which appears to be related to that of fire as constitutive of the universe. It has certain material characteristics, since it is supposed to encompass the world like the *apeiron* of Anaximander and the air of Anaximenes. On the other hand, it is regarded as the source of intelligence in men.[13]

The older "physiologists" have tried to explain the multiplicity of the materials to be found in experience by assuming one kind of matter to be

---

[8] Diels, 22A 1 (7, 8, 9), 5.
[9] Diels, 22B 30, 90, 31.
[10] Diels, 22B 76; see also 36 and 62.
[11] Diels, 12B 2, 3, and A 15.
[12] Diels, 22B 64.
[13] Diels, 22A 16.

basic and showing how the other kinds originated from it. For this reason they have been called "monists" while the term 'pluralist' has been assigned to Empedocles and Anaxagoras, who postulated matter of several kinds, irreducible to one another. This corporeal or material monism, and its opposite, corporeal or material pluralism, should not be confused with what can perhaps best be described as the "structural" monism of the Eleatics, and its corresponding opposite. The philosophers of Elea were not primarily interested in the notion of matter as *"that of which* all things that are consist, *the first from which* they come to be, and *the last unto which* they are resolved", and their structural monism seems to have resulted from their uncompromising rejection of the concept of the void.

As far as one can judge, the concept of the void was introduced into the philosophical vocabulary by the early Pythagoreans. It is only natural that at first they did not see its implications with great clarity. The scanty evidence to be found in Aristotle's *Physics* suggests that the Pythagoreans conceived of the void as encompassing the world or being contained in that which encompassed the world. It was inhaled by the latter like breath or air, and served as the principle of division or differentiation between things.[14] It is most likely that in these early speculations the void was regarded as opposite to concrete or "full" things, yet at the same time it was thought to be real.

Parmenides criticizes this confusion in very strong terms. He is most anxious to establish that the totality of being is one continuous *plenum* with no room for an empty space, and this central thesis of structural monism is hardly a theory which could be ignored by the younger "physiologists" in their inquiries into the nature of primary matter. For structural monism excludes the possibility of reducing the multiplicity of kinds of matter to one substance by invoking the principle of rarefaction and condensation. This was seen by Parmenides himself who rejects the principle most emphatically:

> There is no more of it (i.e., of that which is) in one place than in another, to hinder it from holding together, nor less of it, but everything is full of what is. Wherefore it is wholly continuous; for what is, is in contact with what is.[15]

Similarly Melissus argues that:

> It cannot be dense and rare; for it is not possible for what is rare to be as full as what is dense, but what is rare is at once emptier than what is dense.[16]

Empedocles, who seems to have accepted the structural monism of Par-

---

[14] Aristotle, *Physics* 213b 22 ff.
[15] Diels, 28B 8 (23 ff.).
[16] Diels, 30B 7 (8).

menides, was the first to replace the material monism of the Ionian philosophers by a material pluralism. He assumed four different kinds of matter: earth, water, air, and fire. Mixed in different proportions these elements, or "roots" as they were called by Empedocles, produced the variety of objects given in experience. Change was reduced to a mixing and unmixing of elements, which were themselves eternal and unchangeable. Like the air of Anaximenes, they were divine. And indeed Empedocles assigned to them names of deities. In Empedocles' view the four were enough to account for the whole variety of the phenomenal world. But he thought of them as passive. Left alone they would not enter into the various mixtures. Nor would they separate from one another, were their original state that of a mixture. Thus Empedocles feels compelled to introduce the concept of an *active* principle, and decides upon two such. He refers to them as "love" and "strife", but describes them as if they were kinds of matter.

By introducing these two concepts into his explanation of the changing world Empedocles was in fact exploring the idea of efficient cause. This is at least how the doxographers are anxious to interpret him. According to Empedocles, love and strife appear to be conducive, respectively, to the mixing of the passive elements and to their unmixing. In the great cosmic process of change, love and strife enjoy an alternating predominance. Love leads to the perfect mixture of the four elements while the predominance of strife culminates in the four being entirely separated one from another. Existing things come to be either from the union of the four elements into appropriate mixtures under the rule of love, or from the all-embracing mixture having become differentiated under the influence of strife into portions consisting of uneven shares of each element. Correspondingly, existing things dissolve under the rule of love into the total mixture, but when strife is predominant they break up into the four elements. There seems to be a certain Heraclitean feature in this double scheme of generation and destruction, reminding one of the upward and downward path of the Ephesian.

According to Empedocles then, all existing things consist of different mixtures of the four primary kinds of matter. This he explains with the aid of a very ingenious model:

> Just as when painters are elaborating temple-offerings, men whom wisdom hath well taught their art—they, when they have taken pigments of many colours with their hands, mix them in due proportion, more of some and less of others, and from them produce shapes like unto all things, . . . —so let not the error prevail over thy mind, that there is any other source of all perishable creatures that appear in countless numbers.[17]

[17] Diels, 31B 23.

In every object, then, Empedocles saw a harmonious mixture of the four primary kinds of matter comparable with the mixture of pigments in the work of a painter. No other ingredient, material or non-material, was required except perhaps the presence of love or strife, depending upon whether the object was a result of the unifying process or whether it came to be in the process of decomposition. This model, together with certain other implicit remarks to be found in our sources, suggests that in explaining the variety of objects in the world Empedocles thought in terms of mechanistic mixture rather than in terms of fusion. Galen reports that according to Empedocles, compound bodies came into being from the unchangeable four elements mixed with one another in the same way in which someone, having crushed different kinds of ore into very fine powder, might mix them so that it would not be possible to take from the mixture a portion consisting of only one kind of ore without the admixture of any other kind. Galen points out that Hippocrates was the first to talk about fusion of elements, and that in this respect he differed from Empedocles, who said that men and all other earthly bodies were the result not of fusion of elements but of mixture, whereby small particles were placed side by side and touched one another.[18] If what Galen says is correct, we ought to give Empedocles the credit for preparing the ground for the two most mature theories of matter worked out before Plato and Aristotle, those of Anaxagoras and of the Atomists.

Anaxagoras was probably older than Empedocles but his treatise was written after Empedocles' poem had been in circulation for some time. This seems to be implied by a remark in Aristotle's *Metaphysics*.[19] Both Empedocles and Anaxagoras accept the structural monism of the Eleatics and try to reconcile it with the world of experience by postulating material pluralism. But the material pluralism of Anaxagoras is bolder and more original than that of Empedocles. We saw that according to Empedocles every material object consisted of small particles each of which was pure fire, or pure air, or pure water, or pure earth, but Empedocles did not consider the problem as to whether or not these particles were divisible any further. Anaxagoras, on the other hand, assumed an unlimited number of different kinds of material substance. Moreover, he explicitly accepted infinite divisibility of matter: "Nor is there a least of what is small, but there is always a smaller; for it cannot be that what is should cease to be by being cut."[20]

---

[18] Diels, 31A 34.

[19] *Met.* 984a 11. To interpret Aristotle as wishing to say that compared with those of Empedocles, Anaxagoras' views were inferior, does not appear to do justice either to Anaxagoras' imaginative theorizing or to Aristotle's capability for impartial criticism.

[20] Diels, 59B 3.

The principle of infinite divisibility of matter has proved puzzling even to some modern commentators. Yet there is no evidence that Anaxagoras himself was confused about its far-reaching implications. By assuming it, he was able to contend, without falling into contradiction, that in any portion of determinate matter, say gold, there was a portion of every other kind of matter:

> And since the portions of the great and of the small are equal in amount, for this reason, too, all things will be in everything; nor is it possible for them to be apart but all things have a portion of everything.[21]

Thus there is no pure air, pure water, or pure gold but "each single thing is and was manifestly those things of which it has most in it". The only exception is *Nous,* which is mixed with nothing but is alone, itself by itself.[22] The principle that in everything there are portions or "seeds" of everything else explained the fact that food in the form of bread and water turned into hair, blood, flesh, nerves, and bones, which in their turn contained "seeds" of everything else. For it is quite consistent with the theory of Anaxagoras to hold that in every "seed" there were "seeds" of everything else. In fact this is only a special case of his general principle that "in everything there is a portion of everything", which is secured by the principle of infinite divisibility.

According to the doxographers the "seeds" were not perceptible by the senses. They could, however, be known by reason. Aetius reports that Anaxagoras called them "homeomeries", as they were similar to what they formed when collected in sufficient amount.[23] This sense of the term has to be distinguished from the Aristotelian 'homeomerous' as applied to material substances whose parts were believed to be the same in kind as the wholes. There is no evidence that Anaxagoras used the term 'homeomerous' at all, let alone in the sense comparable to that assigned to it by Aristotle.

We must also note that though progress in the search for an efficient cause is to be credited to Anaxagoras, he failed to arrive at the concept of a non-corporeal being. His *Nous* is "infinite and self-ruled, and mixed with nothing" but it is material. It is "the thinnest of all things and the purest, and it has all knowledge about everything and the greatest strength". Being alone by itself it "has power over all things . . . that have life". "And all things that are mingled together and separated off and distinguished are all known by *Nous*. And *Nous* set in order all things that were to be, and all things that were and are not now and that are . . ."[24] It was the cause

---

[21] Diels, 59B 6.
[22] Diels, 59B 12.
[23] Diels, 59A 46.
[24] Diels, 59B 12.

of rotary motion, which occurred in various areas of the infinite mass of matter and constituted the beginning of worlds like ours.

Since Anaxagoras is inclined to speculate in terms of a "linear" rather than a "cyclic" development of the universe, he is primarily interested in the concept of matter as the concept of *that from which* all things come to be and *that of which* all things consist. The concept of *that into which* all things are eventually resolved does not seem to play a part in his theories.

The structural monism of Parmenides appears to have been derived from the rejection of the reality of the void: it is not true that the void is real or, to put the point in other words, it is not true that the void exists; therefore reality must be a *plenum,* matter must be continuous, portions of matter must touch one another, there must be no gaps, and, as Melissus was to point out, the totality of existing things, i.e., the One, must be infinite in volume. This argument was accepted as valid even by some who questioned its conclusion, like Empedocles and Anaxagoras and even the atomists. As we saw above, the variety of the phenomenal world was explained by Empedocles and Anaxagoras with the aid of the theory of "mingling and separation" of elements or seeds. Now the theory of mingling and separation appeared to imply the concept of motion, which had been flatly rejected by the Eleatics. Empedocles and Anaxagoras took motion for granted and were only concerned with its causal explanation. They did not try to explain its possibility under the conditions presupposed by the structural monism. This difficult problem was left to the atomists. But they, faced with the alternative of denying motion or rejecting the concept of a plenum, made concessions to experience and postulated the discontinuity of matter. In virtue of the Parmenidean argument, discontinuity of matter implied the existence and reality of the void, and the atomists accepted this conclusion. Leucippus held, so we are told by Theophrastus, that "that *what is* is no more real than *what is not,* and that both are alike causes of things that come into being; for he laid down that the substance of the atoms was compact and full, and he called them *what is* while they moved in the void which he called *what is not,* but affirmed to be just as real as *what is*".[25]

It appears that we can press the point even a little further and say that for both the Eleatics and the atomists the denial of existence to the void was equivalent to postulating the *plenum,* and consequently that the denial of the *plenum* was equivalent to asserting the existence of the void. Neither the Eleatics nor the atomists saw that these equivalences did not in fact hold. To say that the void exists may mean a number of things. It may mean (*a*) that the void is something, i.e., that the void is an entity, a being, an

---

[25] Diels, 67A 8.

object. Or it may mean (*b*) that the totality of existing things is an object which, as regards structure, is discrete or discontinuous, i.e., consists of parts which do not touch one another. It may mean (*c*) that the totality of existing things is continuous but porous or finally (*d*) that the totality of existing things is an object that is finite as regards its spatial extension. Now when the Eleatics denied the existence of the void they seemed to understand their thesis as denying (*a*). In their view it was not the case that the void was a being or a real object. When, however, they turned to drawing conclusions from their rejection of the reality of the void, they either treated their assumption as if it were the denial of (*b*), as was the case with Parmenides, or they treated it as if it were the denial of (*b*) and, at the same time, the denial of (*d*), as was the case with Melissus. The possibility of (*c*) was tacitly disregarded. In this way the Eleatics tried to conclude that the totality of existing things was a *plenum*, finite (Parmenides) or infinite (Melissus). They failed to notice that the denial of (*a*) was compatible with (*b*) or (*c*) or(*d*). The atomists make a similar mistake. Their principal thesis implied (*b*), i.e., that the totality of existing things consisted of parts that did not touch one another. This they expressed by saying that the void existed, which in turn was mistakenly equated by them with (*a*), i.e., with the assertion that the void was a real entity, no less real than the atoms. Hence they described it as *rare*, and regarded it, according to Aristotle, as a *material* cause of things on a par with the atoms.[26] Nevertheless, it is very likely that they would have denied the existence of the void in the sense of (*a*), had they only been able to see that this denial was consistent with the thesis asserting the discontinuity of matter.

The atomists' theory of matter can be briefly characterized as structural pluralism and material monism. According to atomists matter, which is conceived as *that from which, that of which,* and *that into which,* consists of an infinite number of atoms each of which is a *plenum*. The atoms are of all shapes and they differ in size, but they are all invisible because of their smallness. No part of an atom can be separated from the rest of it but it can be distinguished by reason. Atoms are eternal, indestructible, and evermoving. In substance they do not differ from one another (material monism), but they differ from any perceptible material. The qualitative differences between perceptible kinds of matter are accounted for by the differences in size, shape, position, and arrangement of the atoms involved, which by their coming together effect the coming of things into being, and by separation, their passing away. Contrary to Empedocles and Anaxagoras the atomists assumed no efficient cause originative of motion. They took motion

---

[26] *Met.* 985b 4 ff.

for granted, just as the early Milesians did, but believed it to be subject to laws, or as they used to put it, to "necessity". They did not, however, give any clear account of these laws.

It seems to be clear that the concept of matter which the Presocratic philosophers began to develop was destined to play a role of significance rather to science than to philosophy. Thus Leucippus and Democritus are regarded as the precursors of John Dalton, and Empedocles is sometimes described as the father of chemistry. The philosopher's concept of matter, on the other hand, seems to require a concept of form as its opposite and complement. While the origins of such a concept of form can perhaps be traced back to the Pythagoreans, its articulate application appears to be recognisable only in the writings of Plato and Aristotle.[27]

University of Manchester.

---

[27] Professor J. W. Scott has kindly read the typescript and offered many stylistic improvements.

COMMENT

REMAINING WITHIN THE CONVENTIONAL PICTURE OF PRESOCRATIC PHILOSOPHY, Professor Lejewski's paper has located the early Greek notion of matter as "*that of which* all things that are consist". Accompanying the notion more or less regularly are the concepts *that from which* all things originate, and *that into which* all things are resolved.—This description isolates a primitive, though workable, concept of matter. At the same time, however, the Presocratics regarded their material principle as endowed with life, and as steering and encompassing and holding together the universe. They looked upon it as something active, intelligent, and divine. They included in it not only what we today would understand by matter, but also nearly everything that we would directly oppose to matter. Aristotle separated these different phases in the Presocratic teachings, and we today can separate them easily enough. But did the Presocratics themselves do so? Did the Presocratics, then, really isolate any concept that could be called matter in contradistinction to form or energy or intelligence or to any other non-material principle? Or on the contrary, is the notion of matter, as it originally emerged in western philosophy, also to be identified with activity, intelligence, and divinity, in such a way that no surprise should be caused by later ascriptions of these attributes to it?

Secondly, Lejewski prefers to leave out the Pythagoreans on the ground that their speculations concern form rather than matter.—Yet their doctrines that the heavens inhale the void and that the unlimited is constrained and limited by the limit, seem to present the closest approximation among the Presocratics to the later contrast of matter with form. At the end of his paper, Lejewski sees in Pythagoreanism a possible origin for the philosopher's, though not for the scientist's, concept of matter. The problem, accordingly, seems to call for more discussion.

Finally, Lejewski offers four possible meanings for the 'void' of the Atomists. —The sponge-like structure in the third alternative does not actually appear in Presocratic philosophy, he acknowledges. Moreover, it would seem to evade the pertinent problems of action at a distance, since it allows labyrinthine material conductors of action to any part whatsoever. The fourth alternative presents an Eleatic rather than Atomistic problem. The problem for the Atomists, accordingly, concerned the equating of the first two alternatives. The Atomists conceived as an entity the discontinuity between the atoms. According to Aristotle, they regarded the void "as a *material* cause of things on a par with the atoms". The interpretation so far is compatible with the Aristotelian text. But Lejewski's further exegesis that the atomists described the void as the rare, is open to question. The text at *Meta.* A 4,985b7 is at least doubtful. The manuscript authority is divided. Recent editors (Ross, Jaeger—see Jaeger's note *ad loc.*) omit the 'rare' at b7, though some translators (Tredennik, Warrington, Tricot) retain it. Further, the text (b10–19) compares the dense and the rare not directly with the atoms and void, but with different shapes, position, and arrangement of the atoms (see Ross's comment at b13). This doctrine of the Atomists reported by Aristotle, however, raises the interesting problem as to whether for them the concept of matter should be extended to the void as well as to the plenum. If, as held today, material things consist of particles and "empty" space, must both be included under the concept of matter? Does the Democritean statement of the problem offer any help towards elucidating the present-day conception of "empty" space?

Joseph Owens, C.Ss.R.
Pontifical Institute of
Mediaeval Studies.

THE MATERIAL SUBSTRATE

IN PLATO

Leonard J. Eslick

... (Plato) used only two causes, that of the essence and the material cause (for the Forms are the causes of the essence of all other things, and the One is the cause of the essence of the Forms); and it is evident what the underlying matter is, of which the Forms are predicated in the case of sensible things, and the One in the case of Forms, viz. that this is a dyad, the great and the small.

—*Aristotle*, Metaphysics, *I, 6, 988a 8-13*

⚑ To speak of "matter" in Plato is, of course, to run the risk of misunderstanding. It is a word, meaning originally wood or timber, which Aristotle seems to be the first to have used in a technical philosophical sense. There are those who deny that Plato, strictly speaking, has any doctrine of matter or material cause.[1] Certainly, even if one is to go as far as Friedlander, who tells us that Plato originated the doctrine of matter[2], it must be recognized that the concept in Plato is not at all the same as Aristotle's *wood*. There is, in both of them, an indeterminate substrate, a principle of limitation of form or essence, but the mode of reality and functioning of this principle are profoundly different in each. The need for positing a material substrate, the nature and mode of its existence, the scope of its causation—all these questions are pertinent, in radically diverse ways, to the undertanding of the most significant oppositions within their thought.

Plato's approach to the existence of matter is for the most part diametrically opposed to that of Aristotle's. It is true that, in a general sense, the Platonic method is determined by an aversion to the fleeting, Heraclitean things of sense, and by a conversion to ideal archetypes, and ultimately, to a preeminently transcendent unity, a principle which at once accounts for the reality of all things and yet falls short of being the total explanation for the way things are. Nevertheless, the fundamental datum for the Platonic philosophy is the world of the concrete; it is *this* world given in experience

[1] Cf. W. D. Ross, *Plato's Theory of Ideas,* Oxford, Clarendon, 1951, pp. 233–34.

[2] P. Friedlander, *Plato,* Vol. 1, *An Introduction.* Translated by Hans Meyerhoff. New York, Pantheon, 1958, p. 249.

which Plato sets out to explain. Yet by all that it is, it is a world of *image* and unreality, a world given not to reason but to sense. Hence, in view of the assumption that the world of sense experience is characterized by intrinsic instability and non-permanence, by *imaging*, Plato's approach to the principles which account for this world cannot be inductive. There is no potential intelligibility to be actualized from that which always becomes and never is, nothing within image-beings which the mind can draw out, no possible content in terms of which human reason can be related to the things of experience and be able to organize them into the unity of science.

My first observation is then: whatever the causes for image-reality these causes cannot themselves be image. They must represent not what is ever the fleeting shadow of some other but what, in its own rights, is and, as such, is permanent and ultimate. These causes must, therefore, be attained aprioristically. The experience of image-reality will be helpful only in a conditional and negative sense, and to the extent that it leads *beyond* the beings which exist by imaging to the principles which explain both their tenuous hold on nature and their image-mode of existing.

How, if possible, does a philosopher explain such a world? How is the not really real, that which is and yet is not, to be brought into the unity requisite for knowledge? To the rationalist, Plato's answer is indeed both evasive and paradoxical. For if the world of becoming is unsubstantial image, knowledge of it properly concerns not it but that of which it is the image. Then to know this world is really not to know it at all.

Now it is clear to Plato first of all that if image-beings exist, there also exists the archetypal reality of which the image-beings are image. An image, by all that it is (or better, by all that it is not) points to the existence of the imaged, and so while we must transcend the order of sense experience to attain the existence of the paradigm reality, this existence is in some way already established in the very existence of the images themselves.[3] Secondly, it is clear to Plato that since images, as such, fall short of the reality imaged[4], there must also exist over and against the reality which the image-beings merely reflect, something *other,* which explains this deficiency, this imitative way of being. For if the reality which is imaged accounts for the *being* imaged, it does not by this line of reasoning explain the *image*-beings, the imagings, the ontological degradation of the copy as compared to the model. The understanding of this seems of utmost importance to what I will

---

[3] In a similar way for Kant, the existence of the phenomenal order points to the necessary existence of the noumenal, of the *ding an sich.*

[4] Cf. L. J. Eslick, "The Two Cratyluses: The Problem of Identity of Indiscernibles", *Atti del XII Congresso Internazionale di Filosofia*, Vol. XI, Firenze, Sansoni, 1960, pp. 81–87.

call "the Platonic dilemma". This dilemma, rooted in the Platonic *chorismos,* is fundamentally this: If that which is imaged (ultimately Unity in the case of the Forms, and the Forms in the case of sensibles) represents the essence of that which is image, and exists nonetheless in a state of ontological separation from them, then the essence imaged cannot formally explain the imagings, i.e. the defective or privative character of the images. Yet to imitate is to imitate something, and this thing imitated is, for Plato, essence itself, so that imaging must in some real sense be explicable by the essence imaged. If image-beings are natureless in themselves and have natures in a purely relational and imitative way then their imitating must somehow be causally related to the nature imitated. Thus by the real separation, on the one hand, and the image-likeness on the other, Plato must both deny and affirm that image-beings *qua* images are explicable in terms of essence or true form. Now the difficulty becomes ever more acute once we find Plato demonstrating the existence of matter as principle from precisely the identical premise upon which he bases the necessity for positing a principle of transcendent essence or true being, namely, the imaging of that which is image. It is necessary to consider this imaging as the basis for matter's existence before I can properly deal with the dilemma I have outlined, and come to any adequate determination of the causality exercised by essence.

On the levels both of being and of becoming the separation of that which participates from the essence participated immediately provides the basis for concluding that all beings separated from their essence are constituted by real difference or otherness. If the separation is ontological the difference is ontological, and there cannot exist real separation unless there exist real difference. Now inasmuch as true Being can render fully intelligible only that which is the same as it and does not suffice to explain what is different, we must look elsewhere for the difference which separates it from the world of images, the things which are its copies. This difference and otherness which accounts for the lack of intrinsic essence and the image character of all that which imitates is, as Plato sees it, matter. Matter must then exist for the general reason: images exist. Particularly, matter must exist on two accounts: because the sensible world is the image-being it is, and as such Being is inadequate to explain it; because Being itself is the image-one it is, and as such Unity does not suffice as explanation.

This reasoning is clearly expressed by Plato in several dialogues. With reference to physical generation in the *Timaeus*[5], Plato concludes that since true reality does not belong to the image-beings generated, which exist "ever as the fleeting shadow of some other", they must be "inferred to be in an-

---

[5] *Timaeus,* 52.

other", or else they could not be at all. It is the lack of substantiality, of inseity and indivisible sameness in sensible things which leads Plato to posit matter as the container of images in the sensible order. Here, then, it is the being contained and the being received which differentiates the image-mode of existing and requires, in view of this differentia, a container and receiver in which this mode of defective existing may be realized. In the second hypothesis of the *Parmenides,* the effort to mingle unity with being leads inexorably to a traumatizing infinite plurality, in which everything participates everything. The therapeutic healing of this traumatic shock, to safeguard both the transcendence of absolute Unity, and to provide for its extrinsic limitation by a material principle of relative non-being which alone can produce the truly differentiated multiplicity which is requisite for a universe of being and discourse, will be the work of the *Sophistes.* Such a principle, in producing many really different beings by extrinsic limitation of absolute Unity, necessarily differentiates only through negation. Only a material principle of this kind, for Plato, which is really distinct from the absolute Unity which is the essence of all beings (as its precise contrary or privative opposite), can guarantee both the possibility of inter-participation of beings in one another, and a restriction of universal relativity and infinite internal relatedness, so that everything does *not* participate in everything. These are the conditions, as the *Sophistes* makes clear,[6] for the possibility of both true and false discourse. In the *Philebus,*[7] the plurality which intrinsically constitutes Being is said to be consequent upon the composition in Being of finite and infinite. Being is finite in respect to having a certain ratio of number and measure, and infinite in regard to non-being and multiplicity.

The ontological basis for the existence of the Platonic matter is evidently the *chorismos* or separation which Plato sets up between Unity and Being.[8] It is not, to be sure, an opposition of contrariety, since contrariety excludes participation, and Being would not *be* unless it somehow participated in Unity, its own essence. But there is nevertheless, in Being's dyadic structure[9], an intrinsic principle of internal relatedness to others which cannot be identified with Being's essential Unity, without a collapse into a universal relativism which destroys the foundation of all real differentiation in Being.[10] This principle, the "material" substrate which grounds all participation in

---

[6] *Sophistes,* 251c—253c.

[7] *Philebus,* 23–25.

[8] Cf. A. C. Pegis, "The Dilemma of Being and Unity", *Essays in Thomism,* New York, 1942, pp. 151–83.

[9] Cf. L. J. Eslick, "The Dyadic Character of Being in Plato", *Modern Schoolman, 21,* 1953, 11–18.

[10] Such a collapse is the consequence of the 2nd hypothesis of the *Parmenides.*

Unity by Being, so that beings are differentiated and multiple *images* of their essential principle, is the "relative non-being" of the *Sophistes,* and *it* is Unity's contrary. Because of its presence in every being, to be Being is not to be One, but to be a mere image-one, to exist as a whole of unlimited parts, to be in as many ways as being can be. For any being, this means that, intrinsic to its very being but distinct from its essential Unity, there is an infinite context or web of internal relatedness, both positive and negative, to all other entities, which alone defines it as differentiated from those others. Being in this sense is without limit or end—like the number series it is always capable of further increase—an infinite surplusage whose infinitude is characterized by an intrinsic indefiniteness. Thus if Being cannot be an absolute One, neither can it be a completely and exhaustively determinate many—it cannot possess, as an intrinsic and proper perfection, an actual limit (for then it would have inherent unity) or a completion, or a realization of itself.

If Being is so bound to plurality, it is only because Unity is above Being and is accorded absolute primacy in the Platonic ontology. This primacy assumed, most probably under Pythagorean influence and facilitated by Plato's own mathematical susceptibilities (for it is the One which is the principle of number which is, as such ontologized), it is not possible to hold that *esse* is itself the act of *ens.* Rather it is Unity which is the perfection and realization of Being—and this is why Being, as such, can never fully be. It is Unity which is the source from whence all that is secondary participates essence and true reality. But it is not unity as intrinsically possessed, so that it is proportionately but really realized in the beings which are image-ones. In Platonic metaphysics an analogy of proper proportionality can never function. The natural posteriority of Being in relation to Unity thus means, for Plato, that Being is inescapably determined to multiplicity. Its essential actuality determined by derivation, not from what is, but from Unity, as other than its essential cause Being must ever be a semblance of itself, of its true essential self, and hence an image-one and a plurality. In this way, it is the pluralism of Being which forces Plato to assume the existence of matter as an ultimate substrate principle of Being's dyadic constitution. Since Being cannot be and be a true One there must exist outside the generic Unity a source from whence originates Being's difference, its mode of being an image-one. And this source, in its function as cause of Being's ontological otherness in relation to Unity, can only be a natureless multiplicity, an indeterminate matrix of relatedness. As such, it is an existing negation of primal reality, a real absence or privation of True being. Matter, in Plato, is not, and cannot be, *potential* being. Aristotle's primary matter is the indeterminate potentiality for substantial existence. Platonic matter is not poten-

63

tially *ousia*—it is precisely that which can never actually become substance, because it is in itself radically non-being and privation.

In the Thomistic formula, potency limits act, but though the act or perfection so received is limited it is not thereby ontologically degraded to the status of unreal image. Such a limitation by potency does not accord with the famous Spinozistic maxim, that all determination is negation. The perfection limited by potency is still properly and truly perfection or act. This is not the case in Platonism. For Plato the limitation of act (in this case, essence) is not by potency, but by relative non-being or privation, and such a limitation is fatal to the integrity of the act or perfection as limited and received. Only degraded images of act can be generated in this way. The existence of non-being is thus intimately contingent upon the existence of being and the certitude with which non-being is known to be is inseparable from that with which is known the being of being. In short, non-being must exist because being is and is an image-one, and the reality and function of non-being as material principle is entirely relative to the lack of unity and essential deficiency which intrinsically constitutes being.

Such being Plato's proofs for the existence of matter, what meaning or character does matter have in the Platonic philosophy? Or, in more precise terms, how are we to understand matter in comparison with that which is image or defective copy, and in comparison with the essence imaged?

It is from the principle that matter accounts for the imaging of the essence imaged that we must infer that matter itself is not and cannot be image. This seems evident from Plato's own insistence that since image-beings (the sensibles) lack the proper inseity to exist in themselves, if they are to exist in the tenuous way possible to them they must exist in another.[11] Certainly this other cannot be image, unless we are to involve Plato in an infinite regress. But especially it is the very meaning Plato attaches to images which prohibits any identification, or even similarity, of the container of images with the images contained. To be an image-being (sensible thing) or an image-one (form) signifies participation in essence, and it is the fact of this participation, mysterious as it is, which renders impossible any relation of likeness between images and their material substrate. For participation signifies a sharing in essence in such a way that that which is participated always remains separate from that which participates. Participation, in this Platonic sense, always involves: the participated which is related to that which participates as its essence or nature; that which participates which is related to the participated as its image or copy; the *chorismos* in virtue of which, on the one hand, the participated is at once the essence of that which

[11] Cf. *Timaeus*, 48e—52.

participates and different from it and, on the other hand, that which participates is simply the image of what is held to be its proper nature. Now in view of this relation of participation set up between images and essence—because images are, to speak metaphorically, the mirrorings and reflections of true essence—the matter which receives them cannot be image. Aside from the fact that the material substrate is ultimate and ungenerated, to what kind of nature could the natureless be so related and to what sort of true Being could existing non-being respond?

Plato tells us, to the contrary, that the substrate of all becoming is to be called a *this* or *that,* while the images themselves are designated *such*.[12] And from Plato's point of view this makes sense. If the images are essentially (yet not intrinsically) nature, if their mode of existing is a mode of participating, it is superfluous to posit a new nature in which they are contained. Indeed, it is contradictory not only to the function of matter but also to the dominant theme of the *chorismos* (to explain which is matter's whole *raison d'être*), that matter be conceived in any sense a nature, for then it will follow that that by which image-beings differ from nature is nothing but nature. True, it is their being contained by matter, and contained necessarily, which serves to explain how that which is separate from its own essence can even exist at all. But if matter rescues image-beings from sheer nothingness, it is neither to supply them with natures in which to inhere, nor to function as a condition for essence or as a principle in the order of essence. Matter contributes simply to their image mode of existing solely by providing the receptacle in which their participation in essence or true form may be realized. Matter is a principle, therefore, not in the order of nature or essence, but in the order of image-existence, and this is why matter, although it is neither nature nor essence, is a non-being which exists. Matter cannot enter into the order of essence, as it does for Aristotle.[13]

This non-image and natureless character of matter is implicitly recognized by Plato in the *Timaeus,* when, after noting that matter is to be called a *this* or *that,* he asserts that while the images themselves are apprehended by opinion and sense, the substrate is grasped only by a "spurious reason".[14] Accordingly, matter is neither sensible nor intelligible (whether *per se* or *per accidens*) but is in the strict sense irrational. Its real irrationality exerts a traumatizing effect even on the higher plane of the objects of science. This is illustrated by the classical case of the incommensurability of the side and diagonal of the square, which cannot be measured by any common unit.

---

[12] *Timaeus,* 49d—50.
[13] Cf. L. J. Eslick, "Aristotle and the Identity of Indiscernibles", *Modern Schoolman,* 36, 1959, 279–90.
[14] *Timaeus,* 52b.

Where unity (and in particular, the unity which is a principle of number, rather than the unity convertible with being of Aristotle and the schoolmen) is the principle and source of intelligibility, the existence of real irrationality is necessitated. *Esse* not being the principle and source of intelligibility, there is something which can exist and yet be irrational. But this irrationality connotes matter's essential negativity and indefiniteness, its lack of limit and nature—in Aristotelian terms it means that matter is *per se* non-being, the knowable neither in itself nor by analogy, as Aristotelian matter is knowable by analogy with substance.[15] As Aristotle points out, the *ratio* of Platonic matter is privation, rather than potency, and as such it is the contrary of form, and hence totally incapable of any assimilation into the order of formal or essential intelligibility.[16]

Now, in so far as matter is "intelligible" only in a purely spurious and counterfeit sort of way, Plato implies not only the naturelessness of the existing subject of image-beings, but also the deceptiveness of matter and the subterfuge it is capable of obtruding upon the human mind. Because it has been necessary to assume a substrate for all things deficient in intrinsic substantiality, must we infer—what indeed appears to be the logical inference— that that in which the image-beings appear is itself substance?[17] For, after all, one might consistently reason that if it is in default of their lack of inseity that these images are determined to existence in matter, matter's mode of existing must necessarily be a substantial mode. Now it is exactly this line of reasoning which Plato would characterize as "spurious". Because the images are, as Plato says, "coming and going" and never the same, non-philosophic reason falls victim to the belief that the changeless substrate is the permanent reality, the substance of which these images are merely the fleeting outward appearance. Thus beguiled, reason nourishes on the fruitless soil of materialism, and finds false delight in rationalizing the irrational, in making nature where nature does not exist.

But matter's power for evil and deception is not exercised exclusively over non-philosophic reason. The philosopher himself, who has with effort transcended the world of sense experience because the imagery therein directs his disciplined reason in reminiscence not to the substrate of images but to the Being imaged, is faced with a system of "intelligibilities" permeated by materiality and irrationality, an order of Forms which, to the

---

[15] Aristotle, *Physics*, 191a 7–11.

[16] *Ibid.*, 192a 4–8. Cf. also *Metaphysics*, 1029a 24–26.

[17] In an analogous metaphysical situation, A. N. Whitehead, in *Science and the Modern World*, compares Creativity, his version of the Platonic Receptacle, with "substance" in the Spinozistic sense. The inadequacies of such a comparison are recognized by Whitehead later in *Process and Reality*.

extent that they resist unity and are subject to non-being, resist intelligibility and are irrational. We have already seen that Being is not convertible with Unity, its own essence. As concerns our present consideration this means that Being for Plato, as composite and as Being, is not the intelligibility of its own essence. Now since matter, as "the Other" or "the Indeterminate Dyad", is Being's difference in relation to its essence, it is matter—Being's *differentia*—which founds the *per se* irrationality of the world of "intelligibilities". There exists an infinite in Being, proper to Being as Being, which is not intelligible. Because of this, as the *Seventh Epistle* makes explicitly clear,[18] the effort of reason to define a Form in its essence is always and necessarily doomed to frustration. This means, since there is no question of individuation in this order (there being only many species, each of them unique,[19] and not many individuals within a species), that the infinity effected by matter is within each Form. To posit multiplicity in this order is simultaneously to posit within the "intelligible" itself—within each species-being—an inexhaustible series of relations. This is, for the philosopher, the traumatizing meaning of being's composition with non-being. It necessitates, for example, that the intelligibility "man" be grasped in immediate conjunction with all the beings "not-man"[20]—but such immediacy is impossible, for both the discursiveness of human reason and the otherness of the innumerable kinds necessitate that these negations be successive; further, there is no limit to the negating, no stoppage or point at which the mind can rest. And finally, even if reason were able to grasp in immediacy this infinity of relations, it would still be in the dark about the "what-is-man".

Yet while we place the burden of responsibility upon matter for the irrationality which pervades the world of Being, we must not neglect the fact—in all fairness to Plato's thought—that were it not for matter, even such relational knowledge would be an impossible dream. For just as matter rescues images from sheer nothingness, so also does it preserve them from utter unknowability. If we can imagine, for the sake of clarification, a pure image subtracted from its receptacle and detached from all that which renders it infinitely relational, we can grasp Plato's meaning.[21] "What" is "left" is neither in itself nor in relation; separated from essence by the fact of participation, it is now separated from its relative identity. Hence we cannot even say of this isolated image that "it is the same as itself". For it is same, or relatively one, only in a relational matrix, in respect to all the others it

---

18 *Epistle VII*, 342—343e.
19 *Republic*, X, 597.
20 *Epistle VII*, 344b.
21 Compare Hypothesis I, *Parmenides*.

is not, and so to know its sameness one must know its difference. The Platonic *chorismos* necessitates a confusion of the logical principle of identity with the real principle of difference: as separated from their own essence the only identity possible to images and capable of exhibition in rational discourse is that of their difference from one another; it is in not being the others that the image is relatively one. This must be carefully understood. For St. Thomas, *ens* and *aliquid* are convertible, so that to be is to be something different and unique. This is possible because being, as analogical, includes its differences, and admits of *essential* differentiation.[22] But this is precisely what cannot be said by Plato. It is not because of its essence that a being differs from and is related to others for Plato. But it must also be remembered that it is separated from its own essence. Even its sameness with "itself" is relational and participated. The *ratio* of sameness which a being has in relation to itself is not identical with its essential and incommunicable unity,[23] but is founded only in its membership in a community of entities which exemplify the same common *ratio*—which participate in the Form *Same*. The *other* is always the only subject which is being talked about,[24] so that even when 'same' is used as a predicate the meaning is relational, and the Platonic *chorismos* between the "thing" and its essence is maintained. Hence the powerfulness of matter as a principle of knowledge is that it makes possible perinoetic discourse around Being, and gives meaning to the only question left for metaphysical discussion in Plato—the question of the relations of beings to one another.

We have yet to determine what it is about matter which enables it to be, as Plato says, an object of "spurious reason." The noetic implication is that matter is falsely designated substance by reason. False reason erects false substance, but is this due to some innate human perversity? It would seem, on the contrary, that Plato puts the blame primarily on matter itself. For there is something about matter that simulates nature and makes it possible that reason be deluded by the natureless and unintelligible.

Plato describes matter in the *Timaeus* as an eternal indestructible and changeless space which never adopts in any way or at any time the forms received from without. Now these notes of eternity, indestructibility, and permanence are equally applicable to true essence, to the One, and reason, in all its searchings, is directed to and finalized by the permanent and in-

---

[22] The ultimate condition for such analogy is the real distinction of existence and essence, related as *act* to *potency*. Cf. L. J. Eslick, "The Real Distinction: Reply to Professor Reese", *Modern Schoolman*, *38*, 1961, 149–60.

[23] *Parmenides*, 139d–e.

[24] Cf. L. J. Eslick, "The Platonic Dialectic of Non-Being", *New Scholasticism*, *29*, 1955, 33–49.

destructible. It would then seem that it is the changelessness and immutability of matter which, beneath the surface of sensible flux, simulates essence and deceives the human mind. But then the permanence of matter, which renders it a fit object of spurious reason, and the permanence of true essence, which determines its suitability as the proper finalization of reason, must signify radically different ratios. What is it that basically determines this equivocity?

Let me say, in anticipation, that the general difference consists in this: while matter is permanently natureless and is always a "that able to receive" but never a "that actually informed", the One is permanently essence and never able to receive or to be informed from without. It can never, therefore, be a *subject* of predication. Nor can matter itself, strictly speaking, be a predicate. Matter and essence thus represent the opposite orders which exhaust the area of immutability.

To explicate this opposition it is necessary to determine the *ratio* of Platonic non-permanence, of images as engaged essentially in becoming. What is the meaning of the "always becoming", as such? Plato says that the images are "too volatile to be detained in any expressions as 'This' or 'That' ... or any other mode of speaking which represents them as permanent".[25] It is the ceaseless change, the becomingness of the image-beings which then resists conceptualization, and makes them unamenable to expression in fixed and static terms. This is why they cannot be the real objects of definition and science. And when we call them "suches", we do not refer to any stability *in them,* to any inner nature, but to a common extrinsic principle of which they are flowing imitations and moving approximations. This, says Plato, is true of "all things generated". Consequently, whatever comes into existence is characterized by an intrinsic instability. Generation as such is thus inseparable from the Platonic notion of participation. All things generated participate in essence, and to so participate is for beings to imitate their Unity, their own essence. And to imitate what is in this way other is to be involved in perpetual becoming, to be always appearing like the nature things are, and never to be at rest. The very idea of participation, imitation, connotes the dynamism intrinsic to the structure of beings generated, and explains this dynamism as the necessary orientation, not merely of the imitating to the imitated, but of the inherently natureless to its formal perfection and identity. All becoming thus denotes the restlessness of participating beings in separation from their proper essence and selfhood, and is made intelligible not in terms of inner form seeking to energize and expand, but by the radical extrinsicism of essence to being itself.

---

[25] *Timaeus,* 49d–e.

From this it appears evident that where essence is intrinsic, where there is inseity and identity, there is permanence but no becoming; for with essence possessed and with nature present by an inwardness, there is nothing to look out to, no need to go beyond what one has to be that which one is. And conversely, where nature is extrinsic and being does not possess the very essence it is, its mode of existing must be a mode of becoming, for there is nothing within it in virtue of which it is stabilized or terminated in true being. Beings generated and involved in becoming thus look to essence or Unity as being at once their formal completion and their finalization. It is the same thing for being to move towards its own nature as it is for it to seek its end. Where essence is the actual determination of being there can be no distinction of final from formal cause.

Seen against this background of the generated and the becoming—becoming which, if explicable at all, is so only in terms of the finality (in a purely formal and non-existential sense) of essence which never becomes—the permanence of matter, ultimate and ungenerated and actually natureless, can be properly estimated. As that which contains images and is not itself image, and which is ever able to receive by never being able to become, matter is permanently closed off from essence and true form.

I have pointed out elsewhere that there is, in Plato, a kind of inverted "real distinction" of essence and existence,[26] in which essence (ultimately, the One) is a transcendent principle of act and supreme ontological perfection. The *existence* of Being (the Forms), and of the domain of becoming, however, is the function not of essence—which is impotent of itself to confer such modes of existence—but of its *material* reception and negative limitation. Existence, in the multiform realm of Being and in the flux of becoming, precisely and necessarily connotes a failure of expression of the inexpressible essential principle, an imperfect and degraded image of a "Reality" which, as existing in these modes, can only *appear* in Otherness and dispersed multiplicity. In such a system, it is not essence or Unity which is creative or emanative of the multiple entities, but rather matter, by negating essence, is the principle of existential actuation in the image worlds.[27] The function of existential actuation is identified with that of existential *differentiation,* performed by the material substrate as the maker of the manifold images of the single essential principle. But this is to make the first, underived prin-

---

[26] Cf. L. J. Eslick, "The Real Distinction: Reply to Professor Reese", *Modern Schoolman, 38,* 1961, 149–60. Also, "Existence and Creativity in Whitehead", *Proceedings American Catholic Philosophical Association, 35,* 1961, 151–62.

[27] A. N. Whitehead, in naming his material substrate "Creativity", is much more authentically Platonic than those neo-Platonists who metaphorically talk of a fertile One which, by itself alone, can engender the many.

ciples of being into contraries, and to destroy any proper proportioning of act (as essence) to the recipient which limits it. We have a *subject* of essence which is absolutely unrelated to it, and which has no potency for it, so that it is totally cut off from *essential* actuality. Between *form* and *privation* there can be no proportion. The absolute and independent status accorded to matter (as an existing privation of essence, rather than Aristotle's potential *ousia*) must signify a total lack of relation between the material substrate and essence. How can such disjoined and unrelated principles function as causes in the production of being and becoming?

While there may be some basis for concluding that imaging and becoming are explicable, through finality, by the essence imaged, there is no such basis possible for setting up a relation between matter and essence. Plato certainly does say, in the *Philebus*, that generation is for the sake of essence,[28] but essence can hardly be the final cause of matter itself. Aristotle speaks of some kind of *eros* which the Platonic indeterminate dyad is supposed to have for the One, identified with the Good, but he points out that since these principles are contraries, this implies that the bad itself (the dyad) must desire its own opposite, and hence its own destruction.[29] But in fact the formula "matter exists for the sake of form" could have no real meaning in Platonic metaphysics. Form cannot be the final cause of matter because it is not through form that matter exists; form cannot as form be causally related to matter because matter is not *potentially such* but *actually this*. Its actuality, to be sure, is neither that of image nor essence, but rather that of existing non-being. Permanently existing in its own right and permanently formless in its actuality, the Platonic matter has no final cause.

This absolute dissociation of matter and form, or of substrate and nature, has disastrous implications in the metaphysics of Plato. For it means that the Platonic metaphysics does not recognize that even though *esse* is not a form or a nature, nothing that is natureless exists. On the contrary, the Platonic position is that essence (the One) is true existence—the original and privileged "Reality" of which even the Being of the Forms is mere appearance—and yet that the natureless necessarily exists. This in turn demands that there are two underived levels of "existence" (as well as two derived levels), irreducible in principle, operative in Plato's thought: the level of true "existence", which is the proper sphere of nature or essence; the level of spurious "existence" which is the proper sphere of the actually formless, of matter and the non-being which is. It is this dualism which explains, at bottom, why Plato's metaphysics is incapable of achieving the unity of science.

[28] *Philebus*, 54.
[29] Aristotle, *Metaphysics*, 1091b–30—1092a–8.

What, then, of the Platonic dilemma? If the image-beings engaged in becoming are separated from true being by a difference which of itself is absolutely unrelated to essence, how is it possible that images as such be explicable by the essence imaged? How is a true causal relationship possible between them, when the *differentia of the effect* from the cause is permanently closed off from the very thing assumed to be the cause?

It might be possible to contend, as Plato does, in fact, that while the existing formless receptacle is the principle of difference, the images received are not so received as to form a unity with their container, but remain somehow different from the principle by which they differ from Unity. And being thus different from their receptacle, they are *like* Unity, and it is this likeness which provides the basis for a true causal relationship.

But this argument proves rather that images *as such* cannot be causally related to Unity. For if they are only related to essence by that by which they differ from their principle of difference, then they are related to essence not as image but as not-image. If that by which they are *like* essence is other than their *differentia*, then the likeness and the causation which explains it are not to be found in the order of image. Thus, the only mode of causation left open to Plato, as concerns the causality of the One, is *final* causality in terms of essence or true form. According to this possibility, the intrinsic *possession* of the One, as unitary essence and true form, could be conceived as being at once the formal completion and the good of all that which participates essence but does not have it. The impossibility of this interpretation is that it demands, between the beings finalized and the end *attained,* identity of nature, and this, for Plato, is identity of true existence. Thus there would be no distinction of cause and effect, and consequently, no conceivable foundation for a causal relationship.

Apart from the intrinsic impossibility of such causation on the part of Unity, the existence of the Platonic matter immutably opposes the supposition that beings engaged in becoming attain to what they are, not as images, but as one with their unitary essence. As long as matter exists, as long as there is multiplicity, Unity cannot be cause according to its mode of being cause.

To understand this, we must, as a final consideration, briefly estimate matter's status as "co-principle" with Unity. The assumption of matter as principle of difference in relation to Unity evidently implies that multiplicity cannot originate from Unity, and this, in turn, is logically dependent upon a *univocal* conception of the One, taken from mathematics. Unity, as primal essence, can only "generate" unity; as univocally conceived, its causation must necessarily be univocal—which means that it cannot generate. The failure of the neo-Platonists to understand this is their greatest departure from Plato. To attribute to Unity the causation of Being is thus equivalent to denying Unity, to inserting duality in that which transcends all composition. From the Platonic point of view, this means that existing matter functions as a sort of metaphysical make-shift, an expedient adopted to safeguard the absolute unicity of the One, and to account for that which Unity, in default of its generic simplicity, cannot explain.

But it also necessitates that the powerfulness of matter as principle is infinitely greater than that of Unity. This is made evident by the effectiveness of matter in the composite being. For if we conceive the generation of Being in terms of an imposition of unity upon matter, we find that the "causality" of the One is purely ineffectual. Unity *received* is merely unity by equivocation, but the only causality possible to the One is that according to a univocal mode. So long as matter is the actual negation of Unity, an existing subject absolutely unrelated to existing nature, the One can in no way exercise its proper causality in conjunction with it. But it is this total absence of mutual relationship between the intrinsic co-principles, and this failure to recognize the reciprocity of causes which must obtain if composite being is to be intrinsically determined to a composite nature, which necessitates in the Platonic theory of generation the absolute causal sufficiency of matter itself—as in Whitehead's "Creativity". Plato's matter thus combines both the roles of existential actuation and differentiation, and achieves the former by means of the latter. The "creative" function of matter is its negation of essential reality.

But how can even this be? For with the real relationship of principles abandoned, the efficacy of both causes is logically nullified. With Plato, however, we have the situation where, while no true relationship of causes obtains, there is nonetheless effected being. But if being is generated and produced by causes so unrelated, it must be that the efficacy of one of the causes is totally destroyed. And since this causation and generation is not in the line of essence, it is the efficacy of essence itself which must be nullified. This explains why matter, although not itself formally altered by the impress of unity, can nonetheless limit and make multiple the unity imposed. It is with this one-sided and independent causation that Plato's defense of participation, of the *chorismos,* must finally rest. Its modern counterpart is found in A. N. Whitehead's doctrine of the creative source of the world as *causa sui*. Ultimately, all developed metaphysical systems which make all determination negation must come to rest in the mystery, or contradiction, of radical self-causation. For unless matter limits and is not informed, unless it receives and is not determined, the separation of the participated and that which participates is wholly inexplicable. And it is because matter exists as the actually formless, and according to a mode of spurious existence, that it

73

is able to limit and not be informed, able to receive and not be determined. For its mode of existing being a privative mode, since privation as such has no potentiality for existence as substance it cannot exist as natured, and nature is powerless to inform it. And being thus powerless to determine matter to existence as nature, unity as received is detemined by matter. This determination by matter is not, of course, in the order of essence. Unity is determined rather by being limited to a mode of spurious existence. Since there are here operative two irreducible levels of "existence", matter then explains why that whose true existence is a nature-mode can nonetheless exist according to a natureless-mode, and in a state of separation from true being. Thus, while it cannot determine essence in the line of essence (or affect absolute Unity), matter can determine it in the line of natureless existence —in the line of relation, of relative non-being. And this is why the image-beings, although they will ever be essentially nature, will never be identical with the nature they are. This is why the imaging, although ever an imaging of essence, will never be explicable in terms of essence imaged. Hence the powerfulness of matter consists in this: while essence cannot produce its own effect in matter, matter can produce *its* own effect by negating essence. The existence of the Platonic material substrate thus bears permanent witness to the impotence of the Platonic One.

St. Louis University

DISCUSSION

McKeon: There are three elements of the "matter" that would be well to separate. Two of them appear in the *Timaeus*: space and the regular solids. Plato distinguishes between causes according to reason and causes according to necessity, and, therefore, the "matters" in question would be respectively either the rational or the necessitating. When we are following reason, there are three principles: There is the maker, or the father; there is the offspring, or that which is made; and then there is the mother, which is part. I think it would be well to separate *Chora* as space from *place*. ('Room' would be the most literal translation.) This kind of space is reminiscent of the analogy that Descartes used, except that Descartes talked about flax and Plato talked about gold, that is, in the gold you have all of the forms that can later be made of the gold, it is not a sphere, it is not square, and so forth. There is justice in Mr. Eslick's relating of this "matter" to space. But, on the other hand, having completed this rational or cosmological form, we then turn to the least parts, and the least parts, the five elements, are equated to the regular solids. By the relation of necessity, you could then build the universe out of these components. The third question concerns the *indeterminate,* which opposes the rational or determinate, and is somehow related with the necessary. We find this not only in the *Theaetetus* but also in the *Philebus* and here we are in the middle range of dialectic, which accounts for the processes of becoming in a world full of— 'contingency' which would be the wrong word, but nonetheless a world which has an indeterminate infinity of possibilities emerging one out of the other.

Sellars: It seems to me that in Plato's *Timaeus*, one finds a notion somewhat analogous to that of Aristotle's matter, but it is the images themselves considered as strivings or yearning. Plato traces the indeterminacy which you are talking about really to the irrationality of impulse, etc. I think this is in a way a material or content aspect which is constrained by the geometrical forms. So that in a way the relationship of the geometrical forms to these urgings, power-strivings, etc. is analogous to the relationship of the limits imposed on an object by an artisan to the raw material with which he works. Then I would say that if this is, as I think, the analogy in Plato's *Timaeus* to Aristotle's matter we must very carefully distinguish it from space or place, because no part of space *becomes* fire; it is where the image, which is the imitation in space of the elemental form fire, appears. The matter-image is not identical, therefore, with space. Space becomes "inflamed" not by becoming hot but by becoming the scene of an image of heat, which in turn becomes intelligible as constrained by mathematical form . . .

* * * * *

McKeon: . . . Suppose you were talking about hydrochloric acid. You can write the formula for it, it fits in equations, it always operates in a particular fashion. You can't take the hydrochloric acid that you buy in the hardware store, and have it operate according to this equation. Even your chemically pure instances of hydrochloric acid will have some imperfections and you will learn how to take account of them. In other words, you can deal with H.Cl. on several levels. You can deal with it in terms of theory or in terms of a chemical analysis, which would isolate the ingredients in an individual case. Chemistry needs to do both of these. You cannot do your chemical work unless you can write your equations in which you take no account of these differences and you must also have the indefinitely large number of varieties of things that are properly labeled hydrochloric acid.

Hanson: But this raises no question of principle whatever. The fact that you can identify the hardware product as deficient in certain ways and can exactly describe where it goes wrong from the equations show that you know to what degree it is imperfect. So that in principle it ought to be possible to eliminate this imperfection, although in practice it might be difficult.

McKeon: But you want to keep, at the level of this imperfection, some radical indetermination that you cannot rationalize completely. What you have to deal with is something like the situations that occur in probability theory; you cannot write the finite equation for the singular transaction.

Eslick: I would say also that knowledge *in principle* cannot be exhausted for Plato. To know hydrochloric acid or anything else exhaustively would involve a knowledge of the total universe. I think this is a predicament very much like that of the absolute idealist of the nineteenth and early twentieth centuries: the problem of knowing everything which something is not, of knowing the infinite context of relatedness to everything else. There is a factor here of real contingency which is incapable in principle of being reduced to the necessity of formal explanation. Now, for practical purposes, you can achieve a working knowledge which is sufficient. You can go as far as you please in the analysis of the infinite, but an exhaustive, perfect knowledge becomes impossible.

Hanson: Well, it becomes impossible because the rules of the game here are being set up in a particular way. If it is one of the rules of the discussion that nothing at all can be known unless everything is known prior to that consideration . . . (*Eslick*: But I think Plato's metaphysics forces him to that.) This seems absurd to me. It seems to me perfectly clear that in the context when I can say I know what is wrong with the hardware sample of hydrochloric acid, then as a matter of principle it ought to be possible to eradicate the imperfections. Now, in statistical examples there will be difficulties, but then I think a further issue is raised: to what degree can you say you are aware of the deficiency in this statistical mode of describing in the instances where, in point of fact, there is no alternative way of describing it? If you've got only one way of describing a physical process and if this involves uncertainties of the quantum-statistical kind, then you are not really contrasting that situation with anything, since there is no alternative way of giving an exact specification of state. I don't see what deficiency you are calling my attention to if you can't describe it to me. And if you can describe it to me, it is not a "deficiency" in the sense you require.

Sellars: I can bring this back to Plato with a kind of paradigm case from his works. Supposing we asked the question of something which is not perfectly a circle: must it be perfectly something else? Now it seems to me that Mr. Hanson is taking for granted that if something isn't perfectly *X*, it must be perfectly something else, and this something else could in principle be specified. In the earlier Plato, there was a definite notion that you could take all possible constructable figures and nothing in the world of becoming was perfectly any of them. To be not perfectly a circle is *not* for Plato to be perfectly something else. It seems to me that this is the crucial issue as far as the historical point is concerned. Professor McKeon's example of the hardware H.Cl. involves a distinction which was in the Platonic metaphysics, whereas the point that Mr. Hanson is making is in the realm of the purely theoretical reason. Already, he is operating at the fourth level of the "line".

Hanson: Well, fortunately for me I put this in the form of a "country boy question". I don't care if Plato's metaphysics had it this way or not. I don't understand it, and I have tried to give the reason why I don't understand it, namely, that if you can describe the deficiency it ought in principle to be possible to patch it up.

Sellars: Just to make you a bit uneasy by pointing out the problem of vagueness in so far as we are dealing with concepts that apply to the world around us: there is an important point in being able to say that this is *not* precisely a triangular shadow and yet this doesn't mean that we can say precisely what shape of shadow it *is*.

Cohen: It seems as though you are responding to Hanson's question by saying that epistemologically it may be very difficult to specify the singular instance. It might require knowing everything to give an answer to this question. Whereas, if I understand the question, he is saying: whether you can know it or not, why *can't* there be exact copies? Now those are quite different questions.

McKeon: I didn't mean to put it on an epistemological basis. I was suggesting that if one is dealing, for example, with particles of gas released into a larger chamber, it's entirely possible that you cannot write the equation in any other form than a statistical one. I'd be quite happy if Plato requires me then to say that I am staying on the third level of the divided line. That's the way this region of reality is built up. There are other aspects of it which allow me to speculate, or write equations of a different sort. And there are always the obstinate optimists who will say that eventually for quantum mechanics a general equation will be written, or that it has probably been written but we can't prove it . . . All of this I would derive from the constitution of matter, viewing it as part of variously delimited experiences. And the contingency is right there, it's not something that is in our ignorance, it's what we experience when we're trying to explain it.

Hanson: I think you would have a stronger reply to Plato if in point of fact you did go through the appropriate description of electrons in a cloud-chamber, say. You would then ask Plato if taking this to be on the third level involves the assumption that the description could be sharpened up somehow in a classically deterministic way. If the answer to this is yes, then I'm sorry I just don't have the concept of what he is talking about. It is not clear to me what it would be like for this description to be raised to the fourth level and still be a description of what we are observing here and now. I don't understand what it would be like for a copy to be somehow claimed to be deficient vis-a-vis the original and yet for the individual making that claim not to be able to specify the respects in which it is different. If he can't *specify* these respects then I can't see he's got any reason for saying it is different or deficient in the first place.

Eslick: From Plato's final point of view, he is really asserting the impossibility of a complete formal system which can account for everything totally without some kind of residue, without some kind of asserted character. From this point of view Plato is the very reverse of the rationalist he has often been accused of being. I think it's matter precisely which limits the possibility of a total formal explanation. Now, you can, as it were, isolate and confine within limits this irrational. The very ancient exhaustion process of approximating the square root of two, is such a method and Plato certainly was aware of it. You can construct images which approximate closer and closer the reality as a limit, but it's an infinite process. You're still dealing with images. There is a kind of existing falsehood in the world itself, a failure of that world to express perfectly the essential reality . . .

"MATTER" IN NATURE AND THE KNOWLEDGE OF NATURE: ARISTOTLE AND THE ARISTOTELIAN TRADITION

John J. FitzGerald

§1 The Problem: Being-in-becoming

This paper undertakes an investigation of matter as one of a pair of primitive concepts which, in the view of Aristotle, their discoverer, are indispensable in any account of nature which purports to assert not only what nature invariably is but why it cannot be otherwise. The concepts in question are systematically introduced into the Aristotelian doctrine in the first two books of the *Physics*. Consistently with his view of science, formulated in the *Posterior Analytics*,[1] Aristotle raises and answers the question as to the number and character of the first, intrinsic "principles, causes or elements" of being-in-becoming, the primary distinctive trait of the universe.[2] As environing and including every human observer, the universe in motion is the first object of experiential knowledge and, as such, had been, from the beginnings of the Western philosophical tradition, the perennial subject of scientific analysis and synthesis. In Aristotle's report, this tradition had, without success, formulated various possible accounts. Because a true and correct account must assimilate all that is true in each of the earlier accounts as well as correct its errors, Aristotle begins his analysis with a criticism of the extreme traditional positions.[3]

By a curious turn, he addresses his most detailed analysis and criticism to the Eleatic position, which involved, as its consequence, the denial of the possibility of being-in-becoming. He does this directly after observing that

---

[1] I, 3, where, from the impossibility of an infinite regression in the premises as well as of the reciprocal demonstration of the conclusion and premises of demonstrative syllogistic, he concludes to the necessity of another kind of knowledge, which he calls the originative source of science, by which the first indemonstrable truths, the primary premises, of a science are discovered.

[2] *Physics*, I, 1, 184a 9–15.

[3] *Ibid.*, I, 2, 3.

no science can be expected or required to resolve such difficulties as arise from the denial of its principles. But in denying the generability and corruptibility of being, the Eleatic position denies both the fact and, with it, the principles of the fact of which physics is the science. Indeed, the physicist must inductively grant that some, if not all, the things that exist are products of what he calls "genesis". At least, all those things of which we are the immediate observers, including the human observer himself, are in existence beings-in-becoming, subjects of generation and corruption. If this is the case, then any response to an Eleatic who denies this first evidence of the experienced real, must be in terms of a higher science or in terms of one common to all human discourse, that is, in terms of metaphysics or in terms of logic.

Accordingly, Aristotle addresses the Eleatic position (that of both Parmenides and Melissus) to show that its premises are (metaphysically) false and its conclusions (logically) invalid. In this way, he is able to introduce the logical and metaphysical presuppositions of his own position (namely, the principles of identity and non-contradiction and the ontological divisions of the given real into a plurality of first substances and their accidents proceeding interminably and in an orderly fashion from one another). Both the subject and predicate terms of the Eleatic formula: "Being is one," exhibit reductively primary meanings, all of which are inconsistent with the assertion that being is one and motionless (i.e. incorruptible and ingenerable). Though the division of the humanly knowable real into substances and their ordered accidents is not a task of natural science, it remains indispensable to any meaningful formulation of the task of natural science as the reasoned account of the changing, and so changeable, world of things and events in terms of their unchangeable necessities. Failing to grasp this division, post-Eleatic Greek thought through Plato, was unable to account for genesis-in-being and so, in each case, ended in failing to account for the first evidence of fact presupposed by all human science.

Though both Anaxagoras and Democritus, in their accounts of that which truly and unmistakably is, admitted a plurality, indeed an infinite plurality, of moving entities, either simply quantitative, or both quantitative and qualitative, these accounts fail no less than that of Parmenides. For an infinity of actual entities is unknowable and cannot therefore make anything known.[4] The Democritean and Anaxagorean accounts of that which is given immediately and from the outset to the human observer, a diversified environing reality in process, respect the factual evidence of genesis but, in Aristotle's view, fail to account for it to the extent that they reduce

---

[4] *Ibid.*, I, 4.

the genesis or coming-in-to-being of the observed universe and its parts to the locomotion, or locomotion plus qualitative motion, of unobserved and unobservable atomic entities, which themselves are said to exist without coming or ceasing to be. If the motion of unseen parts may account for the motion of seen parts, it cannot account for what it presupposes, namely, motion in being, whether seen or inferred. The problem is, in the first instance, therefore, not the reduction of the motion of one section of the real to the motion of another section where, in both sections, the assumed motion is of the accidental order (in respect, that is, of quantity or of both quantity and quality) but rather it is the problem of motion in being, hence motion in the widest sense, whether accidental or substantial.

Nowhere is the originality of the Aristotelian insight more clearly suggested than in his own reformulation of the problem evoked for the human mind by the fact of motion in the only real that we know directly and unmistakably, i.e. the environing physical real in which we find ourselves. The initial imperative question for any human science is neither why being cannot change, nor how the observed changes in being as observed can be reduced to the unobserved changes in being as imagined or supposed, but simply and solely how motion-in-being in any sense, qualified or unqualified, is conceivable both logically and ontologically and so expressible in statements that are not only meaningful and consistent but also true. Quite clearly, the possibility of motion in respect of any or all of the ultimate categories of things is intelligible, like the categories themselves, only if the concept of motion is compatible with the concept of being itself together with its primary laws of identity, non-contradiction and excluded middle.

§2 *Aristotle's Historical Solution*

Because even the "errors" of his predecessors and contemporaries bear some witness to the truth of the matter, Aristotle explores each to extract its element of truth and reject such of each as contradict the relevant facts. All concur in asserting the impossibility of motion-in-being without opposition in being. But in conceiving contradiction as the opposition demanded by motion but excluded by being, Parmenides erred more seriously than did any of the others. For, in rejecting motion, without which there is neither observed nor observer, he suppressed all knowledge of being. All the other thinkers, both pre- and post-Parmenidean, discerned the necessity of an opposition, subsequent to contradiction, but not contradiction since it did not exclude every *tertium quid* or middle. As not between simply being and simply non-being, this opposition is an opposition within being, in the case of the ancient Ionian monists, or within and among beings, for the later pluralists, whether or not atomists; an opposition in respect of second being or accident rather than in respect of first being or substance, an opposition, which not only does not exclude but requires a *tertium quid* or medium; an opposition, in short, of contrariety. Such opposition provided not only for differences, but also for succession, in being and both without contradiction. Further, and most pertinently, such opposition entailed a medium or substratum which, because it is not itself an opposite, assured some unity in being as required by identity. Yet, in fact, the medium or subject for such contraries as were posited by these earlier thinkers was either some existing natural substance or substances or supposed atomic substances and hence, could, at best, account only for process in their accidental being. Process of this sort within and among beings as given, implies unchanging substantive subjects, real or imagined, none of which is either given as such or necessarily required by the given universe of multiple and ordered entities. Without substratum (unity) and non-contradictory opposition (diversity and successivity), motion or process into being would indeed be neither possible nor conceivable. But with substance and contrariety as the substratum and non-contradictory opposition, process in being could only be accidental and expressive, at best, of only the secondary changes and differences in the real world.

Beyond the oppositions of contradiction and contrariety, there must be another. Beyond the subject or substratum of contrariety, the subject of accidental diversity and succession, there must be the subject of another opposition, the subject of substantial diversity and succession, a realm prior to and presupposed by the accidental, a realm without which no process in respect to accidents is thinkable. In short, the inescapable first evidence of ourselves in knowing contact with the diversified and ordered environing real, the fact of motion or process into first being, suggested unequivocally to the reflective, analytic Aristotle the absolute necessity of non-contradictory, non-contrary opposition within substantial or first being together with a subject, as non-contradictory, and a subject that is substantive but not a substance, as non-contrary: the opposition is that of privation and possession; the subject is first matter.

§3 *Aristotle's Analytical Solution*

From his analysis and criticism of the other positions on the number and character of the principles (the necessary and sufficient conditions) of process-in-being, Aristotle concludes that such process involves necessarily an opposition (though not the oppositions which they posited) and a subject or substratum (though none of the subjects or substrata which they posited). Aristotle proceeds to address the problem *ab ovo* in his own terms by explicating the entailments of the simplest statements of the primitive experiential fact of process-in-being. As simply asserting the fact that process-in-being is given in experience, any instance of change whatever its mode (intrinsic or extrinsic, accidental or substantial) will suffice, the depth or mode, at this point in the analysis, being irrelevant. The question thus becomes: What is it that anyone asserts necessarily and inescapably when he truly asserts that something (whether in respect to its accident or to its substance) comes to be? The answer, in Aristotle's analysis of the primary reference and meaning of the true statement: "The unmusical man comes to be musical" is that one asserts invariably and necessarily a subject of change (in this instance: a man), and an opposition, in this instance: the unmusical (man) and the musical (man). In this, as in every instance of truly asserted coming-to-be, that which is the subject is, as such, seen to be equally present in the origin and product of the change. Because the subject of the change, is other, not in itself but in the product, from what it is, again not in itself, but in the origin of the change, Aristotle says of the subject of change, as such, that it is both one and many: one, as surviving the change, and many as other, by extrinsic determination, in the origin and product terms of the change. Thus, the terms of any change, are, precisely as such, other or diverse in reality, but as terms of change, i.e. in their status as origin and product, they are one by the identical subject diversified in each.

Because in the origin of change, the subject of change does not have the determination it has in the product, origin-subject and product-subject are said to be opposed as something in the state of not having what it can have is opposed to that same something in the state of having it. Like contrariety, the opposition of privation and possession, obviously involves a subject but, unlike contrariety, it is not a relation between two positive determinations. To express this condition of any subject of change, Aristotle states that it is one in number but many in determination or meaning. The determining factor which differentiates an identical subject into origin term and product term, he calls the positive form. In the context of change, however, only the form which contracts the subject to the product is essential to change. The absence of this positive form in the subject is precisely that which characterizes the subject in the origin of change and constitutes the origin-thing precisely as origin. The primitive factors or principles asserted necessarily (by entailment) in the assertion of any coming-to-be or genesis are three: a subject, a form and an opposite, which is either a contrary or privative opposite according as the coming-to-be or process into being is "absolute" or "relative", that is, according as the product-term differs from the origin-term of the coming-to-be accidentally or substantially.

That in "qualified or accidental coming-to-be" there is and must always be a subject is evident, granted the Aristotelian doctrine of the Categories, since accidents are and are knowable if and only if substance is, since everything other than substance (i.e., first substance) is and is said to be only if substance is. Further, the positive accidental form that determines the substance-subject in the product of any accidental change is always, in Aristotle's doctrine, as in that of his predecessors, who addressed the problem of motion-into-being, a contrary or an intermediate between contraries of the same genus.[5]

That, in "unqualified or substantial" coming-to-be there is and must be a subject of change is no less evident, given the inescapable conditions of the possibility of change. But what that subject is, what, if anything, beyond the assertion of the necessity of its being, can be said about it is far from evident. The text, in which Aristotle formulates his doctrine on this issue, the key issue which is said to separate him from all his predecessors as well as his master and associates in the Academy, does not speak with any of the decisive clarity of the text in which he writes of "change in the widest sense".[6]

§4 *Primary Matter*

Despite its brevity and obscurity, this text[7] invites the sustained reflection suggested by the indications that the whole Aristotelian systematic philosophy, both physical and metaphysical, rests upon the completely original insight formulated in it. There is unqualified coming-to-be: of individual substances, of this man, of this dog, of this oak, each of which has within itself, as individual substance, all that is required to receive and exercise for itself an existential act of its own and thereby be in a condition of existential autonomy relative to the diverse secondary existential acts or accidental beings of which it is the active center and support. Aristotle is content to point out that such things (substantial thing-products) are observed, in fact, to come to be from other thing-origins, asserting that "we find in every case something that underlies from which proceeds that which comes to be: for instance, animals and plants from seed".

The point here is that there are clearly natural substance-products which as such necessarily entail natural substance-origins. But these natural substance-origins are, in turn, natural products and accordingly themselves entail natural origins. In this cosmic process of continuous genesis of natural

---

[5] *Ibid.*, I, 5.

[6] Solmsen, Friedrich. *Aristotle's System of The Physical World. A Comparison with His Predecessors,* Ithaca, N.Y., 1960, p. 80.

[7] *Ibid.*, I, 7, 190b–191a 15.

substance from natural substance, there is an order such that the more complex animate substance-products cannot come to be without the less complex animate substance-products and these in turn cannot come to be without the more complex inanimate natural substance-products as origins. Reductively, one reaches the "simple inanimate natural substance-origins", simple bodies (whatever they may be) which have no other, simpler, natural substance-origin than themselves but are generated from one another. As generated from and corrupted into one another, these "elements" have the status, in being, of products. As such, they entail necessarily in their being and coming into being a subject or substratum and an opposition. But as simple bodies, or, natural substances having as their origins no substances other than themselves, their substratum can be nothing outside of them nor anything separable in them. It seems to be no more than that indetermination in the first natural bodies and, through them, in all natural bodies, without which cosmic process from cosmic elements, themselves in process, could not begin, advance or continue. It is the primary analogate of that principle of diversifiability of being-in-act to which, in the *Metaphysics*[8], Aristotle will give the name 'potency'. In short, it is the pure potency to come to be which in the scholastic Aristotelian tradition was called "primary matter". Without it, the coming-to-be and being of natural substances would be as contradictory as the Eleatics declared the coming-to-be of being.

Not itself an origin but simply that, without which no thing in being could be an origin, primary matter is obviously not the seed of any biological process but rather that in the seed in virtue of which Aristotle asserts that every complete or mature biological product comes to be from a seed-origin as from an underlying something that survives in the product from the origin. In this account, without the substantial origin, there neither is nor can be any substantial product; without the primary matter there neither is nor can be any substance-origin; without both substance-origin and substance-product, there neither is nor can be any genesis or process into being, natural or artificial, cosmic or technological.

§5 *Substantial Form*

Beyond the matter must be that other, automatically non-material, principle or factor, by which origin and product, indistinguishably one by primary matter, are as origin and product distinguishably other in their substantial unity. In qualified coming-to-be, the determining or actualizing principles which bound the change within its initial and final terms are contrary

---

[8] *Ibid.*, V, 1017a 35-b9; IX, 7.

opposites within any genus of accident and are, therefore, pairs of positive forms so related that the presence of the one in its substance-subject necessitates the absence of the other. In unqualified coming-to-be, the determining principles that differentiate the common subject-matter into the different substance extremes, origin and product, of such coming-to-be are substantial forms. They are not contraries because they differentiate things in the genus of substance and substances cannot be contrary to one another. The subject of such determinations cannot be any substance, for then the coming-to-be would not be unqualified, yet it must be of a substance, otherwise there would be no origin. Because of this substantial otherness of the origin and product terms of unqualified coming-to-be, the origin is said to corrupt when the product is said to be generated. By the substantial form, the primary matter is determined to one natural substance, that is to say, to a substance that is being only because it has come to be from another substance that has ceased to be. *Matter* and *form* thus denote the necessary and sufficient intrinsic conditions of such things as are given in being as substances, but substances that are the origins and products of unqualified coming-to-be.

Not itself a substance, but a necessary constituent of any substance which is only if it has come to be, primary matter is and is known only as determined by substantial form to this or that generable substance. Similarly substantial form is and is known only as determining primary matter in this or that generable substance. What is generated then is neither the matter as such nor the substantial form as such but the substance of which they are the causes of its generability. By this matter-form composition therefore generable substances are distinguished not among themselves but from ingenerable substance, if such there be. Though the division of generable substance into individuals and types (specific and generic) presupposes it, the composition of primary matter and substantial form is not sufficient to account for that division.

If Aristotle can address himself to this problem of the division of generable substance into individuals and types in the second book of the *Physics,* it is only because he has in the first book first disclosed the two intrinsic conditions of generable substance. Of these two, primary matter alone is uniquely Aristotelian in the sense that it is in virtue of it that any natural thing can be said to be an origin or a product substance. It is in virtue of it that Nature throughout is susceptible of being only in becoming. It is in virtue of primary matter that Aristotle rejects every purely mechanistic, atomistic, and even the Platonic account of the cosmos and its ordered parts. It is by primary matter, "the first subject of each thing (given in experience) from which it comes to be without qualification and which persists in the result", that first the environing physical world and ourselves in it and then the whole of being, become consistently and systematically intelligible in the doctrine of the Stagirite. Without the little that can be said about it, nothing else can be said of matter in the language and thought of Aristotle. For these reasons, the analysis in book one of the *Physics,* the preface to the whole of his systematic scientific work, concentrates on the elaboration of this basic concept.

§6 *Nature—Matter and Nature—Form*

Indispensable and utterly primary as is the concept of primary matter to the whole Aristotelian account of Nature and being, it is hardly a sufficient account, as the second book of the *Physics* makes clear. Whatever is said of matter in the first book is said of it first in the context of motion in general and then in the context of genesis as exhibited in unqualified coming-to-be. In the second book, whatever is said of matter is said of it, not as the *primary* subject of unqualified genesis, but as the appropriate subject of the coming-to-be of things, existing outside of human agency, and, in particular such things in respect to the changes by which they achieve their characteristic fulness of substance-being, as expressed in their defining formulas. Of such things, we say that they come to be and behave as they do "by nature" to distinguish them from all those things which come to be by human agency, "by art". In contrast then to art-products, natural products are said to have within themselves, as such, the source or agency of their characteristic motions in respect of place, growth and decrease, or alteration.[9] That there exist such things which come into and develop in existence by virtue of an efficient principle within themselves is manifest for Aristotle in the existence of animals and their parts, plants and their parts, and the "simple bodies". By their nature, natural products are determined as to that from which they come to be, the process by which they develop in being and the limit or measure of being they can achieve. In this sense, nature may be described as that in natural products which is the source of the operations or activities by which they develop and achieve their complete being.

But to differentiate things (natural and artificial) by a factual difference, the possession *in se* or *in alio* of the originative source of their characteristic behavior or motion is not to identify that principle in itself. Though everyone recognized a domain of things that come to be because of a source inward to them, a decisive difference of opinion prevailed as to what it is in such things that is this source. The more ancient but still (in Aristotle's time) current view was that it was that from which they came to be and

---

[9] *Physics II,* 1:*Metaphysics* V, 4.; A. Mansion, *Introduction à la Physique Aristo-télicienne,* Paris, 1945, pp. 226–34; Solmsen, *op. cit.,* pp. 92–117.

into which they are resolved at the term of their natural history, whether that was one or more than one thing. In this opinion, the nature of natural products is the "stuff" in them from which they come to be and which survives after them. Of such residues of natural corruption, some were thought to be ultimate, in the sense that they neither came to be from nor corrupted into anything else and everything else came to be from and corrupted into them, "times without number". This "hulé" or primitive stuff is unique in that, of all things existing, it is the only one (or ones) which neither came to be nor passed away, an eternal thing or things, unalterable in its primary or substantive determinations though alterable in its secondary or accidental determinations. In this view, how and what natural products are, is completely determined by the materials from which they come to be and into which they are (naturally or otherwise) resolved or resoluble. However else these thinkers differed from one another, they were alike in requiring for their primary matter some minimal physical determinations such as extension, inertia and some elementary motion. In these respects, as well as by making matter exist *in se,* their views were opposed to those of Aristotle. Because he, too, believed that something of this sort must be involved in any account of natural process and its products, not, to be sure, as genesis and its term, but as diversified and ordered, he simply reports without approval or disapproval these views on the nature of things. For convenience, we may call these primal stuffs, conceived as that in natural products which is the primary source of motion and rest in them, their "nature-matter".

Other thinkers, from Pythagoras to Plato, acutely sensitive to the indifference of the nature-matters to the multiple successive and simultaneous forms in which they occur in natural products, asserted that the primary source in natural things of their coming-to-be and passing away was their "nature-form" rather than their "nature-matter". Here 'form' can be taken to denote in natural things an immattered structure or design analogous to the blue print or design embodied in and specifying art-products as such. Just as the art product is the embodiment of but not itself the art form, so too are natural products the embodiment of but not themselves the nature-form. Just as the art-product is the term of an art process in a matter which, of itself, must be susceptible of such processing, so the natural product is the term of a process in a nature-matter which, of itself, must be susceptible of such processing. Accordingly, both in art and in nature, determinate products are the terms of processes in which every prior element and stage is what and where it is in the process because of each subsequent element and stage and all the prior is for the last, i.e. for the product itself. In short, in all process into being, whether artistic or natural, what is to be processed (nature-matter) and each step in the process (the coming-to-be) is determined by the form of the product or what the product is. Thus nature-form rather than nature-matter is that which is primarily determining in natural process and its products. In this view, that which is the primary source of the coming to be and being of natural things is their form rather than their matter. The form is that, in them, which determines from what matter they must come to be as well as the process the matter must undergo to yield them.

Such were the two most general views of that in natural process and its products which is the source in them of their coming to be and being what they are. For those who identified this source or principle with nature-matter, natural process and its products were nothing more than variations in "the affections, states or dispositions" of one or more substances, held to be in themselves eternal because ingenerable and indestructible. For those who identified this source or principle with nature-form, natural process and its products were nothing more than the sensible manifestations or reflections in some essentially unintelligible receptor of an eternally complete and ordered set of numbers or idea-existents perfectly intelligible *in se* but imperceptible to the sense. The systematic accounts of the given real available to Aristotle in his confrontation of the fact of change were constructed in terms of one or the other of these primitive concepts of the nature of things, with the result that from the outset of Western science there developed side by side and quite independently, both a physical, largely empirico-descriptive science and a mathematical, largely theoretico-analytic science, both equally realist in their epistemological intention.

§7 "Intelligible" and "Sensible" Matter

Characteristically, Aristotle addresses the issue no longer simply in terms of immediate data of either the sensible or conceptual order but in terms also of the existing systematic accounts of these data. Accordingly, he raises the question whether in treating such objects as points, lines, surfaces and volumes, the Greek physicists and mathematicians were engaged in the same science, or, at least, in a common part of different sciences. His highly elliptical response sufficed to provide the unmistakable grounds for the highly elaborated metaphysical theory of the diversification and classification of the philosophical sciences of the later Aristotelian Scholastics.[10] Granting that though a science is specified by what it studies, i.e. the single genus to which, in the final analysis, all of its statements refer, he argues

[10] Aquinas, *In Librum Boethii de Trinitate*. Qu. V; VI. See: Armand Maurer, C.S.B., *The Division and Methods of the Sciences*. Toronto, 1953.

further that this single genus is, in its turn, characterized not only by things as they are given in existence but also by things as they are displayed in the conceptual intelligence engaged in discerning and articulating the necessary or possible relations involved in the existentially given.

Thus the mathematician and the physicist may both speak truly, of the circularity of such existing things as appear in sense perception to be circular. The mathematician, however, speaks relevantly only when he expresses such elements of the meaning of circularity as are entailed in any and every meaningful assertion that can be made about circularity. The physicist on the other hand speaks relevantly only when, without contradicting any of the mathematically relevant statements about circularity, he asserts additional attributes which belong to the circularity of circular things—not analytically but synthetically, attributes which, in Aristotle's terms, the circle exhibits only as the limit or boundary of some actual physical body or system of bodies, i.e. the actual magnitudes of circular physical surfaces. And if this can in fact be done, as he thinks it can, it is only because any immediately given thing is the conjunction of many objects of knowledge which, though they do not exist separately from one another in the given thing, considered in themselves, in mental separation from the concrete subject in which they are existentially united, they are found not to involve one another in their knowable being. Thus, my being a teacher of philosophy at Notre Dame and my being an American, though, in fact, inseparable in me, remain in themselves different objects of thought, neither entailing the other. My being something human, however, presumably entails my being an animal, though not conversely. In the most general Aristotelian terms, the ultimate genera of the given real, the ten Aristotelian categories, are all such objects of thought that each subsequent one in the series involves in its understandability all the preceding ones; thus, all the accidents involve in their understandability substance and, reductively, first substance, the primary subject of existence.

Though in natural things quantity and substance do not exist in separation from all of the other ultimate genera of accidents, yet they can be thought, without distortion, apart from all the other accidents and the effects in concrete things, of which those accidents are the formal principles. Considered exclusively in terms of those characteristics which belong to them as quantified substances, divisible wholes, natural things were thought to yield the generic object of mathematical investigation. So considered by the mathematical intelligence, objects are said, in the later Aristotelian Scholastic tradition, to be separated in thought from all "sensible matter", abstracted, that is, from all those effects, both necessary and contingent, which belong to quantified substance by virtue of the sensible qualities, with which the quantified substance is united in concrete natural things. By contrast, substance-things, in those inseparable characteristics which were thought to belong to them as *quantified* substances, were designated "intelligible matter". Conceived in terms of their intelligible matter (quantified substance, individual or universal), things are the subjects of predicates whose proper meaning prescinds entirely from motion and therefore from the first necessary conditions of motion, first matter and nature-matter, hence also from natural substance, individual or universal. Statements about objects in this state of abstraction from these formal effects which are principled in existing things by the accidents subsequent to quantity in the Aristotelian Categories, are without physical import. They are therefore independent of empirical verification in their truth value.

As determined by quality, particularly by sensible quality (conceived as the formal source of those determinations of things which have to be sensibly perceived to be known), natural substances were deemed to be incapable of existing or being thought about apart from motion and its necessary conditions, first matter and nature-matter. To the extent that they are constituted in their proper being by these two principles, things were said to be essentially changeable; they are only if they come to be and, once in being, they continue to be only in becoming. Yet, because the operations and affections, of which such things are the agents and the subjects, are known only by reference to sense experience (which inevitably involves a reference to the changes or motions of things), these objects of thought are said, in this later Scholastic tradition, not to be abstracted from "sensible matter". As subjects of predication, such objects of thought involve, in their primary meaning, a reference to perceptual experience (directly or indirectly), and the truth value of statements about them necessarily involves a measure of empirical verification.

Here a distinction must be drawn. 'Individual sensible matter' denotes any perceptible thing in the set of traits which are unique to it and accordingly differentiate if from every other existing thing. Such singular traits cannot be grounded in any of those elements which are the ground in a thing for those traits in respect to which it is *like* anything else. All that such a ground was thought to require was that it allow for the possibility of an indefinite number of singular determinations by which any natural product would be uniquely differentiated from any other. As having no determinations of its own, primary matter is such a ground and was accordingly said to be the first, though not the only, principle of the individuation of changeable or natural entities. Though objects of knowledge in respect to these singular determinations, things are objects of perceptual rather than of conceptual knowledge. Accordingly, the scientific knowledge of nature is, in this theory of science, said to abstract from the individual sensible matter of natural products.

'Specific sensible matter', on the other hand, refers to things in those similar traits (essential constituents and their entailments) which divide them not from one another as concrete and singular generable entities but into definable types of generable beings. Aquinas illustrates the sense of this expression in asserting that though the object of thought, *animal,* can neither exist nor be thought of as not having flesh and bones, it can and must be thought without the determinations which flesh and bones have in this or that actual animal. That which limits what it is to be flesh and bones to the flesh and bones of this or that animal is something extrinsic to what it is to be flesh and bones. Such objects of thought can be understood, even though they cannot exist, apart from that extrinsic factor, which individuates them in concrete first things, namely primary matter, as determined by the unique and contingent qualifications affecting it in the origin- and agent-beings from which any given natural product comes to be. Primary matter, regarded in this way, was later called "determinate or signate matter"; it is the complete—and not just the first—principle of individuation of natural substance. 'Singular sensible matter' thus denotes the concrete individual thing in those of its determinations which are grounded in it by determinate matter, determinations which the thing can be known to have only by observation. 'Specific sensible matter' denotes the same concrete individual thing in those of its determinations which belong to it by nature-matter and nature-form, determinations which the thing can be known to have only in abstraction from singular sensible matter and therefore only by the conceptual intelligence.

In this conception of nature, physical objects are inseparable in existence and conception from "sensible matter"; in conception, from universal sensible matter; in existence, from singular sensible matter. Mathematical objects, on the other hand, are said to be separated in thought from both individual and universal sensible matter but not from intelligible matter. If mathematical concepts signify anything of existing things, it is only such traits and relations as belong to them as quantified substances. Things exhibit these traits to the mind only as it abstracts from that in them which grounds their motions, namely first matter and nature-matter. Mathematics is accordingly said to abstract from things as mobile or in motion. In abstracting from motion, mathematics abstracts from all sensible matter and its principles in existing things. To the extent that such mathematical objects are found to be realized in physical things, they are found there with attributes (e.g. actual physical magnitudes) which belong to them not in themselves but only as the boundaries or magnitudes of physical bodies.

Physical objects, on the contrary, as inseparable in understanding from universal sensible matter and in existence from both individual and universal sensible matter, involve not only quantified but also sensible qualified substance and, hence, involve not only in existence but also, in thought, a reference to motion and its principles and a dependence (direct or indirect) upon sense perception through which alone we know things in their changes or motions and, consequently, in their changeabilities and mobilities.

From this difference in the primary structure of mathematical and physical objects as disclosed in the analysis of such objects as were investigated in the physics and mathematics of his time, Aristotle concludes[12] that whereas the objects studied by physics exhibit quantified attributes which belong to them specifically as the boundaries of actual physical bodies, the objects of mathematics may retain only those attributes which belong to them only in mental separation from physical bodies. As distinguished from mathematical subjects of predication, physical subjects of predication may be called immattered forms and accordingly involve in their definitions both nature-matter and nature-form, that is, both a mobile subject (the origin-term of any natural process) and the discoverable limits of its mobility as exhibited in the type-characteristics of the uniform products of natural process. In short, the form factor in nature (the first principle of the coming-to-be and being of things outside of human agency) appears to be the laws which determine and order the nature-matters in natural process and its products. However necessary and relevant then are the description and analysis of the nature-matter of any natural product, these remain inadequate as an account until one has determined some, if not all, of the necessary reasons (laws) why such a product requires such a matter if it is to come to be what it uniformly is. The discovery of these laws no less than the identification and description of the matters which they determine has been the unending work of many minds in numerous departments of natural science.

In the most general terms, then, the Aristotelian theory of natural science rests upon the assertion of an irreducible ontological duality of matter and form in the nature or originative source of the coming-to-be and actual being of natural products. By the matter, both first (primary matter) and second (nature-matter), such products exist only as terms of process from things already in existence. By the form, both substantial and specific (nature-form), primary matter actually exists in the diversities of nature-matters (origin-things), and these nature-matters achieve in act the other

---

[12] Aristotle. *Physics* II, 2, 193b 31–194a 11.

uniform ways of being-in-becoming which they exhibit in natural process and its products. In principle, then, any natural product, from the simplest known physical bodies through their increasingly complex combinations in the inorganic and organic orders to the whole cosmic order, is at once a natural entity or its part, an origin-thing and a product-thing.

§8 Nature as Agent

As origin, any natural product is not all that it comes to be as intermediate and as product. As intermediate, any natural product is not only other than what it was as origin but also other than what it comes to be as product. Not being as origin what it can come to be as intermediate and product, the existence of any natural product entails the existence of at least one other being and this other being as an agent which, in itself can give to the origin-being that which it does not, but can, have. In this interaction, between agent- and patient-beings, the origin-being passes to the state of intermediate or product-being, relative or absolute (in the case of unqualified coming-to-be). If the agent-being is itself a natural product, it, too, will entail an origin-being and an agent-being other than itself to exist. But not all agent-beings can, without the absurdity of an infinite regress, be natural products. Accordingly Aristotle concludes that there must be an agent which is neither an origin-being nor a product being: a being which moves without itself being in motion and hence has in itself, as such, being without coming-to-be. As unmoved agent, such a being is outside the realm of nature. It has no "material" aspect; it can thus be called "immaterial". The study of it, if not the discovery of it, is beyond physics, the most general science of being-in-becoming.

As given in perceptual experience, the universe of natural process and its products, presents uniformities both within and among its parts, and, in particular, a most general and invariable uniformity such that without the simpler, the more complex products cannot come to be. Here again, to avoid the absurdity of an infinite regress, Aristotle posits a lower limit: the simplest natural products, which in accordance with the prevailing chemistry he identifies with the "simple bodies", and an upper limit: the most complex natural products, i.e. the higher animals. As natural products (i.e. terms of coming-to-be outside of human agency), the simple bodies require an origin or matter. As the simplest, they can have no nature-matter other than one another. If they come to be only from one another, there must be in each something which is identical with none of them but which can be the ground for any of them and through them, as origins, any other natural product; it is thus the absolutely first subject of any generable being, the "primary" matter of natural process and its products. There must also be that in the simple bodies which first divides them according to their natural type, as exhibited in their uniform actions and interactions. This is the substantial form, the absolutely first act by which primary matter in the elements, and through them, in all other natural products, exists precisely as the first subject of unqualified coming-to-be.

In the language of Aristotle's basic account of the universe of natural process and its products, 'matter' and 'form' are primitive terms which have meaning and reference only in the context of things that come into existence in an irreversible order of dependence. For such things to come into existence agents are required of which at least one must exist without coming into existence. Thus, however necessary to account for the coming-to-be of things, matter and form of themselves cannot account for the existence of anything. If physics, in the Aristotelian sense, is the most general science of that which man finds in existence, it cannot be the most general science of that which is in existence.

§9 *Nature as End*[13]

We have seen that Aristotle distinguished between primary matter, the first subject of coming-to-be, unique in its sheer indetermination, and nature-matter (second matter), the first subject of coming-to-be, not simply, but as this or that distinctive natural product (element, compound or organism). Unlike primary matter, nature-matters are as numerous in kind as the kinds of origin-beings, of which the first and simplest are the elements in their unique property of coming-to-be from one another as origins, unlike other natural origins and products which originate from some simpler natural product. At the upper limit of this order of natural products, the product which presupposes all the lower orders of products for its coming-to-be and remaining-in-being, is man, who is unique in not being the origin of any higher natural product. By his art and science man is so related to all the other natural products as to be able to actualize in them virtualities from which, across historical time, he originates, with matchless versatility, the art and technological products which condition the emergence, development and integration of civilized society. In this relatively stable order of the most general types in Nature, Aristotle finds the lower types, as the nature-matters of the higher ones, related to the higher as means to ends. In Nature, however, this ascending order of natural types has no existence

---

[13] For Aristotle's theory of causality in nature and its basis in the matter-form composition of natural products, see: Aristotle, *Physics,* II, 3 and 7; Mansion, *op. cit.,* pp. 226–81.

apart from the ceaselessly changing individual origins and products. Between these irreducible elements of any singular production, no less than between the specific types which fix the limits of their development, Aristotle finds it necessary to assert a similar relation of means to end. For any given individual natural product to be, other natural origins and agents must be at hand in an appropriate way. These others are said to be appropriate, when in interacting they yield invariably or usually the same products in the same way.

Aristotle finds in this absolute or relative invariance of actual natural process and its products and even in the exceptional variances, the sign that in natural production, no less than in art production, everything prior in the productive process is for the sake of (and therefore the necessary means to) the coming-to-be of the product which completes the process. But that which is first in any natural process is the origin (natural substance as unformed matter) and that which is last as completing the process is the product (natural substance as formed nature-matter). In every completed natural process, therefore, the matter at the origin and in the product is related to the form, absent in the origin and present in the product, as means to end. Nature-matter as such has the function of a means in respect to nature-form which has the status of an end throughout natural process and its products. In its prior composition of primary matter and substantial form, no individual natural substance is distinguishable from any other, but all alike are distinguished from such entities as are without coming-to-be, it any such there be. The more specific composition of nature-matter and nature-form presupposes that prior composition. Beyond these specific divisions in natural process and its products are the individual or singular differences which are grounded in them both by their primary matter, as ultimate subject, and by the endlessly variable extrinsic determinations affecting agents and origins and, therefore products, in their actual interactions.

In this assertion of the primacy of nature-form as end over nature-matter as means Aristotle assimilates definitively the finalism or teleology of the Plato of the *Laws*.[14] It is only in terms of this finalism that he is able to formulate his own doctrine of chance and fortune as incidental causes in the sphere of things which come to be always or usually for the sake of something else. Having formulated this doctrine, he rejects the Empedoclean physics which accounted for the coming-to-be and being of natural products in terms of the mixing and unmixing of the four primitive and eternal matters. In the Empedoclean scheme, what is subsequent in natural process (natural products) cannot be other they are because of what is ante-

---

[14] Solmsen, *op. cit.*, pp. 114–17.

cedent in natural process (natural origins). In the Aristotelian scheme, what is subsequent in natural process cannot come to be what they are without what is antecedent. Since, however, there is in the product something that is not the origin as such, matter, though necessary, is not sufficient to account for the product. Thus, besides the matter, there must be in the product that which distinguishes it alike from the origin and from other natural products as well as relating it to both. Whereas in the Empedoclean scheme, the necessity of matter is unconditional, in the Aristotelian scheme it is conditional i.e. if the product is to be, the matter must be, but not conversely.[15] Thus, the form of the product, though last in natural process, is first in natural being as determining matter as well as initiating and completing process. In short, anything is, only to the extent that it is actual and is actual only to the extent that it is or has form. To be an origin of process, natural or artificial, a thing must be and to the extent that it is, it must have form. Yet as origin, it is not all that it can be and to that extent it is matter waiting upon the appropriate agencies (intrinsic and extrinsic) to form or actuate it. To possess those other determinations, it must be acted upon by extrinsic natural agents, the actions and operations of which are in turn grounded in their nature, and in particular, their nature-form.

§10 *Conclusion*

In the first two books of his *Physics,* Aristotle is concerned with the discovery and formulation of those primitive concepts, *form* and *matter,* which, in his view, are entailed in the very possibility of such existing things as confront, everywhere and always, the human observer. Their discernment and formulation do not, in his view, constitute in any sense a "science" of nature but rather the most general *preconditions* of any science of nature both with respect to the *existence* and the scientific *knowability* of nature. Accordingly, they are said to be "principles" precisely in the sense that there is nothing in nature prior to them in being or in concept, and they are entailed in everything else in nature and our knowledge of nature. Granting them, one must grant a sphere of existence outside of nature and related to nature as first cause and last end. Of these two irreducible but inseparable constituents of what is only as it is in process, matter is more characteristic of nature as such, because, without it, being-in-becoming cannot be said to be without contradiction. Inseparable from matter, nature-form is no less primitive and necessary to the being and concept of nature and its products. Yet, in itself as being-in-act, form is simply and solely what is asserted in

---

[15] *Physics* II, 9; Mansion, *op. cit.,* pp. 282–92.

the principles of identity, non-contradiction and excluded middle. In this sense, it is expressive of what is without coming to be. In thus asserting the inseparability of nature-form from nature-matter and stressing the absolute priority of form as such to both matter and immattered form, Aristotle opens the whole realm of being without closing any of the realm of natural being.

University of Notre Dame

MATTER AND PREDICATION
IN ARISTOTLE

Joseph Owens, C.Ss.R

§1 *Introduction*

In describing the basic matter of things, Aristotle removed from it all determinations and so all direct intelligibility. Yet he regarded the basic matter just in itself as a subject for predication. You can say things about it. You can say, for instance, that it is ingenerable and indestructible, and that it is the persistent substrate of generation and corruption. Still more strangely, Aristotle means that a substance or substantial form, like that of a man, of a plant, of a metal, can be predicated of matter.[1] How can this be, if matter is in itself wholly undetermined and entirely unintelligible? How can matter even be indicated, if it exhibits nothing that can halt the gaze of the intellect?

The above observations envisage two ways in which characteristics may be predicated of matter. One is essential (*per se*) predication. Matter is of itself ingenerable and indestructible, somewhat as man is animal and corporeal. The other way is through added forms. Matter is metallic, bovine, human through the forms of a metal, a cow, a man. But these forms are substantial, not accidental. Yet their predication in regard to matter resembles accidental predication, just as the specific differentia in the category of substance is predicated of the genus as though it were a quality. As changes within the category of substance are called by Professor Fisk in the present volume "qualified-like changes", this type of predication may correspondingly be designated "quality-like" predication. It is one type of the medieval *predicatio denominativa*.

---

[1] See Aristotle, *Metaph.*, Z 3, 1029a 20–30. The technical term used by Aristotle for matter was the Greek '*hylê*' or 'wood'. He seems to have been the first to coin a term for this notion, though the philosophic use of '*hylê*' for materials in general was prepared by Plato at *Ti.*, 69A, and *Phlb.*, 54C. In modern times the overall approach to the scientific notion of matter is hardly different; e.g.: "By the building materials I mean what we call matter, . . . ordinary matter is constructed out of two types of ultimate things called "electrons" and "protons." " C. G. Darwin, *The New Conceptions of Matter*, London, 1931, p. 8. Aristotle, however, is approaching the question on a level that does not lead to electrons and protons but to very different principles; cf. Appendix. For texts, see Bonitz' *Index Aristotelicus*, 652b 49–51; 785a 5–43.

In ordinary predication, as treated in Aristotelian logic, the ultimate subject is always actual and concrete. The universal, from a metaphysical viewpoint, is potential (*Metaph.*, M 10, 1087a 15-22). The concrete singular always retains its actuality as its various features are universalized and made potential. It cannot be treated as an undetermined residue that remains after its predicates have been removed. Logical analysis of predication, therefore, leads ultimately in Aristotle to the actual, and not to something wholly potential like matter. Ultimate matter is arrived at through the reasoning of the *Physics*. So reached, it poses problems for metaphysics. How does it have being, and how are forms predicated of it? The Stagirite had here to grapple with a refined concept attained by his scientific thinking and established to the satisfaction of that technical procedure itself, but which broke through the systematized logic presupposed by him for every theoretical science.

The solution reached by Aristotle in this question may or may not provide light for other disciplines when in the course of their reasonings they arrive at concepts that cannot fit into the grooves of the logic they have been using. Such new concepts may well appear self-contradictory when stretched on the Procrustean bed of a closed logical system. Certainly in metaphysics pertinent help for understanding the notion of essence can be obtained from studying Aristotle's procedure in establishing the notion of matter. Whether or not such help may be extended to other disciplines has to be left a question for investigators who specialize in them. But the contingency is one that can be encountered when any discipline pushes its concepts far past the experiences in which human thought commences. Concepts taken from immediate experience sometimes have to be refined in peculiar ways if they are to function in very remote areas of inquiry. The procedure of a first-rate thinker in meeting such a contingency belongs to the common treasury of achievements in the history of thought, and hardly deserves to be forgotten. Aristotle's method in this problem seems, then, *prima facie,* a subject worthy of investigation and critique.

§2 *The Subject of Predication*

First, what is the basic subject of predication in Aristotelian logic? As is well enough known, this ultimate subject of predication is the highly actual concrete singular thing. It is the individual man, or the individual horse, or the individual tree, according to the examples used in the Aristotelian *Categories*.[2] In a logical context, the real individual thing was called "primary substance" by the Stagirite. In Greek the term was '*prôtê ousia*', primary entity. The term characterized the concrete singular thing as ab-

---

[2] See *Cat.*, 5, 2a 13–14; 2b 13.

solutely basic among the subjects with which logic deals, and as the fundamental being that received the predication of all other perfections. Secondary substances, in that logical context, were *man, animal, body,* and the like, taken universally. They were all predicated of a primary substance, of a concrete individual man like Socrates or Plato, or of an individual horse or stone. Accidental characteristics, like *white, large, running,* and so on, were predicated of substances and ultimately of an individual substance. There was nothing more fundamental of which they could be predicated. For Aristotelian logic the concrete individual was the basic subject of predication. It was the primary entity upon which all logical structure was raised. In a logical context it was primary substance in the full sense of the expression.[3]

This doctrine of predication functioned without special difficulty when applied throughout the world of common sense thought and speech. Quite obviously the ultimates with which ordinary conversation deals are shoes and ships and sealing-wax and cabbages and kings, individual pinching shoes and flat-tasting cabbages and uncrowned office kings, as one meets them in the course of everyday life. These are all concrete individual things or persons. Aristotelian logic, it should be kept in mind, was expressly meant as a propaedeutic to the sciences. It did not presuppose knowledge of any theoretical science. Rather, it had to be learned before any theoretical science could be approached.[4] There should be little wonder, then, that Aristotelian logic was not geared to function smoothly in situations brought into being solely through the results of scientific analysis and construction. Yet those situations have to be expressed in concepts and in language. Logic has to be applied to them as they occur. Aristotle, as may be expected, could not go very deeply into any theoretical science without encountering situations that broke through the logical norms presupposed in his hearers. Was he prepared to meet such situations? Was he able to adapt his logic to them as they presented themselves in the course of his scientific investigations? subject of predication in a logic where that ultimate subject is the concrete

§3 *The Problem of Matter*

An instance that could hardly be avoided was that of matter. Matter quite obviously did not come under the notion envisaged for an ultimate

---

[3] *Cat.*, 5, 2b 4–6; 15–17. In a metaphysical context, on the other hand, the form and not the composite was primary substance, as at *Metaph.*, Z 7, 1032b 1–14; 11, 1037a 28. On the category mistake occasioned by this twofold use of 'primary substance' in Aristotle, see my article "Aristotle on Categories," *The Review of Metaphysics, 14,* 1960, 83–84.

[4] See Aristotle, *Metaph.*, Γ 3, 1005b 2–5.

singular thing. In the everyday universe of discourse the material or stuff out of which things are said to be made is always of the concrete individual stamp. The wood of which a house is constructed consists of individual pieces. The bronze in which a statue is cast is a piece of bronze in definite dimensions in a definite place at a definite time. In the later Scholastic vocabulary these concrete materials out of which more complex things were made received the designation, '*materia secunda*', or 'secondary matter'. Bronze and wood and stone were indeed matter, in the sense that things were made out of them. But they were not the basic or ultimate matter out of which those things were made. That was signified by calling them secondary matter. The designation implied that there was a still more basic matter that was not concrete nor individual. Aristotle had not finished the first book of his *Physica* or philosophy of nature before he had established in sensible things a subject still more fundamental than the concrete individual. A visible, tangible, or mobile thing, the Stagirite showed, was necessarily composite. It was literally a *con-cretum*. It was composed of more fundamental elements. These ultimate constituents of sensible things, according to the Aristotelian reasoning, were form and matter. Matter played the role of ultimate subject, and a form was its primary characteristic.

The absolutely basic matter of the Aristotelian *Physics* became known in Scholastic terminology as *materia prima*, "primary matter". By Aristotle himself it was simply called matter. However, Aristotle uses the term 'matter' regularly enough to designate the concrete materials out of which artifacts are made, materials like bricks and stones and wood. So there was ground for the Scholastic insistence on the use of two expressions, 'primary matter' and 'secondary matter,' to mark the important distinction. For convenience in the present study the term 'materials' or 'material' will be used wherever possible to denote what the Scholastics called "secondary matter", and the term 'matter' without any qualification will be used regularly for the absolutely basic substrate of things as established in the Aristotelian *Physics*. By "matter", then, will be meant what the mediaeval vocabulary designated as "primary matter".

With matter in this sense established as subject, and form as its immediate though really distinct characteristic, you may readily expect to hear that the form is considered to be predicable of matter. You will not be disappointed, Aristotle actually does say that substance, in the sense of substantial form, is predicated of matter: ". . . for the predicates other than substance are predicated of substance, while substance is predicated of matter."[5] That is his express statement. What does it mean? At the very

_____
[5] *Metaph.*, Z 3, 1029a 23–24; Oxford tr.

least, it means that matter is the ultimate subject with which predication is concerned. Everything other than substance you can predicate of substance. But what is intelligible about substance can in turn be predicated, denominatively of course, of matter. The principle of intelligibility in a substance is its form, and its form is the primary characteristic of its matter, from the "quality-like" viewpoint.

At first sight, perhaps, nothing could seem more natural than to predicate a form of its corresponding matter. Characteristics are regularly predicated of subjects. A new subject has been unearthed by the Aristotelian philosophy of nature. The substantial characteristic of that subject has been isolated. What is more normal, then, than to say that here as in other cases the characteristic is predicable of its subject?

Yet as soon as one tries to express this type of predication in any definite instance, linguistic and conceptual difficulties arise. How would you word a sentence in which a substance, or a substantial form, is predicated of matter? The first part of Aristotle's assertion was clear enough: "Predicates other than substance are predicated of substance." The predicates other than substance are the accidents. They are quantity, qualities, relations, activities, time, and place. They are predicated without difficulty of a concrete, individual substance. You may indicate a particular tree and say without hesitation that it is large, green, near to you, growing in the yard at the present moment. Each of these accidents is obviously predicated of a substance, the individual tree. But, the Aristotelian text continues: "the substance is predicated of matter". How would you express this in the case of the tree? You would have to say that matter is this particular tree. You would have to say that matter is likewise Socrates, or is Plato, or is this particular table or that particular stone. Such predication is unusual, and requires considerable explanation even to make sense.

Some light may be obtained from the way in which for Aristotle a thing may be defined in terms of the materials of which it is composed. If asked what a house is, you may answer that it is "stones, bricks, and timbers".[6] If

---

[6] *Metaph.*, H 2, 1043a 15; Oxford tr. On this doctrine, and Aristotle's use of the expression 'primary matter' in connection with it, see W. D. Ross, *Aristotle's Metaphysics*, Oxford, 1924, 2, 256–57. 'Primary matter' is found in various senses at *Ph.*, II *1*, 193a 29, *GA*, I *20*, 729a 32, and *Metaph.*, Δ *4*, 1015a 7–10. 'Matter' in its chief or primary sense, however, meant for Aristotle the substrate of generation and corruption (*GC*, I *4*, 320a 2–5), even though the designation 'primary matter' never seems to have been limited by him to that sense. The therapy required by the concept's genesis has to be kept applied in representing the absolutely undetermined matter as that of which things are composed. Such matter is not individual, like any of the materials of which a house is composed. Still less is it something universal, for the universal is subsequent to the individual in Aristotelian doctrine. Rather, it is below the

that may be called a definition, it is surely the least perfect type of definition possible. But Aristotle does refer to it as a definition in terms of the materials that are able to be made into a house. From that viewpoint the house is the materials that constitute it, and conversely the materials are the house insofar as definition and thing defined are convertible. In general, then, in the way in which a thing may be said to be its materials, the materials themselves may be said to be the thing. Awkward though this predication is, what prevents it from being applied in the case of the basic matter of which things are composed? In each particular case it should allow you to say that matter is this individual man, this individual stone, this individual tree. Substance, even the individual substance, would in this way be predicated of matter.

The context in which the present doctrine occurs is one of the central books of the Aristotelian *Metaphysics*. In a metaphysical context, the universal is not substance. When in this context substance is said to be predicated of matter, it can hardly mean just another instance of universal predicated of particular. From the viewpoint of logic, the secondary substance or the substance taken universally is predicated of the particular substance. Even though present as a condition, that logical doctrine can scarcely be what Aristotle meant in saying in the *Metaphysics* that substance is predicated of matter. It is not just another case of predicating universal of singular, as in the assertion: 'Socrates is a man'. Subject and predicate are really the same when a universal substance is predicated of a particular sub-

---

level at which individuality and universality appear. Considered just in itself, it has nothing to distinguish it as found in one thing from itself as found in another. From this viewpoint it parallels the common nature of Duns Scotus, which of itself had nothing to distinguish it as found in Socrates from itself as found in Plato (see Duns Scotus, *Quaest. Metaph.*, 7, 13, no. 21; ed. Vivès, 7, 421b. In contrast to the Scotistic common nature, however, the Aristotelian basic matter lacks all formal determinations, and so not only individual determinations). The absolutely undetermined matter is accordingly one through the removal of all distinguishing characteristics. It is wholly formless in the *Physics* (I 7, 191a 8–12) as well as in the *Metaphysics*. In this sense only, may it be regarded as common. When actuated, it differentiates by its very nature in making possible the spread of the same form in parts outside parts and the multiplication of singulars in a species. In that way it is an individuating principle without being of itself individual. As the substrate of substantial change, it may be said—with the appropriate therapy—to change from one form to another. So doing, it shows itself to be really distinct from its forms, since it really persists while the forms really replace each other. But it is not therefore a really distinct being from the form. In the individual there is but the one being derived from the form to the matter and the composite. Thus any single thing is differentiated from a "heap" (*Metaph.*, Z 17, 1041b 7–31). Subsidiary forms, for instance those indicated in water by the spectra of hydrogen and oxygen, would accordingly be accidental forms for Aristotle, and in a substantial change would be replaced by new though corresponding accidental forms.

stance. If you say: "Matter is a man", however, you have a different type of predication. Matter does not coincide in reality with a man in the way Socrates does. A really distinct principle, the form of man, is added. From this viewpoint the predication resembles rather the assertion of an accidental form in regard to substance, as when one says that a man is pale, or fat. The accidental form is really distinct from the substance, as the substantial form is really distinct from its matter. Such predication will be of the "quality-like" type.

That indeed is the way in which Aristotle presents the situation. As an accidental form, for instance quantity, is predicated of substance, so substance is predicated of matter. What is predicated of matter, accordingly should be the substantial form or act, and not the composite. Later in the same part of the *Metaphysics* it is stated in exactly that manner: ". . . as in substances that which is predicated of the matter is the actuality itself, in all other definitions also it is what most resembles full actuality."[7] As accidental forms are predicated of substances, then, so the substantial form is what is predicated of matter within the category of substance.

The doctrine clearly enough is that form in the category of substance may be predicated of its matter as of a subject. You may accordingly apply the form of man to matter, the form of iron to matter, and so on, and call it predication. But how can you express this in ordinary language? It can hardly be done. Ordinary language has not been developed to meet this contingency. The best you can do, perhaps, is to say that matter is humanized, equinized, lapidified, and so on, as it takes on forms like those of man, horse, and stone. To say that matter is human, equine, lapideous, or that it is a man, a horse, a stone, may be true enough in this context; but with all its linguistic oddity the way of speaking hardly brings out the full import of the situation. It tends to give the impression that matter is of itself these things. The Aristotelian meaning, on the contrary, is that matter is not of itself any of these things, but becomes them by receiving the appropriate substantial forms. As their real subject it remains really distinct from them, somewhat as a substance remains really distinct from its accidents. The assertion that matter is humanized, equinized, lapidified by the reception of different substantial forms expresses the predication with less danger of being misunderstood, though with still less respect for linguistic usage.

The linguistic difficulties, however, turn out to be mild in comparison with the conceptual. The immediate context of the Aristotelian passage that gave rise to this discussion is enough to cause doubts about the very

---

[7] *Metaph.*, H 2, 1043a 5–7; Oxford tr.

possibility of the predication. Matter had just been defined as "that which in itself is neither a particular thing nor of a certain quantity nor assigned to any other of the categories by which being is determined".[8] Matter is not anything definite. It is not a particular thing. It is not a "what" nor at all an "it". It exhibits nothing that could provide a direct answer to the question "What is it?" It has in itself none of the determinations by which a thing can be or be recognized or indicated or known or understood. The text states explicitly that it has no quantitative nor other categorical determination. Of itself, therefore, it has no length nor breadth nor thickness nor number nor parts nor position. It cannot at all be conceived in the fashion of the Cartesian concept of matter. In this concept, matter was identified with extension.[9] Nor can the Aristotelian matter be represented as anything capable of detection by means of a pointer-reading. There is nothing about it, in itself, that could register in quantitative terms. It belongs to a level on which neither quantitative nor qualitative physics has any means of functioning. It eludes quantitative and qualitative and other accidental determinations, as well as all substantial determinations.

Yet it cannot be expressed by negations of known characteristics, as for instance non-being is expressed negatively in terms of being.[10] The nature of matter cannot be represented in terms of what it is not. The same Aristotelian text continues:

> Therefore the ultimate substratum is of itself neither a particular thing nor of a particular quantity nor otherwise positively characterized; nor yet is it the negations of these, for negations also will belong to it only by accident.[11]

All categorical determinations are first denied to matter. They are outside its nature, and in that sense "belong to it only by accident". This has been expressed in the preceding paragraphs of the present study by saying that the forms are really distinct from matter somewhat as accidents are really distinct from substances. But, the Aristotelian text insists, the negations of all the different determinations are just as accidental to matter. None of them can express its nature, as the term 'nature' is used of matter in the *Physics* (II 1, 193a 28-30; 2, 194a 12-13). It eludes even negations. You can indeed say that matter is not something, or better still, that it is a "not-something". What you say is true. But you have not thereby expressed the nature of matter, even negatively. Negations are just as accidental to it as

---

[8] *Metaph.*, Z 3, 1029a 20–21; Oxford tr.

[9] See Descartes, *Principia Philosophiae*, 2, 4–9; *A–T, 8*, 42.4–45.16 (9^2, 65–68).

[10] For Aristotle, predication of being is made through reference to the primary instance of being. Even the negation of being, namely "non-being", is asserted in this way. See *Metaph.*, Γ 2, 1003b 5–10.

[11] *Metaph.*, Z 3, 1029a 24–26; Oxford tr. 'Positively' refers here to determination; cf. a21.

are the determinations it takes on in the actual world. You are still only skimming its accidental manifestations. You have not penetrated to its proper nature. Its nature eludes the negations.

In a word, matter as reached by Aristotle escapes in itself both determinative and negative characterizations. It cannot be conceived or described in any direct fashion, either determinatively or negatively. It is not even a "what" nor an "it" that is capable of being indicated. In terms of modern logic, it is not the "referent" of any "demonstrative" (i.e. monstrative) symbol, because it cannot be presented directly to one's cognition. Nor can the referent be any property or set of properties, because such determinations are lacking to matter in itself.[12]

How, then, is the Aristotelian matter to be conceived and represented? How can it be set up as a subject for predication? Quite obviously, from the above considerations, no direct method, either affirmative or negative, is capable of grasping what Aristotle meant in this regard. The concept will have to be that of a positive subject, able to receive predication. No negation is able to express the nature of matter. Yet from that notion of positive subject every determination will have to be removed, even, or rather especially, the determination expressed by "something". Matter is explicitly not a "something" nor a "what" nor an "it". All determination, even the most elementary, has to be drastically eliminated from the notion of the positive in this concept. The concept that expresses the Aristotelian notion of matter will have to be the concept of a positive object that is wholly indeterminate. Is the human mind able to form such a concept? If so, upon what referents will it be based?

Presumably Aristotle could not have spoken so cogently about matter if he had not worked out its concept to his own satisfaction. The most likely way to learn how the concept is formed, accordingly, should be to follow the steps by which the originator of the concept reasoned to the presence of matter in sensible things. In this context, of course, the referents will be sensible things in themselves, and not Kantian phenomena.

§4 *Substance and Change*

How, then, did Aristotle arrive at the notion of matter as a real subject, and as a subject denominatively characterized by forms that remained really distinct from it? In the first book of the *Physics,* the Stagirite sur-

---

[12] "The referend of a demonstrative symbol (i.e. a word used demonstratively) is *the object directly presented to* the speaker. The referend of a descriptive phrase is a *property,* or *set of properties.*" L. Susan Stebbing, *A Modern Introduction to Logic,* London, 6th ed., 1948, p. 499. On the technical term 'referend', cf.: "We shall find it convenient to use the word 'referend' to stand for *that which is signified.*" *Ibid.,* p. 13.

veyed the teachings of his philosophic predecessors on the basic principles of natural things. Things in the world of nature were known by observation to be capable of motion or change. In the course of his survey, attention is focused upon the universal requirements for change. Any change whatsoever needs three principles. It has to have a subject that loses one form and acquires another. The three principles necessarily involved are therefore the form that is lost, the form that is acquired, and the subject that undergoes the loss of the old form and the acquisition of the new.[13]

The Aristotelian examples meant to illustrate this doctrine are clear enough. They are concrete individual materials that lose and acquire different forms. Bronze is the subject that becomes a statue. At first the bronze has a nondescript form or shape. Then it is cast into the form of a statue, say of the Greek god Hermes. It is the subject that changes from one form or shape to another. The notion of form in this example is readily understood from its ordinary English use. It is the external shape of the bronze. Another Aristotelian example, however, uses 'form' in a more esoteric way. A man from an uneducated state comes to be educated. The man is the subject that changes from uneducated to educated. 'Uneducated' describes the quality of the man who has not had proper schooling. 'Educated' means the quality of adequate instruction and cultural training. Both 'educated' and 'uneducated' mean qualities; and in the Aristotelian vocabulary qualities are forms.

As can be seen in these examples, the original form from which the subject changes is more properly regarded from the viewpoint of a privation of the form to be acquired in the change. It is expressed in a privative way, as in the term '*un*educated'. Any of the Aristotelian categories, like the thing's quantity, its place, its time of occurrence, or any of its relations, is a form in this technical Aristotelian sense. Change can take place in any of the categories of being.[14] But in its very notion, as has emerged from the foregoing analysis, it involves indispensably the three principles—a subject that changes, a form that is lost, a form that is acquired.

This essential notion of change is reached from the changes that are ob-

---

[13] See *Ph.*, I 7, 189b 30–191a 7. The analysis of change or motion is made by Aristotle without dependence on the notion of time. Rather, motion is first defined, and then the notion of time is worked out in terms of motion, that is, as the numbering of motion in respect of prior and subsequent (*Ph.*, IV *11*, 219b 1–2). Since Kant the tendency has been first to establish the notion of time, and then to describe motion in terms of relation to time; e.g.: "Change thus always involves (1) a fixed entity, (2) a three-cornered relation between this entity, another entity, and some but not all, of the moments of time." Bertrand Russell, *Principles of Mathematics*, Cambridge, Eng., 1903, *1*, 469.

[14] *Ph.*, III *1*, 201a 8–9.

served in the accidental categories, like change from place to place, from size to size, from color to color. But the analysis of the notion establishes it as a general concept that will hold wherever change is found, regardless of the particular category. It is accordingly applied by Aristotle in the category of substance. In all other categories the subject of the change is observable. You can see the man who changes from uneducated to educated. You can touch the bronze that is cast from a nondescript form into a statue. You can handle the wood that is made into a bed. But with change in the category of substance you cannot observe the subject that changes, even in principle. This means that you cannot observe the subject changing. Change in the category of substance is accordingly not observable, even in principle.

There need be little wonder, then, that Aristotle is sparing in examples of change in the category of substance. Without too much enthusiasm he accepted the tradition of the four Empedoclean elements as the basic simple bodies, and admitted as generation the change of any one of these bodies into another.[15] But he is very circumspect in determining just where substance is found. Earth, air, and fire, three of the traditional elements, do not seem to him to have sufficient unity in their composition to be recognized as substances. Living things seem to have that unity, yet just where the unity is cannot be located too easily.[16] The one instance that he does mention definitely, though only in a passing way, is the change to plants and animals from seed.[17]

Today this Aristotelian example may not seem any too happy an illustration of substantial change. Without having to call the fertilized ovum of a rhinoceros a little rhinoceros, one may argue either for or against the position that an embryo is the same substance as the fully developed animal. To say that a tadpole is not a frog does not commit you to the stand that the one is a different substance from the other. In general, it may be easy enough to claim that the change from something non-living to something alive is a change in substance. But in regard to pinpointing the change from non-living to living substance, or even to showing definitely that there was change from the truly non-living, are we today in any noticeably further advanced position than was Aristotle? Similarly, with modern chemical knowledge, it is easy to show definitely that air, fire, and earth are not substances in the Aristotelian sense. We no longer share the Stagirite's hesitations in that regard. With respect to water, however, can a definite decision be given? In the higher kinds of living things, Aristotle's criterion was a unity that distinguishes the complex organism from a heap. It is the

---

[15] See *Cael.*, I 2, 268b 26–29; *GC*, II 1, 329a 2–8; 8, 334b 31–335a 23.

[16] *Metaph.*, Z 16, 1040b 5–16.

[17] *Ph.*, I 7, 190b 4–5. Cf. *GA*, I 18, 722b 3–5, and St Paul's simile, *I Cor.*, 15, 36.

same criterion that enables us now to consider the ant a different thing from the sandpile. In man, consciousness adds a still more profound criterion of unity. Every man considers himself a different being from other men, a different being from the substances he absorbs in nutrition and from those into which he will be dissolved when he dies. Apart from preconceived positions arising out of conclusions in metaphysics or in modern physics, and illegitimately transferred to the domain of natural philosophy, the difference of one being from another and the change of one sensible being into another may in general be admitted. *The evidence of pertinent bearing either for or against, though, is scarcely any greater now than it was in Aristotle's day.*

However, the plurality of things in the universe will hardly be contested any more today in a properly physical context than in the Stagirite's time.[18] As long as a plurality of beings in the sensible universe is admitted without subjecting the term 'beings' to intolerable strain, the plurality of substances required for the Aristotelian demonstration of matter is present. 'Substance' in Aristotle's terminology meant the entity or *ousia* of things. Wherever you have a being, simply stated, you have an *ousia*, a substance. Nor should there be too much difficulty about the change of one thing, macroscopically speaking, into another. Molecular compounds are changed into other compounds, transmutation of the elements is no longer a dream. The one real difficulty might lie in the proposal to locate the individuality of things in sub-atomic particles. In that case might not all the changes taking place in the physical universe be merely new combinations of the particles, as in Democritean atomism? There would be only accidental change, not substantial change.

The denial of any unifying principle in things over and above the sub-atomic particles would leave the behavior of every particle wholly unrelated to that of the others. A cosmic puppeteer would have to cause the regularity of the world processes. A principle of unity in each thing itself, on the other hand, would have to be deeper than the division into particles and into quanta, and indeed would have to be of a different order. It would have to function on a more profound level, in order to dominate the polarity of the sub-atomic particles and to maintain the statistical regularity of the quanta. Such a principle would function exactly as the Aristotelian substantial form. It would be the deepest principle of unity in a thing, and so would make a thing "a being" simply and without qualification. It would be the principle that rendered the thing intelligible. It would be the thing's basic determinant, making the thing one kind of thing and not another. It would be

---

[18] See *Ph.*, I 2, 184b 25–185a 16.

deeper than the entire qualitative and quantitative or measurable orders in the thing, and so would enable the thing to exist and function as a unit in spite of the common patterns of atomic and sub-atomic motion that it shares with other things. When this formal principle gave way to its successors in changes like nutrition or death, a radically new thing or things would come into being, in spite of common spectra before and after the change and in spite of the equality of the total weight before and after. It would enable the thing to function as a nature and not just artificially at the hands of a cosmic puppeteer. In a word, this principle would coincide entirely with the Aristotelian form in the category of substance.

The argument for the change of one substance into another, accordingly, seems neither stronger nor weaker in any notable way than it was in fourth century Greece. If you grant that you are a different thing or a different being from the food you absorb in nutrition and from the substances into which you will dissolve in death, you have recognized the data necessary to understand the Aristotelian demonstration. When one substance changes into another, what disappears is the most basic principle of determination and knowability, the principle that most radically made food one thing and man another thing. Without it, nothing in the thing could be knowable or observable. It is of course immediately succeeded by the form of the new thing. But the change of the one thing into the other requires a common subject, according to the very notion of change. Such a common subject will be unobservable both in principle and in fact, because it is what loses and acquires the most basic of forms and so of itself has not even the most rudimentary principle of knowability or observability. It has to be known in virtue of something else. That "something else," quite naturally, will be the observable subject in accidental change, like the wood that becomes a bed or the bronze that becomes a statue. Some corresponding subject has to be present for substantial change. In that analogous way, then, the subject of substantial change, namely matter, is indirectly known. It is known as the conclusion of scientific reasoning in the Aristotelian sense of 'scientific'. In Aristotle's own words:

> The underlying nature is an object of scientific knowledge, by an analogy. For as the bronze is to the statue, the wood to the bed, or the matter and the formless before receiving form to any thing which has form, so is the underlying nature to substance, i.e. the "this" or existent.[19]

The presence of matter is proven stringently from the requirements for change, while the nature of matter is established through analogy with the subject of accidental change. The demonstration presupposes the universal

---

[19] *Ph.*, I 7, 191a 7–12; Oxford tr.

notion of change and the two terms, but not the substrate, of substantial change.

The original referent upon which the Aristotelian concept of matter is based is therefore the subject of accidental change, like wood or bronze. From that notion of "subject", however, all determinations are removed, with the proviso that the negations as well as the determinations are accidental to it. In its own nature, then, this refined notion of subject remains as positive as ever. It was a positive notion from the start, as seen in a positive subject like wood or bronze, and all determinations were denied it under the express condition that none of these pertained to its own nature. In this way the notion *positive* is shown to be independent of *determinate*. For Aristotle, 'actual' was a synonym for 'determinate'. What lacked actuality, or in technical language the potential, could therefore be positive. By establishing the concept of the potential as positive even though non-actual or indeterminate, Aristotle has been able to set up matter as a positive though entirely non-actual subject of predication. Because the potential is positive without being determinate, this concept of matter is possible to the human mind. Its referent is any sensible thing considered potentially as substance. It is the concept of a principle wholly undetermined, yet necessarily posited in reality by any form that is extended, multiplied in singulars, or terminating substantial change.

§5 *Conclusion*

As should be clear from the foregoing considerations, matter in the category of substance can be an object of scientific inquiry only on the level of natural philosophy. It cannot at all be reached by qualitative or quantitative procedures like those of chemistry and modern physics. What is predicated of it, in itself, does not belong to the order of the measurable or the directly observable, even in principle. Its predicates are notions like *purely potential, unknowable of itself, incorruptible,* and so on. Its presence is still necessary to explain substantial change, if such change is admitted. In any case, its presence is absolutely required to account for the extension of a formally identical characteristic in parts outside parts, and for the multiplication of the characteristic in a plurality of individuals, without any formal addition whatsoever. The Aristotelian matter has not been superseded nor even touched by the stupendous progress of modern physics. Nothing that is measurable can perform its function in explaining the nature of sensible things, and by the same token it cannot be brought forward to account for anything that requires explanation in measurable terms. Any type of matter dealt with by chemistry or modern physics would in comparison be secondary matter, and not matter that is a principle in the category of substance. "Matter" in the basic Aristotelian sense is therefore in no way a rival of the "matter" that can be measured or of the mass that can be transformed into energy, but is rather a very different means of explanation for sensible things on another scientific level, the level of natural philosophy.

In distinguishing his two tables, the solid one he wrote on and the "nearly all empty space" table he knew as a physicist, Eddington failed to stress that his knowledge of his scientific table was constructed from his knowledge of the ordinary table.[20] The scientific construct was the result of understanding the ordinary table in quantitative terms. The same ordinary table can also be understood scientifically (in the traditional sense of knowledge through causes) in terms of substantial principles, form and matter, as is done in natural philosophy. It can also be understood in terms of entitative principles, essence and being, as is done in metaphysics. They are all different accounts of the same thing, given on different levels of scientific (again, in the centuries-old meaning of "scientific") investigation. All these different accounts are necessary for a well-rounded understanding of sensible things. None of these accounts can afford to despise any of the others, nor seek to substitute for any of them, nor to interfere with any of them. Each has its own role to play, a role that only itself can play. The Aristotelian matter is a principle for explaining things on the level of natural philosophy. On that level it has its own predicates, predicates that still have to be used today in the properly balanced explanation of nature.

Pontifical Institute of Mediaeval Studies

---

[20] See Arthur Stanley Eddington, *The Nature of the Physical World*, Cambridge, Eng., 1928, pp. ix–xi. Cf.: "The whole reason for accepting the atomic model is that it helps us to explain things we could not explain before. Cut off from these phenomena, the model can only mislead, . . ." Stephen Toulmin, *The Philosophy of Science*, New York, 1953, p. 12.

APPENDIX

On the independence of these different scientific procedures, see my paper "Our Knowledge of Nature", *Proceedings of the American Catholic Philosophical Association*, *29*, 1955, 80–86. A widely accepted view at present is to regard natural philosophy as a sort of dialectic that prepares the way for genuine physics; e.g.: ". . . frontier physics, natural philosophy. It is analysis of the concept of matter; a search for conceptual order amongst puzzling data." Norwood Russell Hanson, *Patterns of Discovery*, Cambridge, Eng., 1958, p. 119. "Not so very long ago the subject now called physics was known as "natural philosophy". The physicist is by origin a philosopher who has specialized in a particular direction." (Arthur S. Eddington, *The Philosophy of Physical Science*, Cambridge, Eng., 1939, p. 8.) It is true that before physics was developed through quantitative procedure as a special science, its problems had in point of historical fact been given over to the non-mathematical treatment of natural philosophy. That way of dealing with its problems was entirely illegitimate. The specific *differentiae* of natural things remain unknown and impenetrable to the human mind. They cannot be made the source for scientific knowledge of the specific traits of corporeal things. For this reason any new attempt to treat the experimental sciences as a continuation of natural philosophy, e.g., C. de Koninck, "Les Sciences Expérimentales sont-elles Distinctes de la Philosophie de la Nature?", *Culture*, *2*, 1941, 465–476, cannot hope to be successful. On the other hand, the view that natural philosophy consists only in "a search for conceptual order amongst puzzling data" seems continuous with the trend that has given rise to the conception of philosophy in general as linguistic analysis, concerned with words and concepts and not with things. Similarly, the notion that natural philosophy is a frontier investigation rather than a full-fledged science in its own right, seems to stem from Comte's law of the three stages, in which speculative philosophy in general was but an immature stage in the unilinear development towards positive science. In this view, philosophical treatment "will naturally be expected to deal with questions on the frontier of knowledge, as to which comparative certainty is not yet attained". Bertrand Russell, *Introduction to Mathematical Philosophy*, London, 1930, p. v. This is nothing but a cavalier dismissal of natural philosophy as a science.

Theoretically, it is indifferent whether the substantial principles (matter and form) used for the explanation of things through natural philosophy are reached by way of substantial change, or of extension, or of individuation. In point of fact, the way used by Aristotle himself was through substantial change. To show that the same two principles are required to explain extension and multiplication of singulars, is not a *tour de force* to safeguard the principles against someone who does not admit substantial change. It is rather a global view of the whole approach, from a theoretical standpoint, to the problem of matter.

May I express my thanks to Msgr. G. B. Phelan for many helpful suggestions, and to Fr. Ernan McMullin for carefully reading the first draft of this paper and pointing out a number of deficiencies. These I have tried to remedy in the final draft. This draft, of course, benefits from the other papers and the discussions at the conference, and in particular from the clear statement of the issues in Professor Fisk's contribution. Friedrich Solmsen's recently published work, *Aristotle's System of the Physical World* (Ithaca, N.Y., 1960), with its illuminating discussion (pp. 118–126) on the historical background of Aristotle's wholly undetermined matter, reached me too late to be of help in preparing the present paper.

COMMENT

As is well known, there are two different definitions of matter in
Aristotle. According to the first (*Phys. I, 9,* 191b 31 f.), matter is the first substratum from which each thing comes to be *per se,* as from an intrinsic principle
(as opposed both to privation and to accidental qualities which may persist in the
product); according to the second (*Met. Z, 3,* 1029a 20 f.), matter is that which
cannot be assigned to any of the categories by which being is determined. The
first definition results from an analysis of change; the second, from an analysis
of predication (cfr. St. Thomas, *In VII Met. 2,* 1287).

Is it obvious that both definitions have the same referent? The least we may
say is that Aristotle never made an attempt to clarify this point. Neither does he
say that the indeterminate subject of predication is identical with the ultimate
substratum of change; nor did he ever suggest that the indeterminateness of matter may be proven by means of an analysis of change. The expression 'λέγω
δ'ὕλην' by which both definitions are introduced, suggests that he did not want
to say that matter, i.e. an identifiable referent, is this and is that; rather, it would
seem that Aristotle is saying: "I will call the first substratum of change, "matter".
I will call ultimate subject of predication, "matter", too". In other words: it is the
ultimate subject of predication which is said to be thoroughly indeterminate; in
order to substantiate the claim that, to Aristotle, *matter* is indeterminate, one
would have to prove that the ultimate substratum of change and the ultimate
subject of predication are identical.

Accordingly, I cannot agree with Fr. Owens that the most likely way to
learn how the difficult concept of an indeterminate matter is formed, would be
to follow the steps by which Aristotle, in the *Physics,* reasoned to the presence of
matter in sensible things. For to reason to the existence of matter in general is
not to reason to the existence of a thoroughly indeterminate matter; and Aristotle
reasoned to the latter by an analysis of predication. (Incidentally, it is worthwhile
mentioning that those philosophers who rely mainly on the "physical" definition of matter are more likely to admit that matter is not *thoroughly* indeterminate; a good example is Suarez, *Disp. metaphys. d.* 13, *s.* 4 ff. Those relying
mainly on the "logical" definition, on the contrary, will be inclined to postulate
matter even in spiritual substances; thus, for example, Ibn Gebirol who initiated
the doctrine of the hylemorphic composition of spiritual substances, argues to the
existence of matter solely on the grounds of an analysis of expressions "Solum
nomen corporis signum est ad sciendum esse materiam . . . quia cum anuntias
aliquid esse corpus, assignas formam et formatum." *Fons Vitae, tr. 2,* ed.

Baeumker (1892), 24. For this whole question, see J. de Vries, *Scholastik*, *32*, 1957, 161 ff.; *33*, 1958, 481 ff.)

What, then, is Aristotle's argument for the indeterminateness of matter? Here is the passage:

> I call "matter" that which of itself is neither a something nor a this-much nor assigned to any other of the categories by which being is determined. For there is something of which each of these is predicated, whose εἶναι differs from that of each of the predicates (for the predicates other than substance are predicated of substance, while the latter is predicated of matter). Therefore, the ultimate (namely, subject) is of itself neither a something nor a this-much nor any other of these (namely, of the determinations of being); nor yet is it their negations, for these also will belong to it by accident (1029a 20–26).

I quote the whole passage in order to correct a sort of optical illusion quite unintentionally suggested by the paper I am commenting on. Indeed, in reading Fr. Owens' paper one might get the idea that, in a number of passages, Aristotle contends that matter is absolutely indeterminate; and that, in a number of further passages, he claims that substantial form can be predicated of matter. Actually, there is only one such passage; moreover, the contention that substance is predicated of matter is brought forward uniquely in order to show that the ultimate subject of predication is strictly indeterminate.

Still, it remains true that Aristotle claims that there is a thoroughly indeterminate ultimate subject of predication; and it would seem quite proper to ask whether his argument is cogent or not. As this question is quite involved, I shall restrict myself to what I consider to be the two main difficulties.

1. Suppose that it is correct to say that whatever can be predicated of another *eo ipso* differs from the latter. Suppose, moreover, that it is correct to say that accidents are predicated of substance, while substance is predicated of something ultimate. Does it follow that this ultimate subject is, in its very being, thoroughly indeterminate? To me, this conclusion is far from being obvious. The only legitimate conclusion, if any, would seem to be that the ultimate subject, precisely because it is ultimate, of itself neither is nor contains anything predicable. However, it is by no means obvious that the absence of anything predicable entails the absence of all determination of an ontological kind. Indeed, such an absence of anything to predicate might as well be explained by saying that matter does not differ from its determinations, i.e. that it is itself an ultimate and consequently unanalysable type of determinate being. Notice that I am not suggesting that it would be possible to *prove* such an assumption; I am only pointing out that it seems impossible to decide whether the ultimate subject of predication is determinate or not. As everything predicated of it by definition is "outside" its very nature, the true nature of such an ultimate subject inevitably escapes us—it is an asymptotic point of reference of all predication, as it were.

2. Aristotle's argument for the thorough indeterminateness of the ultimate subject of predication is based upon the assumption that predicates are related

to the subject as two parts of a whole are related to each other, not as a part is related to the whole. In other words: when I say "This man is white", the expression 'This man' is alleged to stand for this man considered apart from his being white. When I say "This-here is a man", the expression 'This-here' would stand therefore, for this-here considered apart from its being a man. In the first draft of this comment, I criticized this idea by saying that, in that case, the sentence 'This man is white' would mean the same as 'This man, considered apart from his being white, is white' which quite obviously would be nonsense. In the final version of his paper, Fr. Owens has added several passages to illustrate his point that to predicate substance of matter (just as to predicate accidents of substance) would be to predicate *"denominative"*. Now I have to admit that if in the sentence 'This man is white' the expression 'This man' stands only for the substance of this man as opposed to the whole white man, the sentence 'This man is white' must be considered to be an instance of denominative predication. However, in order to know that we have to do with a denominative predication, we have to know *in advance* that there is a substance differing from all accidents. Similarly, if in the sentence 'This-here is a man', the expression 'This-here' stands solely for the subject of humanity as opposed to this whole man, the sentence 'This here is a man' must be taken to be an instance of denominative predication. Again, however, I have to know *in advance* that there is a matter different from all substantial form in order to be able to show that I have to do with a *praedicatio denominativa* as opposed to a *praedicatio per essentiam*. In other words: I grant that substance can be predicated of matter in terms of a denominative predication. However, I cannot see how a reference to this type of predication would help in providing the indeterminateness of the ultimate subject of predication, since the presence of denominative predication can be proven only on the grounds of the *prior* assumption that there *is* a subject bare of all substantial form, i.e. an indeterminate subject of predication.

Incidentally, St. Thomas' analysis of the text in question suffers from exactly the same difficulty. *In VII Met.* 2, 1289:

> Ipsa ergo . . . denominativa praedicatio ostendit, quod sicut substantia est aliud per essentiam ab accidentibus, ita per essentiam aliud est materia a formis substantialibus. Quare sequetur quod illud quod est ultimum subiectum per se loquendo, "neque est quid", idest substantia, neque quantitas neque aliquid aliud quod sit in aliquo genere entium.

Yet how does St. Thomas prove that there really is a denominative predication? By saying in the beginning of the very same paragraph: "iam enim supra (Aristoteles) dixerat quod materia non est quid, neque aliquid aliorum". In other words: since there is an indeterminate matter, the predication of substance is denominative; and the denominative predication shows that the ultimate subject is indeterminate. Of course, St. Thomas' analysis is not as circular as it might seem, since he explicitly (*ibid.*, 1285 f.) presupposes that, in the *Physics*, the indeterminateness of matter has been proven *per viam motus*; to him, the passage in the *Metaphysics* is only a corroboration of a thesis established elsewhere (though, in his commentary to the *Physics,* he would seem to suggest that the "physical" discovery of matter is *per inductionem,* while the corresponding "metaphysical" discovery is *per rationem, In I Phys. 12,* 107).

To put it briefly, Aristotle's only proof for the thorough indeterminateness of matter not only takes for granted that predicability is strictly coextensive with ontological determination, but also depends for its validity upon an assumption which cannot be verified without making the whole proof perfectly circular.

Let me finish by remarking that my criticism applies only to the argument for the indeterminateness of matter *per viam praedicationis quae est propria Logicae.* Other proofs, such as that based upon an analysis of substantial change, still may be valid. However, at least as far as I can see, Aristotle never developed any other than a "logical" proof (though there are some other passages which show that Aristotle *believed* in a purely potential "primary matter", e.g. *Met. IX,* 7, 1049a 20 ff.). Perhaps it is possible to *infer* from his *Physics* as well as from *De Generatione et corruptione* that Aristotle *might* have developed a "physical" proof, too; but actually he never did it—and a commentator, to my mind, should be concerned with the texts in hand instead of engaging in guesslike inferences.

N. Lobkowicz
University of Notre Dame

DISCUSSION

Lobkowicz: There is a problem involved here which I found very well illustrated in a text from the *Commentary to the Physics* of the Salmaticenses. How can a *purely* potential substratum which has no determination whatsoever, no existence of its own, account for continuity of change? If potency has its existence from form, whenever the form disappears, whatever accounts for the existence of potency will disappear too. If a new form, a new existence, is given to the substratum, how could it be numerically the same? It seems to me that in order to maintain the continuity of the substratum, it must be assigned some actuality . . . If *A* changes substantially into *B*, we are told that the whole continuity between them is accounted for by something *wholly* indeterminate, pure potency, etc . . . Now, what allows me to distinguish this change from a pure temporal succession, the annihilation of *A* and the immediate re-creation of *B*, if I do not have some determinations which permit me to identify it? How can I know that there is really a *change*?

Mc Mullin: Could I point this even more sharply? Supposing that in successive moments of time the table in the corner of this room vanishes and a chair appears in another corner of the room. Each of these can, apparently, be said to possess a matter-component which is totally indeterminate. Why would this not count as a substantial change, if a wholly indeterminate substratum is the sufficient guarantee of the continuity of such change?

Sellars: This question goes right to the heart of the matter and involves two elements. One is, it shows the importance of spatial-temporal continuity as a criterion for our identification of physical objects. This is involved in the analogy in which Aristotle gives his notion of an ultimate subject of change. Prime matter, although it is not by its nature at this place or at that place or at this time or at that time, is at some place or at some time or other, and continuity is a criterion of this. The second point is that we are uncomfortable with ultimate capacities of this kind. Supposing we have a case of transmutation of elements. On the Aristotelian scheme we simply have to say that chunks of the elements have an ultimate capacity to turn into each other in certain ways and that this is, in a sense, an unexplainable feature of them. Now, we are tempted to say there must be an explanation, and, in a way, the feeling that this is so fits in very nicely with the subsequent development of science where we *do* get a theoretical substructure in terms of micro-particles etc., which *does* give us an account of it. But what Aristotle is doing, of course, is not constructing hypothetical entities to explain. He is simply saying that in this framework, this is an ultimate capacity, and there must always be such. You can't trace all capacities back to other capacities. I don't see any absurdity in the Aristotelian system on this point . . . The trouble arises in the theory of predication, if one supposes that there is the cold in this water and the wet in this water, so that there must also be another really distinguishable item, although incomplete, which is the prime matter . . .

MATTER AS POTENCY

Norbert M. Luyten, O.P.

§1 *Historical Background*

It seems quite impossible to speak about matter and potency without referring to the history of philosophy, as this aspect of the problem of matter has its roots in early Greek philosophy, and was further elaborated in medieval scholastic thought. The primary aim of this symposium, as I understand it, is not so much historical precision as reflection upon the problems set before us by the notion of matter. As my concern with the proposed problem is systematic rather than historical, let me say from the very beginning that historical data will be considered not for their own sake, but rather as a means of understanding why and how the notion of potency becomes involved in the problem of matter.

The first question we have to ask is: how has the notion of potency become associated with the problem of matter? To answer this, one has to turn to Greek philosophy.[1] It is generally agreed that the original meaning of the word 'matter' (μλη) was "the wood found in the forests". From this primitive meaning was derived the sense of "wood" as the material with which houses can be built. A further extension seems to have led to the wider meaning "every material out of which something can be made". As far as one can see, this widened notion of matter provided the base for the philosophical usage: matter as that out of which something is made in any possible way.

From this origin of the philosophical notion of matter, one can already gather some indications which might prove important for our problem. First of all, one may notice the progressive generalization of its meaning, which is tantamount to endowing it with a more abstract character. But this is not the main point to be stressed here. Much more important is the fact that with the development of the notion, it loses its definite concrete content, and becomes what one might call "functional". The original definite "content", *wood,* disappears; only the idea of the function the wood

---

[1] In a way, it might seem that the notion itself, as well as the problems associated with it, are proper to Western European thought, as influenced by the Greeks. African students (Congo Territory) have assured me that no word corresponding to the idea of matter exists in their languages.

plays in building is maintained and extended to every similar or analogous item. Now, if we ask what kind of function is meant here, the general answer seems to be: the function of being that (indeterminate) out of which something can be made. In a more abstract way, we could say: the availability, the plasticity, the determinability which is presupposed to every action of making something. Productive action is conceived as working on a given "material", which presents a "possibility" of being shaped in a definite way. Here we seem to have the origin of the conception which sees matter as potency: the given *material* with its *possibility* to be shaped, is our matter as *potency*. Matter appears here primarily as correlative to productive action: that out of which something is made. In this context, the relation between matter and the active principle has a certain priority to the relation between matter and "form", although this latter became more important in later philosophical discussions.

To understand the full implications of this further development, one has to consider the broader philosophical context in which the notion of matter was used by Aristotle. The fundamental problem faced by the early Greek philosophers was not so much that of matter as of nature. *Physis* was, indeed, the central theme of their speculations. Considering the world of their experience, they were struck by the fact of ceaseless changing; the spectacle of becoming and disappearing appeared to be the most all-embracing feature of reality. In a remarkable intuition they realized that this infinite variety and multitude could not be the last word about reality. Wherever they looked, they could see transition from one state to another. By a rather unsophisticated, yet penetrating extrapolation, they decided that in a mysterious way every item in reality is somehow linked to every other, because one changes into the other. There must, therefore, be a fundamental kinship between things. The whole multitude of varied things, incessantly changing from one to the other, hide and manifest at the same time a more profound nature common to them all. This common, hidden fundament they called "physis", which means: the nature, the profound and genuine reality, at the bottom of all reality, what in German would be called *Urgrund,* i.e., the most genuine and deepest principle by which things are what they are, not in their ever-varying, rather superficial—since evanescent—aspects, but in their true—because permanent—essence. Diogenes of Apollonia, an early Greek philosopher from the Ionian school states this conception as follows:

> It seems to me, to sum up the whole matter, that all existing things are created by the alteration of the same thing, and are the same thing. This is very obvious. For if the things now existing in this universe—earth and water and air and fire and all the other things which are seen to exist in this

world: if any one of these were different in its own (essential) nature, and were not the same thing which is transformed in many ways and changed, in no way could things mix with one another, nor could there be any profit or damage which accrued from one thing to another, nor could any plant grow out of the earth, nor any animal or any other thing come into being in different forms at different times by changes of the same (substance), and they return to the same.[2]

It is evident, therefore, that a certain parallel between the problem of *physis* and the problem of matter suggests itself. Aristotle in his philosophical lexicon, (*Metaph.*, Book Lambda), indicates as one of the senses of the word 'physis': *the primitive matter out of which things are made,* referring this use of the word to the early Ionian philosophers. For them the two notions converged, so that the "physis", i.e., the very nature of things, was considered to be identical with matter. The parallel here thus leads to a frank identification.

Now, whatever the parallel between the problems of matter and *physis* may be, if we compare the analysis leading up to the notion of *physis* with the brief comments we have already made about matter, some differences become evident. First of all, the consideration of the active principle, which was all-important in the first consideration, is secondary if not non-existent in the discussion of *physis*. Insofar as *physis* is identified with matter, matter is being conceived as correlative to the different forms under which it manifests itself. So that the important relation here is the one between matter and form, not that between matter and agent. But another more important shift in the meaning of 'matter' has to be stressed also. In the first context, matter appeared as possibility, potency; conceived as "physis" it seems, however, to be the opposite of a potentiality. The *physis* being the true nature, the very essence of things, we can hardly consider it in the line of potentiality, but rather have to conceive it as true actuality. So, in this perspective, matter is no longer identified with potency, but is conceived as the true substance in every reality.

We know how the Ionians, still thinking in a very concrete way, tried to identify this fundamental substance with a given nature. So, for instance, Thales of Miletus thought water to be the true essence, the fundamental substance in everything. The important thing in this identification is not so much that the essence should be water, or fire or air, or anything else; what matters is that the true essence of things was identified with a given material reality, so stressing the identification between matter and *physis*.

---

[2] Diels. *Fragmente der Vorsokratiker*, English translation: K. Freeman, *Ancilla to the Pre-Socratic Philosophers*, p. 87.

Now this entails another change in the conception of matter. We saw at the beginning of this paper, how, starting from a concrete substantial meaning (wood), the notion of matter progressively lost this substantial character to become merely "functional", as we called it. In the *physis*-perspective, the contrary seems to happen. 'Matter' does not appear here as a mere functional expression, but once again comes to mean a definite substance, or, better, *the* substance par excellence, the true and universal essence of every reality. Moreover, as the potency-character of matter was connected with its functional conception, it follows that to abandon the functional notion of matter—as is done in the conception of matter as *physis*—is tantamount to giving up the notion of matter as potency. Consequently the identification of matter and potency, which we reached as a provisional result in our introductory reflexion, becomes very problematic when faced with the matter-*physis* conception.

§2 *Aristotle's Position*

This was exactly the problem Aristotle discussed in his criticism of his Ionian predecessors. He blames them for having limited their considerations to the material cause alone, in other words for their having reduced everything to matter. But this criticism does not mean that Aristotle rejects the whole of Ionian speculation as worthless. In a way he reaffirms the most fundamental idea in it: that of a basic kinship between things in our universe. What is more, he agrees on calling the ultimate foundation of this commonness, "matter." But, rejecting the identification between matter and *physis*, he restores the true character of potency attached to the genuine notion of matter.[3] To identify matter with the true nature of things, means to admit a materialistic monism of a sort which contradicts our most immediate experience. To reduce all the rich variety of things to a mere superficial change of a unique permanent substance is to ignore the real nature of things. What things are we know through their manifestations, which indicate different, distinct realities. We have to take these indications seriously, and therefore must see them as manifesting different natures. There is not just one nature; the unique "physis" of the Ionians is broken up into a multitude of different natures, each manifesting itself in a different form. So nature no longer can be considered as a unique substance. We have to admit as many substances as there are different "forms." This leads Aristotle to hold the "form" as the more adequate expression of the true nature

---

[3] What follows is so well-known that it will be sufficient to recall the main lines of the argument briefly.

—the *physis*—of things. 'Form' here no longer means the external shape or quality, but the substantial principle, the intrinsic "nature" underlying and "causing" the exterior appearances. Does this mean that for Aristotle the universe is split up into a multitude of distinct, unrelated "natures", juxtaposed without any connexion? As we pointed out before, Aristotle acknowledges the value of the Ionian intuition: the fact that one thing changes into another indicates a profound community. And as our experience shows us that this fact of change—which in Aristotle's perspective is a substantial change—rather than being an exception, is in fact a general feature of reality, we have to admit a universal community between things. The question is now, what makes this community? Not the *physis* as form because this is distinct in different beings. On the other hand, it must be something intrinsic to things, and in this way, it must belong to their nature.

The only way to explain this seemingly contradictory situation is to admit that the root of the above-mentioned community is intrinsic to the very nature of things. From this it follows that the "physis" in each reality is no longer something simple: it is not only the reason why this latter is different from all others, it is at the same time the reason why it is in communion with them. But it could not be both under the same aspect. Yet one reality can only have one *physis*, one essence. The only solution to this difficulty is to admit a "composition" in the *physis* itself. The reason for the distinctness cannot simply coincide and be strictly identical with the reason for the community. The first—the form—being the reason for the determination of the thing, the other must represent its determinability, its possibility of being determined in some other way (manifested by the fact of transmutation or substantial change). This brings us back to the notion of matter as possibility or potency. But whereas in the earlier context matter appeared mainly as possibility in the context of an agent who produces something from it, in the present perspective its "possibility" relates explicitly to different determined modes of being, to different forms. This brings us to the famous duality of matter and form, terminologically specified in the Aristotelian tradition as primary matter and substantial form.

With this notion of primary matter, the identification of matter and potency is complete. Every aspect of determination in the nature (*physis*) of things is referred to the form. Matter no longer appears as the true (determined) essence of things. It belongs to the essence in a rather negative way. The Aristotelian definition, characterizing matter by its lack of every determined content, sufficiently expresses this negative aspect. As a matter of fact, it is so thoroughly negative that from Aristotle to our own day many philosophers have rejected it as a mere conception of the mind, a logical extrapolation without any value in reality.

§3 *Difficulties*

Now, we must be clear about the fact that this negative notion of matter is intimately connected with its character of fundamental potentiality. As the Scholastic tradition worded it: matter[4] being potentiality in the line of substance, i.e., being fundamental potentiality, must be pure potency. In the words of our earlier argument, we can say that matter, as opposed to substantial determination, cannot be anything more than mere determinability. This, at first glance, might not sound too alarming. But, thinking this through, one seems to be compelled to say that such mere determinability must exclude every determination. In other words, it has to be pure indetermination. Now, this manifestly is no longer a harmless statement. The question immediately arises, whether it is not a contradiction in itself to speak about pure indetermination? Since Aristotle's intention is to give an explanation of *reality,* the expression ought to find its basis somehow in the *real.* But what can a real pure indetermination mean? Can we think of anything real without positing a minimum of determination? But here, by definition, every determination is excluded. Is not this absurd? And, consequently, is not the whole Aristotelian conception of primary matter, i.e., of matter as potency, equally absurd? We mentioned already how generations of philosophers have stressed the absurdity of Aristotle's conceptions. Let it suffice to quote one of the most recent opponents, Prof. A. Wenzl. In the conclusion of a recent paper he wrote:

> It is impossible to deny that the notion of primary matter . . . must be considered as a fiction, i.e. an intrinsically contradictory notion . . . The notion of primary matter, result of a regressive process of abstraction, is not only a 'limit-concept' (*Grenzbegriff*) but an overstepping of the possibilities of conceptual thought (*Grenzüberschreitung des begrifflichen Denkens*).[5]

One could hardly conceive a more radical and definite rejection of Aristotle's conception of primary matter! Let us consider in fuller detail, therefore, what is the case against the conception of matter as pure potency. Why should it be—as Wenzl states—"an overstepping of the possibilities of conceptual thought"? I think one could formulate the argument more or less as follows. Aristotle worked out his notion of potency for the case of "accidental" change: for instance, marble has in itself the possibility of becoming a statue, i.e. of being shaped into a definite form. In this sense, marble is in potency to the statue-form. Applying this analysis to substantial change,

---

[4] We always mean primary matter in this context, unless a different usage be explicitly noted.

[5] *Sitzungsberichte der Bayerischen Akademie,* Philosophisch-Historische Klasse, 1958, 1.

Aristotle posits a "substantial potency" opposed to "substantial form". But this potency seems to be indistinguishable from the marble itself, which can be formed in different ways. In other words, the determinability is intimately connected with a determination: only because marble is what it is (solid, hard) can it be sculptured into a statue. Consequently, we have determinability in marble only insofar as we have determination. We could not make a statue out of water: water is not determinable to a statue because it does not possess the appropriate determination. So, determinability seems to be intrinsically conditioned by determination. How then could we admit pure determinability? Is not this to admit the conditioned without the condition, which is absurd? But, if this is so, we cannot transpose the structure found in accidental change, to substantial change, because in this latter case an essential condition (i.e., the determination supporting determinability) seems to be lacking.

Although this objection might seem decisive, it is not, in fact, cogent. True, a pure indetermination existing in itself would be sheer nonsense. But that is not what the Aristotelian tradition claims. This pure indetermination of primary matter must be seen in its connection with determination. We might call it the constitutive or fundamental inadequacy of substantial determination. Expressed in a more concrete way: a material reality is what it is in such a way that it bears in itself the possibility of simply not being what it is. In this sense it is meaningful to say that *any* determination one considers of itself implies inadequacy. It would not make sense, of course, to posit this inadequacy apart from the determination, no more than it would make sense to speak about the limit of a surface entirely apart from the surface itself. It would be irrational to say that the limit is not real on the grounds that it cannot be examined separately from the surface. To maintain that primary matter is unreal because its pure potentiality cannot be shown apart from the determinate thing is, therefore, unjustified. And so one may conclude that there is no absurdity in admitting a real pure indetermination, provided one does not posit it as a reality existing in itself, but rather as a constitutive deficiency of the given material thing. It is a deficiency, that is, it indicates the possibility of this thing's becoming another thing, in which latter thing it will again have the meaning of fundamental deficiency; it is thus a sort of hallmark of the thing's former—and future—non-being.

However strong this argument may seem, however, experience tells us that many people deny its cogency. The main reason for this, it would seem, is that they are unable to see why the inadequacy or deficiency we spoke about should be really distinct from the determination. They will speak about an "overstepping", contending that the argument above unduly transposes a conceptual distinction into reality. Conceptually, one can distinguish between the substantial determination and its inadequacy, but to claim that this reveals a distinction in reality itself is an undue transition from the logical to the real order. Therefore—their critique runs—the notion of primary matter, expressing this constitutive deficiency (determinability, potency), has value only as an abstractive logical concept. To admit it as a real principle is an error.

This new objection is again inconclusive. To distinguish the determination from its inadequacy (indetermination) is not just a logical exercise. The problem involved in substantial change is not one of mere logical analysis but one of ontological structure. The question is not so much one of ordering concepts as of understanding reality. The necessity of admitting a real distinction between the determination and the determinability (substantial form and primary matter) is evident, I think, from the following consideration. The ontological reason why a thing is what it is, cannot be really identical with the reason why it is not what it is. It does not make sense to derive the "being determined" of a thing as well as its "being undetermined" (and thus determinable) from the same ontological source. The reason for a thing's determinedness cannot really be identical with the reason for its undeterminedness.

But, one might object, this argument would hold good only if we had determination and indetermination under the same aspect. Then it would follow that they could not be really identical. But we do *not* have them under the same aspect here. We have a thing determined in a definite way and able to be determined in another way. Can we not say, in this case, that the actual determination itself is the capacity for another determination (i.e. determinability)? This objection again misses the point. It is incorrect to claim that determination and determinability are not considered here under the same aspect. We may recall that determinability means indetermination. So we can say that in the thing which is changed into another, there is determination and indetermination. The determination is evidently that which makes the thing be what it is. But when it changes substantially, it ceases to be what it is, and becomes something different. Now, why does the thing cease to be what it is? We can point to the active, efficient cause, but this is not the question here. We are looking for the intrinsic reason. It would be absurd to say that its own determination, that which makes the thing what it is, is at the same time the reason why it ceases to be what it is. So we see that the possibility of becoming something else (i.e. determinability or potency) implies an indetermination with regard to a thing's own "suchness" or determination. It implies, indeed, the possibility of its own non-existence; thus the thing bears within itself an indetermination

129

relative to its own existence and relative, therefore, to its own "being determined". What is more, this indetermination is so radical that it contradicts the very fundamental, constitutive (substantial) determination of the thing. To maintain, in spite of all this, that this indetermination simply coincides with the determination by which the thing is what it is seems most unreasonable. From all this it should be clear that the Aristotelian notion of matter as potency, far from being an antiquated and outmoded theory, is an adequate expression of the element of indetermination, necessarily implied in the essence of substantially changing things.

§4 *Primary Matter and Modern Physics*

At this point the question could be raised as to how far this notion of substantial change can be maintained in the face of new conceptions arising from modern physics. As our task in this paper is only to discuss the notion of matter as potency, it would lead us too far afield to discuss this question of substantial change. Let it suffice to note that whoever admits the substantial being of man (and it seems rather difficult to deny this!) must in consequence admit substantial change, whatever the physical picture of the material world may be in its other features.

A question which more properly concerns our subject is that of a direct confrontation of the doctrine of primary matter with the data of modern science. It might seem peculiar, if not absurd, that such a confrontation should be made at all, the two conceptions being so fundamentally different. But, after all, since both theories consider physical reality, it might seem natural to compare them in order to find out whether they contradict each other or not. This is actually what several modern authors have done. The article by Wenzl, already quoted, is a good example of this. He tries to show that in the modern scientific conception of the physical world nothing equivalent to the notion of primary matter can be found. Neither space, nor energy (which, acording to Wenzl, plays a rôle in modern physics analogous to that of primary matter in the Aristotelian system) can be identified with the *materia prima*. From which Wenzl concludes, as we saw, that primary matter is a fiction.

What are we to say to this? I am afraid it must be said that Wenzl fundamentally misunderstands the Aristotelian conception of matter. It is clear from his explicit statements, as well as from his comparisons, that he conceives primary matter as a kind of primitive, preexisting substance, out of which everything is made. Now, even if such a unique primitive substance were to be suggested, it follows, for the reason we have already seen that one would have to distinguish within it the reason why it is what it is from the reason why it becomes something different. So that we would have further to search for primary matter. But apart from this, it should in any case be clear from what we have said above that this notion of primary matter as primitive "stuff" is not the way Aristotle saw it. Primary matter is not an original, preexisting stuff; it is an intrinsic, constitutive inadequacy (potentiality) in actual, existing being. It is not an historical but an onto-logical principle of physical reality. I do not suggest that it is meaningless to ask the question which Wenzl considers. On the contrary, our evolu-tionary view of the universe suggests more and more that all the variety we see in the physical world stems from an original, primitive, relatively undifferentiated reality, from which everything derived by successive dif-ferentiation.[6] But simply to identify this problem with the analysis leading up to Aristotle's concept of primary matter is to misunderstand the whole point of this latter. The mere fact that primary matter is conceived as pure potency should suffice to restrain us from such-like comparisons even though many modern writers delight in making them.

Does this mean that every confrontation of the philosophic notion of pure potency with the data of modern science has to be excluded *a priori*? I think not, provided that we are not looking for a direct counterpart of primary matter in modern physical science. The only possible confrontation is an indirect one. If we hold primary matter to be present in the heart of every physical reality, it seems normal that in one way or another it should manifest itself on the phenomenal level. However, as it is nothing other than the inadequacy of the ontological (substantial) determination, it is only to be expected that the manifestations of this latter will bear the same hallmark of inadequacy. In this way, the fact that a thing ceases to be is a manifestation of its constitutive inadequacy, i.e. of primary matter. Simi-larly, tradition saw in the intrinsic indetermination implied in extension, a typical manifestation of the fundamental substantial indetermination existing in the heart of every physical reality. In this perspective the ques-tion may be asked as to whether modern science did reveal other manifes-tations of primary matter? One suggestion has been that indeterminism in modern physics is a particular manifestation of primary matter as potency, potency being equated with a sort of indeterminism. In this view, in-determinism may easily come to appear as the modern version of Aristo-telian contingency.[7] Leaving the question of the historical accuracy of this

---

[6] I have touched on this problem in a paper—*"Réflexions sur la notion de matière"*—presented to a symposium in Rome, April 1959, published in *Tijdschrift voor Phi-losophie, 21,* 1959, 225–42.

[7] See C. De Koninck, "Le problème de l'indéterminisme," *Rapports de la sixième session de l'Acadèmie canadienne S. Thomas d'Aquin,* 1935; "Thomism and scientific indeterminacy", *Proc. Amer. Cath. Philos. Assoc., 10,* 1936, 58. A. Mansion questions this linking of indeterminism and contingency in his *Introduction à la physique aristo-télicienne,* Louvain, 1945, pp. 332–33.

interpretation aside, what are we to say about the idea that the fundamental potency of primary matter would reveal itself in the indeterminism of modern physics?

First of all, it must be stressed that indeterminism can hardly be considered, even today, as an absolutely certain feature of the physical world. When one remembers that L. de Broglie—in his own way the father of indeterminism—has recently returned to a deterministic interpretation of nature, one is led to treat the physical theory of indeterminism with some caution. But supposing physical science proves in an adequate way that there is "indeterminism" in the heart of material reality, can one regard it as a manifestation of primary matter? Some authors object to this on the grounds that it would be tantamount to attributing an active influence to primary matter, which would be contrary to its character of pure potency. This objection is not quite convincing because indeterminism does not necessarily imply an active influence. If indeterminism can be considered as a lack of determination, an inadequacy of determination in the behavior of the particles, it would not seem to imply an active impulse or influence but rather a deficiency in the way the behavior is determined. It does not seem incongruous to explain this lack of determination on the phenomenal level by a fundamental indetermination on the constitutive, substantial level.

Nevertheless, in order to have an adequate and definitive answer to the question, it would be necessary to show that indeterminism of the quantum type necessarily flows from the hylomorphic constitution of physical reality, in other words from the presence of a principle of indetermination in the core of things. It is difficult to see how this could be deduced in an apodictic way. Nothing, indeed, proves that the domination of the form in a thing, will not pervade all its activity. It is true that there will always be passivity mixed with the activity, but this may be only in respect to exterior influences. There is no necessity whatsoever, it would seem, to suppose that the determined way of acting would be contradicted by an intrinsic passivity. It seems more appropriate to admit that as long as the thing is what it is, under a certain form or principle of determination, it is under the complete domination of this form. Every other determination would affect it only insofar as another extrinsic determining cause would interfere with its own natural determination, and so actualise its determinability in some particular way. The fact that even in substantial change the proper determination is lost only through the influence of another different determination, seems to speak in favour of this last conception. It would seem, then, that indeterminism does not necessarily follow from the presence of pure potency in the heart of physical reality.

The most evident conclusion from all these considerations is, I think, that the notion of matter as potency is a typically philosophic conception. Every endeavor to give it a concrete phenomenal meaning must be a failure. And for this same reason such objections against it as are based on scientific findings, generally miss the point. They overlook that the two are on a different level, give an answer to different problems, and so have different, not incompatible, but incommensurable, meanings. Likewise, to contend that the scientific conception of physical reality as composed of ultimate particles, is opposed to the hylomorphic composition of primary matter and substantial form, is to misunderstand the meaning of at least one of these positions. The two notions of "composition" are quite different, and the only conclusion one can draw is the harmless one that different sorts of questions demand different sorts of answers. There is no question of a contradiction.

This last objection reminds us of the dangers of misunderstanding in any discussion between philosophers of nature and scientists. I would be the last one to deny the necessity of a dialogue between philosophy and science. But it will only be useful and profitable insofar as the parties are aware of the fundamental differences between the two disciplines. Direct comparisons of tenets seldom leads to anything but misunderstanding and fallacious compromise. The only successful way to better comprehension and mutual benefit is a careful examination of what exactly is said on both sides, and an attempt to find how one knowledge might clarify, or complete, or support the other. Only in this way can progress be made in our knowledge of nature.

University of Fribourg

COMMENT

DR. LUYTEN'S PAPER GIVES AN EXCEPTIONALLY CLEAR EXPOSITION OF THE TOPIC, SO clear that some awkward points of juncture in the argument show up much more evidently than they do in customary textbook treatments. I propose to state my difficulties as succinctly as possible under two headings: one is concerned with the linking of potency exclusively with primary matter, and the other with the "purity" of the potency so attributed[1].

The first difficulty is concerned with your proof of the real distinction between matter and form on the basis of your analysis in terms of potency. In the course of the proof, you assume that determinability and indetermination are in fact identical and that a form can in no sense be a principle of potency for some other form. You are holding, then, that the fact that a thing is now an acorn can in *no* sense be the reason for its becoming an oak. My question, then, is: why cannot the form of an acorn be a principle of potency for the thing's becoming an oak? There does not seem to be any reason why a principle which is a principle of act in one regard might not be a principle of potency in another. Connected with this point is another—you suggest that the fact that a thing may become something else is a *defect* of the thing or an "inadequacy" or "deficiency". This, once more, raises a real difficulty because it seems to imply that it is an inadequacy or deficiency of the acorn that it can grow into an oak. Does not this linking of potency with inadequacy seem to lead to a radically Platonic view of the universe in which changeability is necessarily a defect? In a universe of growth and process, surely potency cannot as such be equated with inadequacy. It is proper for the acorn to become an oak. In fact, if it does not become an oak, the form of the acorn itself has somehow or other come to nothing.

The second difficulty is in the context of the notion of *pure* potency. I have some difficulty in knowing what exactly this means and in justifying it. You indicate that because matter is potentiality in the line of substance it must be "pure" potency. I am not sure if I understand this. Are you implying that any given object can in principle become any other object? Would you not agree that there are only certain things a table can become? The restrictions here come from the form, of course, but if one looks at this *particular* table and speaks about the composition of matter and form within it, the matter-principle here regarded as a real co-principle of the table can scarcely be regarded as a princi-

---

[1] These were presented in writing as questions to Dr. Luyten (who was unable to attend the Conference) in case he should wish to respond. His response follows.

ple of pure potency, can it? Even though the limitations on what the table can become proceed from the form, we do not seem to have the right to claim that there is a principle of pure indetermination or pure potency here in the first place. The indeterminacy or "purity" of the potency seem to be properties of the *concept* of prime matter, i.e. of the notion of prime matter abstracting from any particular occurrence or instance of it in a concrete object. If one looks at the totality of material changes, one might want to say that, in general, there is an unspecified series of things into which material objects can change, but the lack of specification here comes from the fact that we are abstracting from the conditions of the *particular* change. It does not seem to come from the ontological character of the matter-principle itself, considered in a concrete instance. If one looks at a material object, then, and claims that there is within it a *real* distinction between matter and form, the "matter" in this instance does not seem to be the principle of pure potency of which you speak but rather a principle of limited potency, the limitation, in this case, proceeding from the quantity, that is, from the form. I suspect that you are using the notion of "principle" or the notion of "pure" potency in a way which is slightly different from mine, one which very likely would allow you to respond to this difficulty easily.

Ernan Mc Mullin

RESPONSE

To answer the first objection, let us first see in what sense I identified determinability and indetermination. There is, I think, nothing very mysterious about this identification. To be "determinable" is precisely not to be determined already by the determination in regard to which the thing is said to be determinable. So e.g. to say that clay is determinable to a spherical shape, means identically that it does not yet have the determination of being spherical.

Does this entail my holding, as it is said in the objection "that a form can in no sense be a principle of potency for some other form"? Here, we must distinguish according to the classical distinction between substantial and accidental form. A substantial form, although perfectly determined in the line of substantial determination, remains determinable in the accidental order. Remaining substantially the same clay (for the sake of our discussion, it is not important to know if clay has really a proper substantiality), it can be modeled in different ways, i.e. it remains determinable to this or that accidental form (figure). But, by no means can I say that a substantial form as such, i.e. as act, as determination, is the possibility of another substantial form, and so determinable (as act) to that other substantial form. Evidently, the proposed objection denies this, and supports this denial by saying: "There does not seem to be any reason why a principle which is a principle of act in one regard might not be a principle of potency in another". The intention is evidently to suggest that a principle can be act of a definite substance and potency in regard to another. But this statement seems to overlook the special character of substantial act (form, determination) which is precisely to be *substantial,* i.e. fundamental, i.e. first constitutive determination. In his mature writings, St. Thomas does not cease to insist on this point: "Cuicumque formae substernitur aliquod ens actu, quocumque modo, illa forma est accidens" (*De spirit. Creat. a.* 3). In other words: it is contradictory to say that a substantial form is a further determination of an already determined substance. But exactly this is implied if we admit that one substantial act is potency in regard to another substantial act.

However, I can scarcely expect that the objector will be satisfied with this answer, because it is evident from the whole context, that he has something else in mind. From the obvious fact that specific antecedent substances give rise to equally determined subsequent substances (in the tradition this was already noticed: *ex quolibet non sequitur quodlibet*), he concludes that the previous substance in this way is a "principle *in fieri*" of the following one, and so, although determined and act in itself, it seems to be determinable and potency in regard to the subsequent substance.

Let it first be said that the given example: the acorn becoming an oak, is mistaken. By no means could one say that the acorn is a different substance from the oak; an embryo is not a different substance from the adult animal. The given example compares different stages of the same being evolving its virtualities. But this is altogether different from a real substantial change. To say that a being in a certain state contains virtualities yet undeveloped—but in its own line—is in no way to admit that one being in act is potency in regard to another one, because in the whole process here considered we have but one being.

Now even if this remark is important, it does not meet the main objection. If we replace the inadequate example by an appropriate one, e.g. bread becoming my body (where, again, it is not important that bread should really be one substance), the objection recovers its full strength.

However strong it may seem, it is anything but convincing. In fact it is based upon a confusion between two very different notions of "principle": one, 'principle' means an extrinsic antecedent in the process of becoming; next it stands for an intrinsic constitutive element in the substantial thing. The bread I eat, in a way is—partially!—at the origin of my bodily substance, and in this sense it could be called a principle of this substance. According to this terminology I can say that bread, being this determined being in act, is in potency to being my body. But it must be understood that, in becoming my body, the actuality of bread simply ceases to exist, and gives way to the new actuality or determination of my body. To say that the act of bread as such becomes potency in regard to my body, would mean that the bread in its own actual substantial determination becomes an intrinsic constitutive principle of my human substance; which in turn would be tantamount to saying that being human is just an aggregate of different substances put together in one way or another. We recognize here the famous theory of plurality of forms.

As I have already treated this subject on another occasion I might as well quote the parts of this former exposé that are relevant for our problem:

"The doctrine of the oneness (*unicitas*) of the form in one substance, as proposed by the Thomistic tradition is at times oversimplified, as though the form as unique excludes purely and simply every contribution of other "forms". Such a conception falls short of the profound concept of hylomorphism, and misconstrues its true meaning. If on the one hand the principle of materiality (primary matter) should be conceived as pure potentiality—which postulates precisely the oneness of the form as counterpart—on the other hand one should not forget that this potentiality of matter is "available" only through a previous form, i.e., within an already existing and determined material substance. Primary matter is therefore "available" for the new form through the previous form, which becomes thereby a condition of the "availability" of primary matter. It is therefore logical that the appearance of a new material being would be conditioned not only by the radical determinability of primary matter, but also by the (particular) availability established by the form. Experience definitely shows us, moreover, that one cannot simply produce a given thing from any other thing at random; a particular determined substance can be reached

137

only from the starting-point of a definite pre-existing substance. This makes it sufficiently clear that the preceding form influences the nature of the being to be produced. But does this violate the oneness of the form? Not at all, provided that one keeps in mind that the new form absorbs within itself everything contributed by the preceding form. The oneness of the form remains intact since all that it takes from the previous form and which would consequently be alien to it, it now assumes and makes its own. Thus the nutritive substance of bread is assumed by man. It exists in a way then within the man and so reveals a true continuity which moreover becomes evident through chemical analysis. But, notwithstanding the (phenomenal) continuity in appearance, which accounts for the "bread" persisting in a way within the man, there is a discontinuity on the ontological level since that which formerly was non-living, bread, becomes formally man. The doctrine of the oneness of the form is the technical expression of this ontological severing of beings which follow each other. However, it is clear from all that we have just said that this ontological severing does not at all mean that the reality is disconnected nor that there is no relationship among the beings which follow each other. To give another example: from the point of view of evolution, man is an absolutely new being, radically different from the brute animal, but nonetheless marked by his animal origins . . .

A material being is not only a thing which *could* be something else, it is also something which *was* something else. What was past becomes present through primary matter, which in a way brings with it the former acquisitions. We have seen in effect that primary matter can perform its role inasmuch as it is rendered receptive by a certain form. This is to say that the pure potentiality of primary matter enters the constitution of a material being only as conditioned by the previous form. This conditioning does not cease purely and simply by the advent of the new form. Of course, formally speaking, every determination within the new being is ontologically reassumed under the new form. However, since this form is joined to the matter, through this latter it falls under the influence of the previous forms which, precisely, have furnished the matter for it. Hence, that which is formally remote from it determines the material being not only as efficient cause, but *in ordine causae materialis*, intrinsically and constitutively. An obvious example is found in the fact of heredity. My parents, who are extrinsic to my being, still determine that being in a most intimate way. One could say the same thing about the nourishment I consume, the climate in which I live, and the cosmic influences I endure. In a very true sense each material being is a function of its milieu, even to its most intimate being. As a material thing, I do not possess an interior closed in upon itself; I am open to the exterior which on the one hand penetrates my very being and on the other hand involves me in a certain way in the multitude as well as in space and time."[2]

After all this it will not be too difficult to answer the last part of the first objection: the "linking of potency with inadequacy". Why should "the fact that

---

[2] Cf. N. A. Luyten, "La condition corporelle de l'homme", p. 35–38.

a thing may become something else be a defect of the thing or an inadequacy or deficiency"? The answer, I think, should not be too difficult. I do not contend that, in the whole of our dynamic universe, it is a deficiency that new things may come from former existing ones. But it is evident that for the thing itself which becomes another, it definitely *is* a deficiency to lose its own being. And in this very clear and definite sense we consider this "possibility of its own non-being" as a fundamental deficiency in the constitution of the thing. Consequently, as I mentioned already in my paper, it would be contradictory to identify *simpliciter* the act of the thing's being, with the radical possibility of its own non-being.

The difficulty brought up in Fr. Mc Mullin's second objection has, I think, already been met by what was said above. To put it briefly, I definitely reject the distinction between a *conceptual* primary matter as *pure* potency and a *real* primary matter as *limited* potency. Not only in abstract conceptual analysis, but in reality itself, the fundamental reason why a thing can cease to be what it is, cannot be identical with the very reason of its being what it is. This latter now manifestly is a principle of substantial, i.e. constitutive and fundamental determination. From this it follows, that the other real, non-identical principle which we have to admit, can by no means be in the line of determination (this being exclusively—because fundamentally—due to substantial form). But that is exactly what we mean by this real "pure potency".

To put it more briefly: the reason why the potentiality of primary matter has to be "pure", i.e. not implying by itself any determination, is not to be found in the fact that it is conceptually abstracted, but formally in its substantial, i.e. radical and fundamental character. And this latter evidently holds true for concrete real substances, not only for abstract concepts. Let us add, in order to avoid misunderstandings that this does not mean that pure potency as such could exist in itself; this would be sheer nonsense. What we maintain is, that in every concrete material reality there is, besides its substantial determination, a real intrinsic reason opposing this very same substantial determination, so that this opposition may result—and actually results—in a *simpliciter* non-being of the given substance. And it is this absolutely fundamental possibility of non-being that we call the absolute, radical, fundamental, pure potency in every concrete material reality.

Norbert Luyten, O.P.

DISCUSSION

Fisk: It seems to me that one could draw a distinction between the two statements, "This man can become something" and "This man can become anything", and what Fr. Mc Mullin is attacking is the claim that this man has a potentiality for becoming *any*thing. Now, I think there is a way in which Prof. Luyten's notion of pure potency can be interpreted as merely the possibility to become something. In other words, this man can become a corpse; that's a determinate possibility and indeed there is something about the form of the man which allows him to become a corpse rather than a carcass. Now, if we say, however, "this man can become *some*thing", we're not pointing to any particular form which he can take on; we're merely saying that he has the possibility for changing so that further forms suit his being. But it seems to me very misleading to say that the possibility for becoming *some*thing is "pure" potency or indetermination. Let's take these two arguments: Derek went to Chicago. Derek went somewhere. Derek had a motion to some place. Motion to some place is not a determinate motion. If something is not a determinate motion, it is a random motion. Therefore, Derek had a random motion. Now, compare this argument with the following: Derek can become a corpse. Derek can become something. This man has the possibility for becoming something. The possibility for becoming something is not a determinate possibility. If something is not a determinate possibility, it is an indeterminate one. Hence, Derek has indetermination, *pure* indetermination. Now, it seems to me that the logical fallacy here is quite obvious. One is taking 'something' to be the name of an indeterminate entity, and quite clearly that is not the implication of 'something' . . .

McKeon: If you had two acorns, one of which was put out where there was plenty of sun and became an oak, the other of which was kept in your bureau drawer and did not become an oak, it would be quite clear that the second one was inadequate, defective, it had not realized its potentiality, and consequently in describing the acorn as such there would be nothing wrong with saying that it represented a privation of the eventual mature form and that this inadequacy is an intrinsic inadequacy of matter.

Mc Mullin: Suppose we put the acorn in the bureau drawer, is it a *defect* of the acorn that it doesn't become an oak?

McKeon: It's rather that we are bringing in those aspects which would prevent the acorn from growing. The acorn in its continuing existence would have an inadequacy which its circumstances have not permitted it to overcome.

Mc Mullin: What is at stake here is the *determinability* of the acorn by outside circumstances. In other words, the reason why the acorn doesn't become an oak is that an acorn is the sort of thing that can be closed up in a bureau drawer.

140

It follows, partly at least then, from its form. And it is a "defect", only if it's considered in the context of the process of becoming an oak. In other words, an acorn has the determinability to be acted upon adversely by lightning, pigs, etc., but this is all a question of its *determinability*, it's not a question of an inherent *defectiveness*, I think, in any proper sense of that term.

McKeon: This is the basis of differentiating determination from determinability. The acorn had the determinability but did not get the determination which made it an oak.

Mc Mullin: Could something have the *form* of an acorn and not be capable of being shut up in a bureau drawer? Further, if change is what reveals inadequacy, an acorn which does *not* change is doing the "better thing", it would seem.

Mc Inerny: I think that the defect of the acorn would be not *not* becoming an oak tree but precisely becoming an oak tree, because you can't say that it is well for the acorn to become an oak tree if the price of becoming this is to cease to be an acorn. It's not good for the acorn because the acorn ceases to be, though it may be good for the oak tree which develops from it.

Mc Mullin: Would you say that natural process is process toward the bad?

Mc Inerny: Well, the growth of the acorn in the sense of becoming an oak tree is the death of the acorn.

Lobkowicz: The process could be as well for the better as for the worse. If there is a determinability toward the better, it seems among all cases of which we know that there is a determinability toward the worse too. So, the fact of being able to develop in any direction whatsoever, higher or lower, requires the possibility of ceasing to be. And I think this would be a way of describing determinability as a "deficiency".

Mc Mullin: The only way in which one could get around this possibility of something bad happening is to have no possibility of something better happening. You are suggesting that the fact that the principle of potency allows worse things makes it on the whole a kind of imperfection. But this is not so unless you suppose that better things, so to speak, are rather unimportant in the overall world-view. If evolution is to be taken at all seriously in cosmology, it is obvious that whatever is responsible for change in the universe, is responsible for the gradual unfolding of new states of being.

Lobkowicz: My point is that non-determinable things are better. They have a lesser chance of destruction. And the fact that they also have less chance of development to the higher is of no importance in this case.

O'Connor: I have the impression that Fr. Luyten's point is a more profound one. It is simply this, that a thing cannot become what it is, it can only become something that it is not, and therefore the precondition for its becoming something is a lack of whatever is there. I don't think you have to discuss whether that which it will be is better or worse than that which it was previously. As far as I can see, all that is involved in this statement is merely that the possibility of becoming involves a defect in the sense that that which is going to become lacks something which it is capable of.

Mc Mullin: But now you are associating "defect" with *privation* rather than

141

potency. Any finite being is "imperfect" in this sense, but it is the form, not the matter, which is the principle of "imperfection" in *this* sense of the term.

Fitzgerald: Would you consider that the notion of "defect" here might refer rather to the correlative of determinability? A determinable thing lacks what is needed in order for it to be what it can be. According to Aristotle, a thing cannot give itself what it doesn't have. That's a defect, isn't it, where it needs what it doesn't have, and can't give it to itself?

Weisheipl: All motion is indicative of imperfection. There are only two possibilities of motion. It may be corruption, in which case the imperfection is already in the thing: the reason for the corruption is the matter which is indeterminable in itself, yet capable of having other forms. This means that the prior one ceases to be. When a man ages, the nature loses its use of the organs; the organs (which are material) now take on the imperfection of the elements, the hardening of the arteries, the ossification of the joints, etc. If the matter itself were not capable of these other accidental forms which render the possession of the mature male form precarious, there wouldn't be any such thing as aging.

Mc Mullin: But what makes the artery behave in the way it does? Surely it is its *form*? You are using 'matter' in the sense of 'second matter' here, and you still haven't shown that *primary* matter is the sole principle of the inadequacy of which you speak.

Weisheipl: But surely you're not saying that there can be corruption without matter?

Mc Mullin: No, I'm not. I'm asking what you *mean* by 'matter' here.

Weisheipl: Let's try to look at the inadequacy which is *the* root of all motion. If one would admit, as Aristotle does, that matter is the cause of corruption, then one could say that within the thing itself because of the matter there is imperfection. Look at the other possibility, namely generation: a thing would not acquire something other than it has now unless it wanted to, unless there were a drive to something better.

Mc Mullin: Would you say, then, that matter is the principle of perfectibility?

Weisheipl: To a certain point. But as such in itself, considered as potency, it is inadequate, imperfect, and therefore needing perfection . . . An acorn would not become an oak unless it were imperfect before.

McKeon: I wonder if we could make the point about inadequacy better if we deserted the acorn for a moment? Aristotle in discussing the career of the individual human being remarks that at the beginning of its life, let's say before the child has attended school, the scope of its potentiality is relatively indeterminate; it could have a number of careers. As the child proceeds through his schooling he approximates more completely the realization of some of his potentialities, but at the expense of not realizing the other potentialities. This would obviously be felt as an inadequacy in his career. Yet, in the beginning these inadequacies taken separately were capable of being overcome.

Mc Mullin: But the "inadequacy" here derives from the finitude of the form as it grows more definite, not from the matter . . . Could I ask how (if at all) the statement that primary matter is to be identified with pure potency is to be translated into a statement about the individual thing? Can we say that it "possesses a pure potency" or something like that?

Sellars: I'll make a stab at it. When we say that prime matter is pure potency we mean that it is not characterized in terms of some empirical character, like hot, cold, moist, or dry, that it is that which is able to become hot and dry or hot and cold, etc., and is one or the other. In other words, it is never in a state in which it is unqualified. (*Mc Mullin*: But you're talking *about* prime matter here. How about acorns?) My point was that prime matter is not characterizable as such in terms of an empirical character.

Fisk: You can make the statement that the acorn can become something. But the question was: How could we formulate a statement which would express the fact that an acorn "has" pure potency?

Sellars: But, like Professor Mc Keon, I would reject the claim that it *has* pure potency; I say it *is* pure potency, in the sense that prime matter as such is not characterized in terms of what quality it has, but in terms of what qualities it *can* have.

Mc Mullin: What bothers me is the suggestion that you can talk about an *M*-principle called "prime matter" in such a way that what you say about it is absolutely incapable of translation into, or even relation with, a statement about that of which it is an *M*-principle.

Sellars: Prime matter is not in Aristotle's system really distinct from the object in the sense in which you presuppose . . . There is no real distinction (in the sense in which you are seeking) between the prime matter of a piece of fire and the piece of fire; the distinction there is of a different sort.

Hanson: The logical function of the designation 'prime matter' seems to me to be simply that of an infinitely variable referent . . . The way of localizing it is to proceed, as it were, along a series of quite practical referring expressions, until one reaches the limit. You automatically find yourself in a situation where the inclination to talk about it in terms of the steps you had to make along the way is very attractive and has to be resisted.

143

THE OCKHAMIST CRITIQUE

Allan B. Wolter, O.F.M.

As Ernest Moody points out,

> Ockham's philosophy was developed with critical fervor and in a spirit of protest, as the reaction of a brilliant and passionately logical mind to the second rate scholasticism which had become established in the universities during the late thirteenth and fourteenth centuries. His criticisms are rarely directed against the "ancients", and where they bear on teachings of Duns Scotus they come nearer to being interpretations or discussions of doctrine, than critical attacks. Ockham's unnamed adversary, for whom he has little sympathy and less respect, is the *communis opinio modernorum*.[1]

His contempt for these "moderns" stands in sharp contrast to his respect for Scotus, whom he cites frequently, and his attitude towards Aquinas, to whom he rarely refers. Obviously Ockham did not go to the latter's works in attacking positions reputedly thomist, for as he presents these views they appear too often as "crude caricatures of the delicately nuanced discussions of St. Thomas". Yet, as Moody shows, Ockham was not out for cheap victories. Few scholastics were more exhaustingly painstaking than he in setting out their opponent's opinions. The most likely target of Ockham's so-called "thomist critique" seems to be none other than Giles of Rome. Moody's careful analysis of certain key doctrines lends considerable strength to this view. And certainly in the years that Ockham was a student at Oxford, "there was no more eminent or authoritative representative of the *communis opinio modernorum* than Aegidius of Rome".[2]

Historians of philosophy in our own day are less likely to accept this "auditor of Aquinas" as his faithful disciple and authentic interpreter. They are too keenly aware of the transformation the saint's doctrines underwent in his hands, especially as regards the real distinction between essence and existence, his notion of quantity as a *res absoluta,* his conception of relation, his development and emphasis on the distinction between *forma partis* and

---

[1] E. A. Moody, "Ockham and Aegidius of Rome", *Franciscan Studies, 10,* 1949, 442.

[2] *Ibid.* Giles of Rome, of course, is not the only *doctor modernus* whom Ockham attacks. A. Maier, for example, has pointed out that in *De sacramento altaris, "quidam doctor modernus"* turns out to be Richard of Mediavilla. Cf. "Zu einigen Problemen der Ockhamforschung", *Archivum Franciscanum Historicum, 46,* 1953, 178 ff.

forma totius, to mention a few that Ockham singles out for special criticism.

All this should be kept in mind in reading Ockham's interpretation of hylomorphism, lest one dismiss his denunciation of certain viewpoints as little more than a clumsy critique of the authentic "thomist" position. There is a sense, of course, in which we could speak of his theory of matter as a criticism of thomism even as we could designate it a defense of scotism, but only because these labels can be so broadly construed as to include any and every independent development that drew some measure of inspiration from Aquinas or the Subtle Duns. But such a characterization says little more than Ockham's hylomorphic theory differs substantially from that of Thomas and comes closer to that of Scotus. Its resemblance to the latter is seen especially in the way Ockham understands the real distinction between matter and form and the actuality of matter. Like Scotus, he rejects the theory of a plurality of forms in inorganic compounds, but accepts it as more probable for living organisms. On the other hand, he disagrees with his Scottish confrère's claim that there is no real distinction between the sensitive and intellective form in man, but follows him in rejecting the Augustinian thesis of seminal reasons or inchoate forms in matter, a view defended by Albertus Magnus and Bonaventure and revived in a more modern garb by some neo-scholastics. But for all its resemblance to the scotist position, Ockham's notion of matter is esssentially the fruit of his personal reflections on the *Physics* of Aristotle. In fact, as he tells us in the introduction to both the *Expositio super octo libros Physicorum* and the *Summulae in libros Physicorum,* he is not even concerned with presenting his personal views as a Catholic and theologian on the philosophy of nature. His aim is rather to explain what he considers to be the authentic interpretation of natural philosophy according to Aristotle's own principles in these two commentaries. When his presentation becomes polemical, it seems directed in the main against the *moderni.*

In presenting his interpretation of Aristotle's theory of matter, I shall draw chiefly upon his own synoptic account in the *Summulae,*[3] using the more extensive *Expositio*[4] for an occasional clarification. For his own novel view on the nature of celestial matter, however, I have drawn upon the *Reportatio* of his questions on the second book of the *Sentences.*[5]

---

[3] *Summulae in libros Physicorum,* Venetiis, 1506.

[4] *Expositio super octo libros Physicorum.* Father Gaudens Mohan, O.F.M., is working on a critical edition of this hitherto unedited work. I am grateful for the use of his collated text on the first two books. I am also indebted to Father Augustine Pujol, O.F.M. who is preparing an extensive study of Ockham's hylomorphism. Without the gracious assistance of these two confrères this paper could not have been written.

[5] *Quaestiones in IV Sententiarum libros,* Lugduni, 1495.

§1 *The Meaning of 'Matter'*

'Matter', like its correlative term 'form', is a word with many meanings. The logician, for example, uses it for the subject of a science; the moralist, for the passions to be moderated by virtue. But these and similar meanings do not directly interest the philosopher of nature. When he speaks of matter, it is in the sense of a material cause, that is, something which is the subject of a change or transformation effected by some agent.

Since this change or transformation can be of two kinds, 'matter' is given a dual meaning. Sometimes, says Ockham, it refers to what is transformed into what is truly a new thing. This is the case with substantial changes, or even with such qualitative accidental changes as involve the acquisition of a positive absolute entity, and do not represent a mere rearrangement or redistribution of the matter. Such a positive quality is acquired, for example, when a body changes color, when the air is illumined, or when water is heated. Here a new form is acquired that is really distinct from the matter. And where a true form is generated, be it substantial or accidental, we have 'matter' or 'material cause' used in a strict and proper sense of the word.

At other times, however, 'matter' and 'material cause' are used in a broad or improper sense to refer to any subject whatsoever of which it can be said: "This is no longer the way it was before". For such a proposition to be true, it suffices that the material as a whole be moved in some way, or that the parts thereof be spatially redistributed. Such is the case, for instance, when brass is molded into a statue, or silver into a drinking cup, or when a wall is built from bricks or a figure is carved in wood. If we speak of "wood" in the last case as "matter" and of the figure as "form", we are using these terms in an extended and improper sense, says Ockham.

> No additional absolute entity really distinct from the wood itself has been added to it. Form properly so called, differs in its entire entity from the matter and together with the latter constitutes a composite which is one thing in itself. Whiteness in this sense would differ from its subject in its entire entity.[6]

This distinction is understandable if we keep in mind that Ockham admits that of the ten Aristotelian categories, only substance and quality can add any positive absolute entity to a thing. He specifically rejects the Aegidian notion that quantity, or the shape or figure it possesses, represents a *res absoluta* distinct from the entity of the material substance itself.[7]

---

[6] *Expositio, lib.* I, *com.* 1; see also *Summulae, Pars* II, *c.* 1, fol. 9*va–b*.

[7] E. A. Moody, *art. cit.*, p. 419 ff.; P. Boehner, *Ockham: Philosophical Writings*, Edinburgh, 1957, p. 137.

We have somewhat greater leeway in using 'matter', says Ockham, than we do in using 'material cause', since something is frequently said to be the "matter" of another thing even when it is neither that thing itself, nor a part thereof. Thus for instance, we speak of matter as the matter of substantial form, even though it is neither the form nor a part of it. The same is true when we call the subject or substance the matter of an accident, even though the subject is not the accident itself (e.g. whiteness) nor a part thereof.

In philosophical parlance, however, 'material cause' could not be properly substituted for 'matter' in the above cases, nor would one be tempted generally to do so. For what is caused materially is not the form, but the composite of matter and form.

In those cases, however, where the so-called "form" does not constitute some new, absolute entity really distinct from the matter, there would be some grounds for saying, for example, "Brass is the material cause of the statue". In such a case, however, we have shifted from a proper, to an improper, use of the term. Such an improper or transferred meaning is justified because of the linguistic similarities between statements which actually express radically distinct types of changes. Given a case where a new entity is generated and where matter, consequently, in the strict sense of the term is involved, one can say what would not have been true earlier: "This composite exists." In a similar way, we could point to a freshly cast statue of bronze, saying: "This statue exists", which it would not have been correct to say before. Yet in this second instance, no real positive entity has been added to the material. All that was altered was the way in which it was distributed in space. Nevertheless, the apparent form of our proposition does not reflect this difference. And because this is so, we can speak of brass being the material cause of the statue in an improper and transferred meaning of the term.[8]

Yet even when matter is used in a strict and proper sense, further distinctions are in order. Contrary to what Baudry seems to imply, Ockham does not restrict 'matter' in the strict sense only to primary matter. What is essential to the proper notion of 'matter' as synonymous with 'material cause' is that it represent only one part of the composite and that it is the recipient of a proper form (i.e. some absolute entity, either substantial like the corporeal form or the intellective soul, or a quality like whiteness, which is really distinct from the subject it informs). He returns to this point again and again in his textual commentary on the first two books of the *Physics*.[9] The acci-

---

[8] *Summulae, ibid.*, fol. 9*vb*.

[9] *Expositio, Prooemium, lib.* I, *com.* 1, 15, 59, 68, etc.; *lib.* II, *com.* 7, 9, 13, 31, etc.

dental quality that air receives on being illumined is a true (accidental) form for Ockham; the material substance (air) would also seem to be a material cause in a proper sense of the term. Furthermore, since Ockham admits that in some composite substances such as living organisms there is more than one substantial form, secondary or composite matter which results when primary matter and the corporeity-form combine would also be matter in the strict sense of the term.

With regard to composite matter, however, Ockham makes a distinction. Sometimes the elements from which compound inorganic substances are generated or formed are called the matter of the latter. Since Ockham like Scotus does not admit a plurality of substantial forms in non-living things, however, he insists that when water is said to be the composite "matter" from which all liquids are formed, 'matter' is used improperly. For in such cases, it is really primary matter, and not the composite matter called "water", that acquires a new substantial form. It is different, however, in the case of a composite (such as man) where more than one substantial form is present; flesh and blood remain flesh and blood whether they are informed by the sensitive or rational soul or not. Composite matter in this second case fulfills the definition of matter in a proper sense.[10]

The most fundamental matter, however, is primary matter as its name indicates. And it is with Ockham's interpretation of this that we shall be concerned in what follows.

§2 *The Existence and Intelligibility of Primary Matter*

Primary matter, like substantial form, is not something we know directly or immediately. It does not belong to the class of simple concepts which we use to categorize our perceptual experience. Neither does it refer to the more abstract or refined conceptions which still have some measure of more or less direct verification at the observational level. *Matter* and *form* are rather theoretical constructs. They are notions we have built up by combining more elementary notions. Some of the latter, taken in themselves, designate something common to matter (or form) and to other things as well. Others, however, refer only to things other than matter (or form). By affirming some and denying others, it is possible to get a combination that applies only to matter and to nothing else. Simply because such "composed concepts" are constructs, does not say that they have no reference to anything in the real world. If we can show that only by the use of such theoretical entities can we account for the changes that are actually ob-

---

[10] *Expositio, lib.* I, *com.* 1; *lib.* II, *com.* 9.

served, then we shall have demonstrated the existence of both matter and form. Scotus refers to such notions as "inferred concepts that have the form of a proposition", because it is only by virtue of some reasoning process that we recognize our construct is more than an empty name and signifies a "real essence", that is, something which at least could exist in the real world. It is in this vein that Ockham writes:

> Primary matter is not intelligible or able to be known in itself, that is, it cannot be grasped by knowledge which is both simple and proper to it. Yet given other simple concepts, both those which are common to, and those which are peculiar to, other things, the intellect can put these together, and through reasoning, can declare that such a combination of certain concepts signifies something in reality and can truly stand for a thing. Thus, if the intellect has this concept: "Something is deprived of some thing which it can be subject to later on", then it can think or conclude that some thing does exist in the realm of nature that is first deprived of a form, but afterwards no longer lacks it, and this it calls matter. But the knowledge of matter acquired in this way, is not simple or non-propositional knowledge. It is by way of a proposition which asserts matter and nothing else, even though each part of such complex knowledge expresses something other than matter, just as every part of this: "A ternary is an uneven number" expresses something other than a ternary number, yet the combination as a whole asserts a ternary number.[11]

The same can be said of 'substantial form' as a correlative of 'primary matter'. Like father and son, neither term can be known if the other is not also known to some extent.

How do we know that primary matter, or that any material cause in the proper sense of the term, exists? There is no *a priori* way of demonstrating this, as Averroes the Commentator correctly points out. It is possible, however, to give some kind of *a posteriori* argument based upon observed changes that occur in the world about us.

If all that is required to explain something new is a local motion or spatial redistribution of materials (as was the case with the form of a brass statue, or the figure given to the wood, or more generally, when any kind of artifact is created), we should not postulate the existence of form as a new and positive entity over and above the matter. Such would be the case, for example, with rarefaction or condensation of air. But this does not seem to account adequately for those cases where animals, plants, etc. are born or die, or explain how natural bodies like fire, air and the like are formed from one another.

None of these came from nothingness. What then pre-existed from which they were formed? Not the thing itself, for its properties are not reducible

---

[11] *Summulae, Pars* I, *cap.* 20, fol. 7ra.

to, or accounted for, by what was there before, plus some simple rearrangement on the part of the efficient cause. On the other hand, what pre-existed was not some reality that is completely distinct from, and extrinsic to, the end product of the change. Otherwise, there would be no cause for speaking of the production as a generation rather than a creation. All these signs then point to the conclusion that one portion of what was generated pre-existed, and this we call matter. Since this presupposes a second entity to complete the thing generated, we are forced to postulate two positive elements at least: one, matter; the other, form. "For generation then", says Ockham, "one must assume that matter and form exist and that they are distinct from one another".[12]

In the *Summulae Physicorum*, and, as far as I have been able to ascertain, in the *Expositio,* Ockham does not try specifically to prove the existence of primary matter. He is concerned after all with explaining what its properties are and what function it serves in Aristotle's natural philosophy. Since he is convinced that Aristotle (if he is consistent with his own principles) believed in both the actuality of matter and plurality of forms, he can introduce *materia prima* as the most fundamental substrate of substantial change. As such it is a subject for all substantial forms and yet it does not possess any as something necessary to itself or as something which always inheres in it. Or as he puts it in the *Expositio*:

> A twofold matter exists, primary matter, namely, which includes no form in its essence but receives in itself a distinct form. And this matter is the same in kind in all things which are able to be generated or corrupted. There is another matter which is composed, namely, it is the whole which results from the combination of primary matter and the corporeity-form which is the first to inform primary matter.[13]

Ockham is obviously concerned to defend the view that if matter is to fulfil its function as a substrate which retains its identity while subject to different forms, it must be really distinct from any and all forms. Matter is something more than a conceptual abstraction apart from form, and the same is true of form apart from matter. Both are positive entities in their own right. This is the only interpretation that will make sense out of Aristotle's teaching as a whole. Some would interpret what he says in the first chapter of the *Physics,* Bk. II, as evidence to the contrary, but this, like Averroes' commentary upon it, must be glossed in the light of his teaching as a whole.

> It must be kept in mind that when the Philosopher says that form is separated from matter only according to reason and the Commentator says in com-

---

12 *Summulae, Pars* I, *cap.* 7, fol. 3*va*.
13 *Expositio, lib.* I, *com.* 1.

ment 11 that form is separated from matter by definition only, they do not mean to say that matter and form are one and the same thing, distinct from one another only by reason and definition. What they wish to say is that form is not separated from matter in such a way that it could exist without matter, as the Commentator says in that very place. But for all that, they are two things, really distinct, even though matter could not be divested of all form so that it existed without a form. And they are distinguished according to to reason and definition because in the soul there are distinct notions of each which make clear that the essence of the one is not that of the other, and by that very fact they are distinct things.[14]

We might note in passing, that Ockham is not concerned with defending this view that matter could not possibly exist under any circumstances apart from all form. This, like his statements about the impossibility of a material substance existing without its parts being circumscriptively present in space, do not reflect his personal views as a theologian.[15] As he warns his readers in the beginning:

> Let everyone know who examines this book that I will not try to give what I firmly hold to be true by Catholic faith or according to theological truth, but rather whatever it seems to me would have to be said according to the mind of Aristotle.[16]

§3 *The Actuality of Matter*

The view that primary matter has some actuality of its own and that God, therefore, could create it apart from any and all form did He choose to do so, seems to have enjoyed a measure of popularity among Franciscans from the English province. Already in Aquinas' day, John Peckham had proposed this thesis, and it was defended a little later again by Richard of Middleton.[17] Still later William of Ware, Duns Scotus and Ockham will champion this view but in a somewhat different philosophical context.[18] In Peckham, the doctrine seems to have derived its inspiration from an

---

[14] *Expositio, lib.* II, *com.* 11.

[15] One of the principles he insists upon as a theologian is that God can cause, produce and conserve independently anything that is a positive reality or thing. Cf. *Reportatio* in *II Sent., q.* 19F. One of the consequences is that matter can be produced without form and vice versa. Cf. Boehner, *op. cit.*, p. xx.

[16] *Summulae, Prooemium,* fol. 1ra.; cf. also Boehner, *op. cit.*, p. 2.

[17] D. E. Sharp, *Franciscan Philosophy at Oxford in the Thirteenth Century,* Oxford, 1930; R. Zavalloni, O.F.M., *Richard de Mediavilla et la controverse sur la pluralité des formes,* Louvain, 1951, pp. 303–309.

[18] Cf. G. Gál, O.F.M., "Guillielmi de Ware, O.F.M., Doctrina philosophica per summa capita proposita", *Franciscan Studies, 14,* 1954, 275–79. On the continent, the Franciscan Vital du Four like the secular master Henry of Ghent also held this view. Aureoli on the contrary denied it.

Augustinian interpretation of matter as the seat of seminal reasons. Ware, Scotus and Ockham all reject this theory of inchoate forms. The actuality of matter is a simple consequence of what Aristotle taught matter to be. This, plus the Christian dogma of creation by an omnipotent God, leads readily to the thesis defended by Peckham.

If matter is everything Aristotle claims it to be, Scotus argues:

> then it is something which is not merely in objective potency, as all the reasons I have given above prove. But then it must be in subjective potency, and existing in act or as act (I don't care how you describe it) to the extent that everything which exists apart from its cause is said to be in act or an act.[19]

And if this be so, he concludes, certainly God could give it existence apart from any substantial form. What would matter be like under such circumstances?

> I say that just as an angel, lacking quantity as it does, will not be in any place circumscriptively, but will be there definitively, presupposing that it is somewhere in the universe, or, if outside the universe where place does not exist, it will be in no place definitively, so too with matter. If it were in the universe without any form, it would be somewhere definitively; if it were beyond the confines of the universe, however, it would not be located anywhere definitively. But for all that it would still exist as a certain type of an absolute nature. If you ask: Would it have parts too? I say that it has substantial parts for these it does not have in virtue of quantity. If you say that [matter] is a being in potency, and therefore, if it were conserved without any form, existence would be accidental to it, I reply that this is not true. For just as man, as he exists in the extramental world, has his own proper essence, so also he has his own proper existence. The same is also true of matter. Jut as it would have its own proper essence, so also it would have its own proper existence. Finally, if you argue that matter, existing apart from form in this way, would at least have a relationship to God who conserves it, and hence would have some form, I reply: As was pointed out earlier in distinction one, this relation is really identical with the matter, for it is not a form added to any created essence, since it is nothing more than the latter's dependence upon God.[20]

In both the *Summulae* and *Expositio* Ockham defends the actuality of matter as the authentic view of Aristotle for much the same reasons as Scotus and Ware. How can primary matter be a real, substantial principle of things if it does not exist as such? And if it does exist, as the facts of generation and corruption prove, then it must have some measure of actuality. For in a broad sense at least, to be actual or in act means to exist in the realm of nature. It is opposed properly to what is at present non-

---

[19] *Opus Oxoniense, lib.* II, *d.* 12, *q.* 1; Vivès, *t.* 12, p. 558.
[20] *Ibid., q.* 2, p. 577.

existent but which can exist. Thus we say that someone whose skin is bronzed by the sun, is only potentially white. Potency in this sense expresses actual privation but possible possession. But matter has its own proper entity or nature and its own proper existence, so it is obviously not in potency so far as these are concerned. True, matter does not always exist under this or that form, but this variation of form is something over and above what the subject matter is in itself. If it were not, there would be no point in speaking of matter as one of the parts of a composite substance.

Furthermore, since a composite substance, according to Aristotle, can only be composed of parts which are themselves substances, matter is a substance in its own right even though, as a part of a composite substance, it is incomplete and capable of being perfected further by the form it receives. Indeed, matter as the subject of form is substance in its literal meaning of a foundation or substrate. Obviously it cannot fulfil this function unless it exists and possesses some actuality of its own.

Conversely, Ockham argues, if matter were not actual in this minimal sense, but only something potential, then it should be possible to produce matter. For what is not actual, but only can be, can be produced and given the existence which it did not previously possess. But matter cannot be produced or brought into existence in this way, since its existence is presupposed as a condition for all generation. Indeed, according to Aristotle, matter has an eternal existence, being incapable in itself of either coming to be or perishing.

Some might protest that form is the actuality of the matter, and since matter is never without some form, there is no need that it be something actual in itself to exist and function as a substantial principle. In fact, since it never exists apart from form, we must deny that it has any actuality in itself. Ockham seems to have some such objection in mind when he argues:

> If matter were not in act, this would only be because it is never without form. But just as matter is never without form, so neither is form ever without matter. Therefore, the argument that says that matter is not in act because it is never without form, would also prove that form is not a being in act because it is never without matter. The consequent is false; so too is that from which it follows.[21]

If Aristotle and his Commentator Averroes declare that matter is not actual but in potency to act, it is only because they are speaking of act in a strict and narrow sense, viz. as synonymous with substantial form itself. In this sense, of course, matter is not act for the simple reason that it is not form, but something really distinct from form. Considered in itself, it is

---

[21] *Summulae, Pars* I, *cap.* 16, fol. 5*vb*.

pure potency because it can receive any substantial form and of itself is none of them actually. But if we take act in its broader meaning as referring to whatever has its own proper nature and existence, then

> I say that matter is a certain kind of act, for matter exists in the realm of nature, and in this sense, it is not in potency to all acts, because it is not in potency to itself.[22]

§4 *Matter as Potency*

But just what does it mean to say "Matter is in potency", or more properly (though authors use the expressions interchangeably) "Matter. is potency"? Is potency of the essence of matter, or is it something distinct from matter?

We might note parenthetically that much of Ockham's discussion of matter in the *Summulae* and *Expositio* takes the form of a logical analysis of such philosophically puzzling statements as "Potency is the matter itself", or "Privation is the matter", or "Quantity is the matter itself, and not something distinct from matter". Certain of his contemporaries have that curious mentality that tends to create philosophical conundrums because they forget how language functions. Just because a word can be meaningfully applied to reality, these "realists" think it must have some concrete reference in the form of a distinct reality or "essence".

Ockham's opponent in the present case is reluctant to identify matter and potency on the grounds that matter is not in potency to all forms at the same time, but only to those forms which it does not actually possess at the moment. Hence, matter's potentialities vary from moment to moment as new forms are generated and others perish. If a statement like: "Matter is potency" or "Matter is in potency" states something about reality, it is only because matter possesses some reality distinct from its essence, which reality we call "potency."

Nonsense! replies Ockham. If potency were something distinct from matter itself, it would have to be either a substance or an accident. But what is gained or lost when the potentialities of matter change is clearly not a substance, for then primary matter would belie its name because it would not be substantially simple or primary. Neither is this "potency" some real accident, for this involves further difficulties. What is the precise subject or substance in which this quality inheres? Since it is obviously destroyed when a new form is actualized, it would seem to be corrupted by this form, yet this type of relationship is characteristic of one substantial form with

---

[22] *Ibid.*, fol. 6*ra*.

respect to a contrary substantial form. It is not something which obtains directly between one substantial form and some contrary accident. Hence we should have to posit some additional substance in which this accidental entity is rooted, and thus be faced with all the difficulties of our first alternative.

But suppose our realist opponent insists that to be real, potency need not be some absolute entity such as substance or quality. It suffices that the accidental reality which potency adds to matter be that of a real relation.

Well, asks Ockham, just what is the term of this relationship? Is it not the non-existent form, for it is precisely this form which matter can possess, and with respect to which it is said to be potency or in potency? How then can a relationship be called real when one term is non-existent?

But that is not all, says Ockham. (We know he was one of the great opponents of the thesis that a predicamental relation adds any positive entity or reality over and above that of the relata). If this potency were a positive something really distinct from the matter, matter would have to contain an actual infinity of such realities, since the forms to which matter is in potency are infinite in number. It will not help to say that potency is distinguished only with reference to such forms as differ specifically, and not to those which are merely numerically different, and there is not an infinity of specifically different forms. For forms are not universals, they are individual. Matter does not possess the whole of a species (e.g. all rational forms) because it happens to be actualized by one member thereof. The only "potency" that matter loses when actualized by a particular form, says Ockham, is the potency to that particular form. If the argument that potency must be distinct from matter because it can be lost or gained proves anything at all, it proves too much. Not only would it follow that matter has some actually infinite reality in it, but other nonsense follows. Matter's potentialities to be in different places would also be distinct realities. If the potentiality to an absent form is a reality, then when the potentiality itself is absent we must postulate a further reality, viz. a potency to potency, and so *ad infinitum*.

The potency of matter, therefore, is not an entity really distinct from the matter itself. But if this be so, one can understand Averroes' comment regarding *materia prima,* namely: "Matter is sustained by potency". Is this not equivalent to asserting: "Potency is the very being or substance of matter", and "Matter is its potency"? For there is a very real sense in which each of these two statements is true. The substance of matter, says Ockham, is always in potency to some form. For even when it receives one form, it is still potency to other forms. And if potency is not some peculiar kind of reality, intermediate between matter and form, which is somehow distinct from, and superadded to, the substance of matter, it would be correct to say: "Potency is the very being or substance of matter", and "Matter is its potency". Nevertheless, it would be more precise to say: "The potency is the substance which is the matter", or "It is the matter which is potency, because matter is a certain potency to a substantial form", or "It is the matter which can receive a form that is the potency itself".

It would be incorrect, however, to conclude from such a statement as "Potency is the very being or substance of matter", that matter must always possess this potency to a particular form so that it could never be without it, or still less, that potency is an essential attribute of matter so that it can be affirmed of it according to the first mode of *per se* predication. Neither could one validly conclude from it that, since actuality and potency are mutually opposed, matter therefore cannot be actual.

Potency is not an absolute term like 'substantial form', 'heat' or 'sensation'. The latter denote but do not connote. They have a primary signification but no secondary one. They point to some substance or to some absolute accident. 'Potency' on the contrary is a connotative term. In its primary signification or denotation, it points to the substance or reality called matter. Secondarily, it connotes some non-existent form. To say that matter is potency, then, is to say nothing more mysterious or puzzling that that this subject matter can have a different form than it has at present. Potency in this sense is not opposed to all actuality. Opposition arises only between two states that are true contraries, viz. "in potency to a particular form" and "actually informed by this particular form".[23]

§5 *Matter as Privation*

In much the same way, Ockham analyzes the notion of privation which Aristotle declared to be the third principle of generation. We must not think that in the existing composite of matter and form, there is some third entity or reality which is neither the matter nor the form nor the composite. Philosophers use the word 'privation' differently in different contexts, however. Sometimes, says Ockham, it refers to the form which perishes with the advent of a new form where the two are contraries. In this sense, whiteness is a privation of blackness, and blackness is a privation of whiteness. Similarly, the form of fire represents a privation of the substantial form of air and vice versa.

In another sense, privation refers to the subject which lacks something

---

[23] *Summulae, Pars* I, *cap.* 16, fol. 6r.

and in this case, 'privation' (*privatio*) and 'that which is deprived of' (*privatum*) can be used interchangeably, since they denote one and the same thing.

In either case it is easy to see to what extent privation can be said to be a real principle, and yet one need not admit that any reality exists that is neither matter nor form nor the composite. Ockham engages in a rather subtle logical analysis, however, of all that is implied by such an admission. But the principal point of the discussion seems to be directed against those unnamed opponents who tend to reify the meaning of every abstract noun used by a philosopher. The fact that all nouns are grammatically similar in the sense that they are subject to the same rules of syntax when used in first order propositions should not blind us to the fact that many are not pure denotative terms, logically speaking. While denoting one reality, they always add some further connotation.

In the last analysis, the reason Aristotle speaks of privation as a third principle distinct from matter and form, Ockham explains, is that you cannot define what is meant by 'generate' or 'generation' without introducing in addition to the notions of the material and formal cause, a third notion, that of 'privation' or 'deprived of'.[24]

§6 *Matter and Quantity*

Like 'potency' and 'privation', 'quantity' is also a connotative term which denotes either the substance (matter or form) or some corporeal quality, and connotes that the integral parts thereof are so arranged that to go from one to the other requires local motion. It is logically equivalent to the adjectives 'extended' or 'quantified' and does not denote some absolute or relational entity over and above the substance or quality of which it is predicated. In this, 'quantity' resembles the word 'duration'. The latter is not the name of any positive entity over and above the thing itself which endures from one moment to the next.

All this indicates that when Ockham speaks of primary matter as a simple substance, this does not mean it lacks all real distinction of parts. The only composition that is excluded is that of matter and form. Since matter is the common element found in all material substances and form is that which distinguishes one specifically from another, matter will be alike in all. But when we say it is form that distinguishes one matter from another, Ockham warns us, this does not mean that the matter of one com-

---

[24] *Summulae, Pars* I, *cap.* 8, fol. 3*va*; see also *cap.* 9–13, fol. 3*va–5rb*.

posite is not numerically distinct from the matter of another by reason of itself and not in virtue of something extrinsic to itself such as form or quantity. Though the primary matter of a donkey is not numerically identical with that of a man, the primary matter of the two could become one. If their bodies were cremated and the ashes collected in a single heap and the gases from the two were fused, matter that was previously numerically distinct would now be numerically one. Conversely, if one were to cut up any corporeal substance, primary matter which was originally one would become numerically distinct.

What can be said of these integral parts of primary matter? For one thing, they can be called "substantial parts", for as Scotus pointed out above,[25] they are something matter possesses in virtue of its intrinsic nature and not by reason of anything extrinsic to itself (be it substantial form or quantity). Furthermore, we must distinguish statements about what the part is from those about the way in which it is. Only in this way can we reconcile the simultaneous predication of seemingly opposite characteristics. Statements about whether the parts form an integral whole or not, or whether they are actually separated or not, refer to the way in which they exist with reference to one another. To characterize a part as "substantial", however, is to say something about what it is. And the same is true of the designation 'really distinct', though this is not so apparent at first sight. For if you accept Ockham's definition of real distinction given above, then it follows that the *possibility* of actual separation (at least by the absolute power of God) is a necessary and sufficient logical condition for a real distinction. And this possibility in turn is a necessary feature of a part, and tells us something of what it is. One does not need first to amputate a man's arm, before he can say for example that the primary matter it contains is something which exists in the realm of nature and hence by definition, is something actual. Furthermore, this existence and actuality is something proper to the matter of this arm, and not something that is only conjointly shared with the primary matter in the rest of the body. In fact it is only because such statements are true that the matter of the arm could be actually separated (by amputation) from that of the body.

Primary matter, for Ockham, has no indivisible or absolute minimal part. Though created agencies may be unable to divide any given portion of matter further, the same is not true of God. Since the possibility of division is sufficient for real distinction, one may ask: How many really distinct and actually existing parts, then, does any given portion of matter possess? An infinity, Ockham answers unhesitatingly. And yet paradoxically, it does not

[25] Confer note 20.

158

follow from this that matter is actually infinite, either in perfection or in quantity. Neither does it follow that one portion of matter is not of greater or lesser quantity than another. Neither is God's omnipotence limited because even He cannot exhaust the divisibility of matter with one single act of division. For there is no one that virtually includes all others in the way that the act of dividing a thing into quarters virtually includes a division into halves. Using his theory of supposition in much the same way as Russell uses his theory of types, Ockham patiently solves the apparent contradictions and paradoxes of the infinite.[26]

Another characteristic of the parts of primary matter is that each is capable of occupying a greater or lesser amount of space without gaining or losing any positive entity. In rarefaction and condensation, matter undergoes quantitative changes by the mere fact that its substantial parts are in a larger or smaller place due to the influence of external agents and the substantial forms they induce. Rarefaction and condensation involve a special kind of "local" movement or change so that the parts of matter which were further distant from one another in a rarefied state such as that characteristic of fire or air come closer together in a denser substance such as water or earth. This is not to be interpreted as meaning that the primary matter of these substances is discrete in the way we consider atoms or molecules to be. It is rather that the primary matter which extended continuously throughout a certain sized place upon condensation now extends continuously throughout only a portion of the original place, and since any given part diminishes proportionately, so too does the interval separating any two really distinct parts that are not immediately adjacent to each other.[27]

Naturally, at least, matter never exists without some spatial extension of its integral parts, but there is nothing fixed or determined about its amount. That is why the Commentator Averroes says that matter of itself has only indeterminate quantity, and that too is why we speak of the quantity of matter where this is determinate as being accidental to matter.

The main point, however, that Ockham wishes to make throughout his discussion of quantity is that the word does not denote some absolute entity over and above the substance of matter itself as the *communis opinio modernorum* maintains.[28]

---

[26] *Sent.* II, q. 8, D, E, F; cf. also *Quaestiones in libros Physicorum, qq.* 66–71 (*Vat. lat.* 956) fol. 43*vb*–45*ra*.

[27] *Sent.* IV, q. 7, P; *Summulae, Pars* III, *cap.* 12, fol. 17*v*–18*r*.

[28] *Summulae, Pars* I, *cap.* 19, fol. 7*r*. As Ockham points out in his theological discussion of the Eucharistic accidents, even though quantity or extension do not add some positive entity over and above the material substance, the latter can exist without being so extended. Cf. G. Buescher, *The Eucharistic Teaching of William Ockham*, St. Bonaventure, N.Y.: Franciscan Institute, 1950, p. 66 ff.

§7 Can Matter Receive Existence?

Like Scotus before him, Ockham rejects the real distinction of essence and existence in the crude form it had taken at the hands of Giles of Rome in his own day. The existence according to this view is represented as a positive something over and above the actualized essence. This is seen by the properties ascribed to it. Whereas the essence is something composite (consisting of matter and form), the existence is not composed but simple. Scotus had already excoriated this notion when he said: "I know nothing about this fiction of existence as something uncomposed which comes over the composed essence."[29] If matter and form exist together, this coexistence is not a positive entity really distinct from, and superadded to, the entity of the matter and the form. It is not something which in virtue of its simplicity wraps up the composite essence, as it were, and holds it together.

The norm or test of a real distinction for Ockham, as for Scotus, is that one thing can be separated from the other, not merely by the mind, but in fact. Hence Ockham writes in his *Summa logicae*:

> If you ask whether the essence and existence of a thing are two extramental things distinct from one another, it seems to me they are not two such things. . . . If they were two things, then for God to conserve the entity in the realm of nature without the existence, or vice versa, would entail no contradiction.[30]

As Moody remarks, "St. Thomas would surely not have acknowledged this formulation as his own, and might have agreed with Ockham that essence and existence are not *duae res*".[31] Those unaware of the development of the notion of the real distinction as well as the so-called "virtual" distinction from the time of Bonaventure and Aquinas to that of Suarez, fail to appreciate that for Aquinas the real distinction has not the precise and sharply defined meaning it has for either Scotus or Ockham.

As Ockham declared earlier in discussing the actuality of matter, if primary matter according to Aristotle is incapable of being generated or perishing, but is itself the prerequisite condition and conserving cause that makes generation possible, then it must have not only its own proper essence but also its own proper existence. It is misleading, therefore, to speak of matter as if it received existence from the form. It would be a mistake, he says, if one were to regard the existence which matter receives as something which is somehow intermediary between matter and form, something really distinct from both, a positive entity which form imparts to the matter

---

[29] *Opus Oxoniense, lib.* IV, *d.* 11, *q.* 3, *n.* 46; Vivès, *t.* 17, p. 429.

[30] *Summa logicae* III, II, *cap.* 27, Venetiis, 1508, fol. 70*r*.

[31] E. A. Moody, *art. cit.*, p. 418.

and matter receives from the form. To believe this is to be deceived about the meaning of such expressions as 'Matter exists under a new form'. The only positive entity primary matter receives when substantially informed is the substantial form itself. When we say that matter exists in a new form, and therefore it has a new form of existence or "being", you must keep in mind that 'existence' or 'being' is an ambivalent term. Sometimes it refers to that which informs a subject; at other times it refers to anything existing in the realm of nature. Taken in the first sense, being is given to matter by the form, but this means nothing more or less than that a form informs matter. But if 'being' is taken in the second sense, then it is not true to say that the form gives being to matter, for matter is something which exists in nature prior to the form that is generated, nor is this existence or being altered by the advent of the form. When the Commentator speaks of primary matter being varied in its being, he does not wish to say anything more profound than that matter possesses different forms at different times.

But you may object: if matter possesses existence or being independently of the form then when it receives a substantial form, the latter will not cause it to become a being in act. And anything that is added to a being already in act will be an accident. Hence, the so-called substantial form will be something accidental to matter and so belie its name.

To this objection Ockham replies: You must distinguish two senses of 'being in act'. It can be taken in a broad sense, as we said previously, and then it is equivalent to 'existing in the realm of nature'. Now it is not true that anything that comes to a being which is in act in this sense is thereby accidental. And it is only in this broad sense that matter is said to be in act. In a more restricted sense, 'being in act' refers to something which is a complete substance, and able to exist naturally in itself and not merely as a substantial part of a composite substance. Understood in this way, 'being in act' does not apply to primary matter, and it is true to say that whatever is added to such a complete substance is accidental.[32]

'Generation', like 'corruption', in the strict sense of the term refers to the existence of the composite substance, the matter of which was formerly deprived of the form which it now has for the first time.[33] In a somewhat broader sense, 'generation' applies to the form which comes to be. But it is only in a loose and improper sense that it applies to what results when the material element is simply rearranged spatially as is the case with the products of art. But where we have a true substantial form which is a positive entity really distinct from the matter, it is easy to see how matter and form are principles of generation or of a composite substance which is

---

[32] *Summulae, Pars* I, *cap.* 17, fol. *6va.*
[33] *Ibid., cap.* 8, fol. *3va.*

generated. This implies nothing more mysterious than that matter and form are together in the same place, that they coexist in such a way that the form is actually received by the matter, and that the form as a whole and every part thereof is newly existent. And if you ask, how is it that matter is able to receive such a form and be substantially united with it, one can only say that such is the nature of matter as potency and of form as act. And if you press further: Why is matter potency and form act? one can only say that it is because matter is matter and form is form. This admittedly is not giving the intrinsic reasons or proper cause thereof. And if you say: Nothing should be assumed or postulated without necessity or reason, I reply that many things must be postulated the causes of which we know not. And this because of experience or reasons based upon empirical observations. And so it is with matter and form and the function ascribed to each.[34]

§8 *Theory of Seminal Reasons*

As we mentioned earlier, Ockham rejected the Augustinian theory of matter as a subject of active potencies in virtue of which it possesses substantial forms in a germinal state. This view, though discarded by most of the later scholastics, still seems to have had a sizeable following in Ockham's day. In his *Summulae* he devotes a chapter to the discussion of the theory:

> Because it is something good and because it was the opinion of Albert someone may be in doubt as to whether anything of the form as such pre-exists in matter, something which is called active potency by some or inchoateness of form by others. For many of the moderns think it necessary that what afterwards develop into perfect forms, are previously present rudimentarily in matter.[35]

Though Ockham seems to have considerable respect for the theory in question, he insists that this is certainly not the mind of Aristotle. His arguments center chiefly around two points: what it means to have potential being, and the inconsistencies that are involved in assuming that a part of the form pre-exists in matter prior to the generation of a composite substance of that form. His arguments do not seem particularly effective, especially against the formulation of the theory as we find it, for instance, in St. Bonaventure.[36] They run somewhat as follows:

---

[34] *Ibid., cap.* 23, fol. 8*ra.*

[35] *Summulae, Pars* I, *cap.* 24, fol. 8*ra.*

[36] St. Bonaventure insists that that out of which the full blown form comes to be is not something which forms a part of that form. Just as an acorn is not a part of the oak nor the rosebud a part of the rose, so neither is this germinal form a part of the perfect form. It is rather a complex of active powers which together with the external agencies cooperate to transform the matter. Cf. *Sent.* II, *d.* 7, *pars* 2, *art.* 2.

If something of the form pre-existed either rudimentarily or as an active power, then one would have to ask: Is this the matter itself or something other than the matter? If the former, since matter functions as a subject and not as a part of the form, whatever it is that pre-exists, it would still be matter and not a part of the form. If it is not the matter itself but something other than the matter, then it would have to be either an accident or a substantial form. It is obviously not an accident, for the substantial form is not born or made up of accidental parts. If it is a substantial form, then we would be confronted with the anomaly of the substantial form existing before it comes to be.

This argument, like the ones that follow, has in mind an opponent who has adopted the Augustinian theory because he is loathe to admit that the natural agencies of generation have truly creative powers. If the form is interpreted as Ockham understands it, it is something positive which is really distinct from, and wholly other than the matter. If the presence of the form in the matter is due only to some extrinsic created agent, then the latter would seem to create the form out of nothing for it is clear that the primary matter is only a part of the composite and not a part of the form as such. Ockham, of course, is willing to admit this consequence: "If you say that the form is created, I grant that in one sense this is true."[37] However, this is not the technical sense of 'creation' or 'create' since two conditions are required for the creation of a thing: (1) prior to its existence as such, no part of what it now is pre-existed, (2) the creative agent requires no subject nor does he need any parts out of which to make it. It is only in this strict sense that the ability to create is regarded as the exclusive property of God. If natural agents are able to produce forms where nothing of the form pre-existed, they are not able to produce forms apart from a subject in which those forms inhere. Hence they are unable to create technically. But if you do not wish to admit such an ability in a natural agent, then you must postulate some pre-existing thing out of which these agents produce or make the form. And this, to Ockham's mind, is tantamount to making the inchoate form a part of the perfect form.

Hence, he argues further: Either the entire form pre-exists or only a part thereof. If the entire form pre-exists, then we no longer have a generation in any genuine sense of the term, because the entire essence of the composite (both its matter and its form) previously exists. But what if it is only a part? Well, argues Ockham, if only a part pre-exists, then there is also a part which does not. This is produced by the agent out of nothing. If this is not a creation, then neither is the production of the entire form. Further-

---

[37] *Summulae, loc. cit.,* fol. 8rb.

more, there is no more reason for assuming that one part of the full blown form pre-exist rather than another for they are all on a par in this respect. Since it is obvious that all parts do not pre-exist, then there is no reason for saying that one part does.

Furthermore, if some part of the form were previously present and afterwards another part came into existence, then the substantial form would be capable of increase or diminution, which no one is willing to admit.

But suppose you object that it is the whole form which exists before, and not just a part thereof, but the whole form is there only potentially or in an imperfect fashion. This will not help, replies Ockham. For what does it mean to be there only potentially? It means something is not there, but can be there. It means that if it is anywhere at all it is not in the matter:

> I say then that by reason of its potential being in matter, a form is no more in the matter than Socrates in Rome is in Paris, because it is possible for him to be in Paris, or that whiteness is in blackness or coldness in heat. For just as one in Rome is not truly in Paris, though he might have been there, so also the form of fire is not in the matter which is actually in the form of air, even though the fire-form could have been there instead.[38]

Ockham's analysis really sidesteps the whole crux of the problem. Granted that the form as such is not truly present when it is only potentially in the matter, how is this potency of matter to be understood? Is it a mere receptive or passive potency or are the potencies from which the form is educed active powers which cooperate with external agencies to produce a new substance?

§9 *The Unity of Primary Matter*

In the *Summulae,* Ockham argues that the primary matter of all terrestrial bodies is alike, differing only numerically in each individual. His proof assumes that any form of a composite substance can be transmuted into any other form either directly or indirectly. If there were any reason for denying that the primary matter of one substance is like that of another, it would be because some substances cannot be directly generated from others but require one or more transitional stages.

This does not require the assumption of different kinds of primary matter, however, nor does the theory that there are such really explain anything. Let us assume that *a* and *b* have different kinds of primary matter because they can only be converted into one another by first becoming *c*. But if *a* can be transmuted into *c* their primary matter must be alike. And if *c* can

---

[38] *Summulae, Pars* I, *cap.* 24, fol. 8*rb*.

be transmuted into *b,* the matter of *c* and *b* must also be alike. Consequently, *a* and *b* must also have the same kind of basic matter.

More interesting, however, is Ockham's personal belief that celestial and terrestrial matter are not fundamentally different. He develops this view-point at some length in one of his questions on the Second Book of the *Sentences.*

To begin with, we postulate matter in the stars as Christians chiefly be-cause of the testimony of the Fathers and Doctors of the Church. They de-clare that in the beginning God created matter from which both the heavenly bodies as well as all other things were formed. But this is not the view of Aristotle or his Commentator Averroes. Both frequently declare that the heavens either lack matter entirely or at least do not have matter as a principle of generation and corruption. The only "potency" the heavenly bodies possess is with regard to place. The "matter" of the heavens is really a substantial form, where form is taken in a broad sense to include pure spirits or the so-called "separate substances". It is this simple substance or form which is subject to such accidents as they possess.

Granting that matter does exist in heavenly bodies, "I say secondly that the matter in the heavens and here below is of the same kind."[39] Admittedly this statement, like the previous, cannot be demonstrated, but persuasive reasons for it can be easily adduced.

Were the matter different, it would be because of the nobility of the form which the heavens are presumed to possess, or because heavenly bodies are incorruptible whereas terrestrial bodies are not. Neither reason, however, is cogent. The first is no good, because those who propose it in these days at least will admit that the rational soul of man is much more noble than the form of the heavenly bodies. Nevertheless, they see no incongruity in assum-ing that the rational soul informs terrestrial matter like any other corporeal form.

The second reason is no better, since the assumption of a different kind of matter is not going to account for the incorruptibility of the heavens. A composite substance can still be corruptible even if composed of two incor-ruptible elements. Take prime matter and the immortal soul of man. Both are incorruptible; they are not generated like composite substances, they are created. But the same is not true of man. So too with celestial bodies. Their matter could be incorruptible as well as their form, but this would not make them incorruptible.

In point of fact, they are not incorruptible in any simple or unqualified sense. God can destroy them or cause them to perish or make terrestrial

---

[39] *Report. in Sent.* II, *q.* 22, D.

bodies out of them. The only sense in which they are incorruptible is that created agents are unable to act upon celestial forms in the way they do on terrestrial forms. And if this be so, the heavens would still be incorruptible in this limited sense even if they have the same primary matter as bodies here below.

> It seems to me then that the matter of the heavens is the same in kind as that of things here below, because as has been frequently said: one must never assume more than is necessary. Now there is no reason in this case that warrants the postulation of a different kind of matter here and there, because every thing explained by assuming different matters can be equally accounted for, or better explained by postulating a single kind.[40]

Matter in the heavens, then, is no different for Ockham than terrestrial matter so far as its intrinsic or inherent characteristics are concerned. If the latter has a natural potentiality or "appetite" for a variety of forms, so too with celestial matter so far as God is concerned. If there is any difference, it will be found only with reference to created agents. But even here, Ockham declares, we are speaking of how things actually are.

It is perfectly conceivable that under different conditions even created agents could induce other forms in what is now the matter of the sun and moon and stars. Suppose God were to replace the celestial substantial form with that of fire, something a created agent is powerless to do. Once this change has been effected, however, whatever created agencies have power to destroy or put out the fire form, could also do so here. Thus, for instance, if enough water were doused on such "celestial fire" it would be extinguished.

It goes without saying that much more could be said of Ockham's hylomorphic theory in general and of his idea of matter in particular[41] But from even such a superficial treatment as this two conclusions at least would seem to emerge. Even such a fundamental philosophical notion as primary matter was given no uniform or monolithic interpretation by the mediaeval schoolmen. Secondly, if Ockham's own philosophizing on the subject is not particularly original for the doctrine of matter it presents, perhaps the way in which he submits traditional formulae on the subject to logical analysis may strike a responsive chord among contemporary philosophers.

Catholic University of America

---

[40] *Ibid.*

[41] A thorough study of Ockham's hylomorphic theory is still a desideratum. As I indicated above, Father Augustine Pujol is preparing such a work. Until it appears, however, the interested reader will find it useful to consult Léon Baudry, *Lexique philosophique de Guillaume d'Ockham*, Paris: 1958, or P. Doncoeur, "La théorie de la matière et de la forme chez Guill. Occam", *Révue des sciences philosophiques et théologiques*, *10*, 1921, 21–51.

PART TWO

Reflections on the Greek and Medieval Problematic

MATTER AS A PRINCIPLE

Ernan Mc Mullin

There is a certain way of appealing to "principles" which effectively marks off nearly all pre-Cartesian philosophy from much of the philosophy of the last few centuries, and especially, as it happens, from that of our own time. It not only marks it off, it cuts it off; some would, indeed, think it the most troublesome of the many barriers to fruitful discussion between those who follow "classical" modes of philosophizing and those who prefer the less "metaphysical" modes that have continued to develop under the impact of experimental science.*

§1 Kinds of Principle

In Book Five of the *Metaphysics,* Aristotle lists many senses of 'principle', and then summarizes: "It is common to all principles to be the first point from which a thing either is, or comes to be, or is known; of these, some are immanent in the thing while others are outside."[1] The emphasis here is on principle as *origin,* whether of being, of becoming, or of intelligibility. In any rational discussion, principles of various sorts will thus play a central role. For our purposes in this essay, it will be helpful to distinguish explicitly between a few of the different senses in which the word 'principle' is used.

Nowadays, when a philosopher (or anyone else, for that matter) speaks of a "principle", he will usually have in mind a general assertion or norm of some sort, one that serves as a basis for a systematic set of inferences, for instance, or one that sums up some very central feature in some subject-matter, or one that expresses a rule governing behavior. Such would be the principle of non-contradiction in logic, the uncertainty principle in quantum physics, or the ethical principle that the end does not justify the means. Each of these is a "principle" in a somewhat different sense, but they share one central characteristic, namely that they are principles in the order of

---

* I would like to acknowledge the suggestions and critiques offered by Dr. W. Sellars of the original version of this paper, especially in the revising of §§ 6 and 7.

[1] *Meta.* 1013a 18-20. Aquinas' definition of the principles of natural things equates them to the "causes" of these things: "those things out of which they are, and from which they become *per se,* not *per accidens*" (*Phys. I, l.*13).

statement, S-principles, let us call them. They are a truth from which inference begins, a starting point for attaining intelligibility (the root meaning
for the corresponding Greek term, *'arché'*). The word 'principle' here does
not name anything physical in the causal order of natures in space-time;
it names a statement, a judgement, a rule, or something of the sort, involving a combination of concepts and some form of assertion.

On the other hand, Aristotle's definition can be turned more directly
towards the concrete order of causally interacting things, so that the "first
point" now becomes itself a thing or some characteristic of a thing. A real
principle (or R-principle, let us say) of this kind is responsible (in part, at
least) for the being or mode of being of something else. Thus, the father
is an R-principle of his child; God is an R-principle of the universe; copper
is an R-principle of a given statue, and so on. Clearly, this sense of 'principle' is quite close to that of 'cause', in its broad Aristotelian usage. But
now a difficulty arises. Supposing that Peter paints the chair green, is he
thereby an "R-principle" of the painting of the chair? He is certainly a
cause of it; and he would satisfy Aristotle's definition of 'principle' above.
In practice, however, 'principle' would hardly ever be used in as broad a
sense as this. There is always some implicit connection with a *science,* with
regular connections of a sort that permits stable inference. The connection
between *explicandum* and R-principle must be such as to lay itself open to
rational analysis, so that the *explicandum* may be seen as an instance of a
law or universal. Thus, John, a carpenter, is an R-principle of the furniture
he makes; wood is an R-principle of it too. And, in general, carpenters and
wood are R-principles of furniture. R-principles are individual substantial
entities or properties of such entities. They are invoked to explain the being
of designated concrete things to which they are *causally* linked, either as
immanent to them or as efficient or finalistic causes of them.

Let us suppose that a given entity is an R-principle of some other being.
It can be referred to in two different ways: either by a term which conveys
the way in which it *is* an R-principle (e.g. 'father', 'carpenter'), or by one
which does not (e.g. 'Peter', 'this person').[2] 'This person' and 'father' may
have the same referent, but they have a different sense; they tell us different

---

[2] Aristotle expresses this (*Meta.* 1013b 36) by saying that the sculptor is a "proper"
cause of the statue, whereas Polyclitus (who is the sculptor) is an "accidental" cause.
Since the referent of the terms is the same, and the difference is at the level of sense,
this way of expressing the distinction leads to obvious semantic difficulties. It makes
the "proper" character or otherwise of the cause depend, not on the entity causing, but
on the way this entity is *described.* It belongs to the order of knowledge, not to the
order of natures being explained.

things *about* the referent. The concept conveyed by 'father' indicates to us the manner in which Peter, the father, is *R*-principle of his child. Let us, therefore, call the concept, *father,* a *C*-(i.e. conceptual) principle, in the sense that it is a basic starting-point for any systematic discussion of those relations between persons of which that between Peter and his child is an instance. This instance would be a rather trivial one because one could not construct much of a schema on it. But all science begins from concepts of this sort which serve as principles of explanation. The simplest *C*-principles are abstractive concepts which directly signify individual concrete entities, themselves *R*-principles. But in even the simplest science, the connection between *C*- and *R*-principles soon gets much more complex, with construct concepts like, for instance, *velocity, mass, evolution.*

The concept, *mass,* is a *C*-principle of Newtonian mechanics. Individual real masses (understood as properties, operationally defined, of concrete bodies) could not serve as principles of mechanics, which is a generalized abstract system. A principle in a science has to be either an *S*-principle (if sententially expressed) or a *C*-principle, if not. Science begins from, and returns to, *R*-principles, but since these latter are individual, neither they nor singular descriptions which fit them individually could serve as the "*principium*" or generalized starting-point of a systematic body of knowledge. If one were asked, however, to explain a *specific* motion, such as the motion of this chair as I push it backwards, the measured mass of the chair would serve as an *R*-principle, and the *concept* of mass would serve as a *C*-principle of the explanation. To put this in another way, if the mass-symbol occurs in a mechanical formula, its referent will be an *R*-principle, its sense a *C*-principle. In an actual problem, where '*m*' will be replaced by a measured number like 8, the *C*-principle will be only *part* of the sense, i.e. that part pertaining to the definition of the measure.

If the problem be an "imaginary" one, (that is, one which is not explicitly referred to as a designated concrete instance, but which *could* be referred to one if an instance which fits the specifications of the problem were to arise), we might still speak of an "*R*-principle", though this would now mean something different. The mass-term in the imaginary problem will not denote a property of a designated individual, but rather a property which is "in suspension" ontologically, so to speak, i.e. it represents in a generic way a property which could be possessed by any number of individuals. The referent of the term is no longer a concrete individual entity but a sort of surrogate fictional entity, the study of which is a help towards the knowledge of real entities. It is a principle of explanation, then, an *R'*-principle, let us say, the prime being a reminder of the surrogate or constructed character of the entity, and the 'R' indicating that it stands in place of (and can at any time be replaced by) a concrete individual entity or some definite aspect of such an individual.

Scientists ordinarily talk in terms of such R'-principles, of electrons, orbits, point-events, and the rest. It is easy to mistake such talk as being about R-principles, and in classical physics the transition from one to the other was not difficult. But in quantum theory, for instance, it is extremely complex. A physicist may present us with a model of the H-atom and make spectroscopic predictions based on it, but it would be an entirely different matter to *localize* a concrete H-atom by space-time measurement and describe it *then* in terms of this model. As Schrödinger and Eddington (in different contexts) pointed out, quantum theory (unlike Newtonian theory) cannot assume that it is dealing with *designated* concrete individuals; even the very notion of designation (presumably relative to a material reference-frame itself composed of atoms in motion) poses very complex and so far unsolved problems. Fortunately, we can leave this aside, but the ontological difference between R- and R'-principles is important to our theme.

The distinction between C- and R'-principles is more complicated. The C-principle is the *sense* of some basic term occurring in an explanatory system; if one understands the term properly, one is able to make various theoretical inferences and explain concrete instances in terms of them. It is thus a general *concept* signifying an indefinitely wide range of instances, and correlated in a complex and interdependent way with the other explanatory concepts of the system.[3] An R'-principle is a "conceptual" entity in a rather different sense. It is the *referent*, not the sense, of a basic term, and the referent in a pseudo-individual way. That is, a fictional situation is created in which terms pick out fictional entities whose career is traced, let us say, through some change whose laws are known. These entities[4] are conceptual representatives of individual objects or properties, so much so that at any moment the fictional situation could be referred to some space-time corner of

---

[3] The word, 'concept', recalls notoriously difficult and important problems. Limitations of space force us to leave them aside; fortunately, they do not affect the distinctions drawn in this section too directly. We shall assume that 'sense' and 'concept' are synonymous here, and that the concept in question is not a modification or feature of an individual mind, but rather the intentional correlate of this in language, thus: 'Peter and Polyclitus have the same concept of equality'. The "having" must be carefully taken here, and the way of speech that permits us to use 'concept' as a referring term must not mislead us into supposing that there is question of an individual conceptual "entity" in some simple sense.

[4] 'Entity' here will be taken in an ontologically noncommittal way to mean: the referent of the subject-term in a meaningful statement, the intentional unity in which the judgement of the speaker terminates.

the concrete order, and then the term whose referent was a fictional (or better, "un-anchored") R'-principle, comes to have a real referent,[5] an R-principle in any explanation of that concrete individual situation. The referring of the "floating" conceptual system to some specific region of space-time does *not,* however, affect the C-principles, or senses of the terms involved. In describing situations of this sort, terms are always used in real reference (the "personal supposition" of the medievals), not logical reference, so that sense and referent will always have a different semantic function within the description.[6]

In a problem of mechanics, the individual mass-particles will be R'-principles, the concept of mass will be a C-principle. The relationship between the concept of mass and the indefinitely great number of instances where it can be *applied* (i.e. where the situation can be described in terms of it) is only superficially similar to—and is, in fact, quite different from—the relation between the particle of specified mass in some fictional problem and the indefinitely great number of concrete instances of such particles it *replaces* conceptually. The concept does not stand in place of the individual referent, it "signifies" it; the fictional referent stands in place of the real one, and is referred to by the term via the sense or concept of the term.[7] (Many of the distinctions drawn above are disputed both in medieval and in modern semantics; they have been listed here without discussion because of the necessity of an agreed terminology for what follows.)

So far, so good. But in order to discuss "matter as a principle", it is necessary to introduce a principle of a more complex sort, the general acceptance or rejection of which marks a fundamental parting of the philosophical

---

[5] The real subject need not be an individual body: with complex terms like 'entropy', 'potential energy', for instance, it will be the concrete system, considered in one of its aspects. So that if 'E' symbolizes the potential energy of a designated actual system, the real subject of a statement which has 'E' as subject-term is the system as a whole, taken from a certain highly constructural point of view. (The further question of the relationship between the referent of 'E' and the *measure* of 'E' can be left aside here.)

[6] Problems about separating sense and referent occur with abstract terms like 'beauty', but these do not arise here, since our terms are assumed to be the type that can be used to single out either individual referents with space-time careers or else properties of such entities. The referents may be complex constructs like electrons, but this does not matter: when the physicist talks about an electron in his equations, he certainly does *not* mean that he is tracing the motion of a *concept* (if the concept is defined as above).

[7] This distinction recalls the medieval semantic distinction between *suppositio* and *significatio* (or *consignificatio*) so important to Aquinas, for example, in many of the problems of the *Prima Pars* of the *Summa Theologica*. The *suppositum* would be the R'-principle, the *significatio* the C-principle.

ways. Classical philosophers were wont to speak of "principles" which were neither things nor concepts, but a sort of real "constituent" or "ingredient" of things, at first sight rather uneasily poised between the logical and real orders, incapable of existing on their own, yet playing a direct role in the activity and being of things. The best known of these would be the famous "six principles" of medieval philosophy: matter-form, substance-accident, essence-existence. These were the anchor-points of the complex ontological structure of reality described by scholastic metaphysicians. Let us call them "M-principles", since the discernment of their nature and number was regarded as the ultimate task of metaphysics. As we have defined them, they would form a special sub-section of the R-(and the R'-) principles, distinguished from the others mainly by their curious ontological "incompleteness". We shall discuss their nature later.

The main concern of this essay is with the question of what it means to speak of "matter" as a "principle" of the physical world, or as a "principle" of natural philosophy, and how these ways of speaking can be justified. Other essays in the collection deal with the different roles it has played in different philosophical systems. Here, however, a prior issue is raised: what are the general functions of a cosmological concept of this sort in philosophy? To answer such a general query, it is desirable to choose some specific philosophical system for analysis. For convenience, we shall concentrate on that of Aristotle, partly because of his pioneer role in delineating a concept of matter, and partly also because the chief problems concerning matter as a cosmological principle are easily located in his writings and those of his followers.

These problems can be reduced to three. First, what sort of analysis is it that yields the matter-form-privation triad of *Physics I*? Second, can they be correlated with other everyday senses of 'matter' and 'form', in the way that is usually assumed? Third comes the thorny question of "primary" matter, its definition, justification and ontological status. Is it an M-principle, and how, in general, are such principles to be understood and justified?

§ 2 *"Empirical" versus "Conceptual" Analysis*

Before we come to discuss the argument of Aristotle's *Physics I*, it will be necessary to draw a basic distinction between two different types of analysis. In order to do so, we shall take an imaginary example: an Ionian who claims that all changes can be reduced to changes of water, that, in fact, the world consists of water in different forms. Such a claim, if it were to be based on evidence at all, would have to be empirical, in the sense that it would presumably rely on observations of different sorts of changes (e.g. evaporation, when water apparently becomes air, or sedimentation, when it seems to become earth) or different sorts of being (e.g. the moisture in seeds and all growing things). An analysis of the *concept* of change could never yield precisions of the sort that would allow one to single out a particular stuff, water, as the basic material ingredient of all change.

The most that a conceptual analysis could yield here would be the necessary and sufficient conditions for the correct application of the term, 'change', to any given situation. It would rest, not on a series of observations of different natural changes and a generalization from them (like the water-theory of our Ionian), but upon the simple ability to use the ordinary-language term, 'change', correctly. This ability would not be entirely independent of experience, of course; to learn how to use the term, 'change' (as an analytic philosopher would put it), or equivalently, to discriminate actual changes in our experience (as a phenomenologist might prefer it to be put), *some* experience of change would be required. So that by contrasting "conceptual" ("*C*") and "empirical" ("*E*") types of analysis, it is not intended to suggest that a conceptual analysis is entirely *a priori* or postulational. But its relevance to experience is of a much more general and unspecific sort, sufficient to let one know the *sense* of the term being analyzed but no more of the referents than is conveyed by the sense. Whereas an empirical analyst will turn to the referents of the term (in this case, individual instances of change), and search for distinctions and correlations between them of a sort that may permit him to understand the referents better. In favorable cases, such an analysis will reveal an internal structure in, or differentiation among, the referents, of a kind that the *sense* of the term (indicating only what the referents, by common consent, have already been believed to have in common) could not reach to. An empirical analysis may thus give rise to a *theory* which will extend our knowledge of the referents in an oblique way, and ultimately perhaps modify the original sense of the class-name of the referents.

If the term to be analyzed were of a more specific sort, 'antelope', for instance, instead of 'change', the sort of experience one would have to have had in order to be able to recognize antelopes (or use the word, 'antelope', correctly), would have to be correspondingly more specific. The conceptual analysis of the notion, *antelope,* as this notion is possessed by some particular person or group, will tell us something of antelopes, in the sense that we will know the minimal conditions an animal must fulfill in order to be labelled 'antelope' by someone or other. But conceptual analysis applied to this sort of instance will not lead to discovery; at best, will only teach someone how to use a language, and to understand definitions *already* implicit in the correct use of this language.

The *extension* of empirical knowledge of the structures of the physical world depends, therefore, on empirical analysis. The formulation and communication of such knowledge will frequently require one to use conceptual analysis, which, however, with such terms as 'antelope' will always remain secondary. Where the term is a basic categorial one ('change', 'quality' ...),[8] conceptual analysis comes into its own. Why this should be so is, of course, highly controverted by philosophers of different schools. But one might suggest that an analysis of the "given" element either in experience or in the ordinary use of language (according to which approach one wishes to emphasize) may well disclose a structure of a very general sort, an *eidos* or a "linguistic fact" reflecting perhaps a more fundamental structure of the experienced world. The fact that such analysis will disclose only what is already there will not bother the philosopher (for by now the reader will have decided that the distinction between the two types of analysis also marks off, roughly at least, the scientist from the philosopher). What is already there may be very interesting when brought into the light and dissected.

Conceptual analysis has considerable power in certain areas involving the general conditions of subjectivity or the most pervasive features of natural language, as contemporary phenomenology and linguistic analysis in their not-after-all-so-different ways have shown. It is more limited in value where the structures involved do not depend in their specificity on man; these will be left to the empirical analyses of science, though the philosopher may still have some help to give in providing analyses of concepts or of methods in a given field of science at a given stage of its development.

These are very rough characterizations, and one would have to fill in a lot of detail and note many exceptions. But even this rough distinction between these two modes of analysis is of the utmost importance in understanding what is going on in Aristotle's discussion of matter. Aristotle's theory of forms-corresponding-to-concepts predisposed him to the method of conceptual analysis; the search for form was most often carried on by methods that could only reveal what the concept of form itself was. Aristotle could say what *form* was; but he could not begin to say what the dif-

---

[8] The distinction between the two sorts of term is not sharp, but it can be roughly indicated by saying that one can use the term, 'change', with complete assurance on the basis of *any* sort of experience of Nature. But this would by no means be true of 'antelope'. To put this in another way, one presumes to know the meaning of 'change' so well that without any need of further enquiry one can be sure what the minimal features are that make something qualify as a change. But one would feel that there would always be more to learn about the "minimal features" that identify an antelope.

ferent *sorts* of form were, because this would have required a different sort of analysis.

In his biological works, he lays down an observational groundwork and ignores for the most part the ambitious canons of conceptual analysis given in the *Posterior Analytics*.[9] But his later scholastic followers for the most part disregarded this empirical trend in the Philosopher, and catalogued forms as one would catalogue dictionary meanings of accepted terms. It was this application of conceptual analysis to problems where the empirical method was the more suited that, more than any other factor, blocked the advance of medieval Aristotelian science. It was this precise weakness in the "philosophy of forms" that was criticized by Galileo and Descartes. In the next section, we shall see how C-analysis *can* be usefully availed of at a very basic descriptive level. It will not disclose elements or M-principles (the work of the scientist and the metaphysician respectively). But it *will* give C-principles.

§ 3 *Matter in Book* I *of the* Physics

At first sight, Aristotle's analysis of change in Book *I* of his *Physics* appears to be in continuity with the cosmological questions of his Ionian predecessors. The frequent use of their terminology and of their very questions heightens this illusion. But what Aristotle is in fact doing here is radically new. He is taking the technique of conceptual analysis which had been brought to a fine point by Socrates and Plato in their discussions of moral and metaphysical concepts like *piety* and *unity,* and applying it systematically for the first time to the domain of cosmology. This is a fateful step, because it turned physics, the "general science of Nature", away from the empirical and scientific (in the modern sense) orientation it was beginning to have with the Ionians, and diverted it for two thousand years into conceptual channels that eventually and predictably ran dry. *Physics I* provides a perfect example of conceptual analysis, of its strength (since it is quite irrefutable) and of its limitations (since it does not penetrate to the diverse empirical properties of things; in fact, this particular analysis does not for the most part get outside the logical order, the order of what later scholastics would call "second intentions"). All it says is this: if a change occurs, it will be describable in terms of two statements of the form: '*S* is non-*P*' (true at one moment); '*S* is *P*' (true at a later moment). This being so, it is clear

---

[9] For an extensive documentation on this point, see the essays by D. M. Balme and I. Düring in *Aristote et les problèmes de méthode,* Louvain, 1961.

that three terms, '*S*', 'non-*P*', '*P*', will be required in the description of any change, even a change in an immaterial being. Aristotle (drawing on Ionian and Platonic analogies) suggests names for each of these categories: 'subject', 'form' and 'privation'. In describing a given change, say a green leaf turning brown, Aristotle says that there must be an *S*-term which names the same subject before and after the change. The subject of this term, the leaf, is called the "underlying subject" (*hypokeimenon*) relative to *this* change, not because of any empirical properties it possesses, but because it functions as subject of the *S*-term used in describing this particular change.

In order to see just how far this is from Ionian science, it will be necessary to recall three features of the Ionian efforts to reduce the complexity of the changing physical world to some sort of intelligible pattern. First, some Ionians apparently sought for a common "stuff", i.e. something with specified empirically determinable properties, like water, in terms of which the different sorts of things in the world and their changes could be understood.[10] The evidence for such a claim would be observations of condensation, evaporation, etc.; elaborate studies of, and theories about, water and its various transformations would be necessary if it were to be substantiated. The notable difficulty about such a claim was that it would mean that everything is made up of the same permanently recognizable "stuff", so that "substantial", or basic, change might seem to be impossible. There would, then, be the temptation to avoid this difficulty by talking about a "featureless stuff", of the kind some suppose Anaximander's "*apeiron*" to have been.[11] But then what sort of analysis could indicate the omnipresence of this undetectable "stuff", no longer in fact a "stuff" at all, properly speaking? Not an ordinary empirical analysis, it would seem. So here, right at the very origins of Greek speculation about the world, we have a tension between the ideals of empirical analysis and the notion of "genesis" or what Aristotle would call "substantial change".

Another Ionian model of physical explanation used the notion of what

---

[10] It is very doubtful that Thales actually *did* hold that things consist of water; his claim was probably the much simpler and not quite so novel one, that the world had *originated* from water, and now *rests upon* water. (See Kirk and Raven, *The Presocratic Philosophers*, Cambridge, 1957, p. 88.) But Aristotle makes Thales say that water is the "material principle" or stuff out of which things are made, and it is this "Aristotelianized" Thales, quite probably imaginary, that we have in mind in sketching the problematic of *Physics I*.

[11] Cornford argues that '*apeiron*', which means *boundless,* also in the context means *indefinite in kind,* since Anaximander does not specify any nature for the *apeiron*-principle, as he might otherwise have been expected to do. Aristotle (incorrectly) supposed the *apeiron* to be a sort of "intermediate" or neutral mixture of the contraries. For a review of the evidence, see Kirk and Raven, *op. cit.*, p. 109.

Aristotle would later call an "element": a primary constituent of complex bodies, itself simple in nature but capable of being transformed into other elements. Obviously, the only sort of analysis that could ever have justified this sort of model was the empirical analysis later to be called "chemistry". Yet Aristotle, unwilling to relinquish Empedocles' convenient four-element view, tried to justify it rather in terms of a reduction of all sense-qualities to two basic pairs of contraries. This influential view rested on an ontology of sense-qualities in which a sort of crude epistemological analysis was substituted for direct ontological analysis. From it, Aristotle's complex cosmology of natural place was in turn constructed. It was not until the time of Galileo and Boyle that people began to see that the notion, *element* (unlike *matter* or *principle*) demanded a different sort of analysis than the philosopher could provide, and one that could not rest on distinctions of sense-quality.

A third point in Ionian cosmology that was to influence Aristotle was the idea of opposing natural substances, the "contraries", whose interactions bring about all changes. The hot and the cold do not simply exist side by side; they "war" on one another, while contraries of the same sort attract one another. This idea (found first in Anaximander and Heraclitus) appears to have been based on rough observations of seasonal change and suchlike. The notion of a "contrary" here was not simply a logical one, but one implying "Love" and "Strife", physical forces that would be specific to the particular contrary.

At the beginning of *Physics I,* Aristotle identifies his quest with that of the Ionians: what are the basic "principles" in terms of which natural change is to be understood? He excludes the views of those who would make the principles one or infinite in number. In Chapter 5, his own argument begins:

> In nature, nothing acts on, or is acted on by, any other thing at random, nor may anything come from something else except in virtue of some concomitant attribute of the latter. For how could White come from Musical, unless Musical happened to be an attribute of the not-White or of the Black? No, White comes from not-White, and not from *any* not-White, but from Black or some intermediate color.[12]

The first statement here sounds like an empirical claim, one that would require evidence about the orderliness of natural events. But then the ground shifts: if Musical comes from White,[13] it can only be because Musical itself

---

[12] *Physics*, 188a 32–188b 1.

[13] This way of speaking is semantically very ambiguous. A white thing comes to be from a musical thing, not because it is musical and not because it is in this instance not-white (since many not-white things never give rise to white things), but presumably because of some other "concomitant attribute". Aristotle is suggesting that if the

was not-White in this instance. This is a new kind of 'because', one which does not, Ionian fashion, give a *reason* for the change but only a tautologous *description* of it. If someone had asked Anaximander: why did this acorn become an oak? he would have considered the reply this question is now getting ("because it was a non-oak") a trifling one, irrelevant to the claim of natural regularity made in Aristotle's first statement. For while one could conceive a world in which things *would* act upon one another at random, one could not conceive a world in which something became an oak from something other than a non-oak. The latter is excluded simply by the principle of non-contradiction. What we have now is not an empirical claim about order in Nature, but a disguised application of a logical principle to the notion of *predication-about-change*. If one is to be able to *talk* about change, these are the categories that will be necessary. It should be noted that this is not only conceptual analysis, it is conceptual analysis of *predication-about*; it is this latter fact that gives it its unassailable logical structure. To mark this, we shall sometimes refer to this analysis below as a conceptual-semantic (*CS*) one.

He now continues:

> If then this is true, everything that comes to be or passes away, comes from or passes into its contrary or an intermediate state. But the intermediates are derived from the contraries, colors, for instance, from black and white. Everything, therefore, that comes to be by a natural process is either a contrary or a product of contraries.[14]

One immediately asks: what are the "contraries" he is talking about? If he means 'contrary' in the technical sense of his own logic, the opposite extreme of a scale, it is quite clear that this conclusion does not follow from his earlier argument. What he has shown is that X must come, not from its contrary, but from its relative *contradictory, non-X* (the *relative* contradictory is one which is restricted in its denotation to the immediate *genus*, e.g. color, to which X belongs). It is incorrect to say (as he does) that "the

---

world is to be an orderly place the *only* attribute one could *invariably* rely on in such cases would be: not-white. But this is confused: to be not-white is a necessary condition of the change, but it is not "in virtue of" this that the change occurs. Nor is there any reason in "science" why one should seek the *same* attribute in each case where White comes to be. This error goes back to Aristotle's misleading distinction between "proper" and "accidental" causes, already criticized above. He is seeking a "proper cause" of the coming-to-be of White here, i.e. one which is conceptually linked to White, whereas he should be (in the context of his initial statement) looking for "accidental" causes, which are "accidental", not in the empirical sense of "random" excluded by him in his initial statement but only in the sense that the given *names* of cause and effect ('Polyclitus', 'statue'; 'musical', 'white') are not conceptually linked.

[14] *Physics*, 188b 21–26.

statue comes from shapelessness"—it comes from a different shape—or that "what is in tune passes not into any untunedness but into the corresponding opposite". Furthermore, the empirical claim he introduces within the conclusion quoted above: "the intermediates are derived from the contraries, colors, for instance, from black and white", is not supported by what went before, and is in fact false. So that his final empirical-seeming conclusion ("everything that comes to be by a natural process is either a contrary or a product of contraries") does not follow at all from the logical analysis he originally gave of relative contradictories.

Why, then, does he talk this way? The Ionian framework is still dominant in his mind: he wishes to reach the sort of conclusion about the identity of principles with contraries that his predecessors would have reached. In addition, one may suppose that, as a scientist, he wished the argument to have the empirical overtone, the air of discovery, that the Ionian speculations had. If he had simply said without further ado: if something becomes X, it must have been non-X, it would have seemed unexciting, to say the least, by comparison with the views of the people he was criticizing. And some question might even have arisen as to whether these categories he was introducing were really "principles" in the sense of accounting for origins, of *explaining*. It was desirable, therefore, that his analysis should seem in continuity with that of his predecessors, with as much relevance and penetration as, and more accuracy than, theirs. The easiest means to this was to retain the Ionian term, 'contrary', and seem to be replacing their contraries simply with different contraries. Whereas what he was in *fact* doing was replacing contraries (and the empirical claim about Nature they permitted) by contradictories (where the claim necessarily ceases to be empirical, even in the broadest sense).

Later on in the *Physics,* he explicitly broadens the notion of "contrary" to admit intermediates as "relative contraries" ("change to a lesser degree of a quality will be called change to the contrary of the quality"—note the stipulative tone of the phrase 'will be called').[15] This reduces contrariety to simple incompatibility (red and green are "contraries" in this new sense). In *this* sense of 'contrary', it is true to say that anything that comes to be in a natural process (or any other process, for that matter) comes from its "contrary". But this statement no longer has the empirical significance it had for the Ionians. And it still will be incorrect to suggest (after the fashion of Empedocles) that intermediates are somehow produced by a mixing of "contraries", in *any* sense of that errant term.

---

[15] *Physics,* 226b 2–8; 224b 30–35. Later in Book *I* he will says that one of the two contraries can be dispensed with in his analysis, because "one of the contraries will effect the change by its successive absence and presence". (191a 6–7).

A few lines later, Aristotle gives his criterion for distinguishing between different proposed sets of principles or tables of contraries. He suggests that in the order of explanation (the one he is interested in at this point), as opposed to the order of sense, the more *universal* the principle, the more satisfactory it is. He clearly thinks that the triad he is about to suggest is more universal than the Great-Small, Hot-Cold, . . . dyads of his predecessors. And in a sense this is true. But it must be added that what has happened here is not a *universalizing,* strictly speaking, in which some specifiable property of even wider reference is proposed, but rather a semantic transfer to a concept, and a type of analysis, of quite a different order. This transfer permits him to propose these principles with complete assurance, with no worry whatever about conceivable refutation in the empirical order (which would always have been possible had he followed the Ionian direction). They are thus prime candidates as starting-points for a "science" of the natural order, as *he* understood "science".

Returning now to the text, he next claims that besides two "contraries" there must also be a *hypokeimenon* (subject or substratum) to carry these "contraries".[16] The first argument he gives for this still speaks of the "contraries" in Ionian fashion as possibly "acting on" one another (relative contradictories, never being present at the same time, cannot act on one another). To have change and not simply succession, there must be something that carries through: opposite contraries are assumed to have nothing in common, so that a substratum must be postulated to support the contraries, something like the "intermediate stuff" of some of the Ionians, Aristotle suggests.

The familiar ambiguity is still here: if the third principle is required on the basis of an analysis in terms of relative contradictories (S is not-P; S is later P), all we can say of it is that it is the subject of the two statements in terms of which the change is described. Let us call this principle the "matter-*subject*". Anything that can serve as the common subject of the subject-term of two true statements of the 'S is P', 'S is later not-P' form will qualify as the "matter-subject" of the change these statements describe. The referent here will itself be an R-principle. But the notion of "matter-subject" is a C-principle of a special sort. When it is applied to individual referents, it is not because of some intrinsic property (e.g. extension, corruptibility) they all have in common, or because of some sort of "indeterminacy" or "featurelessness" they all manifest. It is simply and solely because each is the subject

---

[16] The conclusion of the chapter clearly should say that the contraries are principles, not (as it does) that the principles are contraries. It is the former claim that the argument tends to support, and it will shortly appear that one of the principles is *not,* in fact, a contrary.

of some common-language term, 'S', used in a pair of change-statements. Nothing is said about the ontological character of the subject, about the way in which it "perseveres" in the change, or anything of that kind. The C-analysis began with a particular sort of *description* of change; it examined, not a concrete change, but a formulated set of statements about it. It is *assumed* that there are S- and P-terms available, and that they are correctly used. The S-term is now to be known as the "matter"-term; in a way, there is no more to the analysis than that.

When a leaf turns brown, therefore, the leaf is said to be the "matter-subject" of the change, not because of any "materiality" on its part (we can predicate qualified change of angels just as easily as of leaves), but only because we can name it by the same term before and after. This is why we called the concept of matter used in *this* way a C-principle "of a special sort". Not only is it arrived at on the basis of conceptual analysis, but this analysis is of *predication*, and thus the concept can signify R-principles only by relating them to questions of naming and predication. It is this doubly conceptual and semantic character of Aristotle's triadic analysis (S, P, not- P) that makes discussion of this issue so very involved.

On the other hand, if the emphasis is put on true *contraries* instead of relative contradictories: black and white instead of X and not-X, the character of the analysis will have to change, as we have seen. We will have to find out, for instance, whether black and white, if mixed, really *could* give green. No logical analysis can tell us this, so that we turn away from questions of *predication* about change to actual changes. This means that when we come to describe the matter-principle that persists throughout changes of *true* contraries, we will tend to think of it as a *substratum*, a sort of ontological substructure acting as a carrier of the contraries, rather than as a subject of predication. If the analysis be of this latter sort, we shall use the phrase 'matter-*substratum*' to indicate that the C-principle involved has been arrived at on a quite different basis. In Greek, the same word '*hypokeimenon*' is used both for 'subject' and 'substratum'. It would, of course, be possible for the same entity (the leaf above, for instance) to be both. But it is important to note that the C-principles would still be different here: the leaf might be "matter" both as subject and as substratum, but the justification and sense of these two claims would rest on rather different sorts of analysis.

We come now to the enigmatic Chapter 7 of the *Physics,* where Aristotle remarks that he is giving his "own account" of "becoming in its widest sense". The tension between the two types of analysis is clearest in this chapter; Aristotle seems to be working on two levels at once, so to speak, which makes it very difficult to evaluate the account he gives of "the principles of

183

change". The first part of it is written almost entirely in what Carnap would call the "formal mode". There is constant reference to modes of *saying*: "we say that . . .", "we speak of . . .". Consider this passage, for example:

> There are different senses of 'coming to be'. In some cases, we do not use the expression 'come to be', but 'come to be so-and-so'. Only substances are said to "come to be" in the unqualified sense.[17]

Whereas the latter part of the chapter is rather in the "material mode" of direct description.

He begins with a distinction between "simple things" ('musical', 'man') and "complex things" ('musical man'). The distinction is quite clearly between *predicates,* not between things, and between *expressed* predicates, not just *possessed* ones (e.g. 'rational animal' will be complex, though 'man' is simple). The "various cases of becoming" are now classified in terms of this predicate-level distinction: man becomes musical; what is not-musical becomes musical; not-musical man becomes musical man. All of these actually describe the *same* change. On surveying them, he concludes that:

> there must always be an underlying something, and this, though one numerically, in form at least is not one. By this, I mean that it can be described in different ways. For 'to be man' is not the same as 'to be unmusical'. One part . . . 'man', survives, the other, 'not-musical' or 'unmusical', does not.[18]

The "underlying something" here is clearly matter-subject, not matter-substratum. That is, the analysis shows that the *word* 'man' can be applied both before and after, 'not-musical' only before, 'musical' only after. The "matter" of the change is thus the subject of the statement: "the not-musical man became musical", and the analysis is one of *predication.*

But now the difficulty that has underlain this whole approach comes to the surface at last. What if there be a change for which no S-term is available, i.e. no term which can serve as common subject to the two change-statements (*S is not-P; S is later P*)? To appreciate how shattering this difficulty is, it must be emphasized once again that the analysis so far (apart from the distracting use of the Ionian term, 'contrary') has had as its object, *language about change.* It has been *assumed* that elliptical expressions like 'White comes from not-White' can be paraphrased in pairs of statements in which both 'white' and 'not-white' are predicated of a common subject. It has been explicitly *assumed* that this subject "can be described in different ways" by different predicates. In the list of possible types of change, the change 'man comes from not-man' was most signifi-

---

[17] *Physics,* 190a 32–34. In translating some of the elliptical Greek phrases, the translator often has a choice between the "material" and "formal" modes.
[18] *Physics,* 190a 14–17.

cantly omitted, clearly because in this case Aristotle's argument (that one part of the initial linguistic description, i.e. 'man', survives a change in which non-musical man becomes musical man, and that there is *for this reason* a matter-subject corresponding to this term) would have broken down. But if the analysis purports to be of change (in some sense) and not simply of the available ways of *talking* about change, it must be shown that there is no change which cannot be described, or qualified, in the manner assumed, i.e. by having a subject-term which is applicable throughout the change.

This, it now appears, cannot be done, because there *are* changes, like not-man becoming man, where no such linguistic qualification can be found. One cannot, it appears, describe such "unqualified" changes in the '*S* is not-*P* and *S* is later *P*' form that supported the earlier argument for a matter-subject, *S*. Could this simply be a defect of language, ultimately remediable? In certain cases, it could be; it might happen that no term existed in a particular language to name the common referent, but that one *might* be invented.[19] But are there changes that could *never,* in principle, be described in a "qualified" way? At this point, Aristotle emphatically says: yes, where many other philosophers (Democritus and Hobbes, to mention two) would say: no. Aristotle's assertion of the reality of what he calls "substantial" change is quite fundamental to his ontology; it in nowise rests upon an analysis of language (as the notion of "unqualified" change does).

If one holds for the existence of substantial changes, it immediately follows that there are changes which are *irremediably* "unqualified". For if substance *A* changes into substance *B*, no noun-term can be applicable to whatever substratum links *A* with *B*. If any did, the substratum would itself (according to Aristotle's theory of predication, at least) have to be a substance.[20] But this means that the defender of substantial change must find

---

[19] This underlines a difficulty, often unnoticed. The notion of "unqualified" change is, in its origins, relative to a particular *language*. It simply means a change for which no *S*-term is available. It would be quite possible for an *S*-term for a particular referent to be missing in one language, though present in another.

[20] In *De Gen.* 319b. 20–25, Aristotle remarks that when air becomes water, the property of transparency persists throughout the change, but emphasizes that "the second thing, into which the first changes must not be a property of this persistent identical something, otherwise the change will be alteration", i.e. not a substantial change. His point here is that transparency must not define a substance in such a way that waterness could be construed as a property of this substance. But what is to prevent one from saying: "This transparent thing was air and is now water", or "This white thing was a dog and is now a corpse"? Aristotle would argue that a subject-term of this sort necessarily refers to substance, and if the same term can be used before and after, there has been no real substantial change, and water-ness is now an accident of a transparent underlying substance. So this mode of speaking would be excluded by him,

some new way of analyzing this sort of change, one that does not depend (as the prior analysis did) on questions of predication and language, since no S-term is available now. *In a substantial change, there is no matter-subject,* because there is no term of which it could be the referent. It will not do to talk of an "indeterminate" matter-subject on the grounds of the *lack* of such a term. This is simply a confusion of two orders: from the mere absence of such a term, one can infer nothing about the existence or nature of a substratum, itself un-named in language.

This is the decisive moment in the development of the argument of Book *I*. Far from being the triumphant climax of a smooth development beginning in Chapter 1, it is quite clear that the introduction of unqualified change challenges the adequacy of the previous analysis, and suggests that it is not as universal in its scope as it first seemed. It is often suggested that the appearance of primary matter at this juncture of the argument is somehow the point to which the whole analysis was tending. Nothing, in one sense, could be further from the case. Aristotle is *forced* to raise the issue here (he drops it again, significantly, after a cursory few lines) because the conceptual-semantic analysis around which Book *I* is constructed (which will work only for *qualified* changes) is now seen to be inadequate for a *general* account of change. In any talk about qualified changes, he has shown that terms of the form: 'S', 'not-P', 'P', will inevitably be used, and the categories of matter, privation, form, need no further validation. For such changes, Aristotle's analysis is clearly irrefutable, though not as enlightening as it can seem when mistakenly supposed to yield *M*-principles.

But some quite different approach to the question of change is now necessary. It will not do to patch on a special treatment of unqualified change. Better to try a different mode of analysis, one without the limitations that language imposed on the prior one. So Aristotle brings in some heavy equipment from his ontology—after all, the whole problem was brought on in the first place by an *ontological* claim about the occurrence of substantial changes. He divides changes into two sorts, no longer on the basis of how they are *described*, but rather, following a metaphysical blueprint of What Is. Thus we have "accidental" changes and "substantial" changes. Of the former, one can say that all nine categories of accident "inhere" in substance, so that there must automatically be a matter-substratum in such changes, one

---

because of the equivocal character of the subject-term. 'This white thing is a dog; this white thing is a corpse' would be permitted, but the referents of the two occurrences of the phrase 'this white thing' would necessarily be different. Thus it is not (despite appearances) an instance of a "qualified" change. Every substantial change will thus be an unqualified change. (The converse is not necessarily the case, as the instance of unqualified change most often cited by Aristotle—seed becomes plant—shows).

which is itself a substance. Substantial changes are the ones which pose the problem. How do we prove that *they* must have a substratum?

> But that substances too come to be from some substratum, will appear on examination. For we find in every case something that underlies, from which proceeds that which comes to be; for instance, animals and plants from seed.[21]

This is *all* he has to say about this all-important point. After the complexity and tightness of the chapters of *C*-analysis that preceded it, the meagreness of this lone remark is striking.

We seem to be back in Ionia again, inspecting different sorts of substantial change. But the quest, unfortunately, cannot be the empirical affair it was for the Ionians. For what we are looking for is something that strictly speaking can never be "found", since it has, apparently, no properties, nothing that could serve to identify it for us (though this awkward point Aristotle saves for revelation elsewhere). So that a new sort of analysis, "metaphysical" analysis[22] we can call it, will be necessary. It will not depend on looking "at every case"; it will not be concerned with contraries (in the Ionian sense); it will terminate, if successful, directly in structures of reality, not of predication about reality.

But all of this is only a promise here. No hint of its strategies of proof are given in Aristotle's brief assertion about the existence of a substratum in all substantial changes. Instead, he immediately returns to *C*-analysis of qualified changes as though nothing had happened. The suggestion is that the analysis of qualified change can be simply extended "by analogy" to the special case of unqualified change. We have seen reason to question this assumption, if the original analysis is of the conceptual-semantic type. He continues his discussion by listing different kinds of change (all of them qualified change). Everything that comes to be is "complex", he says, presumably in the sense of "complex-in-predicate" defined some lines previously. But this is precisely *not* the case in unqualified change. When not-man becomes man, the predicate is a simple one, and the example *cannot* be reduced to his paradigm instance, the non-musical man who becomes musical man. He even says:

---

[21] *Physics,* 190b 1–5.

[22] The term is deliberately chosen, even though the entities being analyzed are physical. The 'meta-' is intended to contrast with physics as this science is understood today, because of the marked differences between the methods of, and the sorts of structure disclosed by, this kind of analysis and the empirical analysis of the physicist. 'Ontological' also would do as a label, but in view of the fact that the principles disclosed by this sort of analysis are themselves *not* physical entities, but so-called "incomplete" principles, the label, 'metaphysical', seems slightly more appropriate.

For 'musical man' is composed, in a way, of 'man' and 'musical'; you can analyze this expression into the definitions of its elements. It is clear then that what comes to be will come to be from these elements.[23]

The "elements" he speaks of can only be elements of language or of predication, and the "composition" is thus of the same sort. It does not occur in descriptions of unqualified change, because there the predicates are no longer complex.

Despite the fact that the analysis is once again at the semantic level, Aristotle claims to have discovered:

the principles which constitute natural objects and from which they primarily are or have come to be what each is said to be in its essential nature, not what each is in respect of a concomitant attribute. Plainly, everything comes to be from both *hypokeimenon* and form.[24]

But the principles he has discovered do not "constitute" natural objects, except in the loose sense in which a musical man is "constituted" of *musical* and *man*. And it would not take an analysis of change to produce this information. To describe a change as being from white to musical seems to him "non-essential" in comparison with calling it: non-musical to musical, simply because musical does not always come from white whereas it always comes from non-musical. But this use of 'essential' is a very odd one, because it tells us nothing whatever of the essence of the thing, nor of why it became musical. The regularity connoted by 'essential' in this context is one *at the level of predication only*; though *every* change where something becomes musical can be described as non-musical to musical, this tells us nothing about the constitutive *R*-principles of the varied change-situations covered by this description.

In the remainder of the book, Aristotle speaks more and more clearly in terms of *M*-principles, but since he is only comparing the results he has already obtained with those of his predecessors and adding no new justification for them, the problem still remains. Mention is made of a "formless" nature which "underlies" substance. The word 'matter' (*'hylé'*) makes its appearance for the first time (until now the less cosmological term, *'hypokeimenon'*, 'that which underlies either as subject or substratum', has been

---

[23] *Physics,* 190b 20–22. The Greek text, not having any devices like single quotes to indicate types of reference, can often be taken to be talking indifferently about words, about predicate-properties, or about things. This ambiguity of reference poses a considerable difficulty not only to readers of Aristotle, but also at times to Aristotle himself. In this instance, however, there is little doubt about the reference. Philoponus' reading of a disputed phrase to give 'this expression' above (instead of Ross' more non-committal 'it') seems preferable.

[24] *Physics,* 190b 17–20.

used). It has its original overtone of "stuff" right from the beginning.[25] The two terms are linked in the famous analogy: "as matter and the formless to the thing that has form so is the *hypokeimenon* to substance".[26] This comparison seems to lay the ground in Aristotle's mind for a transfer of what he has just said of *hypokeimenon* as a principle of change, to "matter" as a principle of change; he appears to assume that the same grounds suffice for each.

But this change of name is not as innocuous as it seems at first sight. 'Matter' has an overtone of "stuff", of an ontological similarity between different instances, that *'hypokeimenon'* certainly did not have. The "unity" of the *hypokeimenon* spoken of earlier was no more than the unity of the individual substance throughout a particular change.[27] Now it sounds like something more. The notion of "matter" seems to be reached by a sort of generalizing process; as bronze to the statue and wood to the bed, so is matter to the thing which has form. The *hypokeimenon* could be a man, a leaf, whatever one pleased, depending on what particular change one had in mind: the term *'hypokeimenon'* conveys nothing about the nature of its referent, other than that it *is* a referent of a change-statement. The *term* is "indeterminate" in the sense that it *prescinds from* the form the referent actually possesses. But the *hypokeimenon* itself is by no means indeterminate; as we have seen, it is *necessarily* determinate.

Matter, on the other hand, appears to be "indeterminate" in itself. However, this point is never explicitly made in the *Physics*. The book ends on this note:

> For my definition of matter is just this—the primary *hypokeimenon* of each thing, from which it comes to be without qualification and which persists in the result.[28]

Matter in this sense is said to be "necessarily outside the sphere of becoming and ceasing to be"; it is even said "of its own nature to desire form".[29]

---

[25] Aristotle explicitly identifies his "primary matter" with the "Matrix" or "Nurse" proposed by Plato, which had some of the overtones of "stuff". (*De Gen.* 329a 24; see L. Eslick's essay on Plato in this volume). The first explicit mention of "*hylé*" in the argument of the *Physics* occurs at 190b 9 where it is the matter-stuff of an "alteration", of the sort of change represented by wine turning to vinegar. Ross' comment on this line is worth reproducing: "Since Aristotle is carefully working up to the conception of *hylé*, [the use of the word at this early stage in the argument is] as Mr. Hardie observes, an unfortunate anticipation, or possibly a gloss." (*Aristotle's Physics*, Oxford, 1936, p. 493).

[26] *Physics*, 191a 10–11.

[27] *Physics*, 190b 23–27.

[28] *Physics*, 192a 31–32.

[29] *Physics*, 192a 28, 22.

Gradually by the simple addition of descriptive phrases, it is coming to sound like a common constituent of the physical universe, eternal, determinable, one, featureless. But, the reader will remember, all this rests so far on no more than a single sentence about unqualified change, claiming the necessity of a substratum for each individual change. It said nothing of the ontological character of that substratum, or of the relation between one instance of "it" and another.

§4 *Three Levels of Analysis in* Physics I

It is time now to summarize this lengthy discussion of the argument of *Physics I*. The book moves on three levels at once. First, there is the empirical level of the Ionian background and of the constant reference to "contraries". The "matter" one would get as a result of *this* sort of analysis would be a kind of "intermediate stuff" of the type postulated perhaps by Anaximander. *Empirical* evidence would be required for such claims as: "the intermediate colors are produced by mixing black and white"; "the contraries act upon one another". Aristotle makes no attempt to supply such evidence, and there is every reason to suppose that he thought his view to be in no need of it. Nevertheless, he retains the trappings of the empirical approach.

The second, and main, level of the book is that of conceptual-semantic analysis of predication about (qualified) change. It is C-analysis in the sense defined above since it concerns *predication about* change, not the concept of change itself directly. The triad it yields (subject-form-privation) describes three *linguistic* categories. These C-principles may in turn be applied directly to the order of change itself (so that we will speak of the "subject" of change, and not just the "subject-term of the change-statement"). This gives us R-principles; the subject of the change is still discovered via language, however, since it is defined as the referent of the S-term in the change-statement. Such an analysis can only go as far as language can, and since there is, by definition, no common S-term applicable before and after unqualified changes, there is no "subject" of reference in them either, and the triadic C-structure no longer applies.

This analysis is irrefutable. Even if someone were to hold that what look like continuous changes are really strings of disconnected events or whatnot, this would not disturb Aristotle's C-conclusion. It does not rest on the notion of substance, only on the general referring character of language. Aristotle does think of the "subject" as a substance; in his theory of predication, this would ordinarily be the case. But this is not at all necessary to the analysis. The referent could be strings of events. As long as one is allowed to describe change using meaningful subject-terms, i.e. as long as *any* discourse about change is permitted, the subject-privation-form analysis holds good. It does not tell us very much, true. In particular, it does not have directly ontological implications. But it is certain; it is a part of the "given" of language itself. It is from this level, therefore, that the plausibility and universality of the notion of "matter" mainly derives in the *Physics*. Since practically all of the explicit argument is at the level of the *C*-analysis, its momentum communicates itself to the argument as a whole, and acquires all the empirical and ontological overtones of the latter. The difficulties inherent in drawing conclusions proper to these other two levels may thus be obscured.

The third level is that of metaphysical analysis into *M*-principles. There is very little actual analysis of this sort in Book *I*, as we have seen, but the later chapters more and more tend to assume that the conclusions being reached are, in fact, on this level. Thus by the end of the discussion, one may easily assume, for instance, that an indeterminate stuff-like constituent of all corruptible beings has been isolated on the basis of explicit argument. It appears as the substratum of substantial change, ensuring continuity (and therefore true change) on the one hand, and total discontinuity of formal (predicable) properties (and therefore *substantial* change) on the other. Aristotle's doctrine of "primary matter" as an *M*-principle depends entirely on his doctrine of substance and substantial change. It does so on two scores. First, because without substantial change, it could be argued that all change would be of the "qualified" sort, and then *C*-analysis into subject-form-privation (which involves no explicit metaphysical commitment) would suffice. Second, the notion of matter as a "featureless and incomplete substratum" rests solely on a particular view of the nature and source of substantial unity. But none of this is explicitly adverted to in Book *I*.

The reader may ask at this point: why subject a single Aristotelian text to such detailed discussion and criticism? After all, Aristotle has something to say of primary matter elsewhere, and later Aristotelians have surely remedied the obscurities of this particular analysis. It has seemed worthwhile to proceed in this way simply because the confusion between three different types of analysis, empirical, conceptual-semantic and metaphysical, reappears in much of the later discussion; one is rarely sure, when matter is being claimed as a "principle", whether the analysis backing the claim is intended to present it as an ordinary *R*-principle (e.g. a sort of stuff), a *C*-principle (e.g. matter-subject), or an *M*-principle (primary matter). For this reason, the "classic" text with all its obscurities and changes of level repays the closest scrutiny.

§ 5 *Material Cause as a "Principle"*

In Book *II* of the *Physics,* Aristotle gives the well-known distinction between four different aspects of natural explanation: material, formal, efficient, final. His division is clearly grounded on everyday observation of Nature as well as on analogies from changes brought about artificially.

> Men do not think that they have grasped a thing until they have grasped the "why" of it. . . . In one sense, then, that out of which a thing comes to be and which persists is called a "cause", e.g. the bronze of the statue, the silver of the bowl, and the genera of which the bronze and silver are species.[30]

One feature of any full description of a change, then, will be some mention of the sort of "stuff" that underlies the change. This stuff is called the "material cause" of the change. It is not because of whatever definite properties it possesses that it functions as an "explanation" of the change (this would be to make it a "formal cause"), but rather as an underlying material whose properties are not relevant to a discussion of this particular change.[31]

The transformation from the style of analysis of Book *I* is striking. The fundamental metaphor is now the Platonic one of the craftsman and his material; there is no mention of predication or of subjects of reference. The limitations of the new metaphor are apparent if any *general* account of change is being proposed. Take the not-musical man who becomes musical, the favorite example of Book *I*. Is man to be regarded as the "material" of this change? It would seem so, yet the metaphor is now less appropriate. Aristotle had earlier quoted Antiphon's notion of material cause as "the immediate constituent of a natural object which taken by itself is without arrangement", e.g. as bronze is of the statue.[32] He did not accept this definition, yet something of it persists in the analogies from art that he constantly cites. So that one is tempted to think of the material cause of the not-musical to musical change as being the ultimate homogeneous elements of which the man himself is composed. But this can hardly be what Aristotle intended.

A second point of difference is that the emphasis is now on coming-to-be and passing-away, i.e. substantial change, and "qualified" change gets only a passing nod. Products of art are seen to provide a better starting-point for discussions of this sort of change than language does. As a result, the material cause comes to appear as a permanent constituent of the natural object,

---

[30] *Physics,* 194b 18–26.

[31] For a fuller discussion of this question, see the present author's "Whatever happened to material causality?", *Intern. Philos. Quarterly,* to appear.

[32] *Physics,* 193a 10–11.

apart altogether from any question of actual change. Thus, bronze is said to be *here and now* the material cause of the statue, because it is that "out of which" the statue once came, and that which "persists" in the statue even still. The *'hypokeimenon'* of Book *I* was a relative term, relative to some *particular* change. It would have made no sense to ask (in the context of the discussion in Book *I*): what is the *hypokeimenon* of a man? The answer would depend on which change one had in mind of the myriad possible changes that could occur to such a man. The definition given for material cause is much less relative than the earlier one: "that out of which a thing comes to be and which persists in the result".

The net effect of the introduction of this new notion of "material cause" is to "ontologize" and "cosmologize" the discussion of matter very greatly. The explicit suggestion of a stuff or material is now present. Yet one can still interpret 'material cause' in the light of the earlier analysis of predication by assuming that the "thing" in the definition of 'material cause' has a given name, e.g. 'musical man'; one might then say that musical man comes from not-musical man, and that man is thus "that which persists in the result". This correlation is somewhat artificial and presupposes that the thing whose material cause is being sought has a unique name.

Insofar as 'material cause' is linked with a *specific* change or with a *specific* way of describing the referent, one can still, therefore, identify it with the matter-subject of Book *I*. The notion, *material cause,* would thus be a C-principle, signifying in an unspecific way any entity which serves as the common subject of a pair of "before and after" change-statements. The R-principle would be the individual subject in each case. If the change be a substantial one, however, the material cause is now "primary matter", and since every natural object is taken to come to be "absolutely" in terms of an initial substantial change, the primary matter will be defined as a permanent *constituent* of the thing and not simply as that in the thing which survives a particular qualified change. The R-principle here will still be the individual matter-substratum of the individual change (however we are to describe it); the C-principle is still the generic notion, applicable to qualified as well as unqualified changes. Hence, the "indeterminacy" we associate with it can only be the "indeterminacy" of a generic concept (*material cause*) in relation to specific instances (e.g. this man). It is not the "indeterminacy" of a concept signifying an entity that is itself ontologically featureless.

If, however, it is claimed that since all physical objects are corruptible, they all have a substratum of this sort linking them temporally, but not qualitatively with their pasts, 'material cause' begins to suggest a sort of "intermediate" property-less stuff, common to all physical things, as bronze

193

is common to all bronze objects, but a "stuff" without the definiteness of bronze. The metaphor of the craftsman leads implicitly in this direction: it suggests a community of some sort that links different objects made of the same material. That is the sense in which a material cause would ordinarily be said to help to "explain" an art-work. Of course, the question arises as to whether one *can* carry the notion of "stuff" through to the limit of indetermination, whether the craft analogy still holds, when there is nothing to distinguish one "instance" from another. If one can, the R-principle corresponding to the phrase 'material cause' would become a sort of general material of corruptible beings, taken either collectively or distributively. But whether such a constituent could serve as an adequate substratum for individual changes seems very dubious, and the whole analysis leading to it is open to serious question.[33]

§ 6 *Matter-Subject as an* R-*Principle*

In an earlier section, it was assumed that the "subject" of a change[34] is simply the entity of which 'non-*P*' can be predicated before, and '*P*' after. But what entity is this? Suppose a green leaf turns brown. We say that the "subject" of this change is the leaf, considered apart from such attributes as green, because it is this that survives the change. Clearly the original leaf, greenness and all, does not survive the change. This leads Aristotle to hold that the "subject" in this instance is the *substance,* considered apart from its accidents. The subject of a sentence like: 'The leaf is green', is the leaf-taken-as-a-subject-of-predication. Aquinas puts this succinctly by saying that the *suppositum* (subject) expresses an *intentio* (drawn from the sense of the actual term used to refer); it is, therefore, not just an entity, but an entity-considered-as-the-object-of-a-certain-predication.[35] Predicating green of a leaf is not a simple insertion of accident into bare substance, like a toothpick into an orange:

> What the intellect posits on account of the subject-term, it considers to be the subject; what it posits on account of the predicate-term, it considers to be a form of existing in the subject, according to the saying: predicates are to be taken formally and subjects materially. To this diversity in *idea* corresponds

---

[33] See "Four senses of 'potency' " elsewhere in this volume.

[34] Note that the "subject" of change, as we use the term, is not "that to which the change happens" in one sense of that phrase (the *terminus a quo* considered in its totality; in this instance, the green leaf).

[35] *Summa Theologica,* I, q.29, a.2, c. Thus he says, there are three Divine *supposita,* because the Divine Essence can be regarded as a subject of predication in three quite different ways.

the plurality of predicate and subject terms, but the intellect signifies the identity of the thing by the composition itself.[36]

There has been much controversy over this point in recent semantics, some,
like Quine and Goodman, holding that individual entities in their totality
are the only legitimate subjects of predication, others defending the more
complex forms of referent (X qua Y, etc.). The former are concerned primarily with problems of *verification* of statements (we only find individuals
in the world, so the X-*qua*-Y way of speaking is just an elliptical way of referring to singulars); the latter emphasize rather the intentional unity of
the referent, as the subject of a particular predication, and not just a "raw"
thing untouched by our way of talking about it.

If one comes to the problem of change via a study of predication, one
will define the "subject" of change as that aspect of the changing being
which permits one to predicate the same term of it before and after the
change; thus, the subject of not-musical-man-becoming-musical-man is that
aspect of the changing being which is denominated by 'man'. Just what
that aspect is, and how it is to be related to other aspects, is a further question for ontology. If someone were to object: but how do you know it is the
same man?, the answer would lie within an analysis of predication. If a
univocal predicate continues to be applicable over a period of time, it is because the aspect "grounding" it is the "same" before and after. The 'continues' here involves some space-time *continuity* of reference, so that to
have a subject-of-change one must have a certain minimal continuity of
reference. But how *much* one needs can be decided only by distinguishing
situations where one would predicate change from those where one would
speak rather, for instance, of replacement.

The same can be said of the *unity* which anything that qualifies as a subject-of-change must have. It is the unity required for singular attribution
or predication: if a heap of bricks is replaced, brick by brick, with new
bricks, we do not say that the heap "changes" (though we *would* say that
the *individual* bricks change position). But once again, it must be noted
that in the type of CS-analysis we have been doing, our starting-point has
been *predication-about*-change. We assume that such predications are available. And what we say is that *if* such a predication can be correctly made,
there *is* a subject-of-change, and that this latter requires a certain continuity
and unity in order to qualify via the rules of predication as we know them,
as a subject of this particular sort of predication. But what *sort* of continuity
and unity, what *sort* of ontological status the subject is to be given, is a question for analysis of a different sort.

---

[36] *S.T.*, I, *q.*13, *a.*12, *c.*; see also *q.*85, *a.*5.

This *is* the point, however, at which the two sorts of analysis (*CS*- and *M*-) meet. As we have defined *C*-analysis, it is clear that *C*-analysis *does* reveal something about the world, since concepts do signify the real. (The point of distinguishing conceptual from empirical or metaphysical analysis was rather to separate their starting-points and methods.) But *CS*-analysis posed a special problem, because the difficulties of transferring the results of such analysis to claims about the real order are very much greater than for a simple *C*-analysis. Nevertheless, that such a transfer *can* be made is not being denied, though the mode of doing it is not explored here, since the concern of this essay has been with *separating* the two types of analysis. In the Aristotelian tradition, a simple sort of correspondence between language-structure, concept-structure and real structure was often assumed without question. The point of the essay, then, is that this assumption is not necessarily a safe one, that it has to be justified. It leaves open the crucial questions about which structures *can* in fact be "transferred", so to speak, from one level to another.

Before leaving this point, however, several specific difficulties must still be faced. Is the referent of the *S*-term also the subject of change? When we say, "the leaf is green", and later, "the leaf is brown", the *subject* of the change is that which permits us to use the term, 'leaf', before and after. Whereas the *referent* of the statement, "the leaf is green", is that which the term 'leaf' singles out for the predication, 'is green'. There is no *prima facie* guarantee within the notion of reference itself that the referent of these two statements (*qua* referent) will be the "same", or to put this in a different way, it is not immediately evident what criteria of "sameness" should be applied in this instance. At this point, those who (in terms of the controversy mentioned above) take the referent to be the "total entity" (the leaf *with* its greenness) are either going to have to say that the referent and the subject-of-change are not the same, or are going to have to redefine the latter notion rather radically, or perhaps even refuse it entirely (perhaps on the grounds of the suggestion of persisting ontological unity its conveys). The former alternative seems the more attractive one, since one can quite meaningfully say that the leaf "is no longer the same" after the change, i.e. it is the same *leaf* (subject) but is no longer wholly the *same* (referent).

If, however, to take the other theory of reference, the *referent* of the individual statement be assumed to be "the leaf-considered-apart-from-its-greenness", "referent" and subject-of-change are now identical, and the step from *CS*-analysis to *M*-analysis becomes much simpler. But the difficulty here (as Professor Sellars points out in his *Comment* on the original version of this paper) is that it seems to lead one to the "bare substratum" view of predication, in which each predication is likened to *adding* a predicate to something *lacking* it. Both views of reference have their merits, but we shall

196

have to leave the reader to explore the topic further on his own.[37] For the purpose of the enquiry of this section, we shall continue to differentiate between the terms 'subject' and 'referent', as we have hitherto done. This is, by implication, to separate the question of "matter" as the general subject of predication from the question of "matter" as the subject-of-predication-about-change. (We have already reserved the word 'substratum' for the subject-of-change yielded by *M*-analysis.)

In a famous passage in the *Metaphysics,* Aristotle endeavors to decide whether matter or substance is the final subject of predication, "that of which everything else is predicated, while it is itself not predicated of anything else". His mode of reaching "matter" here is worth noting:

> When all else is stripped off, evidently nothing but matter remains. For while the rest are affections, products, potencies of bodies, length, breadth, and depth are quantities . . . When [they] are taken away, we see nothing left unless there is something that is bounded by those, . . . matter[38]

What is left after this "stripping-away" of predicates is (he says) not substance but matter, because substance itself can be predicated of matter:

> Therefore, the ultimate subject (matter) is of itself neither a particular thing, nor of a particular quantity, nor otherwise positively characterized. . . .[39]

The difficulty here is obvious. As long as one is predicating accidents of substance, there is no problem. The "predication-matter" (i.e. that which is called "matter" *qua* subject of a predication) is the substance itself; "matter" and substance are identical,·and 'matter' is simply a semantic term whose *ratio* is to indicate the function the substance plays in the predication. It is a generic name for the referent of the subject-term in any statement. But in order to reach the "ultimate" matter Aristotle mentions, one will need to present instances where substance is predicated of matter, as he claims it can be. No such instance is given, and there is good reason to suppose from his own description of "matter" (i.e. that which escapes all naming), that no

---

[37] For a recent defence of the so-called "nominalist" position on this point, see W. V. Quine's *Word and Object,* New York, 1960. For the other side, see, for instance, I. C. Lieb's notice of this book in the *International Philosophical Quarterly,* 2, 1962, 92–109. See also the present author's "The problem of universals", *Philosophical Studies* (Maynooth), 8, 1958, 122–39. See also P. T. Geach, *Reference and Generality,* Oxford, 1962.

[38] *Metaphysics,* 1029a 11-18. The idea that substance is predicated of matter is in striking contradiction with the lengthy account of substance in *Categories,* 5. There he insists that primary substance cannot be predicated of a subject.

[39] *Metaphysics,* 1029a 24–25. He adds, unexpectedly, that it is not the negations either, for these belong to it, "only by accident". The unstated conclusion of his argument here is that it is not sufficient to define substance as that of which all else is predicated; we must add that it is individual and complete, in order to distinguish it from matter.

sentence could be formulated in which substance would be the predicate and matter the subject.

At first sight, it may seem plausible that we could keep "stripping away" all predicates, and ultimately "remove" substantial predicates too. The "stripping-away" is a metaphorical way of expressing the separation of S and P in a proposition, and depends entirely upon the availability of linguistic terms for S and P. If we come to a point where S is allegedly property-less and hence unnameable, the whole method breaks down, and the "stripping" metaphor has to be refused. The difficulty is precisely the same as we encountered in §3 when the matter-substratum of substantial change turned out to have no linguistic counterpart, forcing us to reject any attempt to justify such a substratum through a CS-analysis of statements about change. There is one important difference, however. In the case of substantial change, one can replace the analysis of predication by a direct analysis of the change itself, and give a plausible reason for saying that in a substantial change the substratum would have to have such-and-such a character. But if one is analyzing predication itself, and no predications of the desired kind are available, then no *alternative* route to "ultimate" matter is open unless one departs from the problematic of predication entirely. It seems, then, that we must reject the idea that an M-principle, "ultimate matter", can be arrived at solely on the basis of an analysis of predication. *Predication-matter* is a perfectly valid C-principle in describing the referent of ordinary statements, but a stripped-down "ultimate" predication-matter is unacceptable. The impetus towards such an idea clearly comes from the prior establishment of primary matter via substantial change. It seems plausible that if substance is composed of matter and form, one might hope to make the predicate-subject pattern correspond not only with the ontological distinction of accident and substance but also with the distinction between primary matter and substantial form as well. The trouble is that the all-important linguistic examples that would serve as evidence for this latter move are missing, and likely to remain so.[40]

§ 7 Petrifaction and Other Puzzles

Our distinction between matter-subject and primary matter enables us to answer an old problem. In a very critical essay on Aristotle's concept of matter, Professor D. C. Williams recently put it this way:

> If something is to persist, it needn't be the matter, either proximate or prime. In the instances cited [by Aristotle], as it happens, the matter does stay put

---

[40] For a fuller discussion of the relation between "matter" as the subject of predication and "matter" as the subject of change, see J. de Vries, S.J., "Zur Aristotelisch—Scholastischen Problematik von Materie und Form", *Scholastik, 32*, 1957, 161–185.

while the forms are swapped, but there are equally many instances where the form persists and the matter is exchanged. . . . This is obviously true of proximate matter: though a log may keep its woody quality while sawed or nailed in different shapes, it may keep its exact shape and pattern while carbonized into charcoal or petrified into agate . . . [It is true also of primary matter, for Aristotle] generally explicates the persistence of substance by the persistence of its substantial form, exactly as Russell would, while on the other hand, he seems to go along with the Milesians and our moderns on the incessant circulation of the elements. . . . If the thing can either change or not change its qualities while the matter either is exchanged or not, the notion of persistent matter does exactly nothing toward that "explanation" of change of which Aristotelians have boasted more, perhaps, than of anything else in their repertory. Specifically, of course, it is neither necessary nor sufficient for "continuity" of change, as it is often claimed to be: not necessary because forms can differ continuously while matter comes and goes, and not sufficient because forms can flick from one end of the spectrum to the other while the matter sedately stays.[41]

To widen the scope of the problem, let us take three different situations. A tile floor is replaced, tile by tile, with new tiles of a different color. A cube of wood (the word, 'log', has a "woody" overtone that we prefer to lay aside) turns into a cube of stone on being submerged in a certain lake. A human body takes in food and converts it into flesh. Can these be described in terms of the matter-form schema? In all three, the persisting substratum seems to be formal in character, whereas the "matter" comes and goes. "This floor was green and is now red." "This cube was wooden and is now stone." "This man was light and is now heavy." Insofar as these statements are permissible, we have true changes. If 'floor' denotes just the tiles, then the green floor has simply been *replaced* with a red one; it is not a single "change". Because a change has to *happen* to something, and we have not brought anything forward yet which would serve. Suppose, however, that 'floor' denotes a surface situated in a certain way relative to walls, etc. Now we have a matter-subject, and we can use change-terms proper. But this will clearly be a borderline case for which the language of replacement would probably be more suitable.

Now take the wooden cube which has turned to stone. Is this a change? Could we not describe it in terms of a gradual replacement of one set of molecules by another? We *could,* but in this instance the subject-term is better defined; the referent, a material cube, is a nameable entity. So we can speak of it in change-terms. The matter-subject will be the material cube, prescinding from the nature of the material. In the case of the man whose weight increases, the referent is defined by the unity of a living form, so we are not likely to describe what went on in terms of the replacement of individual molecules. It is simpler to speak of the larger unit. And its form

---

[41] "Form and Matter", *Philosophical Review*, 67, 1958, 499–521; see pp. 514–15.

stays the same. As far as matter-*subject* is concerned, then, it makes no difference at all whether what persists through the change is a material or a structure. Whichever does persist, and is the subject of the twin statements describing the change, is the "matter-subject" of the change. If no common *S*-term can be found, it may be necessary to speak in terms of replacement, rather than change. So that Aristotle's conceptual-semantic triad is perfectly well able to handle the situation.

But what of his *M*-pair, matter and form? These are postulated to be absolute, not dependent on the mode of predication used. The floor and the cube are not substances, and the man remains the same substance, so that no substantial change is involved in any of the three examples. Since primary matter is called upon as substratum only where substantial change is involved, these cases can in no way affect it. Could the form remain the same while the primary matter comes and goes? This question makes no sense, because primary matter cannot come and go this way. What comes and goes in each of these examples is *material,* already-formed matter with its own forms, subsidiary to the main form. Where there is a single main form, as in the third instance above, this gives a type of change which is not substantial, yet is something more than an ordinary accidental one. Aristotle is familiar with this sort of change:

> For we must think of the flesh after the image of flowing water that is measured by one and the same measure; particle after particle comes to be and each successive particle is different. When the matter of the flesh grows, some flow out and more flow in fresh.[42]

The floor example above would be regarded from the ontological standpoint as replacement, not as a single change (i.e. each tile is assumed to change place separately). The cube is, however, a borderline case, because one might argue that it is some sort of "active persistence" on the part of the original form that brings about the new being. However, the original wood-form did *not,* in fact, persist, so that there is a touchy problem in causal tracing. This petrifaction example does not, however, bear out Professor Williams' claim for it that it shows the notion of matter to be unnecessary in "explaining" the continuity of change. For one thing, it may be described simply in terms of replacement-changes of the individual particles. In this event, the occurrence *as a whole* would not be regarded as a "change" in the proper sense. The shape *alone* does not seem to suffice to

---

[42] *De Gen.* 321b 25–28. See also Geach and Anscombe, *Three Philosophers,* p. 56. Aquinas raises a similar problem in the context of the Transubstantiation in the Eucharist. Can it be called a "change", since there is no proper *subject* of change? He answers: properly, no. But if one wishes in a *loose* sense to take the persisting accidents as "subject", he has no objection.

provide that spatio-temporal continuity in the material order which is appropriate to "change". If, however, the notion of matter-subject is, in fact, applied here to the wooden cube *qua* cube, then woody quality is being predicated of the cube *qua* this shape by sentences like: 'The cube is wooden', and we are implicitly treating the petrifaction as a unit-change.

Professor Williams' further more radical criticism must likewise be questioned:

> Change as the occurrence of new characters, does not require the persistence of anything at all through the change, except insofar as we are enough more interested in cases where there is persistence so that the Aristotelian can badger us into not *calling* the others "change".[43]

But change is *not* simply the occurrence of new characters (this would cover, for example, creation, which would not normally be called "change"). What he does here is to *redefine* the word, 'change', and then complain that Aristotle's analysis does not fit the new concept. He continues:

> The strict fact is that although there must be persistence for a *thing* to change, this is not because *change* requires persistence but because things do, and trivially so.[44]

This divorce between change and thing is misleading. What Aristotle asserts is that change requires a subject. He is, therefore, analyzing the notion of a changing thing; the "persistence" he discovers is due to its being a "thing" (i.e. a subject of predication), but the non-triviality of the analysis —ask Parmenides or Heraclitus!—comes from the fact that it is a *changing* thing.

§ 8 *M-Principles*

We can return now to what is undoubtedly the most controversial and the crucial point in our exploration of matter as a principle. In §3, we saw that primary matter gradually takes on in Aristotle's work the character of a *constituent* of things, something incomplete in its own right, but capable of being referred to in language, and "really distinct", in some sense, from form. We saw that very little grounds are given for this view in *Physics I*. In other works, Aristotle returns to the question in more detail, shows that primary matter is not an "element" in the Ionian sense,[45] that it is not

---

[43] *Loc cit.,* p. 514.

[44] *Loc. cit.,* p. 514.

[45] "Things which come to be and pass away cannot be called by the name of the material out of which they have come to be. It is only the results of "alteration" that retain the name of the substratum whose "alterations" they are." He adds that the

body,[46] that it is not perceptible,[47] that it guarantees the continuity of coming-to-be,[48] that it is in some sense a source of individuation,[49] and yet that it is "the same in each".[50] He always speaks of it as a "constituent", frequently falling back on the analogy of bronze in the statue. We shall not follow these discussions in detail, but shall limit ourselves to two points:

matter here has "no separate existence but is always bound up with a contrariety" (*De Gen.* 328a 20–22; 26). Elsewhere he argues that it is impossible that there should be only one element because it would follow that there would then be only one natural motion (*De Caelo,* 304b 10–23). An Ionian "intermediate" element is also excluded: matter "is indifferently *any* of the elements or it is nothing" (*De Gen.* 332a 26). It would follow from all this that primary matter can have no predicable properties— for that would make it an element, and thus (Aristotle argues) make unqualified change impossible. He sometimes talks of "matter" as a quantifiable stuff, e.g. *De Caelo,* 278b 1–9, where he speaks of "all the matter of the universe", or 312b, 33, where he alludes to the view that velocity of fall depends upon the "quantity of matter". But 'matter' here means 'natural perceptible body' (278a 9). He also talks of "different kinds of matter" (the elements), "but though they are four, there must be a common matter of all—particularly if they pass into one another—which in each is in being different" (312a 31–312b 1). Aristotle's notion of primary matter as lacking in predicable properties is more persuasive in discussing changes of one "element" into another, because with other types of substantial change, there will always be a problem about the persistence (in some "virtual" fashion, at least) of the various elements in the substratum.

[46] Because if it were, it would either have a natural motion and be an element, or not have, and be a mathematical entity (*De Caelo,* 305a 22–27).

[47] "When nothing perceptible persists in its identity as substratum and the thing changes as a whole (e.g. water into air), such an occurrence is a coming-to-be" (*De Gen.* 319b 15–17). He contrasts the *elements* which are perceptible bodies with the matter that underlies them which is not (*De Gen.* 328b 33–35).

[48] He asks what is the material cause of the "perpetuity of coming to be" in Nature, and answers that it is the *hypokeimenon,* "because it is such as to change from contrary to contrary"; he also notes that the answer here has to be "adequate to account for coming-to-be and passing-away in their general character as they occur in all existing things alike" (*De Gen.* 319a 19; 318a 28–29). The suggestion here is that the "matter" must be described in a manner sufficiently general to allow it to characterize *every* entity capable of the substantial change.

[49] Of the universe as a whole, and of each object in it. It is matter that differentiates circle from particular circle (*De Caelo,* 278a 8–16). Callias and Socrates "are different in virtue of their matter (for that is different), but the same in form" (*Metaphysics,* 1032a 23–1034a 8). This approach to the notion of matter is found only where Aristotle is discussing Plato's theory of Forms.

[50] "Because otherwise the elements would not come to be reciprocally out of one another, i.e. contraries out of contraries". He is puzzled by the paradox implicit in this and concludes: "Perhaps the solution is that the matter [of the elements] is in one sense the same, in another, different. For that which underlies them, whatever its nature may be *qua* underlying them, is the same, but its actual being is not the same" (*De Gen.* 319b 1–4)

why is this question about *M*-principles so important? and what is the typical proof-structure justifying it?

Metaphysics in the later Greek and scholastic traditions was largely a search for such principles. Opposing metaphysical systems made different "cuts" in explaining individual things; distinctions of all sorts were elaborated with considerable complexity and subtlety. The nominalists' reaction against what they took to be the illegitimate reification of the conceptual order gradually turned the focus away from *M*-principles, although the nominalists themselves never question the legitimacy of explanation in terms of them. This was left to the later exponents of the "new science", who found explanation in terms of such "occult" principles purely verbal and ultimately sterile. A new ideal of explanation in terms of hypothetical quantitative models began to replace the older one.

One rule of thumb for separating the "tough-minded" and the "tender-minded" in contemporary philosophy might be to ask: does he make use of *M*-principles? He probably will not use the expression, *'principium quo'*, but if he appeals to constitutive elements that in *some* sense contribute to the being of a thing, though not themselves separate existing things, it does not much matter whether he speaks in terms of "eternal object" or *"En-soi"*, his notion, at least, of what the philosopher should be looking out for is in important respects the same as it was for Plato and Aristotle.[51] It is in the philosophies that are closest to natural science and to logic that opposition to this classical ideal of philosophical "explanation" is strongest: closest to science, because science produces another and more concrete mode of explanation; closest to logic, because the logician is more than ordinarily aware of the dangers inherent in the assumption that terms that are at once name-like and useful necessarily name something real. Positivists, analytic philosophers, logical empiricists, find *M*-principles unacceptable on the whole, though they often retain terms from the "principle" vocabulary. Over against them are ranged neo-Kantians, existentialists, idealists, thinkers like Bergson and Whitehead, and, of course, Thomists.

If there is one area, outside of metaphysics itself, where this divergence is of particular importance, it is the philosophy of nature. The empiricist is, in fact, unlikely to use this title at all. He will speak of the *methodology of science,* in which the logical methods of procedure of empirical science are

---

[51] Obviously, the way in which the *M*-principles *are* constitutive, the extent to which they depend on the subject, etc., will depend on the philosopher chosen. Our characterization of *M*-principles above assumed Aristotelian norms of objectivity. The general point of this paragraph is also made by several of the contributors to *The Nature of Metaphysics,* London, 1957. See also P. F. Strawson's distinction between "descriptive" and "revisionary" metaphysics, *Individuals,* London, 1959, p. 9.

systematically analyzed; he will have an extensive *philosophy of science,* in which the results of science are discussed for the light they throw upon traditional philosophical problems, like those of causality and individuation, and the aid of science is invoked in the articulation of the set of general concepts in which the most pervasive features of our world are to be described (space, time, quality, energy, and so on). He may even admit an *ontology of science* in which the precise nature of the contribution that a hypothetical scientific construct can make to our knowledge of the "real" structure of the physical world is discussed. But in all of this, science is assumed to be the sole source of illumination when it comes to finding out about Nature; in this regard, philosophy is confined to the analytic study of science itself, or to the internal clarification of its results. There is no *philosophy of nature,* strictly speaking, something that would originate for instance in everyday experience, and take shape in a way that would be—in part at least—prior to, or independent of, the progress of science. In particular, the empiricist would tend to deny that any discipline could properly claim to reveal an "ontological structure" of physical reality which would differ in kind from the sort of structure physics and chemistry deal with; he would be inclined to suspect that this is not so much philosophy as primitive or fossilized science.

The philosopher of nature will try to make the opposite case. He will elaborate upon the general features of the world of becoming around us; he may perhaps call upon recent phenomenological methods in doing this, or he may prefer to take language as the initial clue. But his analysis is likely to be an unexciting one, differing from the empiricist philosophy of science only by being restricted to pre-scientific non-hypothetical categories of experience, *unless* on the one hand he enquires (after the manner of Kant) into the sort of structure of the knowing subject which must be postulated in order to account for such categories, or else he tries to discern the source of these categories (after the manner of Aristotle) in the general ontological "structure" of the object known. In the latter case, the validity of his whole procedure is going to rest, implicitly at least, on the notion of an M-principle. It is significant that most scholastic writers on philosophy of nature today make hylemorphism the central point of their exposition; indeed some, like Renoirte, equiparate hylemorphism with philosophy of nature *tout court.* Uppermost in their minds, it is clear, is the thought that their claim to be doing an analysis of Nature that is at once explanatory and different in kind from what one would find in natural science, stands or falls with the cogency of the hylemorphic doctrine and the two M-principles it proposes.

How then does one go about justifying the appeal to M-principles? The

Presocratics spoke in terms of *physical* principles only: elements from which things came to be originally, or of which they presently consist, and so on. In each case, the principle can be specified in terms of ordinary physical predicates. What made them into "principles" was that an appeal to them lent a new sort of intelligibility to the domain of natural change, the domain of primary concern to these thinkers. Plato suggested a much more radical notion of "principle": something that existed apart from the physical world but exercised a manifold influence upon it. The "principle" here is an entity in its own right; in fact, it is the only entity that exists in its own right. Aristotle's "principle" combined features from both traditions. It was ingredient in the entities of the natural world, as the Presocratic principle had been; it exerted an influence on activity in some sense; its existence was asserted on the basis of philosophical reasoning.

The appeal to such principles depends, in turn, upon the legitimacy of two other notions: *ground* and *real distinction*. To ask for the "ground" of some feature of the world is to ask why it should exist, what entities are causally responsible for it. To deny the legitimacy of such a question would be to hold that the world is not intelligible. Suppose one has a yellow ball. To ask what the "ground" is in the ball for its yellowness is to ask in modern terms whether its color can be "reduced" to some other property, ontologically speaking. A physicist today might answer in terms of the energy-levels of the electron-shells of the material on the surface of the ball. This would be to give a "ground". Aristotle, on the other hand, supposed that sense-qualities are irreducible, i.e. that they are their own ground, and that the only question to be raised about them is: in what do they inhere? In this view, one would ask about the "ground" of yellowness in the ball only in the sense in which one would ask about the "ground" of its sphericity, i.e. how does it relate to the substance of the ball? Is it always found in substances of this sort? If so, there might be a reason for this. *Ground* and *invariance* are thus closely linked. The great problem, of course, is the limits to which reductionism can be legitimately pushed. It can be argued that this is one of the principal features dividing philosophical schools.[52]

The classic appearance-reality dichotomy takes its origin from one extreme way of presenting the notion of "ground". In the Neo-Platonic tradition, "ground" becomes "source", and the relation between a given feature of an entity and the ground of that feature in the entity is explained after the analogy of cause and effect. So that a reduction in the order of knowl-

---

[52] For a stimulating discussion of this issue, see R. Rorty, "The limits of reductionism", in *Experience, Existence and the Good,* ed. by I. C. Lieb, Carbondale, Ill., 1961; and "Realism, Categories, and the "Linguistic Turn" ", *International Philosophical Quarterly*, 2, 1962, 307–22.

edge from feature to ground is held to match a causal influence, ground to feature, in the order of being. In medieval philosophy, substance is often said to "cause" its proper accidents in this way;[53] even Aristotle will use this sort of metaphor in describing nature (the ground) as the "cause" of motion in an inanimate body.[54] One danger of this sort of account is that it makes our knowledge of the "cause" entirely inferential and extremely problematic; we think right away of the "occult forms" of later Scholasticism, i.e. named, but otherwise unexplained, "grounds" in things of perceived regularities in their behavior. To say that opium has a "power" to put people to sleep is to give useful information; it can easily come to seem like an *explanation* as well if a pseudo-relation of efficient causality is suggested between form and outward appearance. These hazards in the notion of *ground* should not lead us to reject it entirely, but they do warn us that it must be used with great caution and due justification.

Much more decisive in the setting up of the notion of an *M*-principle is the idea of a "real distinction". Someone might be perfectly prepared to admit that every feature of a thing must have a "ground". But they might claim that this ground is the thing in itself, in its totality. They might object— and many have—to the idea of dividing the thing up into different "grounds", so to speak. If this objection be sustained, the only real principle of a thing will be the thing itself, and essence, form, and the rest will be no more than different ways of describing the same thing, involving no real distinction in the thing itself.

It is here that the crucial point in the argument occurs: if a thing X has two features, Y and Z, and if the concepts of Y and Z are ultimately and demonstrably irreducible to one another, then there is a "real distinction" in X between the grounds of Y and Z, or, to put this in another way, X is "really composed". A typical argument might run: there must be a ground in John for both his specificity and his individuality. But the same ground cannot do for both: what "makes" him be a man cannot be the same as what "makes" him be this man, for if it were, he would be the only man. Therefore, there must be a distinction of some sort in him. It is not a *physical* distinction, as though the two elements could be separated from one another. It would make no sense to separate the ground of specificity from that of individuality. But it must be a *real* distinction, in the sense that the distinction, precisely as a distinction, must have some sort of foundation in the

---

[53] Aquinas, for instance, in discussing the relation between the powers of the soul and its essence, talks of substance as the "efficient cause" of its proper accidents. It is said to "produce" them, and they are said to "flow from it, as from their principle". *S.T.*, I, *q.77, a.6, c.* and *ad 2*.

[54] *Physics, VIII*, 4.

thing itself, i.e. it cannot be purely subjective, imposed entirely *ab extra*.

To defend this argument-schema adequately, one would need to undertake an elaborate discussion of the relationship between the conceptual and real orders, which would carry us far outside the scope of this essay. But a few remarks are in order. First, it should be emphasized once again that the two orders are not disconnected. An analysis of one may be expected to be relevant to the other. To analyze the conceptual is not to turn away from the real. Second, 'real distinction' does not mean a distinction between separable individual entities. Third, its meaning can be gleaned only from a knowledge of the whole system of interpretation within which the phrase occurs, a seeing of it in action, so to speak. In one sense, if someone says: "there is a real distinction between matter and form", part of the *meaning* of the phrase 'real distinction' is likely to be contributed by this very statement. That is, a real distinction is now in a sense partially definable as: the sort of distinction that exists between matter and form, and these latter terms have in turn to be defined by virtue of their function within the system as a whole, as applied to concrete problems. The philosophic concept of matter, for instance, cannot be abstracted in some simple and absolute way from a number of empirical instances. It is part of a highly sophisticated interpretative system, in which each element depends on all the others in a very complex way. If a single thesis in the system be altered, there tends to be a shift over the system as a whole.

The temptation to turn metaphysics into a sort of high-level chemistry is ever-present. The words the metaphysician uses, 'perception', 'quality', 'matter' . . . have the appearance of ordinary concrete nouns; they certainly do not seem to name abstractions, at least. It is easy to assume that there are pigeon-holes "out there" named 'matter', 'perception', etc., in which appropriate samples are available for inspection and analysis. So one proceeds like the chemist who is faced with a number of named substances whose properties have to be discovered, i.e. one assumes that at least the *reference* of one's terms is assured, that one knows which entities one is talking about. But this is precisely what is *not* the case in philosophy, as a rule: one has to establish *both* sense and reference of the terms, and a slight shift in sense may cause a corresponding shift in reference. When one chemist says: "*A* is *X*", and another says: "*A* is not *X*", the two are really contradicting each other. But when this happens in philosophy, the contradiction may well be only apparent, simply because two systems with apparently opposing theses of this sort will ordinarily define their terms (i.e. locate their referents) somewhat differently, so that they are very probably not talking of the same thing in the first place.

The same word, 'matter', is used to designate an *M*-principle in many different philosophical systems. In each case, the M-principle is defined strictly in terms of its explanatory role in the structure as a whole. The concept which serves to single it out (itself a C-principle) is of a special kind, not unlike the constructs of empirical science in some respects, though importantly different in others. It does not involve hypothesis, nor quantitative structure, nor predication-verification, but it *does* involve a systematic interdependence and an apparatus of carefully drawn conceptual distinctions and relations, just as a scientific concept does. It is language-dependent in the strongest sense. This means that different M-systems will make different "cuts" in reality, will bring out different aspects of the concrete object by a small variation in the manner of relating a couple of key terms like 'form' and 'idea'. To question the *uniqueness* of the cuts made by different systems using the same terms (e.g. 'matter', 'form') does *not*, of course, challenge the objectivity of the cuts made. But clearly the notion of an "*objective* cut" here has to be very carefully handled because of the role played by the concept-system in *locating* the cut. The "cut" here is neither the separation between separable things of the chemist nor a purely fictional division. It has a *fundamentum in re,* to use the old term, but the locating of that *fundamentum* depends on the conceptual system in a way that the locating of divisions between the atoms in a molecule does not.

In comparing one philosophical "cut" with another, one must avoid the twin extremes of assuming an identity of M-principle between two systems because they both happen to use the same term, on the one hand, and of assuming that these are necessarily *competing* views about the *same* entity, e.g. matter, on the other. If someone asks: but are matter and form "really" distinct?, the relevant affirmative answer would be that the system in which this distinction is affirmed *and* the terms, 'matter', 'form', 'real', 'distinct', are used in a certain definite way, works pretty well in articulating the complexities of our experience. And we think this affirmative *can* be given. But when it comes to giving the *exact* grounds for the distinction, and, in particular, to probing further into the nature of "substantial" change (upon which the whole notion of a "real distinction" between matter and form must still rest), one cannot but feel that much work remains to be done.

University of Notre Dame

COMMENT[1]

I SHALL SINGLE OUT FOR COMMENT JUST A FEW OF THE POINTS MADE BY FATHER McMullin in his important and stimulating paper. Themes from this paper have been constantly recurring in the course of the discussion, particularly the concept of "M-principle", and of a real distinction "in the thing" between M-principles. It is with the latter that I shall chiefly be concerned.

In §1, Father McMullin writes,

> ... now we come to a subdivision of the R-principles and to a parting of the philosophical ways. Classical philosophers were wont to speak of principles which were neither things nor concepts, but a sort of real "constituent" or "ingredient" of things, incapable of existing on their own, yet playing a direct role in the activity and being of things.

He is clearly right about this, and the point is no mere historical one, for the concept of such real but dependent ingredients of changeable things has turned up again and again in the course of the discussion. He throws out an interesting idea which he doesn't follow through with, and which, I believe, might provide a bridge to an alternative approach. He writes,

> ... the M-principle appears, at first sight, to be rather uneasily poised between the logical and the real orders; it is not a thing, nor simply a concept, but it has something of the character of both. The *essence* of some object, *X*, for instance, seems to be roughly describable as: *X*-regarded-under-the-aspect-of-enduring-intelligibility.

Is Father McMullin thinking of the object, *X*, as an individual? If so, then he is thinking of the essence of an object, e.g. Socrates, as the object itself "regarded under the aspect of enduring intelligibility", e.g. Socrates himself *qua* rational animal. I think that something very important is going on here. The notion of 'something *qua* something' is one to which constant appeal has been made in the course of the discussion, and is one, therefore, which should be submitted to careful scrutiny. What exactly does it mean to speak of Socrates *qua* rational animal? My own conviction is that this way of talking need not commit one to real distinctions between M-principles, and, indeed, that correctly analyzed it

---

[1] This *Comment* is directed to the version of this paper that was presented at the Symposium. The author of the original paper has reorganized and revised it extensively for publication here. It seems preferable to retain the *Comment* in its original form; the reader can judge for himself the extent to which the points it makes are conceded in the new version of the paper. The *Comment* quotes extensively from the original paper, so that the reader can easily identify the positions it discusses.

shows how the latter concept can be avoided. To use my example of this after-noon, the form of a particular shoe can be the shoe *qua* artifact made of some appropriate matter or other, serving to protect and embellish the feet, and the matter of the particular shoe could be, for example, the shoe *qua* this piece of leather. If so, the form and the matter would be the same thing, i.e. the shoe, and to show that a real distinction is involved, it would have to be shown that where a subject can be considered *qua A* and *qua B,* a real distinction in the thing is involved. But, as Father McMullin himself points out, to speak of some-thing *qua* something seems to involve a reference to both the logical and the real orders, and if this is so, as I think it is, the question as to exactly how these references are combined is central to our problem. If we say that Socrates (*qua* rational animal) is immortal or that Socrates (*qua* flesh and bone) is mortal, what is the logical force of the parenthetical phrases? Father McMullin seems to me to suggest that in making the first statement one is *referring* both to Soc-rates in the real order and to a concept in the logical order (rational animality) which is in a special way relevant to the concept *expressed by* the predicate, and which, it is implied, is true of Socrates. Instead, however, of developing this point, Father McMullin commits himself more and more, as his paper goes on, to the conception of *M*-principles as really distinct, i.e. as distinct constituents in the real order of changeable things.

In §6, he writes,

> Returning now to Aristotle's analysis of change-in-general in the *Physics*: when a leaf turns brown, the leaf itself, abstracting from its color, is said to be the "matter" or "subject" or "substratum" of the change, on the grounds that it is the leaf itself that perseveres throughout the change. 'Matter' here de-notes, not the leaf in its totality (for the predicate 'perseveres throughout the change' would not be true of *it*), but the leaf considered apart from its color: thus in a sense the referent is "incomplete". This sort of "incomplete" refer-ent is central to the whole notion of predication in Aristotle.

I shall not be concerned to argue his interpretation of Aristotle, though I think it to be mistaken. What interests me is that in the course of explaining this notion of an "incomplete referent" he seems to me to say much the same sort of thing as he attributes to Donald Williams. Indeed, the main burden of my re-marks on this point will be to emphasize how much there is in common be-tween the ontology in terms of which Father McMullin interprets predication and that in terms of which Donald Williams interprets it.

To begin with, it is surely paradoxical to hold that when we say, "The leaf became brown", and "The leaf persevered throughout the change", that it isn't the *whole* leaf which is said to have become brown, and to have persevered throughout the change. In the ordinary sense of "whole leaf" it is obviously the whole leaf which became brown and endured throughout the change. Thus, when one says, "The leaf itself, abstracting from its color (say, ivy green), became brown", this seems to me to call attention to the fact that when a green leaf be-comes brown, it doesn't become a *brown green leaf,* as contrasted with the case, say, of a rational animal which, when it becomes wise, becomes a *wise rational animal*. It is tempting to move from 'The green leaf did not become a brown green leaf but a brown leaf' to 'The green leaf *qua* leaf, but not *qua* green leaf, became a brown leaf' to 'The green leaf, abstracting from its color, became brown' to 'That "part" of the green leaf other than its color took on the color brown'. If one succumbs to this temptation, how is the "part-whole" relation in question to be construed? A plausible line of thought is to construe things as systems of "aspects", i.e. of "dependent" or "abstract" particulars *à la* Donald Williams.

Father McMullin contrasts two ways of interpreting reference: (a) that which stresses the reference of statements as wholes, which he seems to correlate with the notion of referring to the "complete" thing; (b) that which stresses the reference of the subject-term, which he seems to correlate with the notion of referring to a "part" of the thing. Thus, people who stress the reference of statements as wholes are, as he sees it, thinking of the complete thing as the subject of reference, and he contrasts with this the position according to which it is only in some sense a "part" of a thing (e.g. the leaf) which is the subject of predication (e.g. 'becomes brown' or 'endures through change'), a position which he connects with the idea (in itself correct) that the referring expression is the subject-term rather than the statement as a whole.

Now I think that this is a serious misinterpretation of the situation. In the first place, I believe that very few of the philosophers who object to the substratum analysis of change stress the reference of statements as wholes. They tend to emphasize as much as the Aristotelian that it is the subject-term which refers. They would, however, insist, as I did above, that the subject-term in "The leaf became brown" or "The leaf persevered throughout the change" refers to the leaf as a whole. Later, however, Father McMullin writes, "Returning now to matter-subject . . . it is clear that a leaf-considered-apart-from-its-color is a perfectly legitimate subject of predication." The context to be sure is one in which he is considering matter as a *C*-principle (conceptual principle) rather than an *R*-principle, but it is nevertheless one in which he makes use of a distinction between "the thing in its totality" and something which is presumably *not* the thing in its totality, but in some sense a "part" of the thing. Thus in commenting on the statement 'The leaf-considered-apart-from-its-color remains throughout the change' he writes,

> Of course, one has to be careful in using ordinary predicates such as 'remains' in a context like this; if the subject is not a thing in its totality (as it would ordinarily be), the predicate is being used in an extended sense, the precise import of which would require further elaboration in each instance.

It is difficult to avoid the conclusion that he is ontologizing the leaf-considered-apart-from-its-color into a partial reality which endures through the change of color.

It becomes clearer what Father McMullin has in mind by his contrast between *ordinary* predication (in which the subject is the thing in its totality) and a non-ordinary predication, presumably found primarily in philosophical contexts, in which the subject is something less than the thing in its totality, when one explores his critique of Williams on Aristotle. Williams, like many other philosophers before him, construes individual things or continuants as systems of "dependent" or "abstract" particulars. Thus, although such philosophers would recognize that there is a sense in which *greenness* is a formal universal common to the many green things—needless to say, they differ among themselves as to the *status* of such universals—they claim that in another sense each green object has its own private greenness. Thus, for Donald Williams the "characters" of things, which "characters" come into being and cease to be, are exactly such abstract particulars. A thing which endures through change is a system of abstract particulars, *this greenness, this rectangularity, this smoothness,* etc., and change is the replacing in such a system of abstract particulars by abstract particulars e.g. *this greenness* by *this brownness.* Now as I see it, Father McMullin accepts this analysis, and it is this fact which accounts both for .his remarks on predication and for his defense of a real distinction between *M*-principles. It is not, however, an Aristotelian ontology, and it requires great ingenuity to fit it to Aristotelian terminology.

Father McMullin replies as follows to Williams' criticism of Aristotle which makes use of the at first sight perplexing example of petrifying wood,

> It is the shape, pattern, etc. in such a case which remain the same and which, therefore, by definition are the matter-subject here, while the form of wood has given way to the form of stone. What makes this case paradoxical is that because changes of this sort are not very common—Professor Williams to the contrary—we do not ordinarily predicate woody quality of certain given shapes but rather predicate shapes of the wood.

Notice that Father McMullin is willing to speak of predicating woody quality of a given shape, which implies that he is thinking of the shape as a particular, as "the shape of x", where this does not mean "the shape universal exemplified by x". There is "nothing in semantics", he assures us, to prevent us from making this predication, but because it is the shape that changes in *most* changes involving wood, and because the woody qualities are ordinarily more responsible for continuity than is the mere shape, "we tend to assume that the wood is the substratum by some sort of inherent right". As I see it, therefore, Father McMullin's differences from Donald Williams constitute a family quarrel rather than a quarrel between families.

The fundamentally Williamsian character of his ontology reappears where he writes, "When someone says: This leaf is green, he appears to be saying something about the leaf *as a whole*. It would not be correct to say that the leaf-considered-apart-from-its-color is green." From this, however, he concludes only that "the notion that what we are talking *about* when we predicate a property of a thing is the thing minus this property needs much further discussion;" which implies that it is some such notion to which he has been giving a tentative hearing.

I would really like to press Father McMullin on this question of how he interprets the abiding factor in a changing thing. He says explicitly that

> "matter-cause" in the context of the "four-cause" cosmological explanation of change ... denotes whatever aspects of the changing thing are not directly relevant to the description of the particular change at issue. What is matter-cause in a being relative to one change need not be matter-cause for a different change.

I would like to know what he means by 'aspect' if *not* a Williamsian abstract particular? Indeed, only if "aspects" *are* abstract particulars has a foundation been laid for the subsequent discussion of a real distinction between matter and form. For although abstract particulars are *incomplete* in that they cannot exist apart from the wholes to which they contribute, yet they are really distinct in the sense that they are *in the real order as numerically distinct items*. It is, as I see it, the doctrine of abstract particulars which underlies and gives some measure of plausibility to the thesis that there is a real distinction between matter and form.

In the concluding section of his paper, Father McMullin argues that the different "features" of an object must have different "grounds", where both "features" and "grounds" are in the real order. I would like to comment briefly on the notion of *ground*. It seems to me that this notion is to be explicated in terms of the notion of a *premise,* and that the 'ground-consequent relation' is, in essence, that relation between *propositions* which authorize inference. If so, then an item in the real order is a ground by virtue of some propositional truth or *fact* about it, and it would seem to follow that one and the same *thing* in the real order could, by virtue of different *facts* about it, be the ground of many other *facts* about it. If it is *facts* which are, in the primary sense *grounds*, and *things* are grounds only in a derivative sense by virtue of facts about them, then grounds and consequences in the primary sense belong to the logical or conceptual order, and one thing in the real order could be, in the derivative sense, the ground of many consequences without construing the consequences as "aspects" or abstract particulars in the real order, and without dividing the thing into other "aspects" to be their grounds. The question whether things or individuals in the real order can be grounds or consequences apart from their relation to the logical order, and, if not, how this relationship, and the logical order itself, is to be construed, are, of course, fundamental and classical issues which would take us far beyond the scope of the present discussion. I shall, therefore, limit myself to expressing a general uneasiness about Father McMullin's treatment of things or objects or "aspects" as grounds and consequences, and to expressing the hope that these matters can be explored on a subsequent occasion.

Wilfrid Sellars
Yale University

PRIMARY MATTER AND
UNQUALIFIED CHANGE

Milton Fisk

§1 *Questions about What There Is*

The problem of *primary matter* (*PM*) is an existential rather than an analytic problem. It shares this characteristic with the problem of sense-data and that of universals. Given a small selection of the great number of senses which philosophers have attributed to '*PM*', 'sense-datum', or 'universal', one is concerned to learn whether, in any one of the given senses, *PM* exists, sense-data exist, or universals exist. The problems of perception, of meaningfulness, and of belief are analytic rather than existential. Assured that there are perceptions, meaningful statements, and beliefs, one's concern centers on learning what they are. On problems such as those of physical objects and change, philosophers have been divided. Some have treated these problems as primarily existential; others have treated them as primarily analytic.

Existential problems arise in distinctive settings. I shall mention three such settings. The first two have in common a determination to improve on the customary structure of thought. (1) In some cases the demand for improvement rests on the conviction that a customary concept leads to a contradiction. The remedy prescribed is either the complete elimination of that concept, accompanied by the rejection of a corresponding reality, or the modification of the customary structure of thought and, hence, of the customary concept through the introduction of a further concept, accompanied by the admission of a corresponding reality. The question of the reality of time has, on occasion, been posed and answered negatively, not because it was doubted that people think of events as temporally related but because of the conviction, and a supposed proof in its support, that statements framed in terms of 'past', 'present', and 'future' lead to a contradiction.[1]

(2) In other cases the demand for improvement rests on the conviction that the analysis of a customary concept cannot be sufficiently explanatory unless a new concept is introduced and then built into that analysis. The question

---

[1] Cf. McTaggart, *The Nature of Existence*, Cambridge, Eng., 1927, Vol. II, §§ 331–32.

of the reality of sense-data has, on occasion, been answered affirmatively, but not all of those who have answered it in this way have held that the concept of a sense-datum is an element of our everyday conceptual scheme. When it has been recognized that the concept of a sense-datum is not an everyday concept, its introduction has been justified on the grounds that it permits a redescription of the facts of perception "in a way that is supposed to bring to light distinctions, of philosophical interest, which the ordinary methods of description tend to conceal."[2] This procedure in regard to the analysis of perception exemplifies a familiar pattern of connection between analytic problems (e.g., those of change, understanding-a-predicative-term,[3] and belief[4]) and existential ones (e.g., those of matter, universals,[3] and propositions[4]).

(3) An existential problem can be raised as a problem of finding whether a given structure of thought directly presupposes, without detour through entity-introducing explanations of that structure, entities of a certain kind. "There are those who feel that our ability to understand general terms . . . would be inexplicable unless there were universals. . . . And there are those who fail to detect, in such an appeal . . . , any explanatory value. Without settling that issue, it should be possible to point to certain forms of discourse as *explicitly* presupposing entities of one or another given kind, say universals."[5] But how is one to decide which elements of a structure of thought or of a form of discourse directly presuppose entities? At least as regards the constant terms of a form of discourse, we are to understand 'directly presupposes an entity' as follows: If a form of discourse contains a term and that term is construed, in respect to the use of that form of discourse, as referring to an entity, then that form of discourse will be said to presuppose directly the entity in question. An answer to the question what entities a form of discourse directly presupposes, depends, then, on a division of terms into categorematic and syncategorematic ones, into those which make discourse to be about something and those which do not. It depends, let us say, on the adoption of a criterion of existence. Nevertheless, in this third setting, the debate over the criterion of existence goes on against a background of agreement not to add or eliminate concepts the addition or elimination of which would require changes in the structure of thought or the form of discourse considered.

In view of the difference between settings (2) and (3), the same existen-

---

[2] Ayer, *The Problem of Knowledge*, Baltimore, 1956, p. 108.

[3] Cf. Russell, *The Problems of Philosophy*, London, 1912, pp. 58, 93, 104, 106.

[4] Cf. Church, "On Carnap's Analysis of Statements of Assertion and Belief", *Analysis, 10*, pp. 97–99.

[5] Quine, *From a Logical Point of View*, Cambridge, Mass., 1953, p. 102.

tial conclusion may be the result of importantly different trains of thought. In setting (3), theorist *A* might hold that discourse containing predicates, such as 'is wise', but lacking singular terms for universals, such as 'wisdom', is not about universals. Yet, in setting (2), theorist *A* might defend the introduction of discourse about universals on the grounds that without such an introduction an adequate analysis of 'Peter understands 'is wise' ' cannot be given. To carry out such an analysis the original form of discourse must, he would claim, be supplemented so that the statement 'Peter grasps the universal, wisdom' can be formed in it. On the other hand, theorist *B* might defend the existence of universals, with respect to the original form of discourse, entirely within setting (3), *B*'s criterion of existence would then be said to be more liberal than *A*'s. *B* would claim that a form of discourse containing predicates but lacking singular terms for universals is, without undergoing any additions, about universals, since, for him, predicates are names of universals. On the other hand, *A*'s more restricted criterion of existence leads him to require that the form of discourse be broadened to contain singular terms for universals before it explicitly presupposes universals.

§ 2 *The Subject of Change and the Subject of Predication*

There have been two problems of *PM*. There has been (i) the problem of whether there is an ultimate subject of change and (ii) the problem of whether there is an ultimate subject of predication. I shall be concerned with (i). I shall leave (ii) aside, except for brief notice in the following paragraph. Moreover, there will be no mention of the implied problem of whether, if they are not empty, the descriptions 'the ultimate subject of change' and 'the ultimate subject of predication' have, of necessity, the same descriptum.

In raising the problem of *PM* in the form of (ii), the following question, or some variant of it, has played a central role: If a certain flower is the subject of which 'red' is predicated in asserting 'This flower is red', then what is the subject of which 'flower' is predicated in asserting 'This is a flower'? One might plausibly interpret the following as an answer to just such a question: Predicates other than substance are predicated of substance while substance is predicated of *PM*.[6] When interpreted as an answer to the above question, and we are here interested in it only when it is so interpreted, this claim has been countered with the objection that, despite grammatical similarity, the function of sentences such as 'This is a flower' cannot be

---

[6] Aristotle, *Meta.* 1029a 18–20; cf. also Locke, *Essay*, Bk. II, Chap. XXIII, Sec. 2.

216

identified with that of those such as 'This flower is red'. 'This is a flower', having the force of 'Here we have a flower', is used to assert that a presented object is correctly called a flower.[7] 'This flower' in 'This flower is red' serves to bring the hearer's attention to an object of a certain kind. But 'This' in 'This is a flower' is not used to bring the hearer's attention to an object which fits no kind, a bit of *PM* let us say. Rather, the demonstrative in 'This is a flower' serves to bring attention to an object for the sake of saying what kind of an object it is, not for the sake of characterizing an object of a certain kind or an object which belongs to no kind. For, if I ask 'What is a flower?' on hearing 'This is a flower', I might be answered with 'Come over here and look behind the bush, and you will see it', but not with 'A certain bit of *PM* is a flower'.[8] On the other hand, 'This flower is red' or 'This flower is a rose' is used to assert, not just the presence of an object of a certain kind, but the presence of a certain characteristic in an object referred to as belonging to a certain kind or the membership in a subordinate kind of an object referred to as belonging to a wider kind. Yet being at odds with such facts about the different functions of these sentences will not deter the theorist[9] who finds greater satisfaction in judging grammatical similarity a sufficient basis for assimilating the function of 'This is a flower' to that of 'This flower is red' or 'This flower is a rose'. We shall find the same attitude on the part of the theorist who calls for an ultimate subject of change. He will attempt to assimilate, despite obvious differences, the function of a statement of *unqualified change* (*UC*), such as 'Smith's cow drowned in the flood', to that of a statement of *qualified change* (*QC*), such as 'Smith got tanned at the beach'.

Four questions will be considered. First, does the unsophisticated language with which we make assertions of *UC* (ἁπλῆ γένεσις or ἁπλῆ φθορά, *De Gen. et Corr.* 318a 12) explicitly presuppose *PM*? Here we are in setting (3) for existential problems. It will be found that the ontology of ordinary assertions of *UC* does not comprise *PM*. Second, what are the rules of a language for change which has a *PM* ontology? Third, are paradoxes derivable from ordinary assertions of *UC* which can be resolved only by the addition of expressions purportedly designating *PM*? Here we place ourselves in setting

---

[7] "The difficulty arises in all these cases through mixing up 'is' and 'is called'" (Wittgenstein, *Remarks on the Foundations of Mathematics*, Oxford, 1956, I, §127).

[8] Cf. Macdonald, "The Philosopher's Use of Analogy," in *Logic and Language, First Series*, ed. Flew, Oxford, 1951, pp. 88–91; Lazerowitz, "Substratum," in *Philosophical Analysis*, ed. Black, Ithaca, 1950, pp. 176–94; and Warnock, *Berkeley*, Baltimore, 1953, pp. 108–109.

[9] Cf., e.g., Van Melsen, *The Philosophy of Nature*, Pittsburgh, 1954, pp. 115–25. "Thus 'thisness' and 'glassness' refer to different aspects or "parts" of the same concrete thing."

(1) for existential problems. The alleged paradoxes of change-without-a-substratum-of-change and of coming-to-be-out-of-nothing will be shown to be real only when a *PM* ontology is already assumed, and spurious otherwise. Fourth, even if there are no paradoxes, must we not add *PM* designators to the language in which assertions of *UC* are made in order to give a philosophically adequate analysis or explanation of *UC?* Here we are in setting (2). I shall show that *PM* cannot enter into an analysis of *UC* and that there is no way in which a *PM* language explains the customary language of change.

§3 *Unqualified Change and Everyday Speech*

(A) To justify the answer just given to our first question we must begin by pointing out differences between assertions of *UC* and those of *QC*. But it has not yet been indicated which changes we would classify as unqualified and which as qualified. For our purposes an enumeration will suffice. Most familiar uses of 'to burn up', 'to be born', 'to die', 'to cut down', 'to kill', 'to turn into', 'to germinate', 'to abolish', and such-like verbs will be said to express *UC*. On the other hand, most familiar uses of 'to sink', 'to grow', 'to darken', 'to learn', 'to walk', 'to stop', 'to fidget', and such-like verbs will be said to express *QC*. The task of pointing out differences between *UC* and *QC* shall be treated as one of formulating entailments of statements formed with verbs of the first of these groups which stand opposed to entailments of statements formed with verbs of the second group. We shall not undertake to point out all differences. The most pertinent difference for us consists in the fact that in a *UC* a thing comes to be or passes away and, hence, is not persistent in respect to this change, whereas in a *QC* there is no thing which is initiated or terminated. The appropriateness of using the terms 'unqualified' and 'qualified' is evident upon noting, (i) that the result of a change described by a verb of the first group (the *UC* group) is a thing itself, while the result of a change described by a verb of the second group (the *QC* group) is a thing under a certain qualification, and (ii) that the source of a change described by a verb of the *UC* group—the that-from-which of the change—is a thing itself, while the source of a change described by a verb of the *QC* group is a thing under a certain qualification. An example of the kind of situation which would count as evidence for (i) is as follows: A man who is born may be a talented man, but 'talented' can be dropped from 'In 1724 a talented boy was born to a saddler' without a nonsensical result; on the other hand, we get a queer result by dropping 'crooked' from 'A crooked tree grew from that tree'. An example of the kind of situation which would count as evidence for (ii) is as follows: A cow which was killed may have been a brindled cow, but loss of information rather than nonsense results by dropping 'brindled' from 'This carcass is what remains of the brindled cow'; on the other hand we cannot drop 'poor' from 'From being a poor man he grew wealthy over-night' unless 'man' is to have a significance other than the customary one.

Suppose I report that Smith's cow was drowned last night in the flood. Someone then asks, 'Which cow?' A study of admissible answers to a question of this sort reveals restrictions which must be placed on the formation of descriptive phrases referring to something which has passed away. I could reply with 'The cow walking through the gate' only if by the report of the drowning I had meant that Smith's cow had gotten very wet last night, or something of the like. If I reply with 'That cow by the creek bank with its feet in the air and its head buried in the mud', I would be understood to be referring to the carcass of the drowned cow and not to a cow which had miraculously survived a drowning in the flood and a suffocation in the mud. In respect to cows, drowning is terminal. But suppose the question had been, 'What drowned?' A study of admissible answers to a question of this sort reveals which types of expressions can and which cannot be employed as subjects of a given verb for passing away. If I answered with 'The animal on the bank drowned last night', then, since drowning is terminal for animals of all kinds, my answer is to be understood in the same way as 'The carcass on the bank is what remains of the animal drowned last night'. Yet, could one not say that the body on the bank was drowned last night? There is a body on the bank, even if there is not a cow there. But bodies don't drown, they float or sink. Before it drowns the cow has a body. From this one cannot conclude that the cow's body is *both* something persisting through the drowning (a substratum) *and* something undergoing the drowning (a subject[10]). The cow, not its body, drowns.

Now consider: 'The day after it rained grass came up where Smith had scattered seeds'. The question 'Which grass?' would prompt the answer 'The grass which the previous tenant cultivated' only if the original state-ment had meant that, even though the seeds had failed, old roots had pushed up new shoots. But, if grass had come up from Smith's seeds, this coming-up did not happen to something already there before the rain. Coming-up is initiative in respect to grass. Suppose the question had been 'What came up?' We do speak of seeds coming up, but without expecting to find them hovering so many inches above the places to which they originally fell. In

---

[10] In what follows, the term 'subject' will do double duty. According to the context, it will mean either the thing which undergoes a change, or the grammatical subject of a change verb which is functioning intransitively. In parallel fashion, the expression 'a substratum role' will mean, according to the context, either the role a thing has in persisting through a change, or the role a term has when it can be used to refer to a thing both before and after an asserted change.

the sense in which grass is said to come up from seeds, seeds are not said to come up when they germinate. Seeds come up only in the sense that something comes up from them. Yet some of the material of the seed finds its way into the blade of grass; seed-stuff persists as grass-stuff. Depite this continuity, the seed-stuff is not the subject of a coming-up. Just as the persistent body of the cow does not drown, so too the persistent seed-stuff does not come up. The expression for UC ('to drown', 'to come up') is not predicated of the expression for a persistent factor or a substratum[11] ('body', 'seed-stuff'). The cow, which has a body, drowns; the blade of grass, which contains seed-stuff, comes up. The subject of UC is not a substratum.

Let us turn to examine some features of a report of a QC. Consider: 'Smith got a tan at the beach last week'. On being asked 'Who?' the speaker could answer in two significantly different ways. He could identify Smith by means of a descriptive phrase ('the man who was chairman last year', e.g.) referring both to a time prior to last week and to Smith. But one could not identify the grass which came up after the rain by a single description referring both to a time prior to the rain and to the grass. The speaker could also identify Smith by means of a descriptive phrase ('the man who is standing in the door', e.g.) referring both to a time after last week and to Smith. But one could not identify the cow drowned last night by a single description referring both to a time after last night and to the cow. Thus, in regard to Smith's being, the tanning is not initiative, and it need not be terminal. Depending on the context of the question, either 'Smith got tanned' or 'Smith's back got tanned' could be appropriate as a response to 'What got tanned?' And either Smith or his back both persists through and undergoes the tanning. Where the first answer is appropriate, Smith is not only a substratum but also a subject of the QC in question.[12] Where the second answer is appropriate, Smith's back is both a subject and a substratum of the tanning.

(B) Now consider 'PM' understood as follows:

$$D1 \qquad PM =_{df} \text{ the substratum which is the subject of } UC.[13]$$

[11] Substratum, but not substance. For, before it drowns, the cow and its body are not, in one and the same context of discourse, two substances. Cf. *Meta.* 1039a 3 ff.

[12] The principle 'In a QC there is a substratum which is a subject' is not trivially analytic; 'being a subject of change' is not part of the definiens of 'substratum'. "When a 'simple' thing is said to become something, in the one case ['man becomes musical'] it survives the process, in the other case ['non-musical becomes musical'] it does not" (*Phys.* 190a 8–9). Nevertheless, seeing that there is a substratum which is a subject of a QC is seeing something about the structure of our thought about QC and is, thus, unlike finding that the suicide rate is higher in northern countries.

[13] " 'Matter', in the most proper sense of the term, is to be identified with the substratum which is receptive of coming-to-be and passing away" (*De Gen. et Corrup.* 320a 3–5).

Consider *D1* in respect to passing away, first. When a cow drowns, an oak is felled, hay burns, a criminal is executed, or a city is destroyed the subject of the change does not persist and is, hence, not a substratum. In the sentences 'The cow drowned', 'The oak has been felled', 'The hay burnt', etc. the referents of the grammatical subjects of the change verbs are clearly the subjects of the changes. The cow, the oak, the hay, etc. undergo the changes in question; they are receptive of passing away. In 'The flood drowned the cow', 'Jones felled the oak', and 'Bombing destroyed the city' the grammatical subjects of the *UC* verbs do not refer to the subjects of the changes in question. In these cases the *UC* verbs are transitive. Where they function intransitively, i.e. where the verbs are either intransitive or in the passive voice as in 'The cow drowned', 'The criminal was executed', and 'The city was destroyed', the grammatical subjects do refer to the subjects of changes. In what follows, when we speak of the grammatical subject of a *UC* verb for passing away we shall mean the grammatical subject of a *UC* verb for passing away which is functioning intransitively.

Now consider *D1* in respect to coming to be. That which comes up, is born, or results from a metamorphosis (as a frog does from a tadpole) is not a substratum. Is it a subject of *UC*; is it receptive of coming to be? The grass comes to be when it comes up and the man comes to be when he is born. Thus we shall say that the grass and the man are subjects of *UC*. The fact that prior to coming up there is no grass and that prior to being born there is no man does not mean that the grass and the man cannot be subjects of coming to be. It means only that the subjects of coming to be have a different temporal relationship to coming to be than do the subjects of passing away to passing away. In 'Abraham begot Isaac' and 'The rain brought up the grass' the grammatical subjects do not refer to the subjects of the changes in question. Here the coming-to-be verbs are transitive. When they function intransitively as in 'Isaac was born', 'Isaac was generated from a fertilized ovum', 'The grass came up', and 'The grass came up from the seed' the grammatical subjects do refer to the subjects of change. In what follows when we speak of the grammatical subject of a *UC* verb for coming to be we shall mean the grammatical subject of a *UC* verb for coming to be which is functioning intransitively. Thus we have the general convention that whenever we speak of the grammatical subject of a *UC* verb for passing away or of one for coming to be, we shall mean the grammatical subject of a *UC* verb which is functioning intransitively.

Special treatment needs to be given to 'becomes' and related verbs. 'Becomes' is unlike both the *UC* verbs for passing away and the *UC* verbs for coming to be thus far mentioned. We might say that the seed became, came to be, or turned into grass, but we would not say that the grass came up *something*. The grass simply came up or came up from seed. Moreover, we might say that the cow became, came to be, or turned into a carcass, but we would not say that the cow drowned *something*. The cow simply drowned. Since 'becomes' and 'comes to be' are convertible one might urge that that which becomes something is, as such, a subject of coming to be. Thus when seed becomes grass both seed and grass come to be. This is a mistake resulting from a failure to distinguish coming to be something from coming to be—'comes to be' with a direct object from 'comes to be' without a direct object. In the previous paragraph the *UC* verbs for coming to be were such that with them one could assert coming to be, but not coming to be something. Taking this as a defining feature of verbs for coming to be, it follows that verbs of the 'becomes' family are not verbs for coming to be. Certainly the referent of a subject of 'becomes' (with an object) undergoes change. It is then a subject of change even though it is not a subject in the sense of that which comes to be. In unqualifiedly becoming something a thing passes away into something. Thus that which becomes something is a subject of change in that it passes away. In view of the special nature of the 'becomes'-family, we shall not place its members, even when they are used to report *UC*'s, under either the category of *UC* verbs for passing away or that of *UC* verbs for coming to be. Nonetheless, a similarity remains in that the subject of an unqualified becoming-something is not a substratum.

Ordinary language is, thus, such that a substantive attached, as subject, to a verb for *UC*—be it a *UC* verb for passing away, coming to be, or becoming—cannot be treated as referring to a substratum of the change asserted. For, if one were to treat such a substantive in this manner, it would be permissible to attempt to identify that to which it supposedly refers both by means of a description referring exclusively to a time before and by means of a description referring exclusively to a time after the occurrence of the asserted change. But, as is clear from the discussion of admissible answers to the questions 'Which cow?' and 'Which grass?', both descriptions cannot be used without displaying a misunderstanding of the *UC* verb in question.

It is now possible to decide, in the third setting for existential problems, whether everyday assertions of *UC* commit us to the existence of *PM* in the sense of *D1*. Note that *PM* in the sense of *D1* is a subject of *UC* and that subjects of change enter discourse through substantives alone. But our discourse cannot, for the reason given in the last paragraph, contain substantives playing a subject-substratum role for *UC* verbs. Thus, even under a liberal ontological criterion which treats every substantive as designative, everyday discourse lacks a *PM* ontology, since it can have no substantives playing a subject-substratum role. Moreover, since *PM* could enter discourse only through substantives, a more liberal criterion which treats predicates and other expressions as designative would fail to show that ordinary assertions of UC commit us to the existence of PM in the sense of $D1$. But suppose 'PM' is understood as follows:

> $D2$ $PM =_{df}$ that from which a thing comes to be without qualification and which persists in the result.[14]

Learning makes a literate person from an illiterate one, but literacy does not come to be without qualification ($\mu\dot{\eta}$ $\kappa\alpha\tau\dot{\alpha}$ $\sigma\upsilon\mu\beta\epsilon\beta\eta\kappa\acute{o}s$) either from an illiterate person or from illiteracy. Literacy comes to be in virtue of the qualification ($\kappa\alpha\tau\dot{\alpha}$ $\sigma\upsilon\mu\beta\epsilon\beta\eta\kappa\acute{o}s$), illiteracy. But a blade of grass is said to come up from a seed. Usage requires no mention of a qualification. The blade of grass comes to be from the seed without qualification. Yet the that-from-which, the seed, does not persist in the blade of grass. Seed-stuff, however, does persist. To determine whether the seed-stuff is also a that-from-which the blade comes to be without qualification we must keep in mind that the object of 'comes to be without qualification from' is a substantival word or phrase. We would, then, not have 'comes to be from wise, chloric, or glucosic', but rather 'comes to be from a wise father, from hydrochloric acid, or from a seed containing glucose'. But 'The blade of grass came up from a seed containing glucose' deprives glucose of the role of a that-from-which, giving this role to the seed which contains glucose. On the other hand, to say 'The blade came up from glucose' might suggest to our hearers that the blade had been artificially synthesized. If, in fact, grass could be synthesized from glucose and 'The blade came up from glucose' could then be used in a straight-forward manner, glucose, like the seed in the natural process, would not persist as a substance in the result. Thus, whether there is a natural or a synthetic coming-up of the grass, seed-stuff cannot satisfy both of the conditions of $D2$. It either persists and is not a that-from-which or does not persist and is a that-from-which.

is the result of the UC in question'. For, if (i) is true, (ii) can be true only

In our conceptual scheme for UC the concept of a that-from-which-something-comes-to-be-without-qualification and that of an element-persisting-in-the-result-of-a-change are incompatible. That is, the following sentences cannot be jointly true when 'A' has the same significance in both: (i) 'A is that from which B came to be unqualifiedly' and (ii) 'A persists in B which if it is equivalent to 'B, which is the result of the UC, contains A-stuff or

---

[14] "For my definition of matter is just this—the primary substratum of each thing, from which it comes to be without qualification, and which persists in the result" (*Phys.* 192a 31–2). *Gloss:* If one regards 'persists in the result' as a defining predicate for 'substratum', and 'from which it comes to be without qualification' as tantamount to 'primary', then what follows 'the primary substratum of each thing' will not be viewed as giving a differentia in respect to, but as expressing a definition of, 'primary substratum' and, hence, of 'matter'.

has the character of an *A* thing'. Thus, if 'Glucose is that from which grass comes up' (i') is true, then 'Glucose persists in the grass' (ii') can be true only if (ii') means the same as 'The grass which comes up is a glucosic thing'. "As for that out of which as matter they are produced, some things are said, when they have been produced, to be not that but 'thaten'; e.g. the statue is not gold but golden."[15] One could say of the glucose mentioned in (i') that it is on the ground or in a pan, in the same sense that one could say of a block that it is in a box, of a diamond that it is in a ring, or of a board that it is in a scaffold. But the glucose mentioned in (ii'), like iron in the blood stream or sodium in salt, is in something in quite a different sense. It is in grass in the sense that grass is glucosic. In order to label this distinction, we can say that in (i') 'glucose' has a *substantial* while in (ii') it has an *aspectual* significance. Conversely, if (ii) is true, (i) can be true only if '*A*' changes its sense in an identical fashion. In (ii) '*A*' will have an aspectual significance, if *B* is the result of a *UC* rather than of a spatial re-arrangement of things. Thus, with (ii) true and *B* the result of a *UC*, '*A*' in (i) will undoubtedly have a substantial significance. It is essential to note that the incompatibility of (i) and (ii) with univocal '*A*' results here from the way our use of change-words construes '*A*'. It does not result from a restriction independently imposed by ordinary discourse on the variety of types of things '*A*' could signify. The ordinary concept of *UC* is, then, such that it is incompatible with a *PM* ontology, when '*PM*' is taken in the sense of *D2*.

The compatibility of (i) and (ii) with univocal '*A*' would require a twofold change in the customary conceptual scheme. First, the concept of *UC* would have to be modified so that consistently with it one could speak of something which is both a that-from-which and persistent. Second, a concept would have to be added which can play the substratum—that-from-which role opened up by the modified concept of *UC*. For otherwise the conceptual scheme containing the modified concept of *UC* would be inadequate in an important respect. The modified scheme is adequate only if in it there is a way of expressing those changes which in the customary scheme are expressed as *UC*. Linguistically this means that one will need a translation of 'The grass came up from seed', e.g., into the language of the modified scheme. In expressing a *UC* in the modified scheme one will make use of the modified concept of *UC*. But an actual substance, such as a seed, does not play the substratum—that-from-which role needed in a modified *UC*. Thus unless a restriction is to be placed on the adequacy of the modified scheme for expressing changes, there is a need for an added concept, a concept of

15 *Meta.* 1033a 5–7.

"something which *potentially* 'is', but *actually* 'is not'."[16] The linguistic counterpart of the addition of this concept is the introduction of a new type of substantive, the *PM* designator, which conforms to the role opened by the modified concept of *UC*. It cannot be maintained that the addition of a concept of something which can be a substratum—that-from-which is alone sufficient. For this concept cannot, in view of the last paragraph, be applied along with the customary concept of *UC*.

§4 *The Concept of Change in a Primary-Matter Language*

Now I shall sketch the outlines of a *PM* language whose rules for '*PM*' itself jointly correspond to the Aristotelian concept of *PM*.

Through *D1-2* of §3 (B), two senses of *PM* have been introduced. What relation can be established between them? Suppose that in our *PM* language, call it *PMese*, we formulate the following sentences: '*PM* comes to be'[17] and '*PM* comes to be from *PM*'.[18] Assume that both sentences are used to refer to the same change. The first occurrence of '*PM*' in both sentences has a subject role, and the second occurrence of '*PM*' in the second sentence has a that-from-which-role. Does '*PM*' have the same reference in both

---

[16] *De Gen. et Corrup.* 317b 16–18. Here Aristotle argues that, if there is to be *UC*, something must come to be without qualification from something which is not a substance, not indeed from unqualified not-being but from something which is potentially. For a discussion of this argument see §5(B), below.

[17] "The matter comes to be and ceases to be in one sense, while in another it does not. As that which contains the privation, it ceases to be in its own nature . . ." (*Phys.* 192a 25–7). Thus we are permitted to say '*PM* comes up', '*PM* is born', '*PM* is destroyed', and '*PM* burns up'. But a regress results (*Ibid.*, 27–33) if these sentences are understood in the same way that 'The grass comes up', 'The man is born', 'The city is destroyed', and 'The hay burns up' are understood. Coming to be and passing away are initiative and terminal, respectively, for substances. But coming to be and passing away are neither initiative nor terminal for *PM*. Thus when 'comes up', 'is born', 'is destroyed', or 'burns up' takes '*PM*' as subject, the verb must be allowed to change its meaning in such a way that the substantive used as its subject refers to a substratum. The sense in which *PM* comes to be or passes away is the sense in which a substance undergoes a *QC*. With *PM* designators as subjects, *UC* verbs take on the grammar of *QC* verbs. '*PM* comes up' is like 'Smith walks' in that, in both, the subject has the role of a substratum.

[18] "Matter, which is being in potency, is that-from-which something comes to be unqualifiedly, because this is what enters into the substance of the thing made" (Aquinas, *In I Phys., l.*14, §8). Now just as we can say in ordinary discourse both that *the grass* came up and that *the grass* came up from the seed, so too we will say in *PMese* both that *PM* comes to be and *PM* comes to be from *PM*. I.e., when in *PMese* the subject of 'comes to be' (without an object) is '*PM*', the subject of 'comes to be from' will be '*PM*'.

roles? In respect to ordinary talk about UCs, subject and that-from-which are distinct: the blade of grass comes up from the seed but, in the intended sense, the seed does not come up. Now, by definition, both the PM which comes to be and the PM which is a that-from-which persist through the coming to be. But for them to do this does not make them the same. There is another similarity between the two: as is clear from §3, neither a subject-substratum nor a that-from-which-substratum of UC is a substance. Thus not only are they alike in being substrata but they are alike in being non-substances on the order of substances[19] or, if you like, potential substances. But still the PM which comes to be and the PM which is a that-from-which may be different potential substances. We can then say that $D1$-2 leave open the question whether 'PM' in the subject role and 'PM' in the that-from-which role in the above sentences refer to the same bit of PM. In a particular case this indeterminacy would show itself in our being unable to say whether, if 'The PM of B comes to be from the PM of A' is true, then 'The PM of A comes to be' is true, and conversely. $D1$ can be regarded as a rule to the effect that a PM designator can be used as a subject in a PMese rendering of a statement of UC. $D2$ can be regarded as a rule to the effect that a PM designator can be used in a that-from-which role in such a statement. To eliminate the indeterminacy just mentioned a further rule is required. Since a separation of subject-substrata from that-from-which—substrata would be a complication without advantage, the rule we choose will assert their identity. It can be stated as follows:

> $R1$ The PM of B comes to be from (passes away into) the PM
> of A if and only if the PM of A comes to be (passes away).

This rule has the effect of uniting into a single concept the two senses of PM introduced by $D1$-2. Those definitions staked out two grammatical roles for PM designators; $R1$ allows, in a context in which a single change is being described, one and the same PM designator to play both of those roles.

In PMese there will be no use for 'this PM' or 'the PM to the left of this PM', when the *linguistic* context fails to specify further which PM *this PM* is. In English, by contrast, we have a use for 'this cow' and for 'the building to the left of this tree' without additional linguistic specification of the *this*. The use of 'PM' in PMese is governed by the following rule:

> $R2$ 'PM' will occur only in descriptions containing definite or
> indefinite references to substances or in contexts which can
> be straightforwardly expanded to contain such descriptions.

---

[19] "This [the underlying nature] is one principle (though not one or existent in the same sense as the 'this')" (*Phys.* 191a 12).

Nothing then is to count as *PM* unless it is the *PM* of some substance,[20] just as nobody is called a king unless there is a kingdom which he rules or pretends to rule. Thus we are to identify a bit of *PM* by means of a description such as 'the *PM* of this seed', 'the *PM* of the last tree in this row', or 'the *PM* of the executive who hired Smith'. If instead of wishing to identify a bit of *PM*, we wish only to refer indefinitely to some bit or other of it, then we will use 'the *PM* of something'. Nonetheless, we will allow '*PM* came up from *PM*' and '*PM* came up'. But we are to understand these sentences as meaning the same as 'The *PM* of something came up from the *PM* of something' and 'The *PM* of something came up'. Compare: 'It germinated in water', which has as an expansion 'It germinated in some volume of water'.

How are we to identify the *PM* underlying a given *UC*? The descriptions 'the *PM* from which the *PM* of *A* comes to be' and 'the *PM* which comes to be' are unavailing. For, using them, we get not synthetic but analytic statements of change: 'The *PM* of *A* comes to be from the *PM* from which the *PM* of *A* comes to be' and 'The *PM* which comes to be comes to be'. We shall choose the following means. It is already agreed that, for a given *UC*, a substratum which is a *subject* is the same as a substratum which is a *that-from-which*. To identify the one is also to identify the other. Thus for the purpose at hand we need only one further rule:

> *R3* The persistent *that-from-which* of a *UC* in which *B* comes to be from *A* and from nothing else, while nothing else comes to be from *A*, is identical with the *PM* of *A*.

Hence, by *R1*, the persistent *subject* of a *UC* in which *B* comes to be from *A* and from nothing else, while nothing else comes to be from *A*, is the *PM* of *A*. Since, by *D2*, *PM* persists in the result, the *PM* of *A* is identical with the *PM* of *B*, provided that *B* comes to be from *A* and nothing else and that nothing else comes to be from *A*. Thus either 'the *PM* of *A*' or 'the *PM* of *B*' can be used to make an identifying reference to the *PM* from which the *PM* of *B* comes to be as well as to the *PM* which comes to be. So far it would seem that the *PM* of a given *UC* depends, as regards making an identification of it,[21] either on the substance which comes to be, *B*, or on one which passes away, *A*, in *that UC*. But we can widen the alternatives for such a dependence. Suppose that *B* comes to be from *A*, that there is something else, *A'*, which contributes to *B*, and that there is something else, *B'*, to which *A* contributes. Then we can say only that some part of the *PM* of *B*

---

[20] "In all instances of coming-to-be the matter is inseparable, being numerically identical and one with the 'containing' body, though isolated from it by definition" (*De Gen. et Corr.* 320b 13–4).

[21] Cf. Strawson, *Individuals*, London, 1959, Part I, Chap. I, Sec. 3.

is identical with some part of the *PM* of *A*.[22] It is now clear that, if *C* comes to be from *B* and *B* comes to be from *A*, the *PM* of *C* is, at least in part, some part at least of the *PM* of *A*. If, however, *C* is connected with *A* neither directly nor by a chain of several comings-to-be-from, then we shall say that the *PM* of *C* is neither in whole nor in part identical with that of *A* or that of part of *A*. Recognition of a chain of change is a condition for re-identifying part or all of the *PM* of *A* as now part or all of the *PM* of *C*.

PM designators cannot be used in assertions of change unless the meanings of customary *UC* verbs are altered (cf. §3(B) *ad fin.*). 'Comes up' in '*PM* comes up' and in 'The grass comes up' does not have the same meaning. When grass comes up, the grass does not exist before the coming up. But, in *PM*ese, coming-to-be verbs are used in such a way that it is possible for their subjects to have a substratum role. Moreover, while the seed does not last through the grass' coming up, the *PM* from which the *PM* of the blade of grass comes up is in the blade once it comes up. Change verbs in *PM*ese corresponding to *UC* verbs in ordinary discourse are such that designators which play a subject or a that-from-which role in respect to them also play a substratum role in respect to them. Whether 'comes up', e.g., in *PM*ese is to have a different meaning in *all* or only in *some* of its uses from that which it has in English depends on a further choice. There is a "pure" and a "mixed" *PM*ese. (i) In the pure language there are no statements of *UC*. In it every use of 'comes up', 'dies', 'is born', or 'drowns' is in certain respects like a use of 'walks', 'tans', 'fidgets', or 'warms up' in the assertion of a *QC*. The subjects of all changes will be persistent. Since, then, the behavior of change-verbs in pure *PM*ese no longer warrants a distinction between *UC* and *QC*, we shall call all changes *qualified-like changes* (*Q-LCs*).[23] Abolishing this distinction represents a conceptual economy as regards kinds of change. It involves replacing the *UC* statements 'The cow drowned' and 'The grass came up from the seed' by the *Q-LC* statements 'The *PM* of

---

[22] This passage provides a rule for the use of the part-whole distinction in respect to the *PM* of any given thing. Further rules can be obtained by a deployment in *PM*ese of familiar rules for 'part' and 'whole' as applied to particulars. Thus, just as, if *A* is not the whole of *B*, there is something besides *A* which in part or whole is a part of *B*; so too, if the *PM* of *A* is not the whole of the *PM* of *B*, there is something besides *A* whose *PM* in part or whole is part of the *PM* of *B*.

[23] In grouping both 'comes up' and 'grows' together as *Q-LC* verbs, rather than as *QC* verbs, of pure *PM*ese, we are recognizing both a similarity and a difference between them. The difference consists in the fact that in pure *PM*ese 'comes up' takes *PM* designators as subjects, while 'grows', 'warms', 'tans', and the like take names of substances as subjects. The similarity consists in the fact that in pure *PM*ese both 'comes up' and 'grows' are unlike ordinary *UC* verbs in that subjects for both 'comes up' and 'grows' have a substratum role.

the cow drowned' and 'The *PM* of the grass came up from the *PM* of the seed'.[24] In pure *PMese* substances do not come to be or come to be from something. Rather, they only come to be in such and such ways ('The man came to be darker' and 'The fruit vendor came to be wealthy'); they only undergo what in ordinary discourse would be *QCs*.[25] Only *PM* comes to be *simpliciter* or comes to be from something, but it does this in a changed sense of coming to be. As regards verbs of the 'becomes' family, one cannot in pure *PMese* say that one substance becomes another. Rather, the *PM* of one becomes the *PM* of another. Substances only become in such and such ways. In effect, ordinary *UC* verbs for coming to be, for passing away, and for becoming give way in pure *PMese* in favor of *Q-LC* verbs for coming to be, passing away, and becoming. (ii) In the mixed language, however, statements of *UC* can still be formed. But, in the mixed language, each statement of *UC* can be paired with what is to be regarded as an equivalent statement using one or more *PM* designators. 'Comes up', e.g., will have both its English use and a use which makes it a verb for *Q-LC*. Whether one chooses a pure or a mixed *PMese*, it is to be noted that *PM* designators can have neither the subject nor the that-from-which role in assertions of change which employ verbs in their *UC* senses.

Could pure *PMese* be used in communicating about changes? Clearly not, if there were no way of learning in which situations a given *PM* designator applies and in which it does not. Offhand, one might think that a *PM* designator, like the stereotype of a "metaphysical" expression, has no rules for its application to empirical situations. Thus it could be objected that the use of a *PM* designator in a statement of change makes of that statement a non-factual one which, since it is not analytic, must be a pseudo-statement. If there are no rules for the correct application of a *PM* designator, then to say that the *PM* of grass comes up from the *PM* of seed is to give no factual information about the origin of this change. But this objection need not apply to pure *PMese*. (i) In teaching pure *PMese* as a first language one would teach the use of certain change verbs only in contexts containing '*PM*'. The contexts 'The *PM* of . . . came up' and 'the *PM* of _____ came up from the *PM* of . . .' would be learned as units. Thus, in its basic use 'the *PM* of' would be part of a change verb in the way that 'ne' is a part of 'ne . . . pas'. To the extent then that there are empirical situations in regard to which one learns to apply or withhold change verbs, there are empirical situations in regard to which one learns to apply or withhold 'the *PM* of'. However, 'the *PM* of',

---

[24] Following Aristotle (*De Gen. et Corr.* 317b 23–5), 'The cow passed away into the cow-carcass' would give way to 'The *PM* of the cow passed away into the *PM* of the cow-carcass'. (Cf. *R1*.)

[25] Cf. *De Gen. et Corr.* 318a 32–5.

M. Fisk

but not 'comes up', 'is born', 'drowns', and the like, would have derivative uses outside of the mentioned contexts. Thus one would be taught that, in a context in which 'the *PM* of *A* came up from the *PM* of *B*' would be appropriate, one could say that the *PM* of *A* is all or part of the *PM* of *B*. (ii) In teaching pure *PM*ese, not as a first language, but through rules relating it to e.g., English, the question whether change statements in *PM*ese are empirically testable reduces to the question whether the rules are such that they determine the truth values of *PM*ese statements through the truth values of English statements of change whose testability is not here in question. *D1-2* of §3(B) can be regarded as telling us how *PM* designators are to function in statements in *PM*ese which correspond to statements of *UC* in an ordinary language. So regarded they suggest this co-ordinating procedure: the English statement '*A* comes to be (ceases to be)' is true if and only if the *PM*ese statement 'The *PM* of *A* comes to be (ceases to be)' is true; and '*A* comes to be from (passes away into) *B*' is true if and only if 'The *PM* of *A* comes to be from (passes away into) the *PM* of *B*' is true. *R1-3*, by which *D1-2* were supplemented, provide further coordinating procedures with the net effect that pure *PM*ese learned through another language receives the needed empirical grounding. (Since mixed *PM*ese can be considered the result of combining a natural language with pure *PM*ese, the problem whether in mixed *PM*ese sentences containing change verbs and *PM* designators can be used to convey information about changes reduces to the problem just discussed regarding pure *PM*ese.)

We have before us now the major differences between the customary scheme with its concepts of *UC* and *QC* and both the pure *PM* scheme with its single concept of *Q-LC* and the mixed scheme with its concepts of *UC* and *Q-LC*. Is there any reason recommending either of the latter for philosophic employment? Does the customary scheme hide a contradiction (cf. §5)? Would an analysis of concepts of the customary scheme fail to bring philosophic inquiry to its goal, unless the concept of *PM* were introduced (cf. §6)?

§5 *Two Supposed Proofs of Primary Matter*

(A) If there is substantial change, there must be a substantial subject which through corruption loses its substantial being and through generation acquires a new substantial being. But a subject which can lose or acquire some kind of being is in potency to it. Therefore, we must admit a substantial principle which is ordered to something else as potency is to act. This subject we call primary matter.[26]

[26] E. Hugon, *Philosophia Naturalis*, Paris, no date, p. 118, reprinted in translation in *Readings in the Philosophy of Nature*, ed. Koren, Westminster, Md., 1958, p. 135.

230

Here in a nutshell is a little questioned but, for many, the only prop for the claim that commitment to a *PM* ontology is a necessity for thought about change. The argument contains a *petitio principii* which has gone unnoticed for so long because of a failure to see in the argument a hopeless confusion of the customary and the *PM* conceptual schemes.

We shall let S stand for 'If there is UC, then there is a subject-substratum', which has the same force as the conditional with which the above quotation begins. Those who would employ the argument outlined in that quotation would treat S as an indisputable truth of reason. We shall let S' stand for 'If there is UC, then there is no subject-substratum', which, in view of §3 and §4, follows, not from the fact that in everyday speech one does not or has not yet used noun expressions with a substratum role as subjects of UC verbs, but from the fact that one cannot use them in this way without changing the UC verbs into non-ordinary Q-LC verbs. The result of joining S and S' with 'There is UC' is the contradiction that there is and there is not a subject-substratum. The claim that there is UC is not here in question. To avoid this contradiction, while respecting the indisputability of S, it would seem necessary to reject the customary scheme in favor of either the pure or the mixed *PM* scheme. In this way S', which is true only relative to the customary scheme, could no longer command assent.

But we must ask which conceptual scheme it is that gives S its indisputability. S is true only if concepts of drowning, coming-up, and the like are structured in essential respects like concepts of QC. Thus S is true only in respect to a conceptual scheme in which either the concept of Q-LC has replaced the concept of UC (the pure scheme) or the concept of Q-LC has been paired with that of UC (the mixed scheme). This imposes the further restriction that S cannot be true unless its antecedent, 'there is UC', is construed as meaning the same as 'there is a type of change which in the customary scheme would be UC'. It follows that: (1) *The contradiction arising from the conjunction of S and S' is innocuous*. It results from a combination of statements true only in different conceptual schemes. It damages the customary scheme of concepts of change no more than Euclidean geometry is damaged by the fact that a contradiction arises from the conjunction of Euclid's axioms with the non-Euclidean theorem that similar triangles do not always have corresponding equal angles. (2) *One begs the question in using S to prove that PM exists*. Suppose S is true in respect to a given scheme. Could one know that it is true without appealing directly to the fact that the scheme in question has a *PM* ontology? To come to know that S is true of a given scheme one must first come to know that the concepts of coming-up, drowning, and the like, of that scheme, are Q-LC concepts, not UC concepts. But in order to come to know this one must know that these concepts are applied along with that of *PM* (cf. §3(B) *ad fin.*). I.e., one must come to know that 'comes up', 'drowns', and the like are used together with *PM* designators in assertions of change. Thus to come to know that *S* is true of a given scheme requires that one first come to know that the scheme in question has a *PM* ontology. Using *S* to prove that *PM* exists begs the question.[27]

(B) "As the saying goes, it is impossible that anything should be produced if there were nothing existing before. Obviously then some part of the result will pre-exist of necessity."[28] But what pre-exists and persists in a *UC*? The seed pre-existed, but, as a seed, it does not persist. Both the seed and the grass are organic things, but considered just as an organic thing the grass does not come up, for no change would be needed to produce an organic thing from an organic thing.[29] The grass comes up from a glucose-containing-thing, and the grass itself is composed of glucose. Yet neither the glucose-containing-thing nor, in the hypothetical case of a synthesis, an initially isolated quantity of glucose persists as a substance in the grass. But, it will be said, if *UC* is not to be a kind of "creation", something on the order of substance must be posited which both pre-exists and persists.[30] Not being an actual substance, the posited element will be a potential substance from which the change proceeds.[31] By *D2* of §3, it will be *PM*.

We shall let *T* stand for 'If there is *UC*, some part of the result will pre-exist', on which the above argument for *PM* rests. We shall let *T'* stand for 'If there is *UC*, no part of the result pre-exists', which is a consequence of our examination of the customary scheme, or, indeed, of any scheme in which *UC* verbs are not changed to function as *Q-LC* verbs. The conjunction of *T* and *T'* with 'There is *UC*' leads to the contradiction that there is and there is not a persistent that-from-which. To avoid the contradiction while respecting the indisputable "saying" *T*, it would seem necessary to reject the customary scheme in favor of either the pure or the mixed *PM* scheme.

---

[27] It is often said by scholastics that all change involves substratum since the principles of *QC* must be verified in *UC*, because in both there is coming-to-be. (Cf., e.g., D. O'Donoghue, "The Nature of Prime Matter and Substantial Form," *Philosophical Studies* (Maynooth), 3, 1953, p. 35.) But they engender confusion by failing to note that such a claim is true only on the assumption that change is a concept of the pure or of the mixed *PM* scheme.

[28] *Meta.* 1032b 30–31.

[29] *Phys.* 191b 17–25.

[30] Cf. Aquinas, *In I Phys. l.*14, 7, where a variant form of this conclusion runs as follows: "If being comes to be *per accidens* from both being and non-being, we must posit something from which being comes to be *per se* because everything which is *per accidens* is reduced to that which is *per se*." That from which "being comes to be *per se*" pre-exists and persists, for "something comes to be *per se* from something else because the latter is in the thing after the thing is already made (*Ibid.*, 5).

[31] *Meta.* 1069b 19–20.

But in reference to what scheme is T indisputable? Doesn't, one might ask, T merely deny the identity of UC and creation? And, if it does only this, then it surely stands on all fours as a truth about the everyday scheme. We must reply that 'creation' is used in a non-ordinary sense when T is identified with 'UC is not creation'. Most people would be satisfied that grass hasn't been created—if there had been any doubt—when they find that grass comes up from seed. Yet 'creation' has a quite different use as employed by the philosopher who says that T means the same as 'UC is not creation' and who is then led to say that, without PM, UC would be creation. For him it is not enough that grass should come up from seed for its doing so to fall short of creation. For him there is no creation only if there is a persistent that-from-which. But with 'creation' used in this non-ordinary way, the statement 'UC is not creation', and hence T itself, is false in regard to the customary scheme. When 'UC is not creation' is true, as it is in regard to the customary scheme, provided that 'creation' has its customary sense, it cannot be identified with T.

We must, then, say that T is true only if concepts of drowning, coming-up, and the like are structured in essential respects like concepts of QC. Thus T is true only in respect to the pure or the mixed PM scheme. It follows that: (1) *The contradiction arising from the conjunction of T and T' is innocuous*. It is not a contradiction within the customary QC-UC scheme. It can be regarded as seriously damaging the worth of the QC-UC scheme only if one fails to distinguish that scheme from the pure and the mixed PM schemes. (2) *One begs the question in using T to prove that PM exists.* T is true only in a scheme containing Q-LC concepts. But to recognize a concept such as that of coming-up or drowning as a Q-LC concept requires knowing that it is applied, in some instances at least, along with a concept of PM. For it is through its application together with PM that such a Q-LC concept is distinct from a UC concept. Thus to recognize that T or, more exactly, 'If there is a change which in the customary scheme would be a UC, some part of the result will pre-exist' is true, requires knowing that the conceptual scheme in respect to which it is true has a PM ontology.

§6 *Is There Need for an Artificial Language of Change?*

We now face the question of the explanatory value of the concept of PM. There are two ways in which it might be claimed that PM serves to explain customary UC. (A) It might be claimed that an analysis of the customary concept of UC reveals the concept of PM as one of its components.[32] (B) It might be claimed that theoretical advantages flow from the

---

[32] *Phys.* 190b 1–3.

replacement of the customary scheme containing the concept of *UC* with a non-customary scheme containing the concept of *PM* and its correlative the concept of *Q-LC*.[33] It will be shown that the concept of *PM* is explanatory in neither of the above senses.

(A) As is clear from §§3-4, analyses of customary statements of *UC* cannot be expressed by entailments mentioning *PM*. For, analyses of customary uses of 'is born', 'drowns', and other *UC* verbs reveal that the rules of use for these verbs are such as to deny to subjects of these verbs a substratum role. In addition, these analyses reveal that the that-from-or-into-which of a *UC* is not persistent. Only when 'is born' or 'drowns' is governed by the rules of pure or mixed *PM*ese can we say that that which is born or drowns is persistent and that, in respect to being born or drowning, there is a persistent that-from-which or a persistent that-into-which. But the concept of being born or of drowning in the pure or the mixed scheme is a replacement for the customary concept. If one sees that the pure or the mixed scheme is used to replace the customary scheme, one can avoid the mistake of treating an analysis of a change verb governed by the rules of pure or mixed *PM*ese as an analysis of a customary *UC* verb.[34] But if, while recognizing the difference between the two schemes, one insists that an analysis of customary *UC* reveals a persistent subject and a persistent that-from-which, then one betrays a lack of attention to the difference between the customary use of *QC* verbs and that of *UC* verbs. Introducing *PM* defeats the purpose of analyzing customary *UC*. For, introducing *PM* involves replacing the concept to be analyzed (viz., *UC*) by a different one (viz., *Q-LC*).

(B) "The underlying nature [*PM*] is an object of scientific knowledge by analogy."[35] This is not an analogy in the sense in which one might argue by analogy from the fact that Mars moves in an ellipse to the fact that Jupiter moves in an ellipse. 'Jupiter moves in an ellipse' is more probable relative to 'Mars moves in an ellipse' than in isolation, only if the meaning of 'Jupiter moves in an ellipse' leaves open the possibility of a verification independent of that of 'Mars moves in an ellipse'. In addition to having a use in arguments, analogy also has a use in the replacement of one conceptual scheme by another. (i) Suppose that, contrary to fact, 'Jupiter moves in an ellipse' is such that it is in principle impossible to obtain an independent verifica-

---

[33] We can, e.g., speak of replacing the family of qualitative temperature concepts with the concept of a numerical temperature functor, the Newtonian with the relativistic concept of temporal interval, and the family of concepts of conditionals with the concept of the material conditional for purposes of truth functional analysis.

[34] "Whenever one is clearly aware that one is . . . using one method of representation *as opposed to another*, one is likely to be careful not to make the mistake of mixing up the grammar of the two systems" (W. H. Watson, *On Understanding Physics*, New York, 1959; first ed., Cambridge, Eng., 1938, p. 49).

[35] *Phys.* 191a 8.

tion of it. Then to say that Jupiter moves in an ellipse *because* Mars does is tantamount to staying that henceforth we shall treat 'Jupiter is a planet' as entailing 'Jupiter moves in an ellipse' for by doing so we shall increase the number of respects in which Jupiter and Mars are alike. The *'because'* only *seems* to be that of an analogical argument. In fact, it serves to introduce the consideration of analogy which suggested the decision to replace the customary concept of planet by one which now entails elliptical motion. The replacing concept, planet, is such that Jupiter will necessarily possess, in so far as it is a planet, a characteristic which Mars possessed contingently in respect to the original concept of planet. But once the replacing concept is introduced, it will entail elliptical motion in its application to Mars also. We shall say that a conceptual replacement like this one is "based on analogy". It is based on analogy because it serves to increase the number of respects in which things to which the concept of planet applies are alike. (ii) Laws of physics which are based on regularities confirmed in domains in which length can be measured are used to tell us the diameter of the electron. Here one cannot argue by analogy that the dimensions of immeasurably small objects which are given by calculations in terms of these laws are correct because the dimensions predicted in terms of these laws for other objects have been verified by measurement. Rather, one decides to accept a concept of length which is interlocked with the other concepts of electrodynamics in such a way that numerical determinations of the latter entail determinations of the former.[36] The decision to introduce such a concept of length is based on analogy in that it increases the number of respects in which macrophysical and microphysical thought show structural similarities. (iii) We cannot hope to interpret "For as the bronze is to the statue . . . so is the underlying nature to substance"[37] as an analogical argument, but only as a prescription for a conceptual replacement based on analogy. The statement expresses a decision to harmonize the grammar of expressions for UC with that of those for artificial coming-to-be. By harmonizing the grammar of the two sets of expressions one increases the analogy between them. The analogy is significantly increased by the decision to replace every UC verb by a verb which can take PM designators as subjects. Thus the decision to make this replacement is based on analogy. Clearly then the sharp contrast which appears in the customary scheme between QC and

---

[36] "If these space coordinates cannot be given an independent meaning apart from the equations, . . . the attempted verification of the equations is impossible. . . . If we stick to the concept of length by itself, we are landed in a vicious circle. As a matter of fact, the concept of length disappears as an independent thing, and fuses in a complicated way with other concepts, all of which are themselves altered thereby" (Bridgman, "The Logic of Modern Physics", in *Readings in the Philosophy of Science*, ed. Feigl and Brodbeck, New York, 1953, pp. 44–45).

[37] *Phys.* 191a 9–12.

UC will disappear in the replacing scheme. But is the decision to introduce such a replacing scheme a philosophically fruitful one?

Physics, mathematics, and logic grow from conceptual replacement to conceptual replacement. In respect to these disciplines Carnap's counsel is unexceptionable: "Let us grant to those who work in any special field of investigation the freedom to use any form of expression which seems useful to them."[38] We can extend this toleration to those who work in the field of philosophical investigation. But being tolerant doesn't require being blind to whether or not it is philosophically pointless to choose a non-customary scheme. What does a *PM* language accomplish which ordinary English, say, does not? (i) It economizes on categories of change. True: but only at the expense of a double outlay for categories of being, actual and potential. (ii) It contains the intelligible principles[39] in respect to which change can be understood. Indeed, the mixed scheme contains concepts, among them that of *PM,* used in expressing entailments from any statement of *UC* as understood in the mixed scheme. But the concept of *UC* in the customary scheme cannot be correctly identified by just those entailments. (iii) It comports with corpuscular scientific theories to the extent that these theories are expressed in a language devoid of any vestige of a sharp distinction between *QC* and *UC.*[40] True again; but those theories have achieved a conceptual economy as regards change by the fruitful course of replacing the substances of the everyday world by corpuscular multiplicities, while in a *PM* scheme the substantial units of the replaced scheme remain intact. The scientific fruitlessness of the rules of a *PM* scheme contrasts with the scientific fruitfulness of the rules of a corpuscular scheme.

Thus we can point neither to a philosophical nor to a scientific advantage

---

[38] "Empiricism, Semantics, and Ontology", in *Meaning and Necessity,* Chicago, enlarged edition, 1956, Suppl. A, p. 221.

[39] "It is evident that in the generic sphere of intelligibility of the first order of abstraction, the notions and definitions resulting either from empiriological analysis, wherein all is resolved into the observable, or from ontological analysis, wherein everything is resolved into intelligible being, correspond to distinct kinds of knowledge" (Maritain, *La philosophie de la nature,* Paris, no date, p. 88). How else is resolution into "intelligible being" to be understood than as replacement by concepts of a non-customary scheme? But then "ontological analysis" need not be analysis of a customary concept in respect to which philosophical controversy arose. As we have seen, when *PM* is regarded as an "intelligible being" into which *UC* is resolved, *UC* has already undergone a transformation into *Q-LC.*

[40] Cf., e.g., Meyerson, *Identité et réalité,* Paris, 1908, Chap. 2, "Les théories mé-chaniques". More recently, pair production and pair annihilation have presented difficulties for theories with a univocal concept of change. Yet the hold of this concept is such that repairs in terms of an interpretation involving a particle's travelling part of its path by going backward in time have been judged feasible (cf. Reichenbach, *The Direction of Time,* Berkeley, 1956, Sec. 30).

stemming from a *PM* language. A proposal to adopt a *PM* language comes to resemble a proposal to speak Russian mid-way in a conversation which has thus far been carried on unhampered in English. The only purpose of the proposal is to show ourselves that we can do what is proposed. In occupying himself, as in §4, with piecing together the rules of *PM*ese, the philosopher abandons the question of the nature of changes asserted by means of *UC* verbs. He abandons analysis for the construction of an artificial language. And his procedure lacks philosophical importance so long as there is no way in which *PM* serves to explain *UC*.

$$* \quad * \quad * \quad * \quad *$$

I have regarded the question 'Does *PM* exist?' as a meaningful one, for I have assumed that, depending on the context in which it is raised, it could, without remainder, be replaced by one or another of the following meaningful questions: (1) Are there expressions used in customary assertions of *UC* which behave like *PM* designators (cf. §3)? (2) Do customary assertions of *UC* lead to contradictions which can be eliminated only by the addition of *PM* designators (cf §5)? (3) Do customary assertions of *UC* entail statements which, to be expressed, require the use of *PM* designators (cf. §6 (A))? (4) Is any theoretical advantage, beyond avoiding contradiction, to be derived from adopting a *PM* language for assertions of *UC* (cf. §6(B))? These questions have been answered negatively. Thus, when the question 'Does *PM* exist?' is raised in a wide variety of contexts relating to *UC*, it is, I believe, to be answered negatively.[41]

---

[41] This, of course, applies only to *PM* understood in the sense of *D1* or *D2* of §3(B) or in the sense of both, as is possible if one accepts *R1* of §4. I have not denied the existence of *PM* in other senses. (a) Suppose one were to define *PM* simply as a substratum of *UC*. The discussion of §3(B) serves to indicate that there is no objection to the claim that *PM* in this sense exists. That discussion serves to indicate also that a substratum of *UC* is neither a subject nor a that-from-which. (b) *PM* might be defined in terms of a that-from-which when this is taken in a derivative sense. When grass comes up from seed, the seed is a that-from-which in a primary sense. The glucose of the seed is a that-from-which in a derivative sense. It is a constituent, with aspectual significance, of the seed which is a that-from-which in the primary sense. Thus *A* is a that-from-which in a derivative sense when *A* is a constituent, with aspectual significance, of *B* which is a that-from-which. One could then define *PM* as a substratum—that-from-which (derivative sense) of *UC*. There is no trouble about the existence of *PM* in this sense. Even so *PM* in this sense lacks the indeterminacy or qualificationlessness classically associated with *PM* and derivable from *PM* in the sense of *D1* or *D2*. For glucose is a substratum—that-from-which (derivative sense) but is not indeterminate.

University of Notre Dame

COMMENT

For different reasons, lack of space among them, i shall not comment on MF's excellently argued paper in all its fine details, as it would deserve. I shall make some beginning comments on his §3, and on his footnote 41; these appear to be the basic comments to be made.

1. Apropos of §3, in which MF argues in his setting (3). — If *PM does not exist* is taken to mean: ordinary *assertions* of *UC* do not explicitly presuppose *PM*, then it is to be granted to MF that *PM does not exist*. But there are statements in ordinary language which, though they are *not assertions* of *UC*, nonetheless pertain to the context of *UC*, and which appear to me to presuppose *PM* implicitly.

In ordinary *assertions* of *UC*, there is no *subject*-substratum (*D1*), nor is there a *that-from-which*–substratum (*D2*). In ordinary assertions of *UC*, the *subject* and the *that-from-which* are a substance, and this substance ceases to be; hence it cannot be a substratum. Or, in the case of a *UC* verb for *coming to be* (used intransitively; e.g., the grass came up), the subject (grass) did not exist before the *UC*, and hence cannot be a substratum.

But there is a formulation of a sense of *PM* which is implied by ordinary statements, which are *not* ordinary *assertions* of *UC*, but which belong to the context of *UC*. — Consider the *UC*: *seed comes to be grass*. There are at least two other descriptions for the term *a quo*, i.e., the that-from-which, or for the subject, of this *UC*, namely: 1) *what-is-not-grass* comes to be grass, and 2) *what-can-be-grass* comes to be grass. Clearly, *seed* does not persist; for grass is not seed. *What-is-not-grass* does not persist; for grass is not· what-is-not-grass. And lastly, one will want to say on the pattern of the above that what-can-be-grass does not persist, for grass is not what-can-be-grass. But, if one considers this further, one can perhaps see a sense in which it can be maintained that what-can-be-grass does persist. Consider this example of a *QC* as an aid: *marble becomes statue*. Marble persists. But something else is to be noticed. Not just any kind of material can become a statue; for example, *water in its liquid state* cannot; water in this state is not such that it *can acquire and maintain* the shape or form of statue. Wood, however, along with marble, and glass, and clay, and metal—all of these *can acquire and maintain* the form which is the shape of statue, that whereby statue (after the change) differs from marble (before the change). This yields two senses for the potentiality-actuality or subject-received relation:

$$\text{sense 1}): \quad \frac{\text{potentiality (or subject)}}{\text{actuality (or received)}} : \frac{\text{something perfecti}ble\ (before\ \text{change})}{\text{perfection}\ (after\ \text{change})}$$

238

sense 2): $\dfrac{\text{''}}{\text{''}}$: $\dfrac{\text{something perfect}ed\ (after\ \text{change})}{\text{perfection}\ (after\ \text{change})}$

Apropos of sense 2), even *after* marble has become statue, it is clear that the shape is *an addition* to the marble as such.

Now, to return to the *UC*: *seed becomes grass. That* something survives is clear; MF indicates this himself when he writes: ". . . yet something of the material of the seed finds its way into the blade of grass; seed-stuff persists as grass-stuff . . ." The problem becomes *to give an acceptable description or definition* of what survives; this is perhaps the best way to formulate the problem of *PM*. One must notice here, as in the *QC: marble becomes statue,* that not just anything *can acquire and maintain* the form of grass. (By *form of grass* I do *not* mean the shape of the blade; I mean that whereby grass differs from seed; if grass does not differ from seed, then no *UC* has occurred.) A bar of iron, e.g., cannot. But that which we call *seed,* before the change, can. And that which we call *water* (before the change; not necessarily the same change in which seed becomes grass) can; and that which we call *nutriment in the soil* (before the change) can. Thus:

$\dfrac{\text{seed + water + nutriment}\ (\text{before the change})}{\text{form of grass}\ (\text{after the change})}$: $\dfrac{\text{something perfect}ible\ (\text{or subject})}{\text{perfection}\ (\text{or received})}$

$\dfrac{\text{seed-stuff (MF's phrase) + water-stuff + nutriment-stuff}\ (\text{after the change})}{\text{form of grass}\ (\text{after the change})}$: $\dfrac{\text{something perfect}ed\ (\text{or subject})}{\text{perfection}\ (\text{or received})}$

Thus, *PM* can be defined or described as *that which survives in a UC,* and which as surviving has a potentiality (sense 2) for substanitial form (*SF*), or is a subject (sense 2) of *SF*. (*SF* = df., that whereby the term *ad quem* in *UC* differs from the term *a quo*). — Some ordinary statements, which are *not assertions* of *UC*, but which belong to the context of *UC*, and which imply *PM* in the sense just described, are these: "A stone cannot come up grass, but grass seed can"; "A stick cannot come up a tree, but an acorn can."

Thus, since *PM* is a *subject* which survives, we appear to have D1. But *subject* does *not* mean *substance*. For *UC* can be defined as a change such that the substance which undergoes it ceases to be; and *QC* can be defined as a change such that the substance which undergoes it does not cease to be. From the very definition of *UC* it follows clearly that what survives is not the substance which undergoes *UC*. But something does survive. How describe it? As *part* of the *newly generated* substance, that part which is related to the new *SF* (this will be the other part) as potentiality to actuality (sense 2), or as subject to received (sense 2). — We seem also to have D2, for if *PM* is *what survives* the *UC, PM* must have pre-existed the *UC;* and hence is that-from-which the *UC* proceeds.

But it is *not* a *substance*. Pursuing the seed-stuff which persists, MF concludes that seed-stuff "either persists and is not a substantial that-from-which, or does not persist and is a substantial that-from-which". *PM*, I believe, can be described as what persists and is *not* a *substantial* that-from-which; but it is a that-from-which. Seed-stuff is one way of describing what persists; *PM* is another way of describing what persists, sc. in relation to the *one SF* of the substance which has come to be. (See below §2, the comment on MF's footnote 41).

The question to which MF addresses himself in §3 is this: ". . . does the unsophisticated language with which we make assertions of *UC* . . . explicitly presuppose *PM*?" His answer is negative; and I think I can agree with that answer. Yet, it seems that it must be allowed that the unsophisticated language with which we make statements pertaining to the context of *UC* implicitly presuppose *PM*. To speak of things like seed-stuff which persists in a change like: *seed comes up grass*, is to imply *PM*. To make statements like: "A stick cannot come up a tree, but an acorn can", is to imply *PM*.

I cannot at present (nor perhaps would I ever want to) defend the above formulated sense for *PM* as that of Aristotle. I am able at present to do only this much. In the *Physics*, Bk. I, ch. 7 (where he begins his analysis of *UC*, with the aid of an accompanying analysis of *QC*, which ultimately terminates in the definition (*D2*) of *PM* which MF records in his footnote 14), Aristotle states *explicitly* that he intends to approach becoming or change *in the widest possible sense*. This suggests that one consider individual instances of *UC* in an attempt to uncover the *most general possible description* of the principles involved in it. *PM*, according to the definition proposed above, is the *most general possible description* of *what survives* in a *UC*.

2.   Apropos of the second of the two senses of *PM* in which MF does not deny its existence (see footnote 41, sense *b*). — *PM*'s classical indeterminacy or qualificationlessness cannot be derived from MF's sense of *D1* and *D2*, since he takes *subject* in *D1* and *that-from-which* in *D2* as *substances*. Secondly, since there can be but one *SF* in each one substance, then *whatever survives in UC* (however it may be described or describable in whatever other relation or frame of reference) *when it is taken in relation to the substance which has come to be*, it must be absolutely indeterminate (i.e., must have neither substantial nor accidental determinations). For *SF* is the source of all the substantial determinations of a composed substance.

Joseph Bobik
University of Notre Dame

DISCUSSION

Sellars: If we make use of the example of the seed becoming grass, there's a danger that we make the mistake of thinking of a boy becoming a man as being a case of substantial change. In the latter case, we are all clear that the same form is involved and that in no sense is boy matter for man. Now, I think the seed case is a tricky one because there's an important sense in which the form is in the seed, so that in a way an acorn or a seed is, you might say, the completely undeveloped oak or man. That's why I think it is very important to make the step from seed to seed-stuff. And now the question is: can the seed-stuff be said to be that which continues, because it's granted that the seed does not? The fundamental metaphor of the Aristotelian four-cause system of explaining coming-to-be is the craftsman making something out of a certain material. You may want to reject the Aristotelian explanatory scheme, but I think the first discussion of prime matter should go in the context of this specific categorical framework of explanation. And here it seems to me perfectly clear that Aristotle is committed to the view that all corruptibles are generated in this way from an antecedent "stuff from which", which is "substance" only in an ordinary, non-technical sense. Our ordinary statements about unqualified change may not contain a term referring to prime matter. We have to ask ourselves: what is the character of our ordinary concepts of the things that do come into being? And then the Aristotelian question would be: are they conceptually accommodations to the form-matter metaphor? In other words, we have to ask: is the concept of matter involved in the very concept of a thing that can come into being? And, of course, in most cases it seems clear that this is so. Certainly it is the case with respect to shoes and so on. Aristotle extends this and finds it to be a characteristic of *all* concepts of changeable things: these things are something arranged after a definite fashion, a matter somehow qualified. Looking at the Aristotelian framework of explanation of genesis, we are led inevitably to the notion of prime matter. But I think the question is now: Is this the most fruitful way of conceptualizing the process of physical change? And I think that the correct answer to the question: "does prime matter exist?" is that in the Aristotelian scheme it does, but it is not as exciting a sort of thing as it is sometimes made out to be. (I don't think for instance that it is a kind of bare particular.) And a second question then arises: do we need it in another framework? It may be that another framework would be more adequate. The fundamental metaphysical metaphor of the craftsman is illuminating with respect to a world in which things are known to be fashioned from materials, but it may not be the most fruitful way ultimately of understanding how the world really hangs together.

* * * * *

McKeon: Most of the instances of unqualified change that have been adduced are biological. But in the treatise *On Generation and Corruption,* Aristotle fights back until eventually the unqualified change that he is interested in turns out to be that of the "elements" themselves. If this is a possible process, (as against those philosophers who would say that the elements are themselves eternal) it would be by virtue of a kind of matter which is somehow between fire and water, a sort of "medium"; it has no other description than this. If one wished, then, to move to the transmutation of *elements,* what kind of matter is involved there? Could one get away without *any* "matter" in such changes?

Fisk: There is a that-from-which here and there may be a substratum, but there is nothing that qualifies as both together.

* * * * *

Hanson: It's interesting to notice that in the recent development of microphysics, some of the properties of the fundamental particles seem in the classical sense to be simply inconsistent. You get a series of attempts, on the one hand, to find a basis in something like a hydrodynamic substratum-model as in quantum field theory, and to treat the point-events of particle-type behavior as a kind of molar manifestation of this. Then, on the other hand, there are those who are trying to find a point-substratum, and then the "wave" phenomena would be statistical manifestations. Some years ago, Heisenberg and Pauli tried to find a wave-equation for a matter which would be fundamentally lacking in any specific physical properties. I think that the way in which this fits into the discussion of primary matter is interesting. The argument was that, if they attributed any properties whatever to the fundamental substratum, that property would have to remain inexplicable in the whole. It very often happens in the development of fundamental particle theories that some particle, like the proton for example, is taken as a typical way of combining the field and singularity properties. In so far as you do this, the properties of the proton itself will remain inexplicable in the expansion of the theory. So they tried to get a fundamentally uninterpretable, or at least a fundamentally propertyless, wave equation for all of matter. Now, the fact of the matter is that it didn't work. The numbers didn't come out properly. But it looks as if there is here the same impetus toward something which lacks any determination, in the total explanation of change.

Misner: This field was not lacking in *all* properties; they were reduced to a minimum but there *was* something there to be discussed.

Hanson: It was lacking in the familiar properties, at least; it had to have *some* properties if an equation were to be used at all. But these properties will always appear as vulnerable to the question: What are they properties of? If "minimal matter" has any properties at all, this issue will continue to be a live one. And the very use of equations involves properties of some kind.

Sellars: To put it in this way seems to make the philosophical howler that

242

every synthetic proposition must have an explanation. In a system of explanation, there must be unexplained explainers. You suppose it to be legitimate for a philosopher to ask a physicist why his theory goes this way rather than that. But this is legitimate only where the theory is not working properly in some area.

Hanson: Why cannot prime matter be the "unexplained explainer"?

Sellars: Prime matter does not, I think, come into this context at all . . .

THE REFERENT OF

'PRIMARY MATTER'

Harry A. Nielsen

☫ Primary matter, so the doctrine goes, is one principle of physical beings. What does this mean? How can someone assure himself that he has arrived at precisely Aristotle's view and not something that only sounds like it? Not least, what are its applications? In other words, does holding this doctrine amount to anything more than putting on Aristotle's locutions? All these questions come down to one of pedagogy: Can this doctrine be taught to 20th Century students? Can it be set over without remainder into their ways of speaking?

Textbooks are full of attempts to do this. In proposing yet another I do not claim to have gone beyond these in labor or scholarship; the account to be given here merely seeks to keep the pedagogical question in focus throughout. That question is momentarily lost sight of, I believe, when philosophers try to characterize Aristotelian physics as "knowledge through intelligible principles" or "knowledge of mobile being through its causes". These and similar locutions have no sure place in 20th Century ways of speaking. This holds also for characterizing Aristotle's method by saying that it differs from experimental methods as 'Why?' differs from 'How?'[1] A determinate method guides our steps so as to bring independent inquirers to the same result. It is how one goes on, then, and not the wording of a question, that shows method. Nor does the account of science in *Posterior Analytics* reveal a method that fits Book I of the *Physics*. Turning elsewhere, when we are told that the doctrine of primary matter rests finally upon induction or experience,[2] we find that non-controversial canons of experimental reasoning take us very little of the way toward clarifying the concept of primary matter. That is, experience is consulted only to the extent of establishing philosophical starting points, facts such as "There are substantial changes", "There are real specific diversities in the world of bodies", etc.[3] A man might agree that these are faithful to common sense and yet

---

[1] See for example A. N. Whitehead, *Science and the Modern World*, Ch. I.

[2] J. Maritain, *Degrees of Knowledge*, tr. Gerald B. Phelan. New York, 1959, p. 179.

[3] *Loc. cit.*

244

find no clear path from them to the doctrine of primary matter. To be told that the path is deductive or demonstrative[4] is one thing; to exhibit it in terms of non-controversial deductive paradigms is another.

Such references to Aristotle's method do not by themselves distinguish between (a) arriving at his doctrine and (b) merely putting on his ways of speaking. In this respect they leave the pedagogical question and the status of the doctrine up in the air. When we ask how the doctrine was arrived at, it is good to remind ourselves that logic is a limited instrument for tracing the movement of a man's thought. For one thing, logic takes *inference* to be the general type of such movement. This wants defending. Nothing forces us to suppose that the primary matter doctrine has to come *via* a process we should want to call inference. If we suppose that much, we find ourselves too soon nailed to a twofold division of inference, such as deductive/experimental or analytic/synthetic, into whose forms not only Book I of the *Physics* but a great many other philosophic doctrines refuse to fit. Nor is it clear that by adding a further division, dialectic, we solve the pedagogical problem.

The aim of this essay is to suggest a clear status for the doctrine of primary matter, a way of reading it which will go over into 20th Century concepts. This means locating the referent of the term 'primary matter' among our everyday, uncontrived, non-technical conceptual tools. The method here consists in reminding ourselves of certain uses of language in connection with the physical world. I refer to language as our point of departure in order to make clear that no special empirical knowledge, i.e., none beyond what anyone knows who can make his way in a natural language, will be brought in. Our emphasis, however, will fall upon *uses* of language (as opposed, for example, to the invention and study of toy languages, and as opposed to the practice of drawing conclusions from the way people speak) and therefore will deal with concerns which occasion a great deal of human discourse. Such concerns—touching birth and death, production of foodstuffs, manufacture of goods, etc.—occasion the uses of language which we shall notice, and are addressed to physical reality with a directness which no second-thoughts can match.

One prefatory question remains. Why assume that the doctrine of primary matter corresponds to anything in our everyday concepts? Few of us would care to make this assumption for a doctrine of things-in-themselves or of monads. The answer, I believe, is that the familiar Aristotelian overture "All men agree . . ." marks him as reluctant to go against truths which men generally allow, and his account of philosophical science shows him to be concerned with truths which fall within that allowance.

---

[4] *Loc. cit.*

To proceed, the question which Aristotle's doctrine of matter and form proposes to settle is: What is essential to something's being a new physical being? If we see a mere shard or shred of something that already existed, like the chip off a plate or the lint from a coat, nothing is easier to state than its relation to "the unbroken continuity of becoming."[5] It came off the plate or the coat. If we see something put in a new state by crumpling or discoloration, we have concepts ready on the top of our mind as it were, concepts intimately connected with the senses of touch and sight, which enable us to take the event as a matter of course. But consider a baby chick. This is a new physical being, new at least without the kind of qualification we applied to a chip or wrinkle. It belongs to the class of things that come to be and pass away "by nature". Normally, to be sure, people do not rack their brains over the hatching of a chick any more than over the chipping of a plate; the one event is as commonplace as the other. But why are we not puzzled by the chick? That is, what concepts stand guard to protect us from the puzzles of a Melissus or Anaxagoras? Here we cannot appeal to concepts close to sight and touch, such as *breaking off* or *wearing off*, as though the processes of reproduction were similarly open to view.

Aristotle's predecessors had been unable to put their finger on the concepts which enable most humans to take the appearance of radically new beings as a matter of course. Our problem of the moment, then, is to identify those concepts and to ask whether Aristotle's doctrine of matter and form can be understood as calling attention to them.

How is the solution of this problem supposed to come? Two points need to be made about this. First, the concepts we seek to identify are already in our possession. In other words, our knowledge of what is essential to new physical beings as such is manifest in our ability to take account of such beings and to speak without confusion about such matters as birthdays, new models of cars, next year's crops, and so on. We know the answer "in a manner",[6] yet we ask the question anyway; we wish to bring out the answer as doctrine, as settled knowledge. Aristotle's aim in Book I, as we read him, is to give articulation to what was before only the absence of confusion. The purposes behind this modest aim will be discussed later.

Second, the method of arriving at the concepts we seek is not inferential but consists in giving voice to concepts which are already with us. The

---

[5] *On Generation and Corruption*, 318a 13–14.

[6] "Before he was led on to recognition or before he actually drew a conclusion, we should perhaps say that in a manner he knew, in a manner not. . . . I imagine there is nothing to prevent a man in one sense knowing what he is learning, in another not knowing it . . ." *Post. Anal.* 71a–72b. This could not be said in connection with empirical sciences.

applications of these concepts are nowhere listed in full, yet their full mastery belongs to anyone who knows a natural language. It is not part of my purpose to propose a theory connecting or identifying language with the having of concepts. One may notice, however, that we expect the full norm of ability to apply concepts only from those who have the use of a language. In any case, what Aristotle depends on in Book I is nothing more than the knowledge everyone has in virtue of knowing a language. Knowledge of a language answers better than any other thing his description of "the originative source of scientific knowledge" (100b 14-15) which "enables us to recognize the definitions" (72b 24). Knowledge of a language is clearly "pre-existent" with regard to any kind of science, and agrees with his description of the vehicle of our "primary immediate premisses" (72b 5-17) which, although we do not possess them from birth, would not come to be in us if we had no developed state in which they were implicitly known to us (cf. 99b 25-30).

We turn now to certain uses of language. Concerning physical beings people can and often do use expressions like these:

> 'What is it made of?' 'What does it come from?'
> 'How is it manufactured?' 'What does it need for growth?'
> 'How does it form?' etc.

It will become clear as we go on that our reference to these expressions does not put us at the mercy of idiomatic kinks peculiar to Greek, English, or some other language. That danger would certainly be present if Aristotle were asserting a simple isomorphism between his 'primary matter' and some linguistic unit that can be parsed out of Greek sentences. Nor will primary matter correspond to part of "a basic structure common to all languages", whatever that might look like. Both of those possibilities bring in language as a kind of existent in its own right, standing over against the world as a second existent, and posing problems about how the two existents are related.

Our reference to questions like 'What is it made of?' is concerned only with the uses people make of them, the varieties of human concerns they serve. In this sense these questions belong to every language; the things we do with these questions and their answers all men do: train our children, help control our food supply, care for livestock, etc. The fact that such questions are asked leads us to one of the concepts we are after, or to one of the principles of new physical beings which Aristotle sought. The principle can be introduced in this way: a physical being (e.g., a chick, a star, a deposit of petroleum) is continuous with temporally prior physical beings which went into its making. As to what the makings are in any particular instance —sand, beef, cosmic dust, water, ferns, microbes, etc.—there is no generalizing. What we are noticing is that *the idea of having makings, of a thing's being constituted out of other beings that were once independent of it,* belongs to the concept of a new physical being.

A new physical being, then, is continuous with past ones. We do not need an inference to arrive at this principle; it can be given voice out of what everyone knows. To nail this phrase 'what everyone knows' to something definite, we need only recall that when a person acquires the use of a natural language he finds himself able to ask questions like 'How does it form?' in connection with physical beings, and to look for answers. This is important in relation to disputes about the "method" of Book I, *Physics.* If articulating what normally goes without saying can be called a method, then Aristotle employs a method. However, attempts to characterize the movement of his thought in terms of more sequential or paradigmatic methods, whether deductive or experimental, tend to be disappointing.

'Primary matter' or 'underlying substratum' is the name Aristotle gives to that continuousness-with-past-beings, that having of makings, which stands out when we explore the concept of a new physical being. Unhappily, any inevitability in his movement of thought stops short at his choice of these names, as Jacques Maritain observes.[7] At the start Aristotle had no name for it, and neither does the 20th Century. 'Continuousness' is hardly an improvement. Aristotle chose a 'stuff' word, a word with a substantival soul, and brought on endless disputes of the form 'There is/There isn't any such stuff as primary matter'. These disputes show the tendency on both sides to think of primary matter, and indeed of principles generally in the Aristotelian sense, in terms of either *ingredients* or *reagent properties.*

In asking what is essential to the concept of a new physical being, Aristotle is not concerned with the elements (fire, etc.) that make up physical beings, the kinds of particle they have in common, nor their common reagent properties such as the power to displace other physical beings, to suffer change, or in the case of living things, to reproduce. The concept of a new physical being is one which we employ in advance of, and independently of, special experimental knowledge of elements and reagent properties. 'Primary matter' has neither of these as its referent.

Primary matter is first of all not an ingredient or component. A pool of petroleum, for example, is not made up of carbon compounds *plus* continuousness with paleozoic plant life, unless we tolerate a serious ambiguity in the phrase 'made up of'. Rather, the concept of petroleum, as of any physical being we encounter, carries with it the possibility of people asking e.g. 'How does it form?' and pursuing empirical answers. Such questions

---

[7] *Degrees of Knowledge,* p. 181.

tie up importantly with human concerns about finding more petroleum, laying up reserves, synthesizing it, and so on.

Nor is this fact of having makings a property, like the specific density of petroleum, its flotation, crackability, or color. The continuousness-with-makings we are speaking of does not belong to petroleum as something it wears on its sleeve or, if you prefer, as part of its definition. That continuousness stands on a different footing from properties such as combustibility which petroleum exhibits on demand. Taking primary matter to be a "principle" of petroleum amounts, in other words, to honoring questions about its sources, its makings, its past.

At the beginning we set out to identify the concepts which as it were do sentinel duty by warding off, for most people, the puzzles which troubled Aristotle's predecessors when they wondered about becoming. One of those concepts, we have seen, may be identified with *the possibility of asking and answering questions about the making of a new physical being*.[8] It is this possibility which enables us to take the appearance of new physical beings as a matter of course instead of feeling that we have bumped into a wall of utter mystery each time we see something like a baby chick. If we can now see this continuousness-with-makings as the referent of Aristotle's term 'primary matter', the status of his doctrine will be clear and our pedagogical problem solved.

Our account raises some textual problems concerning the *Physics* directly, and others concerning the medieval and modern commentaries. These issues, it seems to me, arise from Aristotle's choice of 'stuff' words for his principle. In the *Physics* his choice of the substantives 'matter' and 'substratum' makes it appear that he is positing an unheard of stuff in ordinary animals, vegetables, and minerals. This stuff is the same for all, and it has no determinations of its own but can take on any. If we may for a moment think of this idea as a misunderstanding, there are texts which attempt to clear it up:

> (Speaking of the four elements) Perhaps the solution is that their matter is in one sense the same, but in another sense different. For that which underlies them, whatever its nature may be *qua* underlying them, is the same: but its actual being is not the same.[9]

---

[8] Aristotle's second principle, form, refers us to countless uses of language in which we declare or imply the identification of (a) kinds of being (e.g., of a strain of bacilli through its virulence) and (b) particular beings (e.g., my house). 'Form' stands for the discontinuousness between a new physical being and its makings, i.e., for the fact that once it comes to be it has ways of its own which may differ radically from those of its makings. For example, a caterpillar is easy to catch, a butterfly hard.

[9] *On Generation and Corruption*, 319b 2–4.

Here as in other places Aristotle hedges at the thought of identifying his "matter" with a stuff which is the same for all. The awkwardness following upon his choice of substantives is something he struggles against consciously: "... matter is nearly, in a sense *is*, substance ...".[10] Words like 'underlying' and 'substratum' are applied, then, to something that is *nearly* substance. But what is that like? One could suggest that it means materiality thought in abstraction from all specific determinations; this, I believe, amounts to what we have been calling 'continuousness' or, participially, 'having makings'. Still, how could he have meant that (one wants to ask) and yet said things like:

> Matter, in the most proper sense of the term, is to be identified with the *substratum* which is receptive to coming-to-be and passing-away ...[11]

> ... my definition of matter is just this—the primary substratum of each thing, from which it comes to be without qualification, and which persists in the result ...[12]

Such passages seem to call for a "stuff", a "this", but the fact of having makings is not a "this". But he hedges just as often. For example, primary matter "is not one or existent in the same sense as the 'this' ".[13] Remarks like this suggest that the whole issue of primary matter *as existent* arises out of his choice of a substantive name for the principle, a choice which steadily nags him for retraction, and which he therefore repeatedly seeks to qualify by means of expressions like 'nearly', 'in another sense', etc. If the reader sets himself this question: "What kind of existence does the continuousness we are discussing have?" I think he will find, as he runs through common categories such as substance, accident, property, and component, that we have no ready name for that feature of reality. Aristotle gave it a name, and to the question how he could possibly have meant 'continuousness' by it, I would answer that his assertions together with his gestures of qualification indicate as much.

It is easy to see that the doctrine of primary matter has some connection with the fact that new physical beings are continuous with prior ones. Contemporary Aristotelians would protest, I believe, our pointing to that continuousness-with-makings as the *referent* of the term 'primary matter'. Primary matter, they would say, is rather the *source* of that continuousness. This protest, it seems to me, is faithful to Aristotle's substantival way of speaking. However, if we try to get beneath the continuousness to a deeper

[10] *Physics*, 192a 5.
[11] *On Generation and Corruption*, 320a 3–4.
[12] *Physics*, 192a 30–34.
[13] *Physics*, 191a 12.

"source" we create dilemma. That is, the source will either be ordinary matter—bronze, water, etc.—and we shall not have gone deeper after all, or the source will be occult. If it is occult, we are back where we began in the attempt to state the doctrine of primary matter so that anyone can understand it.

We now turn to the applications of the primary matter doctrine. The uses of it are not made clear just by our viewing it as an articulation of something that ordinarily goes without saying. What good comes of giving voice to what everyone knows already? For one thing, the primary matter doctrine marks a contrast between physical beings and mathematicals. Secondly it marks a contrast, less important in Aristotle's day than in ours, between physical beings and "mere appearances, which have no existence independent of our minds" or, switching from Kant to Hume, "impressions".

On the first point, Aristotle is often at pains to show the contrast between physical beings and mathematicals, although he does not explicitly invoke the idea of primary matter for that purpose.[14] There are heady analogies between the grammars or ways of speaking associated with the two kinds of being, analogies which underlie philosophical issues as diverse as the paradoxes of Zeno and the mathematical antinomies discovered by Kant. These issues arise as a result of applying to the physical world a concept of infinity which applies in the first instance to mathematicals. As a rule people do not confuse physical with mathematical beings, yet the history of philosophy from Pythagoras to Russell shows the power of the temptation to think of each kind of being in terms appropriate to the other, and justifies an analysis that will keep their boundary-markers clear. To develop the contrast in terms of our interpretation of primary matter: a physical being both inherits from past physical beings and exhibits ways of its own by which it can resist us. Mathematicals, on the other hand, neither incorporate other such beings so as to use them up, nor exhibit ways of their own that would enable them to act up and resist our operations upon them.

In our time the more important contrast is between physical beings and "impressions" or "mere appearances". These, as the several varieties of phenomenalism conceive them, have no inheritance, no makings. In Hume's words they spring fully made up "from unknown causes" and stand in relation to past impressions only in so far as the mind associates them with remembered ones. Physical beings, on the other hand, take on existence from past ones, and furthermore come into being as a result of causes to which empirical modes of inquiry give us adequate access. No

---

[14] See for example *Physics*, 231a 21–233b 17; 239b 5–240a 18; *Metaphysics*, 1068b 26–1069a 14.

contrast could be more striking, and none, if overlooked, could cause more wasted motion in philosophy.

Within philosophy, then, the point of giving voice to the primary matter doctrine is plain enough. Outside philosophy it helps boundarize an area of common and certain knowledge in which neither philosophy nor natural science can surprise or confound us or get in the way of deeper human concerns.

A final word is in order concerning the procedure followed in this discussion. The attempt here was to see the principle of primary matter as something open to anyone's gaze. Our point of departure consisted in noticing a number of ordinary questions people ask in connection with new physical beings, and then articulating the primary matter doctrine with those in mind. The doctrine, as here interpreted, brings in nothing occult, and, I should want to say, nothing deep. Still, what sort of knowledge is it? As we read it, the principle of primary matter as an articulation of something known to everyone, falls within the "given" of experimental physics and does not conflict with it, though it carries a clear reference to the same physical world. Experimental physicists, like everybody else, use the expressions we have referred to which ring with the notion of continuousness. At the same time, Aristotle's principle sounds *a priori*. There is a familiar stumbling-block to many modern thinkers in the fact that Aristotle's science couples existence with necessity, or that its propositions are at once empirical and *a priori*. This fact, it seems to me, ceases to be puzzling when we remind ourselves that our knowledge of a natural language has both of those aspects. First, the uses of language which we have picked out are occasioned by the hard knocks of existence. On the other hand, the fact that we can ask and answer questions about the makings of physical beings is given with mastery of a language in advance of any particular occasion for asking and answering those questions. We know *a priori,* in other words, that questions about the makings of any physical being make sense.[15]

University of Notre Dame

---

[15] My thanks to Profs. Joseph Bobik, Milton Fisk, and Ernan McMullin, all of Notre Dame University, for helpful criticism of these ideas.

COMMENT

Dr. Nielsen's interpretation of Aristotle's doctrine of primary matter rests upon the argument that "Knowledge of a language . . . answers better than any other thing Aristotle's description of 'the originative source of scientific knowledge' ".

Granting that the knowledge of the use of a natural language does pre-exist the learning of any kind of science, that is not the pre-existent knowledge to which Aristotle refers as the necessary condition of demonstrative syllogistic, scientific knowledge, in the *Posterior Analytics*. Far from being the mere articulation of something already known to everyone by virtue of knowing a natural language, the knowledge of indemonstrable premises, the originative source of science, is the knowledge of the cause of the necessary inherence of the predicate in the subject of the conclusion of a demonstrative syllogism. The cause in question occurs as the middle term in such syllogistic and is the definition of the generic subject upon which the science bears. Thus, the pre-existent knowledge, which is the necessary condition of scientific knowledge in the Aristotelian sense, far from being the knowledge of something already known through the possession of a natural language, is rather the result of an inductive analysis of a primary datum of experience in the light of the first principles of being, identity and non-contradiction. The term of such an analysis, when successfully executed, is an insight into the reason why things cannot be otherwise than they present themselves as being primarily in experience. Though such causes or reasons why are, in Aristotle's view, more knowable in themselves, they are, in the beginning, less knowable to us by virtue of being farthest removed from that which is most knowable to us, namely, things in their sensible presences.

The burden of *Physics I* is to show that primary matter is such a cause in the domain of physical reality and our scientific knowledge of it. As the result of his analysis of what is necessarily involved in the unqualified coming to be of physical beings, Aristotle finds in the substance of each such being a first subject from which it comes to be and which remains in it. As that in a physical being from and by which it comes to be and is such a being, the first subject or, as it is commonly named, the primary matter, is prior to every category of accident. As not any physical substance but that by which any substance is physical, the primary matter is said to be "nearly" a substance. In this context, it is clearly distinguished from those "second" matters, discussed in *Physics II*, by which physical beings are not simply generable beings but this or that kind of generable being. Though one may consistently with the texts construe these second matters as "stuffs", one may not so construe the primary matter. In both usages of the term 'matter' by Aristotle, what is referred to is unmistakably something of the *substantial* constitution of physical beings so that he can, as he does, properly write that "matter is nearly, in a sense *is*, substance". In these circumstances, his choice of a word "with a substantival soul" represents no linguistic contingency whose awkwardness he is never quite able to transcend, but a technical expression transcending the basic categories of ordinary names and hence explicatable only in analogies. It may also be noted that there is no warrant in the notion of "continuousness" for a distinction between "second" and "primary" matter; the most one could do would be to show a connection between continuousness and the notion of *matter,* prior to any distinction (based e.g. on types of change) into "primary" and "second".

If the grounds for the doctrine of primary matter in the texts of Aristotle are as I have suggested, then the grounds for the doctrine of primary matter as formulated by Dr. Nielsen must be sought elsewhere than in the Aristotelian texts.

John J. FitzGerald
University of Notre Dame

RAW MATERIALS,
SUBJECTS AND SUBSTRATA

Wilfrid Sellars

§1 *Introduction*

The "matter" of the Aristotelian system is raw material for changing things or substances, the fundamental model of the system being that of the craftsman who brings ingredients together in terms of a recipe to produce an artifact which serves a purpose. Substances proper, living things, are characterized by internal teleology. They are self-developing and self-regulating agencies the activity of which is to be understood in terms of the analogical conception of a craftsman who consciously and deliberately enlarges his body, regulates its activity and makes copies of himself.

Whereas living things are artisan-analogues, artifact-analogues, goal-analogues and means-analogues all rolled into one, and are *beings* in their own right, artifacts-proper, as such, have being only in relation to the purposes of men. Thus the *fundamenta* of the analogy whereby we understand beings proper are themselves beings or substances in a derivative sense.

The elements, like living things, have an internal teleology. For their motion, like the growth of plants, is conceived by analogy with the pursuit of goals. But they are more like slaves than craftsmen, for they are essentially raw material for living things, and are therefore essentially characterized by an external teleology which is conceived by analogy with the status of a list of ingredients in a recipe for, say, a cake.

But my aim is not to explore the familiar structure of the Aristotelian system as a whole. I shall limit myself to some logical features of the role played by matter as raw material in this system, with particular reference to the theory of predication.

§2 *Matter and Materials*

Words like 'marble', 'leather', 'cloth' and 'salt' are words for kinds of material. The context in which they belong is that of a recipe, thus:

a cubic yard of marble
20 bricks of brick
a piece of cloth 2″ x 10″

One speaks of a "dog" (a substance in the philosopher's sense) but not of a "cement" (a substance in the ordinary sense). Words like 'cloth' and 'brick' are ambiguous, thus 'cloth' in one sense means piece of cloth in the other, and 'brick' in one sense means standard chunk of brick in the other. 'Material' as a noun is the generic term which can take the place of words for specific kinds of material in the above contexts, thus,

> a cubic yard of material
> 20 chunks of material
> a piece of material

In English, the term 'matter' does not seem to function as a synonym for 'material'. Thus we don't ordinarily speak of a piece of matter. Philosophers, however, bully this term to serve their purposes by using the phrase 'the matter of x' to have the sense of: *the material of which x consists or is made*. 'Matter' in this sense, of course, is not to be confused with 'matter' as a collective term for material things. Nor should it be assumed that 'material thing' means 'thing made of (or consisting of) matter'. For this is equivalent to construing 'material thing' as 'thing made of or consisting of a portion of some *material* or other', and to view the world in terms of the framework of raw materials, tools and ends to be achieved.

A universe in which "matter alone is real" where this has the sense of "all individual things are simply portions of matter (material)" is as logically impossible as a wife without a husband. There must "be" the things for which the "matter" is the material. On the other hand, a universe in which "matter alone is real" where this has the sense of "all individual things are material things" is not in the same way absurd, if absurd it is.

§3 *The Credentials of the "Bare Substratum"*

A second recurrent theme in classical discussions of matter has its fundamental source in a mistaken interpretation of statements of the form 'S is P'. Consider the statement

(A) Socrates is wise (courageous, snubnosed, etc.)

This is clearly logically equivalent to

(A′) Socrates has (or is characterized by) wisdom (courage, snubnosedness, etc.)

It is only too easy to conclude that the former is not only logically equivalent to but has the same sense as the latter.[1] This by itself would not suffice

---

[1] This is the exact counterpart of supposing that because 'p' and 'It is true that p' are logically equivalent, they have the same sense.

to generate the idea of a substratum. But suppose the argument to continue as follows:

Socrates is not identical with the wisdom which he has, nor with the courage which he has, nor the snubnosedness which he has, etc.

This, of course, is true. Socrates is not identical with his attributes taken severally. At this stage the temptation arises to ask "What does 'Socrates' refer to or name, if it is something distinct from all his attributes taken severally?" and to answer:

It refers to a substratum which is neither wise nor courageous nor snubnosed, etc.

which is surely false as stating in somewhat different terms a logical contrary of the original statement, (A), with which we began.

Put thus explicitly, the fallacy is so transparent that no one would be taken in by it. The step from:

What 'Socrates' refers to is not (i.e. is not identical with) wisdom

to:

What 'Socrates' refers to is not wise

is so obviously fallacious that no one would take it. But before adding a missing step which explains why philosophers have, on occasion, made this move, let me first sketch the final outcome of this line of thought. It is the thesis that what we refer to strictly or philosophically speaking is *bare substrata*, i.e. substrata which are neither hot nor cold not white nor wise, etc. Items which *are* hot or cold or white or wise, etc. are *wholes* consisting of a substratum and an adequate bunch of attributes. (The truth, of course, is that it is not *things* but *facts* which consist of individuals and attributes).

The missing link which disguises the above howler is the role of such expressions as:

> the greenness of this leaf
> the wisdom of Socrates
> the rectangularity of this table top

These expressions obviously refer to *singulars,* that is to say, to "individuals" in that broad sense in which anything properly referred to by a singular term is an individual. But it can readily be seen, I believe, that these singulars or individuals are universals. Thus, consider the sentence:

The greenness of this leaf is identical with (or different from) the greenness of that leaf.

Notice that whereas the expressions listed above are singular terms, the occurrences in them of 'greenness', 'wisdom' and 'rectangularity' are *not*.

Rather they are common noun expressions, 'the greeness of this leaf' having the same form as 'the owner of this house', and the above sentence the same form as:

The owner of this house is identical with (or different from) the owner of that house.

But it is easy to confuse the fact that *the greenness* of this leaf is an individual (in the *broad* sense—the sense in which formal universals as well as perceptible things are individuals or singulars) which is *a greenness* with the idea that the greenness of this leaf is an individual (in the *narrow* sense which connotes spatio-temporal location) which *is green*.[2] Thus is born the widespread conception of changeable things as consisting of, or at least containing as ingredients, dependent or "abstract" particulars of which the greenness of this leaf, thus construed, would be an example. For, once one is committed to the idea that the greenness of the leaf is a spatio-temporally individuated green item, the inevitable conclusion is that greennesses are the *primary* green items and that ordinary changeable things are green by virtue of *having greennesses*. And we can now appreciate how, thinking of the leaf as green in a derivative sense,

$$L \text{ is green} = \text{a greenness belong to } L$$

one inevitably concludes either that there is a subject which is not a greenness or sweetness, etc., in which these qualia inhere, so that

$$L \text{ is green} = \text{a greenness inheres in } L;$$

or one takes the line that things are patterns of greennesses, sweetnesses, etc., in which case we have the formula

$$L \text{ is green} = \text{a greenness is an element of } L$$

It is not my purpose to examine the view that changeable things are "patterns" of greennesses, sweetnesses, etc. It is a venerable position, and is certainly to be found in Plato. I shall limit myself to pointing out that Aristotle rejects the view that the elements could be hotnesses, coldnesses, moistnesses and drynesses on the ground that it makes interaction unintelligible. For, as Plato emphasized in the *Phaedo* (a dialogue to which Aristotle is closer than is the Plato of the *Timaeus*), a coldness cannot become hot without ceasing to be. But what else could a hotness *do* but warm

---

[2] A note on the dangers of the use of color examples in discussing the problem of predication might not be out of place. Color words are radically ambiguous in a way which easily leads to serious confusion. Thus, 'red' is (1) an adjective which applies to things, e.g. this is red; (2) a common noun which applies to *shades* of red, e.g. crimson is a red; (3) a singular term (equivalent to 'redness') e.g. red is a color.

that on which it *acts?* One must either abandon the very idea of interaction, or say that it is subjects qualified by opposites which interact, rather than the opposites themselves. It is important to note that Aristotle need not have construed (if he did construe) these subjects as substrata in the dubious sense generated by the above described misinterpretation of predication.

It is also interesting to note that the argument which Aristotle gives in the *De Generatione* for a matter more basic than the elements rests on physical considerations pertaining to the transmutation of the elements. Yet it would be a mistake to construe the argument as physical *rather than,* in a broad sense, logical. The core of the argument is the idea that one's willingness to speak of water as "changing into" rather than as "ceasing to exist and being replaced by air" does imply an identical subject which is first moist and cold and then moist and hot. Once again it should be emphasized that this subject does not have to be construed as a substratum which is neither hot nor cold nor moist nor dry, though, of course, this is what one will be tempted to say if one is already committed to the theory of predication examined above. It would suffice to say that the identical subject is capable of being at different times cold-dry, cold-moist, warm-moist, warm-dry, and is, at every moment in one or other of these states.

Of course, if one already has as one's paradigm of qualitative change:

$$\text{This-}X \text{ was } f \text{ and is } f'$$

where 'X' replaces thing-kind expressions (e.g. 'man', 'house') or, at a lower level, expressions of the form 'portion of M' (e.g. 'chunk of marble') which are the analogues of thing-kind expressions proper, then when one comes to the elements and tries to use the formula:

$$\text{This portion of } PM \text{ was cold-moist and is hot-moist}$$

one runs up against the fact that whereas there are empirical criteria for being a dog or a piece of marble which are present both before and after qualitative change, there would seem to be no such criteria for being a portion of primary matter. To be sure, the *capacity* to be characterized (in sequence) by pairs from the list of fundamental opposites would persist through transmutation. But to accept this capacity as the criterion for being a portion of PM is, or so it might seem, to commit oneself to the idea that PM "as such" has no "positive" or "intrinsic" nature.

Notice however, that if instead of the above our paradigm of qualitative change were:

$$S \text{ was } f \text{ and is } f'$$

where 'S' is simply a referring expression, e.g. a demonstrative, then to grant that there are no "occurrent" (as contrasted with "dispositional") characteristics which persist through transmutation, e.g.

S was cold-moist and is hot-moist

is not to grant that *S* has no "positive" or "intrinsic" nature, unless one assumes that the nature of a continuant, if it is to be "positive" or "intrinsic" must include abiding "occurrent" qualities. One can, of course, stipulate a usage according to which this would be true *ex vi terminorum*—but then it does not seem that there must be anything particularly perplexing about subjects which do not have, in this stipulated sense, a "positive" or "intrinsic" nature.

Certainly from the fact that *S* has no occurrent qualities which abide through transmutation one could infer neither that there were no empirical characteristics in terms of which it could be identified, nor that it has no empirical qualities. '*S* is not *abidingly* hot' doesn't entail '*S* is not hot'. Thus, while transmutation would be a radical change, it would not lead us to speak of a qualityless substratum unless we were already doing so because of a faulty theory of predication.

Suppose, now, we return to the idea that every proper subject of change must in principle be identifiable as either a *"K"*, where '*K*' is a thing-kind expression proper, or a portion of *M,* where '*M*' is a word for a kind of material. We now notice that where the context is one of craftsmanship, the immediate raw material for an artifact has and, it would seem (logically), *must* have "occurrent" qualities which abide through the changes involved in working it up into a finished product. (Compare processed leather before and after it is worked into a shoe). Let us call these occurrent characteristics the "positive" or "intrinsic" nature of the material. From this standpoint transmutation would involve a "material" which "has no positive or intrinsic nature". But again, that this is so does not mean that in any paradoxical sense transmutation would involve a qualityless substratum. It would simply mean that the '*M*' of the procrustean formula

S is either a *K* or a portion of *M*

(which presents the alternatives for answering the question "What is *S*?") is being by analogy to cover what are now recognized as proper subjects of change which are not in the literal craftsman sense pieces of raw material. But that Aristotle's concept of matter, and of primary matter in particular, is a concept by analogy is scarcely news.

These considerations lend weight to the idea that the concept of primary matter, though rooted in the form 'this portion of *M*', is simply the concept of the ultimate subject of predication with respect to changeable things in space and time,[3] the concept showing in its formula the traces of its analogical formation route, but having no correspondingly overt expression of the qualifications which, in effect, limit the analogy to the essential of an abiding subject of change.

But surely, it will be said, the qualifications do not remove the "indeterminateness" of primary matter, a trait on which Aristotle insists, and which gives it a richer metaphysical role than that of the bare concept of an abiding subject of change. There is *something* to this challenge, and it must be taken seriously; though it does not, in my opinion, militate against the essential correctness of the above interpretation. Let us examine the sense in which secondary matter is indeterminate. This indeterminateness is logically necessary, and is a consequence of the fact that words for materials belong in the context:

Amount x of M.

A raw material which came in indivisible chunks which could not be put together would be a "degenerate" case of material. There would be no point in giving it a name with a grammar akin to that of 'leather' or 'marble'. A common noun would suffice. The recipes involving it would read ". . . take a glub".

This indeterminateness belongs primarily to the kind, not to the individual. It is *marble* which is indeterminate, not (save in a derivative sense) this piece of marble. And Marble is indeterminate only in the sense that 'x is a piece of marble' doesn't entail 'x is (say), one cubic foot in size'. Clearly indeterminateness in this sense is a feature of the Aristotelian elements.

Now something akin to this indeterminateness is a feature of the ultimate subject of predication with respect to changeable things, even where the concept of such a subject has not been formed by analogy in the Aristotelian manner. For it is a necessary feature of the concept of such a subject that it have *some location or other* in space and time. The indeterminateness to which 'some . . . or other' gives expression is, again, an indeterminateness pertaining to the "kind" and not to the individual. Now if 'having some location or other in space and time' entails and is entailed by 'having some size or other', one can see how the formula:

This portion of *PM* (every portion of which has some size or other)

could have a philosophical force which was indistinguishable, save by its conceptual roots—a distinction which should not, however, be minimized —from the more familiar:

---

[3] For a discussion of the idea that the ultimate subject of predication is in some cases matter and in other cases primary substances, see the next section.

This ultimate subject of predication (every one of which was some location in space and time or other).

§4 *The Ultimate Subject of Predication*

The above remarks need to be supplemented by some comments on the notion of an ultimate subject of predication. The contrast between ultimate and "non-ultimate" which I have in mind does not concern the distinction between individuals and universals. I would, indeed, defend the thesis that individual things and persons in space and time are the ultimate subjects of predication. Also the more radical thesis that they are the *only* subjects of predication. But that is a story for another occasion. The contrast I now have in mind is developed by Aristotle in *Metaphysics,* 1049a 19–b2. He writes:

> For the subject or substratum is differentiated by being a "this" or not being one, i.e. the substratum of modifications is e.g. a man i.e. a body and a soul, while the modification is 'musical' or 'pale'. Whenever this is so, then, the ultimate subject is a substance; but when this is not so, but the predicate is a form and a "this", the ultimate subject is matter and material substance.

Aristotle is here contrasting predication which can be represented by the formula:

(A) /substance/ is /modification/

with that which can be represented by the schema:

(B) /matter/ is /substance/

In (A) the substance in question is an individual substance, a *synholon* consisting of form and matter, thus an individual man. In (B) the word 'substance' is place-holding for a substance-kind expression, e.g. 'man'. To be a "this" in the sense of the passage quoted is to be an instance of a thing-kind. Indeed, Aristotle uses 'is a this' as we might use 'is a K' where 'K' is a representative expression for thing-kind words such as 'man'. Thus the conclusion of the passage quoted could be written: ". . . but when this is not so, but the predicate is a form and a K, the ultimate subject is matter and material being." Now it is important to see that while Aristotle is committing himself to the thesis that whenever a statement classifies a changeable subject under a thing-kind expression, the subject is matter, he is *not* committing himself to the thesis that where the predicate is not a thing-kind expression, the subject is a substance consisting of both matter and form (a synholon). In other words he is not committing himself to the thesis that the *only* predication in which matter is the ultimate subject is predication in which the subject is brought under a thing-kind.

Rather, what he is claiming is that whereas all thing-kind predications

262

have matter as their ultimate subject, *some* non-thing-kind predicates presuppose that their subject is a *substance*, i.e. falls under a thing-kind. The examples he gives are essential. He could not have used 'heavy' instead of 'musical' or 'white' instead of 'pale'.[4] The point he is making could be put by saying that a sentence which classifies a subject under a thing-kind is an answer to the question: "What is *x*?" This question cannot presuppose that the subject is a *synholon*, for the answer could very well be (for example): "*x* is (nothing but) a piece of marble". Thus even though *x* is in point of fact a *synholon*, the statement, "*x* is a *K*", does not refer to, it *qua synholon*. It refers to it *qua* something which may or may not be a *synholon*, i.e. *qua* denotable portion of some matter or other.

§5 *Are Matter and Form Distinct?*

In conclusion, I want to touch briefly on the nature of Aristotle's distinction between form and matter, and on the question whether a "real distinction" exists between the form and the matter of an individual substance. As I see it, the primary mode of being of a form, e.g. the form Shoe or the form Man, is its being as a *this* or individual, the individual form of this shoe or this man. As individual form it is, so to speak, private to the individual of which it is the form. For the form of an individual substance is, according to Aristotle, the "substance of" the substance, and, he insists, the substance of an individual cannot be common to many. We must, therefore, distinguish between form as individual matter and matter taken universally. It is essential to see that if a changeable thing is a *synholon* or "whole", its "parts", in the primary sense, are an individual form and an individual piece of matter. It is only in a derivative sense that the form taken universally is a "part" of the changeable thing.

But how is this "part-whole" relationship to be understood? Clearly a metaphor is involved. How is it to be interpreted? Are we to suppose that as in the *ordinary* sense the *spatial* togetherness of two individuals (the parts) constitutes a new individual (the whole), so in the *metaphorical* sense a nonspatial, metaphysical, togetherness of individual matter and individual form (the "parts") constitutes a new (and complete) individual (the "whole")? The answer, I submit, is no, for the simple reason that the individual matter and form of an individual substance are not *two* individuals but *one*. The individual form of this shoe is the shoe itself; the individual matter of this shoe is *also* the shoe itself, and there can scarcely be a real distinction between the shoe and itself.

---

[4] It is interesting to note that in the first edition of his translation of the *Metaphysics*, Ross translated 'leukos' as 'white' instead of the 'pale' to which he subsequently changed it.

What, then, is the difference between the individual form and matter of this shoe if they are the same *thing?* The answer should, by now, be obvious. The individual form of this shoe is the shoe *qua:*

(piece of some appropriate material or other—in this case leather) *serving the purpose of protecting and embellishing the feet.*

The individual matter of this shoe is the shoe *qua:*

piece of leather (so worked as to serve some purpose or other—in this case to protect and embellish the feet).

Thus, the "parts" involved are not incomplete individuals in the real order, but the importantly different parts of the formula

(piece of leather) (serving to protect and embellish the feet)

projected on the individual thing of which they are true.

§6 *Forms and Individuals*

It is important to see that although Aristotle flirted, in the *Categories* and elsewhere, with the Platonic doctrine that changeable things have dependent or abstract particulars as ingredients, neither his argument for, nor his interpretation of, the thesis that the forms of individual changeable things are themselves, in their primary mode of being, individuals, depends on this doctrine. I believe that the real nature of Aristotle's thought on this topic can be brought out most effectively by a careful re-examination of a much misunderstood example.

This bronze ball is a spherical piece of bronze. Its matter is the piece of bronze—not, however, *qua* having the spherical shape it in point of fact has, but rather *qua* capable of a variety of shapes, one of which is the spherical. There is little difficulty, clearly, about the distinction between the matter of this bronze sphere, and the matter of this bronze sphere taken universally. The distinction is represented by the distinction between the referring expression: 'This piece of bronze', and the predicative expression '. . . a piece of bronze', which stands for a quasi-thing-kind. Bronze is a kind of matter, and "piece of bronze" is an analogue of a thing-kind in the basic sense illustrated by Tiger or Shoe. Thus we can say, as a first approximation, that this bronze ball is this piece of bronze *qua* spherical, and, in general, that bronze balls are spherical pieces of bronze.

But what of the form? We have already abandoned the idea that the form of this bronze ball is the supposed abstract particular which is its shape ('this sphericity' it might be called, if there were such a thing). Is it, then, the universal *sphericity*, or, perhaps, *sphere?* To say that it is either, is to run counter to explicit and reiterated statements to the effect that the "substance of" a substance cannot be a universal. But if so, *what* is the alternative? Part of the answer lies in distinguishing between the referring and the predicative uses of the phrase 'a sphere' as illustrated by the two sentences: 'That is a sphere', and 'A sphere is on the table'. We have been using such expressions as 'this sphere' as equivalent to 'a sphere' in its use to refer to an individual sphere as a sphere. In these terms we might say that the form of the bronze sphere is the bronze sphere itself, not, however, qua *bronze* sphere, but simply *qua sphere*. We might add that spheres can be made of many materials and that while to characterize an item as a sphere is to imply that it is made of some appropriate material or other, to characterize it as a bronze sphere is to class it as a sphere *and* to pin it down to one specific kind of material.

But while it is more accurate to say that the "individual form" is *this sphere* rather than what we referred to as "this sphericity", it is still only an approximation to the truth. The final step is to distinguish between 'a sphere' and 'a ball'. When they are carefully distinguished, the former concerns a class of mathematical objects, the latter a class of material objects. Thus, 'a sphere' has a referring use in which it refers to a particular instance of a certain mathematical kind, and a predicative use in which it says that a certain region of Space (or Extension—*not* Extendedness) is so bounded as to constitute a (mathematical) sphere. Space or Extension plays a role analogous to that of matter in changeable things, and can be called 'intelligible matter'. It is, of course, a central Aristotelian theme that mathematical objects[5] and the intelligible matter 'in' which they exist are dependent beings. Just how the dependence of this domain on that of material things is to be construed is left somewhat of a mystery. As I see it, we have here a prime example of Aristotle's ability to rest content with partial insights, repressing the temptation to push them into a "complete" but erroneous system.[6]

---

[5] The descendants of the *"ta mathematika"* which hover around the Platonic dialogues.

[6] In a paper dealing primarily with Time, I have suggested that Space (and Time) are "metrical entities" related to the domain of physical objects by "correspondence rules" so designed that an object or event occupies a region determined by discounting not only error, but all physical forces pertaining to observed measurement. Though they share many of the logical features of theoretical frameworks with, e.g. atomic theory, this discounting or division of labor accounts for the *Unding*-ish character of Space and Time, correctly stressed by Kant. The correspondence rules which correlate operationally defined metrical properties with the occupation of regions of Space (or Time) occupied are the counterpart of Aristotle's notion that mathematicals exist when boundaries are marked out by *physical* differences. Further elaboration of these points would bring out the essential truth of Carnap's contention that Space is an ordered set of triads of real numbers *qua* coordinated with a certain family of measuring operations.

While 'sphere', then, marks out a class of mathematicals, 'ball' marks out a class of physical things. It should not however be taken to mark out certain physical things merely *qua* having a certain shape. As a true thing-kind expression, or, more to the point, as a means of clarifying the status of true thing-kind expressions, it should be taken in the sense of 'spherical material object serving a certain purpose', as, for example, 'tennis ball'. The reader is invited to think of a game in which a ball is used which might be made of any of a number of materials[7] including bronze, thus "pusho"; and in that context to distinguish between 'a pusho ball' and 'a bronze pusho ball.'

In its predicative use, the expression 'a bronze pusho ball' stands for a materiate thing-kind in which *pusho ball* is the formal element and *bronze* the material. In its referring use, it refers to a "this" *qua* bronze pusho ball, i.e. *qua* a pusho ball and *qua* made of bronze. Thus the individual which is *a bronze pusho ball* is necessarily *a piece of bronze* which is *a pusho ball*. What it is *essentially* is *a pusho ball*. It is a pusho ball by virtue of the fact that being a piece of matter of a kind which can satisfy the criteria for being a pusho ball, it does in point of fact satisfy these criteria. And even though 'a pusho ball' refers to the individual in an *indeterminate* way in the sense that there is much that is true of the individual, including the material of which it is made, which we cannot infer from this referring expression, the reference is determinate in the sense that the criteria specify the material of which the object is to be made with reference to a determinate purpose which the object is to serve. Thus to refer to something as a pusho ball is to refer determinately as one would not be doing if one referred to it as *a ball played in some game or other*. For unless there are varieties of the game of pusho ball, there is no more determinate purpose to which the materials for making pusho balls are to be selected. It is the *teleological* character of artifact kinds which enables us to understand why *bronze pusho ball* is not a species of *pusho ball* as *soccer ball* is a species of *football*.

The answer to our question, thus, is that it is *this piece of bronze qua* pusho ball, i.e. *this pusho ball,* which is what *this essentially* is. It is *this* bronze pusho ball *as a whole* and not an abstract particular (in the sense of the *Categories*) which is an instance of the formal element in the materiate universal *bronze pusho ball*. The sense in which the form of the bronze pusho ball is a this which is "in" the bronze pusho ball is *not* that in which

---

[7] Even if *in point of fact* it can satisfy the purpose of the game only by being made of a specific material (e.g. as having a certain size and weight it must be made of bronze). The "logical possibility" remains—as long as the purpose doesn't specify that the ball be made of bronze (a topic for further exploration)—that it might be made of some other material.

a quale is a this which is "present in" a substance. The form can indeed be said to be an "abstract particular" but only in the sense of a particular *considered abstractly,* i.e. a particular *qua* what it essentially is. To consider it as a bronze pusho ball is, of course, also to consider it abstractly, but as an instance of a materiate thing-kind, rather than as an instance of a thing-kind *simpliciter.* Obviously, then, the sense in which the form of a thing is "in" the thing is different from that in which the qualities of a thing are "in" the thing. But this should surprise no one who has reflected on the multitudinous uses of 'in'. And similar considerations obtain in connection with the statement that changeable things "consist of" matter and form.

Before we consider the relationship between the sense in which the form of a materiate substance is "in" the substance, and that in which one of its *qualia* is "present in" it, let us tentatively apply the above considerations to the case where the primary substance is Socrates and the secondary substance or thing-kind is *man.* We can cut through the preliminaries by turning directly to the question: "Is man *essentially* a being of flesh and bone?" To this question Aristotle's answer is that there is an essence, *rational animal of flesh and bone* only in the sense in which there is the essence *bronze (pusho)* ball, which is to say that in that narrow sense of essence in which the essence of something is its form, flesh and bone do not belong to the essence of man. Here we must be careful, for there is a sense in which flesh and bone do belong to the essence of man, and, indeed, bronze to the pusho ball. For while being a pusho ball does not include being made of bronze, it does include *being made of some appropriate material or other.* Similarly being a man includes being made of some appropriate material or other, and hence includes being made of flesh and bone, in that sense in which *somebody* includes *Smith.*

Thus the fact that the essence of Socrates is his form (i.e. his soul) is the parallel of the fact that the essence of this bronze pusho ball is this pusho ball. And if it be granted that we use the name 'Socrates' to refer to a certain substance *qua rational animal made of this mixture of flesh and bone,* the above suffices to show that it would be more tidily used to refer to it *qua rational animal made of this piece of appropriate material.* Using it thus we could say not only that the essence of Socrates is his form but that Socrates is identical with his essence, i.e. with his form. And the above analysis makes it clear that we could do so without implying that Socrates is an immaterial substance. For in exactly the same way, given that a certain pusho ball is called 'Beauty', we could say that the essence of Beauty is its form and that Beauty is identical with its essence, i.e. its form. The fact that Socrates is identical with his form no more implies that Socrates can exist apart from matter than does the similar fact about Beauty.

If this analysis of Aristotle's account of forms as "thises" is correct, we can say that he distinguishes between the primary mode of being of forms, which is to be, for example, this bronze pusho ball qua this pusho ball, and a secondary mode of being, which is to be, for example, the universal *pusho ball*. Thus, while in the primary sense, forms are "thises", there is a secondary sense in which they are universals. It is only to be expected, then, that in many passages Aristotle clearly has universals in mind when he speaks of form. That the forms of perishable things are individuals enables us to understand how "pure forms" or "immaterial beings" can be individuals. For if we think of the form of a perishable thing as a universal "in" a piece of matter, one will think of an immaterial substance as a universal which is not "in" a piece of matter.

Yet while the form that is "in" the bronze ball is, in the primary sense, a "this" or individual, Aristotle finds it also appropriate to say that the universal ball is "in" the bronze ball. For although he does not clearly distinguish between the ball (of which the universal is *not* a constituent) and the fact that the ball exists (of which it *is*), he does the next best thing by distinguishing between the sense in which the form as "this" is "in" the bronze ball from the sense in which the form as universal is "in" it.

That the forms of perishable things are "thises" in the sense analyzed above is no mere incidental feature of Aristotle's metaphysics. For if the primary mode of being of forms were that of universals, then instead of being as perishable as the individuals of which they are the forms, they would be imperishable and eternal, and a central theme in Aristotle's theology would be lost. It is just because the forms of perishable things are as perishable as the things themselves that beings which are pure forms and, therefore, imperishable individuals are required to be the real foundation of beginningless and endless time.

Yale University

COMMENT[1]

THE TARGET OF PROF. SELLARS' PAPER IS THE NOTION OF BARE OR QUALITYLESS
substratum. He will allow, it would seem, covered or qualitied substrata. But
he will not have bare or qualityless substrata. His attack on the latter is two-
pronged, the first prong being directed against bare substrata introduced in an
analysis of predication and the second prong being directed against bare substrata introduced in an analysis of change. In attacking the notion of bare substratum Prof. Sellars does not regard himself as attacking the classical notion of
primary matter. He interprets prime matter as a covered or qualitied substratum.

How are we to conceive of a bare substratum? A bare substratum would be
an entity of which we could not say that it is wise or foolish, that it is heavy or
light, that it is a man or a beast. Correspondingly, a bare-substratum designator
would be one of which we could predicate neither thing-kind words nor quality
words. Subject-predicate sentences with bare-substratum designators as subjects are meaningful only when the predicates transcend the categories of substance and accident. To say that a word is a bare-substratum designator is to
say that as a subject it is 'is'-shy. By contrast, substance words like 'Socrates',
'this', and 'the man' do take thing-kind words and quality words as predicates.
In a language supplied with bare-substrata designators, relations between bare
substrata and thing-kinds and qualities could be expressed by means of either 'is
a constituent of a substance which is' (when substances are the primary individuals) or 'exemplifies the thing-kind or quality' (when bare substrata and universals are the primary individuals). Thus we would have 'This bare substratum is a constituent of Socrates who is a man' or 'This bare substratum
exemplifies the thing-kind manness' rather than 'This bare substratum is a
man'. Bare substrata, although they can be related to thing-kinds and qualities
in these ways, cannot be related to them in the manner of subjects to predicates.

The first prong of Prof. Sellars' attack is directed against an argument which
begins with an analysis of 'Socrates is wise' and ends with the claim that
'Socrates' is a bare-substratum designator. He asks: Can ordinary singular terms
for particulars be construed as bare-substratum designators, as this argument
contends? The answer must be No. Ordinary singular terms for particulars
are *not*, as subjects, 'is'-shy. Beginning the argument with 'Socrates is wise'
grants this point. But the conclusion, that 'Socrates' is a bare-substratum designator, contradicts this admission and, hence, makes nonsense of 'Socrates is
wise'.

---

[1] This comment concerns §1–§4 only; §§5, 6 were added subsequently.

I concur with Prof. Sellars in rejecting the contention that ordinary singular terms for particular are bare-substratum designators. Can we not, however, find another form of the argument through predication to bare substrata, a form which, though perhaps objectionable, cannot be objected to on the same grounds?

The following argument is grounded in an analysis of the statement that Socrates is wise and is guided by the postulate that it is legitimate to submit this statement to two questions, (a) What in Socrates accounts for his being a man? and (b) What in Socrates accounts for his being (predicatively) anything, i.e., what in him makes him a subject of predication? The manness of Socrates satisfies (a). But what accounts for his being this or that cannot account for the fact that he can be something. Moreover, we cannot account for this fact by Socrates, the substance. For as substance he is subject; thus to account for the mentioned fact in this manner would in effect be to say that substance is the reason that substance can be something. Clearly then (b) takes us beyond forms and substances. To answer (b), something is needed which is not form and is not, like a substance, a subject of predication. The bare substratum of Socrates is tailored to the demands of (b). It is not (identical with) a form and it is not (predicatively) a thing-kind or a quality.

The difficulty encountered before does not arise here. In place of an ordinary singular term we have used the artificial singular term 'the bare substratum of Socrates'. No contradiction results from the requirement that such a term be used in an 'is'-shy way. In the partially artificial language supplied with such-like terms a shorthand is inevitable and, once habitual, misleading. We either introduce 'is' in place of 'is a constituent of a substance which is' thus allowing 'This bare substratum is a constituent of Socrates who is white' to go as 'The bare substratum of Socrates is white', or we replace 'This bare substratum exemplifies whiteness' with 'This bare substratum is white'. Uncritical use of this new 'is' might lead us to think that the substratum introduced was, after all, covered or qualitied. But, if so, it could not answer (b).

The second prong of Prof. Sellars' attack is directed against an argument to the conclusion that unqualified change requires a bare substratum. I interpret him as saying that the argument:

> Unqualified change requires an enduring subject of predication.
> An enduring subject of predication in an unqualified change is a bare substratum.
> Therefore unqualified change requires a bare substratum.

is ineffective, since its second promise is analytically false. A bare-substratum designator is 'is'-shy. Thus a subject of predication cannot be a bare substratum.

In reply, I wish to note that the principle: "Unqualified change requires an enduring subject of predication", admits of two interpretations. Let S be the enduring subject of predication in an unqualified change from a K to a J. We can then interpret the principle as requiring either that

(1) S was$_1$ a K and is$_1$ a J.

is true, where 'was$_1$' and 'is$_1$' have the sense of the verbs in 'Socrates was in the Academy and is in the *stoa'*, or that

(2) S was$_2$ a K and is$_2$ a J.

is true, where 'was$_2$' and 'is$_2$' are such that the statement as a whole means the same as 'S was a constituent of a K and is a constituent of a J'. If correct interpretation of the principle requires the truth of (1), then the second premise of the above argument is indeed false. If it requires the truth of (2), then there is no reason for denying the second premise. Which interpretation is the more plausible?

It must be admitted, I think, that the analysis of change which leads to the requirement of an enduring subject of predication is neutral in regard to the two interpretations. Suppose that a cow becomes a carcass. The one does not just cease to be and the other then come to be. There is, the analysis runs, an element of continuity requiring a substratum which in this case cannot be a substance. But this leaves us with several routes. The substratum for the change of a cow into a carcass may be described as a component of the cow and of the carcass which neither was$_1$ a cow nor is$_1$ a carcass. Or the substratum may be described as a component of the cow and of the carcass which was$_1$ a cow and is$_1$ a carcass. The continuity requirement is upheld whether the substratum be bare or covered. If it is bare we can still call it an enduring subject of predication by introducing 'is$_2$'.

Consequently, Prof. Sellars' choice of interpretation, his choice of the covered or qualitied substratum, must rest on the conviction that one must keep one's substrata covered when one can avoid having them bare. I find no further context in which this conviction is given a foundation. It should be remembered that a covered substratum which can be successively a K and a J not only differs from a bare substratum but also from ordinary substances, for it can be successively two different substances. One might feel as strongly that no entity can be successively two different substances as Prof. Sellars feels that substrata must be covered. His preference for covered substrata would be matched by a preference for bare substrata. In both cases one departs from customary concepts; neither the bare substratum nor the covered substratum which survives change of thing-kind is the referent of an ordinary singular term. Nevertheless, one can make empirical assertions of change while using bare-substratum and covered-substratum designators; for of necessity such designators will be complexes of the sort 'the bare (covered) substratum of Socrates' and will thus derive their criteria of application from those of ordinary singular terms. In these and other regards neither interpretation gains an advantage. It is then futile to dispute in the context of the analysis of change whether the substratum of unqualified change is bare or covered. This points to a conceptual difference between the substratum of unqualified change and the bare substratum posited in the previous analysis of predication.

Milton Fisk
University of Notre Dame

DISCUSSION

Lobkowicz: According to you, Aristotle does not think of matter and form as "really" distinct. Would you say then, that 'matter' and 'form' are only generic terms for things which would have, so to say, the same extension when applied to things themselves?

Sellars: Yes, it is individuals as wholes which are the referents of both terms. I'm concerned here with matter and form as *this* matter, *this* form, as opposed to matter and form taken universally: this shoe rather than shoe as universal.

Eslick: Why, in that case, wouldn't the definition of a shoe be simply in terms of enumeration of its material parts?

Sellars: Because you cannot define the shoe by enumerating its parts. You have to specify the form in which they stand to one another.

Eslick: Doesn't that presuppose some sort of a real distinction?

Sellars: Well, there are real distinctions involved. The question is whether there is a real distinction between the form and the matter. I have a bundle, for example; there is a real distinction between the twigs but the question is whether there is a real distinction between the form, *bundle,* and the matter.

Eslick: The formal actuality of the shoe is still not formulated simply in terms of the material components.

Sellars: In the case of artifacts, the definition involves specifications of qualities of the material and also involves a reference to purpose, so that the defining traits would not be simply traits of the matter as it would be found apart from the artifacts.

Eslick: Is there a distinction between formal and material causality?

Sellars: There is explanation in terms of the matter of which a thing is made. There is explanation in terms of the form. I understand the term 'causation' in terms of *explanation,* the variety of explanations we can give. I don't think that one has to require a real distinction in the sense I am objecting to in order to allow for these modes of explanation. A "real distinction" is a distinction between reals, in the sense of items in the real order as opposed to the logical order. But then, of course, there is a more colloquial sense in which a real distinction is a genuine distinction. The distinction between form and matter, is, of course, a genuine distinction. But it is not a distinction between reals.

Johann: This piece of plastic in my hand can be shaped in some other way. The plastic material can take on another form, so that these aspects must be in some sense really distinct, though not themselves things.

Sellars: I indicated there are all kinds of distinctions involved. I was addressing myself simply to the question: is there in the technical sense a *real*

272

distinction? I understand the term 'real distinction' to involve subjects and predication. Let me illustrate in terms of Donald Williams' system. Take for example a substance which has two accidents. In addition to the mental words, *square* and *green,* there is the square of this object, there is the green of this object. These latter are not universal; they do not belong to the logical order; they would in a sense be individuals or "thises", but they would not be substance. They would be incomplete or second-class "thises", so to speak. This would give a real distinction in the thing between its aspects.

Eslick: Take, for example, the Thomistic real distinction between *esse* and essence. *Esse,* I would say, is certainly not a subject, so it doesn't seem to me that you have given a necessary property of really distinct principles.

Sellars: The existing of an individual thing is a possible object of reference; we have, in fact, been referring to it. This is what I mean by calling it a "subject". The form likewise could be a subject, but it would not be a substance.

Eslick: But you can't subsume the color, green, in the sense of a genuine subject, that is, as having some kind of determinability, some kind of indetermination in which a higher specification is somehow removed, can you?

Sellars: But you see the green which is present in this green thing is not the green that you are talking about. There are certainly problems about the states of "absolute natures" of the Thomistic system. I'm not talking about an absolute nature now, I'm talking about the green of this green book, you see, and that is a *this*.

*　　*　　*　　*　　*

Fisk: Your objections to bare particulars seem to me inconclusive. Your "covered substrata" require an artificial language just as much. The covered substratum represented by your designator S, which is used in the description of the transmutation from one element to another, is of such a sort that it can take two thing-kind predicates successively. Yet there is no designator in ordinary language which can do this.

Sellars: I don't agree. A piece of skin can become a piece of leather.

Fisk: You are using *two* designators there.

Sellars: S was a piece of skin and now S is leather. The referent of S is an identifiable object enduring through time, through the change from skin to leather, for example.

Fisk: This is precisely what I am worried about, because if I say: "this is a piece of leather and was a piece of skin", then, it seems to me that the 'this' has a reference to what actually it is now, the physical object as it is now.

Sellars: This I regard as unwarranted. I don't see why I can't call this piece of skin 'Tom', and I don't see why Tom shouldn't be the same physical object, first being a piece of skin and then a piece of leather. Returning now to your original objection, my "covered" particulars do not involve any artificial designators because 'Socrates' or 'the man next door' will suffice, and this involves no artificiality. The point I was making was that in order to introduce the bare particulars you have to introduce an artificial language and my suspicion was that it is going to have to be a far more complex artificial language than you ingeniously suggested.

Fisk: Suppose we take the change from John to a corpse. It seems to me that it is not true that if we say this corpse was a man, we are referring by means of the 'this' to some particular which endures and is successively a man and a corpse. In the case of a radical change of this sort, I don't know what designator could refer to the perduring covered substratum.

Sellars: Supposing I say this flesh and bone and hank of hair was once a man. I think that there are certain rhetorical commitments of the examples you use that make them ring sounder than they are.

Fisk: But when you refer to something by means of 'this', you are referring to it as it is presented to you now.

Sellars: I refer to something *as* something if I say this as something is something. To refer to something considered as colored is to say this colored object is something; to refer to it without its color is simply to refer to it in a way which doesn't bring in its color.

Fisk: But then, if the 'this' does have the effect of referring to a perduring body then I don't see that we have anything here which we could call a "radical" change because it is characteristic of such a change that you can't use the same designator to refer to the thing before and after the change.

Sellars: It is true that designators ordinarily presuppose that the objects designated have certain features. For example, a name like 'Jones' presupposes that the item is a person who lives. If I say: this corpse was once a man, you're objecting: well, after, all to be a corpse is to be dead. But when I say this, I am using 'corpse' as a means of reference only. This does not require that every expression substantive to this expression must be logically in its presuppositions compatible with the presuppositions of that reference. So I can say: this man will be a corpse.

*   *   *   *   *

Lobkowicz: Are you not in a way committed to something like a real distinction once you speak of matter as something that things consist of? You cannot say that matter alone is enough, because there must at least be something which is material. Now, in this sense, it would seem that you have to add something to the material in order to make something consist of matter. You need to have a sort of co-principle.

Sellars: You mean that, in order for there to be material, there must be things like chairs and tables?

Lobkowicz: If matter is what something consists of, there must moreover be the thing besides.

Sellars: There must "moreover"? I said there must be the things—I didn't say "moreover", because I suspect that the little word 'moreover' carries an overwhelming overtone.

Lobkowicz: Yet it *does* seem that there must be "moreover" some kind of co-principle, because otherwise you would be obliged to say that the thing simply *is* this material and it would not be logically possible to say that matter is what the thing consists of.

Sellars: This is compatible with saying that this is a shoe and this is a piece of leather. In order for there to be materials, there must be "things" in several senses. In the conceptual order there must be the proper universals. But we are not talking about the conceptual order. There must be the various kinds: species and genera, etc. But we are not talking about that either. The issue is: is this piece of leather identical with this shoe? I am maintaining that this piece of leather is a shoe. I'm not saying that it is shoeness.

Lobkowicz: But why then is it inconsistent (as you suggest in your paper) to say that matter alone is real?

Sellars: There would be no materials in the Aristotelian sense unless there were the things. The word 'material' is a category word in a broad sense for structuring the world. A "material" would have no point in a universe of discourse which was not conceived of in terms of artifacts in which e.g. the leather could be made into something. In the Aristotelian scheme, a universe consisting merely of pieces of material would be incoherent, a Hamlet without the Prince of Denmark, you might say, because the whole point of matter is to be matter for form.

*   *   *   *   *

Owens: For your "real distinction", do you require two beings in the Aristotelian sense?

Sellars: I would draw a distinction between varieties of real distinction. Let me illustrate. There is a "real distinction", in some sense, for instance, between individual things in the real order and conceptual things: genera, species, etc. (We all know of course that items in the conceptual order are also in some sense in the real order, and this is the place where one has to tie philosophical threads together.) But, of course, although they are both real, they are not in the same order.

Owens: Would you say that the universal for Aristotle adds something real to the individual?

Sellars: No, because the universal is in no sense a constituent of the individual.

Owens: But for Aristotle, matter and form are certainly constituents of things.

Sellars: It is true of this shoe both that it serves to cover the feet and that it is a piece of leather. But, although these two facts are essential to the shoe's being a shoe, nevertheless this does not give us two individual things in the real order.

Owens: To use Aristotelian terminology, then, you would say that there is one *ousia* there, and that it is located primarily in the form; the composite substance is being only in virtue of the form, so that you will just have one being there. (*Sellars*: That's right.) Now take the question of what it is that endures after a substantial change. In such a process, there are only two things, yet there are three real principles: the initial form, say, of uranium, that made it one being, the final form of lead that makes it one being, and the substratum.

Sellars: The word 'form', as you know, is ambiguous with respect to individual form and the form universally considered. Now, the form as the "this" is not something that makes the individual something, it is the individual considered in that which makes it intelligible.

Owens: So that if there is any individuality, then, in either of those two things, it comes in each case from the form.

Sellars: Of course, the material has, in a secondary sense, its thisness. For

275

example, for Aristotle, a shoe is a this, but it is a this which owes its intelligibility to the existence of shoes, etc., so that the shoe is both a this as a piece of leather, and in a way that brings intelligibility to it as a shoe.

Owens: But now admitting matter as a permanent substratum, the secondary thisness of the uranium derives from the form of uranium, is that correct?

Sellars: Well, I'd prefer the case of the piece of leather. I'm dubious about these high-powered scientific examples. Let's talk in terms of earth, fire, air, and water. I don't like to mix theoretical and observational discourse.

Owens: Well, take the change, say, from fire to water: does the form of fire and the matter that is in that fire derive its secondary thisness from the form of fire?

Sellars: Well, the matter, of course, here is primary, and the primary matter is the object qua identifiable object in space and time, having *some* basic physical character or other. It is indefinite or indeterminate in the *disjunctive* sense: it has some character or other, some location or other. So that the object would be "this" *qua* this very indeterminate specification.

MATTER AND INDIVIDUATION

Joseph Bobik

§1 *The Problem*

The problem to be treated in this paper is a very modest one, and it can be conveniently presented if we begin by quoting Karl Popper's formulation of a problem which falls under the heading of the principle of individuation:

> Given two or more qualitatively indistinguishable bits of matter, we may be able to count them, or to say how many they are, which presupposes that they are not identical. Wherein lies their difference or non-identity?[1]

However alike *two* given material bodies or bits of matter[2] may be—e.g., they may be alike in being sugar cookies, or in being black swans, or in being men, or in being white, or even in all their qualities,—they are nonetheless clearly *two* bodies. What accounts for their being two?[3] What role, if any, does matter have in this account?[4]

It will be helpful, first of all, toward making unmistakable the sense of our problem, to notice that whereas Karl Popper asks for "something like a *sufficient condition,* i.e., a criterion, of difference or non-identity of material bodies, or bits of matter . . .",[5] this paper asks for an explanation of, or an account of, numerical plurality, where explanation means identifying some characteristic of material bodies from which (characteristic) it can be seen why two bodies are two. We want to be able to see why two bodies are two in a way similar to the way in which a plane triangle can be seen to be a plane figure with an exterior angle equal to the sum of the opposite interior angles from its character as a plane figure bounded by three straight lines.

It will be helpful, secondly, toward formulating a solution (see below, §2), to notice that the problem just posed can be conveniently posed as two

---

[1] Karl R. Popper, "Symposium: The Principle of Individuation, III", *Aristotelian Society Proceedings,* Suppl. Vol. 27, 1953, p. 100.

[2] Our problem is posed at the macrophysical level.

[3] This question is treated in §§2 and 3.

[4] This question is treated in §4.

[5] Karl Popper, *art. cit.,* p. 101.

problems; for if there *is* a plurality of sugar cookies, that plurality is *possible*. The two problems are these: 1) what accounts for the *possibility of a plurality* (numerical or countable) of individuals within a same type? Most generally put: what accounts for the possibility of a numerical plurality of qualitatively indistinguishable material things? 2) What accounts for the *factual plurality* (numerical or countable) of individuals within a same type? Most generally put: why are two or more qualitatively indistinguishable material things two or more?

There are other questions (perhaps more interesting, but which this paper will not consider) which go by the name of the problem of individuation, or which at least are asked in the context of the problem of individuation:[6]

1) What accounts for the fact of the *perduring identity* (over a span of time) of an individual? For example, what is it that accounts for my identity as an individual from birth until now?

2) How account for the fact that an individual is a *unity*, although it consists of many parts? For example, a man consists of countless small "material particles, whether of atoms, electrons or something else, this must be left to the physicists, . . ."[7] What accounts for the fact that a man is a *unity* or a *whole*, though composed of this multitude of parts?

3) The problem of *individual differences* amounts to a careful enumeration of the unique or distinguishing qualitative features of an individual followed by an attempt to account for these features. This problem has a psychological as well as a biological level.

4) In biology, is the colony or the member the individual? For example, in what we call sponges, much of the vital activity like engulfing food, digestion, respiration, and excretion, is by the separate cells. What we call sponges appear to be cell aggregates, and not organic unities. Is the colony, i.e., that which we call the sponge, the individual; or is the member, i.e.,

---

[6] For a consideration of some of these questions see the following by the author of this paper:
   a) *Saint Thomas on the Individuation of Bodily Substances*, an unpublished doctoral dissertation presented at the University of Notre Dame, Notre Dame, Indiana, August 1953.
   b) "Dimensions in the Individuation of Bodily Substances", *Philosophical Studies* (Maynooth), 1954, *4*, 60–79.
   c) "St. Thomas on the Individuation of Bodily Substances", *Readings in the Philosophy of Nature* (ed. by Henry J. Koren, C.S.Sp.), Westminster, Md., 1958; pp. 327–40.
   d) "A Note on a Problem about Individuality", *Australasian Journal of Philosophy*, 36, 1958, 210–15.

[7] Jan Lukasiewicz, "Symposium: The Principle of Individuation, I", *Aristotelian Society Proceedings*, Suppl. Vol. 27, 1953, pp. 81–82.

the cell, the individual? Further, what is the criterion for determining the biological individual, whether macroscopic or microscopic?

5) In physics, what is the ultimate (in the direction of smallness) physical individual, if it is meaningful to speak of an individual in this context? Further, what would be the criterion for determining the minimal physical individual? Physicists do not appear to be concerned with the problem of the *possibility of plurality* and the *factual plurality* of elementary particles (this is the problem of the present paper, but at the macrophysical level); rather they are concerned with the propriety of calling an elementary particle an individual, since it lacks "sameness". Erwin Schrödinger writes: ". . . the elementary particle is not an individual; it cannot be identified, it lacks "sameness". The fact is known to every physicist, but is rarely given any prominence in surveys readable by nonspecialists. In technical language it is covered by saying that the particles "obey" new-fangled statistics, either Einstein-Bose or Fermi-Dirac statistics. The implication, far from obvious, is that the unsuspected epithet 'this' is not quite properly applicable to, say, an electron, except with caution, in a restricted sense, and sometimes not at all."[8] "If we wish to retain atomism we are forced by observed facts to deny the ultimate constituents of matter the character of identifiable individuals."[9] Elementary particles do not appear to have the feature mentioned above in problem 1), sc. *perduring identity,* in the way in which macrophysical things have it.

6) What kind of identity and difference belong to whatever it is which is the principle of the individuation of macrophysical indivduals?[10]

§2 *Three Dimensional Quantification and Circumscription*

If the matter of the things of the physical universe (our consideration is macrophysical) were not quantified, there could not be a plurality of these things. (Matter by definition is that out of which a thing comes to be in change, and which survives in it, sc. in that which comes to be).[11] Consider the sugar cookie. Suppose that the matter of sugar cookies, i.e., sugar cookie batter, were not quantified. It would be impossible for a plurality of sugar cookies to come to be; for quantification is the source of divisibility. There could be but *one* sugar cookie; or, perhaps more precisely, there

---

[8] Erwin Schrödinger, "What is an Elementary Particle?", reprinted in *Readings in the Philosophy of Nature,* p. 341.

[9] *Ibid.,* p. 347.

[10] See D. C. Stove, "Two Problems About Individuality", *Australasian Journal of Philosophy,* 3, 1955, 183–88.

[11] The definition just given abstracts from the differences between matter in unqualified change and matter in qualified change; see below, footnote 22.

could be *neither one nor more than one* sugar cookie; there could at most be sugar-cookieness, which as such is neither one nor more than one, which as such does not give rise even to the possibility of its being one or more than one, which as such neither comes to be nor ceases to be, and which would as such (i.e., by virtue of its being sugar-cookieness) be distinct from all other things. As another example, consider bits of white paper. Suppose that the sheet of white paper out of which (as out of matter) the bits were supposed to have come to be were not quantified. It would have been impossible for the bits to have come to be; for bits of white paper come to be out of a sheet only as a result of tearing or cutting (i.e., any process which actually divides, and by dividing circumscribes), which presupposes tearability or cutability (i.e., divisibility), which in turn presupposes quantification. Only quantity is divisible and actually circumscribed *per se;*[12] all else is divisible and actually circumscribed *per accidens,* i.e., through quantity.

Thus, the three dimensional quantity of the matter (i.e., of that out of which they come to be, and which survives in them) of qualitatively indistinguishable material things accounts for the *possibility of their plurality.* The actual circumscription (effected sometimes by physical acts of dividing, sometimes by acts of composing) of their quantified matter accounts for their *factual plurality.*

§3 *Clarification*[13]

Someone may rightly point out that: 1) if one says that A is three dimensionally quantified and that B is three dimensionally quantified, A and B may well be the same individual. Further, someone may rightly point out that: 2) if one says that A is three dimensionally quantified *and circumscribed* and that B is three dimensionally quantified *and circumscribed,* again A and B may well be the same individual. Thus, someone may want to conclude that it does *not* seem to be *sufficient,* though it is necessary, that two qualitatively indistinguishable individuals be *quantified and circumscribed,* in order that they be *two.* Someone may then ask: what, then, along with, but in addition to circumscribed quantification accounts for the fact that A is an individual distinct from the individual B?—One wants to say right off that A is distinct from B, if A and B occupy different

---

[12] Divisibility and circumscribability are intrinsic attributes of quantity; although actual circumscription has an extrinsic cause, only that which is quantified is circumscribed.

[13] I am deeply indebted and grateful to Milton Fisk of the Notre Dame philosophy department for occasioning this attempt at clarification.

regions of space, in addition to being quantified and circumscribed. But here one wants to, and perhaps must, ask: why are different regions of space different? Are different regions of space to be distinguished by different individuals; or are different individuals to be distinguished by different regions of space?

Karl Popper's article on individuation, already cited, affords an excellent take-off point for trying to say something apropos of the immediately preceding paragraph. Because of the way in which the existence of space depends on the existence of quantified and circumscribed individuals,[14] it does not appear legitimate to say that individuals are differentiated by reason of different regions of space. Rather, it is to be said that different regions of space are differentiated by reason of different individuals. At most, it appears that individuals can be differentiated by different regions of space *quoad nos,* i.e., *we* can tell that *A* and *B* are different individuals if they occupy different regions of space. Thus, it appears that Karl Popper's sufficient condition of non-identity, namely: "Two qualitatively undistinguishable material bodies or bits of matter differ if they occupy at the same time different regions of space",[15] is at most a sufficient condition *quoad nos.*

It is desirable to seek a sufficient condition which is such *quoad res* as well as *quoad nos.*[16] In describing Miss Anscombe's method of tackling the problem of individuation,[17] Karl Popper distinguishes between the "logical or ontological side" of the problem ('logical' and 'ontological' appear to be equivalents here) and the "epistemological or operational side" of the problem ('epistemological' and 'operational' appear to be equivalents here,

---

[14] The existence of space appears to be notional, i.e., to speak of the existence of space is to speak of our notion of it, which involves a reference to existing quantified and circumscribed individuals. Our notion of space appears to be that of a receptacle for existing quantified and circumscribed individuals; this is not to say that there is such a receptacle, at least not one which exists independently of existing and circumscribed individuals.

[15] Karl Popper, *art. cit.,* p. 107.

[16] The difference between *quoad nos* and *quoad res et nos* can be seen by considering the example of fresh human footprints in the sand. One might want to argue: there is a man on this island, because there are fresh footprints in the sand. If this means anything, it means only this: *I know* there is a man on this island, *because I know* there are fresh footprints; that is, *my knowledge* of the existence of the fresh footprints causes *my knowledge* of the existence of the man. In arguing, the *causes in knowledge* (the fresh footprints in the sand are causes in knowledge) may but need not be *causes in the things which enter our knowledge* (the man is such a cause of the footprints); when they are, we have an instance of something *quoad res et nos.*

[17] See Karl Popper, *art. cit.,* p. 106. Popper's reference is to an article of Miss Anscombe's in the same supplementary volume of the *Aristotelian Society Proceedings, 27,* 1953, pp. 83–96.

and though I cannot understand 'epistemological,' I think I can understand 'operational').

Now, if one considers what Karl Popper calls the operational side, i.e., *how to make* many different qualitatively indistinguishable individuals, all one needs to do, for example, is to take some evenly rolled out cookie dough, but larger than the cookie cutter, and proceed to cut. Each cookie will be in every respect qualitatively indistinguishable from every other (even down to the shape of the cookie, if the same cookie cutter is used); but there will be many different (countably different) cookies. It is obviously important that the dough be larger than the cookie cutter; otherwise one will not be able to cut *two* or *more*. It is also obviously important that the cookie dough be quantified, and that each cookie be quantified and circumscribed.

For a thing *to be quantified* is for it to be such that it is constituted out of mutually excluding, contiguous, circumscribable parts. If one *actually divides* a quantified thing (like rolled out cookie dough), this is all one need do in order to have countably two (or more) individuals; for the actual cutting, though it affects the circumscribability of some of the parts of the quantified thing which has been divided, *in no way affects the mutual exclusion of the parts*. That is, whether the parts of a quantified thing are circumscribable (as they are before the cutting) or actually circumscribed (as they are after the cutting), in either case they mutually exclude each other. Their mutual exclusion is the basic ground of their countability. Thus, operationally tackled, the principle of individuation is the *mutual exclusion* of the parts (whether circumscribable or circumscribed) of dimensive quantity. *Qua* circumscrib*able*, the mutually excluding parts are potentially countable; *qua* circumscrib*ed*, actually countable.

The given physical universe is like the cookie dough *after* it has been cut; or better, like many different types of cookie dough after they have been cut. The physical universe is a collection of things each of which is quantified and circumscribed, some of which are qualitatively (in some respects at least) indistinguishable from others. Beyond this, the things of the physical universe are *like cookie cutters* in that they cut or circumscribe parts of the matter of the physical universe; they are *unlike* cookie cutters in that their cutting-out or circumscribing activity is not as simple as that of the cookie cutter, for they combine physical things with other physical things, or *parts* of some with *parts* of others, and introduce by appropriate processes new forms into the cut out or circumscribed matters. For example, the male uses food, and in a natural process circumscribes some of this food and gives it the form of a sperm; the female gives it the form of an ovum.—It appears clear now that Karl Popper's distinction between an *operational tackle* and an *ontological tackle* is precisely the distinction between a tackle *quoad nos* (Popper's ontological) and a tackle *quoad res et nos* (Popper's operational).

The preceding may be summarized in this way. How do *we tell* that two qualitatively indistinguishable things are two? By noticing that they occupy different regions of space (Popper's sufficient condition). But we must point out, because of the way in which the existence of space depends on the existence of quantified and circumscribed individuals, that two individuals occupy different regions of space because they are two; it is not the case that *two* individuals are *two* because they occupy different regions of space. We ask, therefore: why are two individuals two? The appropriate answer appears to be this: because of the *mutual exclusion* of the parts (whether circumscribable or circumscribed) of the dimensive quantity of the matter of the things of the physical universe.

Apropos of the comments made in the first paragraph of this section, this may be said: a) Comments 1) and 2) are unassailable. We cannot tell from the predicate 'three dimensionally quantified' that A and B are different individuals. Nor can we tell this from the predicate 'three dimensionally quantified and circumscribed.' For it is characteristic of any individual of the physical universe, considered precisely as a physical individual, to be both three dimensionally quantified and circumscribed. Apropos of 3), the *addition asked for* appears to be only this: noticing that being quantified means being constituted out of *mutually excluding circumscribable parts* which do not cease to be mutually excluding when a physical act of cutting renders them actually circumscribed parts.

Apropos of what Karl Popper calls a *sufficient condition,* one can perhaps say that *in essence* it does not differ from what this paper has called an *account* (briefly outlined above, in §2, namely, that the principle of individuation is the mutual exclusion of the parts (whether circumscribable or circumscribed) of the dimensive quantity of the matter of the things of the physical universe. One can perhaps say this, because Karl Popper attempts[18] to invalidate a *prima facie* objection to his criterion, namely this objection: that his criterion merely shifts the problem, by replacing the problem of the *difference of bits of matter* by that of the difference of *spatial regions.* His attempt at invalidating this objection amounts to formulating his criterion in absolutely general terms, which appear to me to be applicable to anything which is quantified, whether material individuals, space, mathematical lines, or whatever else, *and precisely because it is quantified.* This absolutely general formulation has the obvious ad-

---

18 Karl Popper, *art. cit.,* pp. 107–108.

vantage of avoiding the question: does the existence of space depend on the existence of quantified and circumscribed material individuals? The first formulation of his criterion or sufficient condition[19] is open to the objection which he notes; but his improved versions of the criterion are not.[20]

§4 *Matter and Individuation*

It is often said that matter is the principle of individuation. But if accounting for individuation is taken to mean accounting for the *possibility of plurality* and for the *factual plurality* of qualitatively indistinguishable material substances, matter cannot be the principle of individuation. This can be seen if one considers what matter is.

One can see what matter is when one considers unqualified change (UC),[21] and asks the question: what are the intrinsic constituents of a substance which comes to be in UC? Matter is that out of which a substance comes to be in UC and which survives in it, sc. in the substance which comes to be. This is primary matter (PM).[22] Since the generation of a substance is always the corruption of a previously existing substance, PM is not a substance. PM can be described as a constituent (this does not mean quantitative constituent) of the newly generated substance, the other constituent of the substance being its substantial form (SF).[23] But SF is not a

---

[19] Criterion (C), p. 107.

[20] It may be helpful here to quote his improved versions.

"$(3')$ If x is in the region occupied by A and y is in the region occupied by B, and if no path connecting x and y lies entirely within the region or regions occupied by A or by B, then $A \neq B$." (*Art. cit.*, p. 109)

"The letters 'x,' 'y,' 'z,' 'w' will be used to denote *points* (or perhaps marks) on the surface or within physical bodies or spatial regions; 'A,' 'B,' to denote physical bodies; and 'P,' 'Q,' to denote spatial regions." (*Ibid.*, p. 108)

"$(3'')$ If the body A lies within the region P, and the body B lies within the region Q, and if P and Q are separated by a gap, then $A \neq B$." (*Ibid.*, p. 110)

[21] UC is a change such that the substance which undergoes it ceases to be. For example, a man dies, or a seed and an ovum become a man. Qualified change (QC), on the other hand, is a change such that the substance which undergoes it does not cease to be. For example, a man grows, a man learns.

[22] PM is the expression used to refer to what survives in a UC, e.g., to what survives in the man from the seed and the ovum. *Second matter*, on the other hand, is the expression used to refer to what survives in a QC. For example, in the QC, the man became tan, man is second matter. Second matter is always a substance.

[23] Whereas 'PM' is the expression used to refer to that which survives in a UC, 'SF' is the expression used to designate *both* that in the substance which comes to be whereby it differs from the substance which has ceased to be *and* that in the substance which has ceased to be whereby it differs from the substance which comes to be.

284

constituent of *PM*. Since *PM* is not a substance, it is impossible for *PM* to have the determination of any accidental form. Since *SF* is not a constituent of *PM*, *PM* has no substantial determinations. It follows that *PM* is absolutely indeterminate. From which it clearly follows that *PM* cannot account for the *possibility of plurality* and for the *factual plurality* of qualitatively indistinguishable material substances. Thus, something other than *PM*, something to which divisibility belongs *per se*, must be introduced. This is clearly the observed three dimensional quantity of the substances of the physical universe.

At this point, one wants to ask this question: if matter cannot be the principle of individuation, and if quantity must be introduced, why not say that quantity alone is the principle of individuaton?; why say, as some do, that matter is the principle of individuation along with quantity?

The following immediately suggests itself. When one is concerned to account for the individuation of material substances as such (i.e., of things which exist *simply*, as for example: Jack exists, rather than of things which exist qualifiedly, as for example: Jack's height exists), one should perhaps propose an individuating principle which pertains to the intrinsic constitution of these substances. Any other kind of proposal would appear to be irrelevant or *per accidens*. *PM* and *SF* are the intrinsic constitutents of a substance-which-comes-to-be-in-*UC* as well as of a substance-which-ceases-to-be-in-*UC*;[24] there are no other intrinsic constituents. At this point, the following things suggest themselves:

1) One may say: Hence either *SF* or *PM* or the composite of *SF* and *PM* is the principle of individuation. But *SF* is neither one nor more than one, nor does it give rise to the possibility of its being one or more than one. The same is to be said about *PM*. The same, therefore, will have to be said about the composite of *PM* and *SF*. On this showing, therefore, not only is *PM* not the principle of individuation of material substances, but there is no principle of individuation at all which pertains to the intrinsic constituents of a material substance. Quantity and circumscripton have to be introduced at this point, if one is to account for individuation.

2) Or one may point out, in an attempt to give a reason for saying that *PM* is the principle of individuation (along with quantity), that: *PM* exists prior to the coming to be of a newly generated substance, whereas the *SF* of that substance does not. Thus, the *SF* of that substance can be said to come to be in *PM*, much the same as the form, i.e., the shape, of a statue can be said to come to be in some already existing chunk of marble. And just as the *shape* of the statue can be said to be individuated by the

---

[24] See above, footnote 23.

already-existing chunk of marble in which it comes to be (which would be another way of saying that the *statue* was individuated by that chunk of marble), so too the *SF* of a newly generated substance can be said to be individuated by the already-existing *PM* in which it comes to be (which would be another way of saying that the newly generated substance was individuated by *PM*). Having said this, however, one is still faced with the fact that *PM* cannot be the principle of individuation.[25] Thus, if one wants to say that *PM* is the principle of individuation *because it exists prior to the coming to be of a newly generated substance whereas the SF of that substance does not,* one gives, if one gives anything at all, only an incomplete account of individuation; quantity and circumscription would have to be added to complete the account.

Suggestion 2) just above amounts to proposing, for one who wants to assign a principle of individuation which is among the intrinsic constituents of a material substance, a reason for assigning *PM* rather than *SF*. But the reason appears to be a weak one. First of all, it is restricted to the context of generation, i.e., it attempts an account of the individuation of a substance which *comes to be* in *UC,* but attempts no account of the individuation of the substance which *ceases to be* in *UC.* Secondly, to assign *PM* as principle of individuation is to assign a principle which is at best incomplete; for quantity and circumscription must be added.—Suggestion 1) above (along with what we earlier had to say about the nature of *PM*), on the other hand, proposes a rather compelling reason for not assigning *PM* at all. Further, the reason is not restricted to the context of the substance which comes to be in *UC;* it extends also to the context of the substance which ceases to be in *UC.* Further still, to assign quantity and circumscription as the principle of individuation is not to assign a principle which is incomplete. The preceding suggestions, thus, offer no good reason for saying that *matter along with quantity* is the principle of individuation.

In the writings of St. Thomas Aquinas one finds a perhaps more acceptable reason for saying that matter along with quantity is the principle of individuation.[26] Whereas quantity (and circumscription) accounts for the *possibility of plurality* and for *factual plurality,* matter accounts for something else, so that *matter along with quantity* accounts for more than possibility of plurality and factual plurality. What this is can be seen if one considers further what matter is.

---

[25] If one had said that an *SF* is individuated by the *bit* or *chunk* of *PM* in which it comes to be, one would have begun to face the fact that *PM* cannot be the principle of individuation; for to speak of *bits* or *chunks* of *PM* is to have introduced *quantity* and *circumscription.*

[26] What follows takes us outside the bounds we have set for ourselves in this paper; we will be very brief.

PM is the primary potential or receptive principle, or subject, in a material substance. That is, whereas accidental forms (*AF*'s) are related to the substance composed of *PM* and *SF* as inherents to a receptive subject, and *SF* is related to *PM* as inherent to a receptive subject, there is nothing to which *PM* is related as inherent to receptive subject. *PM* does not inhere in anything; there is nothing in which it could inhere. *PM* is an absolutely irreceivable subject.

It is this irreceivable character of *PM*, according to St. Thomas Aquinas, which accounts for the irreceivable character of an individual material substance.[27] One of the differences between the individual nature and the specific nature, according to St. Thomas, is that the latter is communicable to others as to inferiors (sc. to individuals), whereas the former is not. What can account for this incommunicability or irreceivability? In the material individual we find only three things: *PM*, *SF*, and *AF*'s. *AF*'s cannot account for this irreceivability, for they are themselves receivable. Neither can *SF*, for it too is receivable. *PM*, first of all by elimination, must account for it. But more importantly, *PM* is an absolutely irreceivable subject.

Our intention here is not to defend the position that *PM* accounts for the irreceivable character of the material individual. Our intention is simply to indicate that one can speak acceptably of *matter along with quantity* as the principle of individuation if one is attempting to account

---

[27] "Est . . . de ratione individui quod non possit in pluribus esse. Quod quidem contingit dupliciter. Uno modo, quia non est natum in aliquo esse: et hoc modo formae immateriales separatae, per se subsistentes, sunt etiam per seipsas individuae. Alio modo, ex eo quod forma substantialis vel accidentalis est quidem nata in aliquo esse, non tamen in pluribus: sicut haec albedo, quae est in hoc corpore. Quantum igitur ad primum, materia est individuationis principium omnibus formis inhaerentibus: quia, cum hujusmodi formae, quantum est de se, sint natae in aliquo esse sicut in subjecto, ex quo aliqua earum recipitur in materia, quae non est in alio, jam nec ipsa forma sic existens potest in alio esse. Quantum autem ad secundum, dicendum est quod in-dividuationis principium est quantitas dimensiva. Ex hoc enim aliquid est natum esse in uno solo, quod illud est in se indivisum et divisum ab omnibus aliis. Divisio autem accidit substantiae ratione quantitatis, . . ." (St. Thomas Aquinas, *S.T.*, III, *q.* 77, *a.* 2, *c.*) ". . . formae quae sunt receptibiles in materia, individuantur per materiam, quae non potest esse in alio, cum sit primum subjectum substans: forma vero, quantum est de se, nisi aliquid aliud impediat, recipi potest a pluribus. Sed illa forma quae non est receptibilis in materia, sed est per se subsistens, ex hoc ipso individuatur, quod non potest recipi in alio: et hujusmodi forma est Deus." (St. Thomas, *S.T.*, I, *q.* 3, *a.* 2, *ad* 3) Sylvester of Ferrara expresses the role of *PM* in individuation in this way: ". . . ad individuationem et materia et quantitas concurrit. Materia quidem, inquantum in-dividuum est incommunicabile per exclusionem communicationis illius qua universale communicatur particulari: nam quia materia primum subjectum est, in nullo receptum inferiori, ideo natura in materia recepta, ut sic, nulli inferiori communicari potest." (*In C.G.*, I, *cap.* 21, IV).

J. Bobik

for more than just the possibility of plurality and the factual plurality of qualitatively indistinguishable material individuals. If one is attempting to account for no more than this, quantity alone is the principle of individuation.[28]

University of Notre Dame

[28] We are thus, it may be of interest to some to note, in agreement with the explicit opinion of St. Thomas Aquinas on this point: ". . . quia sola quantitas dimensiva de sui ratione habet unde multiplicatio individuorum in eadem specie possit accidere, prima radix hujusmodi multiplicationis ex dimensione esse videtur: quia et in genere substantiae multiplicatio fit secundum divisionem materiae; quae nec intelligi posset nisi secundum quod materia sub dimensionibus consideratur: nam, remota quantitate, substantia omnis indivisibilis est, ut patet per Philosophum in *I Physicorum*." (*C.G.*, IV, cap. 65).—Many thanks to Ernan McMullin and to Harry Nielsen, both of the Notre Dame philosophy faculty, for many enlightening criticisms of this paper.

COMMENT

MR. BOBIK FORMULATES THE CLASSICAL PROBLEM OF INDIVIDUATION BY MEANS OF the question, "What accounts for the numerical plurality of qualitatively indistinguishable macrophysical individuals?" In asking for an account or for an explanation of plurality, I understand him to be asking the question "What entails and is entailed by the concept of plurality?" or the question "What entails and is entailed by the fact that A and B are not numerically identical?" It is clear that if such a question can be answered, the answer to the correlative question "What entails and is entailed by the fact that A is numerically one individual?" would follow immediately. Thus to pose the problem of individuality in terms of plurality, as Mr. Bobik does, is not to shrug off the problem of individuation conceived as a problem of unity.

For Mr. Bobik it is the mutual exclusion of the parts (whether circumscribable or circumscribed) of the dimensive quantity of the matter of the universe which accounts fully for the numerical plurality of individuals. This then is his principle of individuation. I am in agreement with this solution to the problem of individuation. In what follows I shall give it a more explicit formulation and attempt to defend it against a serious objection.

There is a conceptual difference between the two predicates:

> is an individual
> is a part of an individual.

Mr. Bobik's analysis relies on this difference, for he treats distinct individuals as parts of a more encompassing individual in order to explain how, as individuals but not as parts, they are distinct. But one might ask: Doesn't this procedure pose the problem of individuation at another level, not at that of individuals but at that of parts of individuals? I shall show that this is not the case.

Let us reformulate Mr. Bobik's solution to the problem of individuation as follows:

> The fact that A and B are numerically distinct individuals entails and is entailed by the fact that A and B are mutually excluding parts of some individual.

Thus, e.g., Kelley's right arm and his left leg are countably two if and only if they are mutually excluding parts of Kelley or of something including Kelley. Likewise, Kelley and Johnson are countably two if and only if they are mutually excluding parts of this room or of something including this room. The concept of distinct individuals A and B is, then, analyzed in terms of the concept of mutually excluding parts A and B of some encompassing individual.

289

The problem of individuation would be posed by Mr. Bobik's solution at the level of parts of individuals only if in order to understand the notion of mutually excluding parts we have to introduce that of numerically distinct parts. We shall now examine the notion of mutually excluding parts of something. Take Kelley's right arm and his left leg. The arm and the leg are parts of Kelley. Further they exclude one another. That is, there is no further part of Kelley which as a whole is part of Kelley's arm and also part of Kelley's leg. Thus:

> A and B are mutually excluding parts of some individual D if and only if A and B are parts of D and there is no part of D, say C, such that C as a whole is a part of A and a part of B.

Suppose, however, that A and B are numerically identical parts of D. There is a part of D, say C, which as a whole is part of A and B, viz. either A or some part of A, either B or some part of B. Thus under the supposition of identity of parts the condition for mutual exclusion of parts is not satisfied. We do not then need to add to this condition for mutual exclusion the condition that A and B be non-identical parts. Since mutual exclusion of parts can be understood without the notion of plurality of parts, solving the problem of individuation for individuals in terms of mutual exclusion of parts does not pose the problem of individuation at the level of parts of individuals.

We are now in a position to give a more explicit formulation to Mr. Bobik's solution:

> The fact that A and B are numerically distinct individuals entails and is entailed by the fact that A and B are parts of some individual D and there is no part of D, say C, such that C as a whole is a part of A and a part of B.

I wish to make three remarks about his solution as so formulated. First, if one accepts this solution then one expresses it only in a partial fashion by saying that quantity is the principle of individuation. D must be quantified to have A and B as mutually excluding parts. Thus quantity features in Mr. Bobik's solution in no such direct way as it would if we could say that A and B are numerically distinct if and only if A and B are quantified, which we can't. As a slogan representing Mr. Bobik's position the sentence 'Quantity is the principle of individuation' is misleading. Second, Mr. Bobik's solution fails for a universe containing only a single individual. Even though according to the assumption of a unitary universe 'A' and 'B' would be names of the same individual, A and B would according to Mr. Bobik's criterion for numerical distinctness be distinct. But I see no reason to take this as an objection to his criterion. One and many are codeterminables. The assumption of a unitary universe is conceptually indefensible. And that Mr. Bobik's thesis encounters a difficulty under such an assumption is no argument against it. Third, in his original formulation of the principle of individuation Mr. Bobik uses the phrase, 'parts of the dimensive quantity of the matter of the universe'. In my formulation of his principle I have replaced this by the phrase 'parts of some individual'. My objections to Mr. Bobik's phrase are twofold. 'Parts of the dimensive quantity of' suggests, against his intention, that the parts are spatial regions rather than individuals considered as parts of more encompassing individuals. 'Matter of the universe' introduces the troublesome term 'universe' (Is it a class term? Does it reintroduce the problem of plurality?) into an analysis in which we wish our concepts to be as well understood as possible.

In conclusion I want to emphasize that the key to the success of Mr. Bobik's solution is his treatment of the individuals whose plurality is to be explained in terms of the concept of parts-of-a-more-encompassing-individual. The proof of the success of his solution consists, negatively at least, in producing an analysis of the notion of mutually excluding parts which does not rest on the notion of the non-identity of parts.

Milton Fisk
University of Notre Dame

DISCUSSION

Weisheipl: With regard to Mr. Bobik's paper and Mr. Fisk's comment, it seems to me that there are two things to talk about. First of all, the position, or the supposed position, of St. Thomas and, secondly, the intelligibility of the problem and the solution. With regard to the first, it comes to me as a considerable surprise that Mr. Bobik attributes this position to St. Thomas. In the Thomistic tradition there are two interpretations: (1) That St. Thomas maintained a dual principle, namely, prime matter and quantity. And (2) the other tradition which interprets St. Thomas as insisting upon prime matter alone, as such, although understood through quantity. In both of these interpretations it is still prime matter which has the significant role to play. There is no tradition, as far as I know, which excludes prime matter from individuating. With regard to the text of St. Thomas, it is always *haec materia* which is said to individuate. It is true that in two or three places, St. Thomas does bring in dimensive quantity, but I think in each one of those passages the position of quantity is very clear: the term 'individual' involves terms which directly pertain to quantity, such as 'division', 'indivision', 'one', 'many' . . . Yet we must remember that, in the Aristotelian scheme, quantity is an accident and the big difficulty Aristotelians, for the most part, felt and all Thomists feel, is that an accident cannot possibly make a substance individual. We are still dealing with individuals even if we get down to the ultimate particle; the ultimate part is still an individual part; and nothing posterior or accidental to substance can render this thing an individual. Now, it's true that we *understand* an individual through quantity and through qualitative characteristics, but is that the same thing as to say that quantity is the responsible cause, the principle, from which an individual substance is derived?

St. Thomas recognized that the difficulty about making matter the principle of individuation, is that matter is supposed to be absolutely indeterminate. But if we remember there's a difference between prime matter in the abstract, (that's what we were discussing yesterday: prime matter as pure potentiality, is an abstraction) and prime matter in the concrete. What really exists is *this* matter, this thing given a nature, *haec materia, materia signata,* as St. Thomas frequently calls it, or *materia designata,* the ultimately given. Well, that distinction between an abstract *materia communis* and a concrete *materia designata,* is very clear in St. Thomas, while the principle of individuation is certainly not the abstract. What we were discussing yesterday cannot *be,* precisely because it is an abstraction, it is common. It's common to many things, it's common to the entire universe. All material things have matter. You see, in

292

that sense it's common, but each individual has *this* matter. Now, what does 'this matter' mean? It means: this ultimate individual substantial thing designated in terms of quantitative characteristics of being here, now, this much, actually distinct from other things, but in itself undivided. The classic definition of individual, is that which is in itself undivided, but divided from all other things. Now, the first part of this doesn't mean that it doesn't have any parts. Quite the contrary. It means that it itself is not in any subject, that in itself is not multiple, it's not like a form which can be many things. The first part refers to the substantial individuality of the body being discussed. The second part of the definition giving the reason for its distinction from other things involves, of course, the accident of quantity.

I am much happier with Mr. Fisk's insistence on parts of individuals rather than on parts of quantity. After all, Kelley's right arm and left arm are his arms; they are substantial. It's not quite proper to speak about parts of quantity. But in an organism such as man, the parts are quite clear; you can speak of Kelley's right arm and when you get down to the arm you can speak of the shoulder, the fingers; when you get down to the ultimate part, that too is quantified, and we say of each of the parts of that ultimate part, (ultimate insofar as nature or we can divide not mathematically but physically) that even *that* has parts. In what sense, though? Actually distinct parts? No, distinguishable parts, distinguishable in the sense that there is a this side or a that side. The quantity, the accident, doesn't give any matter, doesn't really give any parts, merely gives distinguishableness of parts which are themselves substantial.

Fisk: I would just like to make this remark. I find some difficulty in understanding your formulation of the problem of individuation. What "makes" X and Y distinct individuals or what "makes" X one, by itself, alone? If you raise the question in this form then you do find that it is difficult to say that an accident "makes" the substance be an individual or an accident "makes" one substance to be distinct from another. But I think Mr. Bobik has put the problem in a way which avoids the possible difficulties of the word 'makes', for what he has asked for is an "account" or an "explanation" and by this I understand him to be asking: "When we use expressions for plurality or expressions for unity, what do we mean?" In this form I think that one avoids a type of ontological cookery, which would demand ingredients or elements which have the task of individuation. The formulation in terms of an "account" gets away from this, and thus I don't think that we can be worried by its being said that quantity by itself cannot individuate. And furthermore, I would like to ask if there are any objections to Mr. Bobik's formulation of the principle of individuation other than those arising from the historical point of view. If you do find that as an account of plurality this does not fail then why should matter be introduced into the account?

Owens: To get the record straight on a remark of Fr. Weisheipl's that all day yesterday we were talking about an abstraction. In the Thomistic context you could have the abstraction of a universal from a particular or a form from matter. There is certainly no question here of the abstraction of the universal from the particular and since we are talking about matter, the abstraction could not be that of a form either . . . All day yesterday we were talking about a *concrete* principle, even though we were talking about it universally.

Weisheipl: It's true we're not abstracting a form, but we have been discussing prime matter in common, and in that sense I meant 'abstract'. That is to say, it is not a thing as it physically exists, while *'haec materia'* denotes a thing as it exists, and it's that ultimate thing which is *de facto* given and which we, of course, universalize.

Owens: So, the fact that we are talking about it universally doesn't destroy its reality?

Weisheipl: No, I didn't mean that, but I did mean that there is a real distinction between discussing prime matter as pure potentiality and seeing it as the ultimate root of individuation.

Misner: Do we account by this procedure for the plurality of objects? Are we shedding light on that question? And here, as in many things I hear here, I wonder what one is trying to explain? What's the purpose of it? It would seem to me that there aren't any immediate practical problems involved in being able to decide whether I have one cookie or two cookies in front of me. I have an intuitive idea of how the word 'several' is to be applied to ordinary everyday objects, an idea which has never failed me, not given me any problems. It would seem that a philosophical analysis of this idea should be for the purpose of getting a stronger, clearer concept of plurality which would allow me to talk about the number of angels or the number of elementary particles, or something like that that isn't everyday, ordinary. Yet that is precisely what this analysis won't do. It fails completely for elementary particles at the microscopic level, because I can have two electrons and know they are two electrons and that they fill the same area of space and thus can't be circumscribed and set apart; yet they are distinctly two, not individual, but two. So, I ask why does one talk about the intuitive concept, which as far as I know, doesn't cause people trouble, without deepening it to an extent that it is a stronger, more powerful concept? . . .

294

FOUR SENSES OF 'POTENCY'

Ernan Mc Mullin

§ 1 *Historical Note: Aristotle*

Aristotle defines the "primary kind of potency" as "an originative source of change in another thing or in the thing itself *qua* other",[1] and suggests that the other senses in which he uses the term can be simply reduced to this one. Most of his modern commentators would disagree firmly with him on this point:

> Applying the same word to these diverse representations of potency obviously does not suffice to prove a real unity of the concept. . . . The mere unity of the term very often leads (Aristotle) to deceive himself about the unity of the thought.[2]

In fact, the writer just cited would go on to say that the diversity of ways in which the notion of potency may be taken is "one of the most important sources of obscurity in Aristotle's thought".[3] Be this as it may, there can be no doubt that one of the reasons we have had so much difficulty in deciding whether, and in what sense, primary matter can be described as "pure potency", lies in the ambiguity of the term 'potency' itself. It seems worthwhile, then, to spend some more time at this point.

Potency, as defined above, is relative to *change;* it points to the future. Something is said to be "in potency" only insofar as it is capable of change. If it is incorruptible, it has no substantial potency, though it may still have an incidental potency e.g. for local motion, as in the case of the celestial bodies.[4] Against the Megaric school, Aristotle stresses that although potency necessarily involves privation, it is of itself more than privation. To say that *A* is capable of becoming *B* is to tell us more than that *A* is simply non-*B*. Potency would thus seem to lie somewhere between the fullness of actuality and the non-being of privation. To put this in another way, potency has two

---

[1] *Meta.* 1046a 11. I would like to thank Dr. N. Lobkowicz for his critical reading of the first draft of this essay.

[2] J. Le Blond, S.J., *Logique et méthode chez Aristote,* Paris, 1939, p. 426.

[3] *Op. cit.,* p. 417.

[4] *Meta.* 1050b 7–27. Aristotle is notoriously unsure how to handle this obviously peculiar situation: the celestial bodies are essentially "in act" and thus non-material, yet, if they are to move at all, they must be assumed to have some "local matter" (*Meta.* 1042b 6) of a non-essential sort, whatever that could be.

aspects, one the negative aspect of privation and the other the positive (though intermediate) actuality of matter.

Aristotle distinguishes between *active* potency or power (the original sense of δύναμις) which is the ability to act upon something else, and *passive* potency which is the capacity of being acted upon by something else. The two are clearly correlative: each is conceptually related to the other. Each is relative to a specific "something else"; thus we do not simply say that *A* is in passive potency, but that it is in passive potency to being acted upon in a *specific* way by a *specific* entity, *B*.[5] If notions of purpose or value be introduced, the definition of 'potency' will have to be altered; there will now be question of an active (or passive) potency, specified as being for the *better or worse*.[6] In natural motion, especially living motion, Aristotle pictures the active potency as a sort of striving (ὁρμή) intrinsic to the being, a power that, if not impeded, carries the being to its goal. Thus the acorn has the intrinsic *active* potency to become an oak; it has an intrinsic *passive* potency to be stepped upon.

Potency, possibility and contingency are closely linked in Aristotle's mind. He sometimes equates potency with the possible (δυνατόν), but more often distinguishes between indeterminate logical possibility and determinate potency.[7] Potency is regarded as a *proximate* possibility, one that will lead to its result if no actual hindrance be interposed. Thus:

> The seed is not yet potentially a man, for it must be deposited in something other than itself and undergo a change. But when, through its own motive principle, it has already got such and such attributes, in this state it is already potentially a man. . . . Earth is not yet potentially a statue, for it must first change in order to become brass.[8]

The criterion is not altogether clear; 'proximate' is a relative term. How close must possibility approach to actuality in order to qualify as "potency"? When we say of the sleeping man and of the human foetus that they have a "potency" for rational thought, for example, it is evident that two somewhat different senses of 'potency' are in question, the one involving non-exercise of a power presently possessed and the other indicating a capacity to develop (at a later time) this same power. The latter is a "second-order" potency, it would appear, a sort of "capacity to develop a capacity", involving time or process in two different ways.

Further, how are potency and *contingency* to be related? Aristotle sug-

[5] *Meta.* 1046a 25.

[6] *Meta.* 1019b 13; 1046a 17.

[7] *Meta.* 1019b 35. See L. Robin, *Aristote,* Paris, 1944, "La matière comme puissance", p. 80 *seq.*

[8] *Meta.* 1049a 13–19.

gests that "every potency is at one and the same time a potency for opposites",[9] implying non-necessity of the outcome, i.e. contingency. But he also holds that non-rational potencies are determined to act in one specific way (if properly aided and not impeded). The contingency in these cases could not, it would appear, lie in the individual natures as such, but only in the manner in which different natures come to interlock with one another.

This point is a notoriously controverted one among commentators on Aristotle. Though he links potency and contingency, it seems in keeping with his over-all philosophy to suppose that he is saying: (1) a determinate non-free being will always act in the same way under the same sort of physical conditions; the matter-component of a physical being does not bring about some sort of *radical* contingency or defect that would lead to an indeterminism independent of physical context; (2) rather, a physical being has a potency for different outcomes simply because it can be acted upon by different agencies, and because there is no way *intrinsic to the being itself* of telling which of these will come about. The contingency (or lack of necessity) about the outcome is thus due to *passive* potency (because passive potency is not ordinarily determined to a *single* sort of uniformly-acting outside agency); it is not due to some sort of occasional "faltering" in the *active* potency of the being, as some writers on Aristotle have suggested. Where the interlocking of different natures and potencies is itself of a "necessary" sort, i.e. in the case of the celestial motions, one would expect, therefore, to find him admitting a potency without contingency. This is, in fact, the case. He says that the eternal motion of the stars is without potency as to its existence but involves potency in respect to "whence and whither"; yet this potency is without contingency—he explicitly modifies his initial linking of potency and contingency—because there are no "opposites" involved in celestial motion.[10]

At the beginning of Book 9 of the *Metaphysics*, Aristotle remarks that "potency and actuality extend beyond the cases that involve a reference to motion", and that this broader sense of 'potency' in fact furnishes the reason for the inquiry of Book 9. He promises that this broader sense will become clear from his discussion of actuality in the later chapters of the book. Unfortunately, this crucial point never *is* quite clarified. It is difficult to decide just what the broader sense is, because each of the later references to potency still involves *some* reference, at least, to possible change. A statue of Hermes is said to be potentially present in the block of wood "because it might be separated out", and, more generally, if we can say that X is Y–en (e.g. the casket is wooden; wood is earthen), then Y contains X in potency. X is here

---

[9] *Meta.* 1050b 9.
[10] *Meta.* 1050b 18–27.

regarded as a sort of stuff which contains an infinite number of determinate "potential" forms; each is relative to a specific change that could be wrought on X.

> And if there is a first thing which is no longer, in reference to something else, called "that-en", this is primary matter; e.g. if earth is "airy" and air is not fire but fiery, fire is primary matter, which is not a this.[11]

The difference between this sort of potency and the earlier ones is not very clear-cut; Aristotle even uses an example (the person able to build but not actually building) he had already given for the motion-potency. He is apparently urging that the statue-form potentially present in the uncut wood ought to be described as something other than simply a passive potency of wood to be acted upon in a particular way.[12] The point becomes somewhat clearer with the "potency" that goes with mathematical divisibility: "the fact that the process of dividing never comes to an end ensures that this activity exists potentially but not that the infinite exists separately". This is a potency which, though related with motion, can never reach to actuality; the infinity of divisions exists only potentially, for knowledge.

§ 2 Historical Note: Plotinus and Aquinas

There is no suggestion in Aristotle's work, nor for that matter in the work of any classical Greek thinker, of the well-known medieval dictum about potency: "actuality can be limited only by potency", i.e. no actuality can be found in a limited degree in any being unless it is conjoined with a really distinct limiting principle whose nature is to be a potency for that actuality.[13] Aristotle would have rejected this usage of his terms 'actuality' and 'potency'; for him, "actuality" was something sufficient to itself, definite, possessing its own limit; unlimit connoted for him imperfection and incompleteness, while "potency" for him was always linked with privation and change. Once the wood is fashioned into a casket it is no longer in potency to the casket-form, simply because that form is now actualized, and the actuality and potency are defined to be exclusive of one another. The idea, for example, of a "potency"—like the angelic essence—which excludes all change and is merely a static receiving principle, would have made no

---

[11] *Meta.* 1049a 23–26.

[12] J. Souilhé, *Étude sur le terme 'dunamis' dans les dialogues de Platon*, Paris, 1919, p. 183 *seq.*

[13] This is discussed in detail by Fr. Norris Clarke, S.J., in his important essay, "The Limitation of Act by Potency", *New Scholasticism, 26,* 1952, 167–94. See also the classic work by P. Descoqs, S.J., *Essai Critique sur le Hylemorphisme,* Paris, 1924, Part 2, chapter 2.

sense to him; he expressly insisted that the celestial bodies, because incorruptible, had no essential potency.

This odd inversion of the Aristotelian roles of 'actuality' and 'potency' took place in two stages. Plotinus identified the One with the Unlimited, and hence was led to re-define the philosopher's key term, 'actuality', by associating it with the infinite rather than the finite. Thus, limitation now becomes a sign of imperfection and incompleteness instead of the opposite. The change here is in the notion of what constitutes intelligibility itself: it is now seen not in limits, structures, definite boundaries, but rather in "perfections", in a participating in unlimited "actualities". Hence, one must look for limit now on the "lower" or "material" side of a being rather than on the formal or intelligible side. Aquinas completed the inversion by using the Aristotelian term 'potency' for this principle of limit, even though Aristotle had made act, not potency, *his* principle of limit.

St. Thomas' justification for doing this must be sought in his distinctly non-Greek metaphysics of creation and participation. The act-potency relation is generalized so as to provide a schema for the new essence-existence distinction; this allows him to regard existence as a sort of quasi-form or actuality, which is unlimited in itself but can be shared in different degrees. Since there can be no *process* towards existence, strictly speaking (and thus no potency-act time-progression in the Greek sense), if the term 'potency' is to be applied here at all (which Aristotle would presumably have questioned), it will be in a strikingly novel sense. The notes of present privation and aptitude for specified change are eliminated; only a sort of static "grasping towards a perfection not possessed of itself" reminds us of the former sense. The "actuality" and the "potency" now *co-exist,* and qualify one another mutually. Each is an ontologically incomplete principle, though one has to be careful here not to ask whether existence exists of itself, a question that obviously makes no sense. One of the principles (actuality, perfection) links a being with "higher" realities; the other (potency) marks the reason for its falling short of these actualities.

'Potency' is now to be understood differently. It is not, of course, as though Aquinas had discovered some new property of a well-defined entity called "potency", a property which Aristotle had never suspected—though this is unfortunately the way in which this sort of development can easily be represented. It is a matter of re-definition of the terms, 'potency', 'existence', 'limit', 'actuality'. . . . The internal relations between them are altered and the corresponding concepts, because of this internal shift, are different. The complication arises here from the fact that such terms cannot be defined operationally nor by ordinary *genus-differentia* techniques; they are in fact defined by the very formulae in which they are employed.

These have, therefore, a quasi-definitional character, as well as being quasi-theoretical, because the structure to which they belong must ultimately be evaluated in terms of consistency and explanatory power. Thus, Aquinas would have to defend his conceptual shift by claiming that the new internal relations he has proposed between Aristotle's terms give a better, richer account of what is.

That they do so for problems of essence and existence and creation can easily enough be defended. But a real difficulty arises with the matter-form distinction, to which the act-potency relation had already been applied in its earlier sense. In the new usage, matter is said to be "potency", not because its indeterminacy will be replaced, via change, by the determinacy of actuality, but rather because it is the principle of limitation and negation which will serve to determine the "unlimit" of form. Previously, primary matter had been regarded as unbounded; the root metaphor was one of *making,* in which a formless stuff received a knowable structure. Now it is the form which is unbounded in the line of actuality. Nothing could more clearly indicate the change than the Neoplatonic formula Aquinas often quotes: "every separated form is infinite".[14] If we wish to describe the matter-form distinction by contrasting a principle of determination and a principle of determinability, our dilemma is now obvious. Because of the new ambiguity in the notion of what it is to "determine", we could link the two pairs either way. Matter can be regarded either (in the manner of Plotinus) as a principle of "limitation" or (in the manner of Aristotle) as a principle of "determinability". If the formula about potency as limiting act be stressed, then the former description will be preferred, and we may even find ourselves saying that matter is a principle of "indetermination", besides also being a principle of limitation, a combination of roles that has given mental cramps to many a textbook writer.

This new mode of linking matter and potency immediately leads to a stress on the role of matter as *individuating.* Matter is what superimposes multiplicity upon the undifferentiated unity of actuality. Not unexpectedly, then, we find the ontological problem of individuation to be quite central to Aquinas' natural philosophy. Here he is somewhat more in the spirit of Plato than in that of Aristotle, for whom individuation had been more often of epistemological concern. Another consequence of the change was a vastly increased emphasis on the notion of *primary* matter, which, when all is said and done, is mentioned only a handful of times in Aristotle's own writings. If matter is defined to be a "potency" for the form which presently qualifies it, it is plain that much more interest will attach to the way in which pri-

---

[14] See the references given by Clarke, *op. cit.,* p. 192.

mary matter plays "potency" to substantial form than to the way in which second matter will be a "potency" for the accidental forms that qualify it.

Primary matter is said to *be* a potency, not to *have* a potency (as would be said of second matter):

> The potency of matter is not some property superadded to its essence; matter according to its very substance *is* a potency for substantial existence.[15]

One of Aquinas' modern commentators enlarges upon this:

> A piece of wax . . . is a total potency in the order of figure, because it requires no particular figure and can contain all figures in itself. The same is true of primary matter, but in the substantial not the accidental order. Primary matter can take to itself *any* substantial form, stone, man. . . . It is not something which *has* a potency (as it would be were it accidental), it *is* a potency in itself because substantial.[16]

We have come some way here from matter as substratum. And the assumption that the metaphysical principle of individuation can also account for the continuity underlying substantial change is going to require a clear and explicit proof—not just an assumption based on the fact that the same term 'matter' is used in each instance.

§ 3 *Historical Note: The Virtual Presence of Form*

One last complication in the story of 'potency' still remains to be chronicled. Early in the thirteenth century a vigorous controversy arose concerning the unity of the substantial form in man and in other composite beings. The Platonic view that there are three types of soul linked in man, each associated with a different organ, was reinforced by arguments from embryology (the human foetus does not seem to have a fully human form at the instant of conception; different forms successively appear) and from theology (only the rational soul in man is immortal, so it must be separable from his lower powers). Relatively few writers admitted this sort of plurality in man, however, because of the strong counter-arguments. But everyone—until Aquinas—admitted some form of actual plurality in inorganic composites. Aristotle had raised this same question about composites in some detail:

> Since, however, some things are-potentially while others are-actually, the constituents combined in a compound can "be" in a sense and yet "not be". The compound may be-actually other than the constituents from which it has resulted; nevertheless, each of them may still be-potentially what it was before

---

[15] Aquinas, *Phys. 1, l.15.*
[16] R. Masi, *Cosmologia,* Rome, 1961, p. 101.

they were combined and may survive undestroyed. . . . They not only coalesce, having formerly existed in separation, but also can again be separated out from the compound. These constituents thus do not persist *actually* (as *body* and *white* persist), nor are they *destroyed,* for their power of action is preserved.[17]

The "potential" presence of the constituent in the composite is specified here in two significantly different ways. The constituents are "potentially" present because: (1) though not "actually" present here and now, they can be separated off by the decay of the composite, often in their original form; or because (2) though dominated for the moment by a "higher form", their *power of action* is preserved here and now. Clearly, if the former is the reason, there is question of potency in the normal Aristotelian sense (i.e. capacity for possible future change). But the second introduces a new strand in our tangled rope: potency as a present *"virtus"*. Aristotle did not develop the latter idea further, and when he speaks of the "potential" presence of the four elements in all terrestrial composites, it is almost always in the original sense of potency as involving possible future decomposition.[18]

But in the medieval discussion of composites, it was more and more the latter sense of potency as "virtual" presence that dominated.[19] The pluralists held that in the composite some forms were subordinated to others, either "essentially" (in which case the subordinated form was said to be "in potency" to the "actuality" of the subordinating form) or else "dispositively" (when each form is "actually" present and the unity of the composite is assured only by the primary matter which each equally qualifies). The anti-pluralists rejected this sort of subordination of one "actual" form to another. To them, "actually present" clearly meant *autonomously* present, with a proper *esse,* and it seemed obvious to them that if a plurality of forms, each autonomous in its own order, were admitted in the composite, its unity would be destroyed. The pluralists, who had never held for pluralism in *this* sense, were—as one might expect—unconvinced. For them, the unity of the composite was a complex one, involving internal relations of subordination. Their view gave a better account of the obvious permanence of subsidiary structures in composites. St. Thomas, stressing the unity of the composite and somewhat altering the senses of '*esse*', 'form' and 'actuality', could, however, claim a better over-all scheme for the purposes of a metaphysics of participation.

It was obvious to both sides that elementary forms are present *"aliqualiter"*, as St. Thomas puts it, in the composite. It would not do to describe

---

[17] *De Gen. 1,* 10; 327b 24–32.

[18] See, for example, *De Caelo, 3,* 3.

[19] R. Zavalloni, *Richard de Mediavilla et le controverse sur la pluralité des formes,* Louvain, 1951; also Masi, *op. cit.,* pp. 125–55.

their presence as "potential" in the classical Aristotelian sense (in which the form of the tree is "potentially present" in the acorn), because the properties of the elements are present *at this moment* in the composite, just as they would be if the composite were destroyed and the elements suddenly dissociated. So it seems to be something more than ordinary potency. The pluralist answer is that it is "actuality" of a subordinate kind; the "unitist" answer is that it is a special sort of potency called "virtual":

> (The elements) do not altogether cease to be (in the composite) but remain virtually, insofar as the proper accidents of the elements remain with a diminished intensity according to some "mode" in which the *virtus* of the element is retained. . . .
> The elements remain, according to the Philosopher, not in act but *in virtute;* for their proper qualities (in which the *virtus* of the elementary forms exists), though diminished, remain.[20]

To which the pluralist would respond: if the properties and *virtus* of the form are there, why can one not say that the form itself is there? Aquinas answers that these have been "taken over" by a higher form, and offers the analogy:

> Substantial forms are related to one another as numbers or figures are (as it said in *Meta. 7* and *De An. 2*). The greater number or figure contains the smaller *in virtute.* . . . Thus the more perfect form contains the less perfect in *virtute.*[21]

The root-metaphor here, of one form "containing" the other, is Aquinas' answer to the pluralist's idea of *subordination* of one form to another. The relation between "form" and "property" is clearly different for the two; they do not agree, in consequence, as to the criteria to be used in deciding when the activity of a given body indicates the presence of "different forms" or the "same form".

Aquinas makes of physical composition a juxtaposition of interacting qualities: the contrary qualities of the elements interact so as to produce a "*qualitas media*" (e.g. black and white give gray), of a sort that is characteristic of composites. The separate elemental qualities then exist in a "diminished mode" in the intermediate quality.[22] The ontology here is radically qualitative in one sense, since in the explanation of change the basic permanences are sought in the domain of quality and not at all in quantitative sub-structure. While it is "substantivist" in an even more fundamental sense, because of the way in which qualities and forms are assumed to be "absorbable" without residue in other qualities and forms, especially in a "higher" substantial form.

---

[20] Aquinas, *Q.D. de An. a.9 ad* 10; *S.T.* I, *q.76, a.4 ad* 4.
[21] *Quod. 1, a.6.*
[22] *De Mixtione elementorum, ad fin.*

If one applies this terminology of "virtuality" to a modern context, what does it mean to say that a water molecule is "virtually" present in a living cell? It does *not* mean that the decay of the cell would give water as a by-product; this would be described rather as the "potential" presence—in the Aristotelian sense—of water in the cell. It does *not* mean that water is a particularly proximate potency of the cell in the line of its normal changes.[23] It means that in the behavior of the living cell there are facets that make a comparison with the behavior of water-molecules possible; it is not that there "are" (in the Thomistic sense of actuality) water-molecules in the cell, but rather that a complexus of water-molecule-qualities are "contained within" the substantial unity of the cell. That more is required for an adequate analysis of the sense in which a water-molecule is "present" in a cell scarcely needs to be said, but our purpose here is only to decipher the Thomist sense of "virtual potency" and to show how closely it is linked with an ontology of qualities. To the extent, however, that one thinks of a molecule as (among other things) a *spatial* structure (and the philosopher has to do this just as much as the scientist has), there is no room for an intermediate "virtual" presence; the structure is either there or it isn't. And the normal criteria for deciding whether this structure is the "same" now as it was yesterday do not depend critically upon whether or not a "substantial" change has occurred in the meantime.

We have now seen the main historical contexts in which the notion of "potency" occurred. In the remainder of this essay, we shall attempt to analyze these senses of 'potency' in some detail with a view to determining the exact relationship of each to the notion of matter. This will allow us to come to grips once more with the theme-problem, one of the two crucial ones in the classical doctrine of primary matter (the other one being that of the ontological status of matter). In what sense can matter be said to be pure potency?

§ 4 C-*Potency*

When X is capable of taking on a determination Y that it presently lacks, X is said to be "in potency" to Y. This is Aristotle's main usage of the term.

---

[23] By locating virtuality somewhere between "pure potency" and "act", Masi (*op. cit.*, p. 143) implies that it can be defined (for St. Thomas) not only in terms of *virtue*, as we have done above, but also "in regard to whether the potency is more or less remote from act". He thus contrasts "virtual" potency with "pure" potency; one of his theses is that the elements are not present in the composite "merely in pure potency". But this confuses matters considerably, because this way of defining "virtual potency" is by no means the same as that which would link it to present *virtus*. It might well be that a form could be in proximate potency without being "virtually present", in the sense of this latter phrase found in the Thomistic texts cited by Masi.

Since it is always correlative to possible future *change*, let us call it *C*-potency. Thus an acorn is in *C*-potency to becoming an oak, or as we more familiarly put it, has the *capacity* to become an oak. *C*-potency involves privation: if *X* is in *C*-potency to *Y*, then *X* is not now characterized by *Y*. It may be either active or passive (*CA* or *CP*), as we have seen. The acorn. has a *CA*-potency to becoming an oak or to cause a stomach-ache if swallowed whole; it has a *CP*-potency of being stepped upon or being soaked by rain.

What is it that becomes? Or, as this is sometimes put, what is the "subject" of becoming? Here a distinction must be made between two sorts of change, or, if you wish, between two uses of the term, 'become'. Take two changes: acorn-becomes-oak, acorn-becomes-brown. Let us describe these from the point of view of the substratum of the change, that which perseveres.[24] First, something which was an acorn becomes an oak; second, something which was green becomes brown. In the first case, there is no word for the referent of the term 'something'; in the second case, 'something' refers to an acorn. If the descriptions of these changes be abbreviated to '*X* becomes *Y*' form, it is clear that '*X*' will denote the *terminus a quo* in the case of acorn-becoming-oak, whereas it will denote the substratum of the change in the case of acorn-becoming-brown.[25] The subject of the term 'become' (which is what is usually meant by the phrase, 'the subject of becoming') is thus different in each case. Though the same term 'acorn' be used in each instance, it *refers* in different ways. The notion of "becoming" is, therefore, itself different in each case. For *X* to "become" *Y* in one sense, automatically means that *X* itself, *qua X*, ceases to be; in the other sense, *X* remains even when it has "become" *Y*. The linguistic fact that the word 'become' has two senses follows from (1) the lack of a name for the substratum of certain sorts of change, yet (2) the desirability of being able to describe such changes in the standard form, '*X* becomes *Y*'.[26]

---

[24] The phrase 'substratum of change' is to be preferred here to 'subject of change' (though the two are often taken to be synonymous); the latter notion is, however, ambiguous. The "subject" of a change is what the change happens to, but this might be either the substratum, or that from which the change began (i.e. the *terminus a quo*), depending on how the phrase 'happens to' is understood.

[25] Two linguistic notes: One would not ordinarily say that an acorn "comes to be" an oak (because '*X* comes to be *Y*' is usually understood to imply that *X* itself remains), so that the terms 'becoming' and 'coming to be' are not quite equivalent in English, only the former having the ambiguity noted in the text. Also, one would not ordinarily say that an acorn which was painted blue had "become" blue, because 'becoming' would tend to suggest a more active role on the part of the acorn, a *CA*-potency of sorts.

[26] This point is fully discussed, from different points of view, in the essays of Dr. Fisk and Father Owens elsewhere in the book. See also P. Geach and E. Anscombe, *Three Philosophers*, Oxford, 1961, p. 47.

In discussing a change such as acorn-becoming-oak, there is a tendency to confuse three different questions: "What is the subject of 'becoming'?" "What is the (subject-) substratum of the change?" "Where does the C-potency for this change reside?" We have already seen that the first two of these are not equivalent. Now it must be added that the third question, concerning the "locus" of C-potency, cannot be answered by answering the first, i.e. by giving a semantic analysis of 'become'. The question about potency is *not* primarily one of predication, as though potency were a simple property like triangularity, and we were asking: "of what should it be predicated?" To ask of acorn-becoming-oak, "in what does the C-potency for this change reside?", is the same as asking less technically: "what is it about the acorn that makes it able to grow into an oak?", or more technically, "where should we look to find the ontological ground that enables such a change to occur?"

Quite commonly, the answer given to this question is that C-potency resides in the matter-substratum of the acorn. This is incorrect, or at least incomplete. C-potency clearly resides in the matter-form composite. It is not simply the matter of the acorn that gives it the capacity to grow into an oak or to be squashed, it is the fact that it is an *acorn* here and now, and not for instance, a drop of water. Again, C-potency involves a specific privation: an acorn has no C-potency to become an acorn. Such a privation follows from form, not from matter: to say that X is non-acorn (in the sense required for C-potency) is to say that X has the *form* of something other than acorn. The "privation" which is peculiar to matter would not suffice: the matter of an acorn is "non-acorn" by definition, but it by no means follows from this that an acorn could have the capacity to become an acorn. Aristotle's analogy from sculpture can mislead here: a piece of marble "has the potency" to take on different shapes, it is true, but this is not just an intrinsic characteristic of the marble-matter, prescinding from all questions of form. It also depends on its present shape. Just because the unworked marble is loosely called "shapeless", we should not be misled into assuming that it really *has* no shape or that this shape is irrelevant to what can be done with the piece of marble in the future.

It is true, of course, that it is the marble-matter, not the composite, that will later take on the new shape. But to infer from this that C-potency lies in the matter alone, so to speak, is too hasty. There is a broad sense in which matter, considered apart from any particular form "has the potency to take on" different forms. But this sort of "potency", the mere ability to be limited by form, is not at all the concrete pointing-at-the-future that one needs in the Aristotelian analysis of individual changes. One *could* define 'potency' in such a way as to pertain to matter alone, but then it would be of little use in philosophical analysis. The question: "what is it that *has* the

C-potency?" has a deceptive clarity about it, as though "having" a potency were like "having" a nose. If it were, the question could be answered by specifying the referent of '*X*', where *X* is what is said to "have" the potency. But, in fact, this phrase cannot be simply analyzed in this way, and it is much more satisfactory to rephrase the question as: on what does the capacity for change depend? Then the answer is unequivocal: on the composite, on the form just as much as on the matter.

It is important to have this answer straight before we come to the more complex question: what is the "principle", or the ontological ground, of potency for change? Because one might be tempted to answer "matter", which would be wrong. This common mistake derives not only from the shaky analysis of *C*-potency, already criticized, but even more directly from a Platonic notion of "form", according to which the form of an acorn would be a sort of principle of static determination were it not to be immersed in "matter", from which flows the defectibility that leads to change. The fallacy here lies in arguing that if form is the correlate of scientific knowledge, then it must of itself somehow be "static", if such knowledge is to have the desired "immutability" of science. Since an acorn-form could not exist on its own, it is a category-mistake to apply predicates like 'static' or 'mutable' to it in the first place. But even apart from this, the essential mutability of the acorn cannot be attributed exclusively to the presence of "matter". What makes the acorn liable to cease being an acorn is not merely that it is material, but that it is an *acorn,* and acorns are the sort of thing that do not remain acorns indefinitely.

It would make no sense to suggest that the formal principle which makes a certain thing an acorn would also of itself tend to make the thing unchanging were it not "defeated" in this effort by the matter. If the form of something tended to make that thing unchanging, the thing would not be an acorn, whatever else it might be. The Platonist and the rationalist tend too easily to see in change a defect of intelligibility, and thus to push responsibility for it entirely over to matter, the "non-intelligible". But in the natural—as opposed to the mathematical—order, change is the very key to nature and intelligibility itself. An acorn has a *C*-potency, involving both active and passive elements, to grow in virtue of its present form into an oak. A dog has a *C*-potency to die, whereas an angel has not. It is misleading to put this latter point, as it is sometimes put, by saying that dogs have matter whereas angels have not. This is only half the story. Dogs have the sort of forms that imply mortality; angels do not. An angelic form could not be realized in matter in the first place, precisely because it is the form of an immortal being. It is not as though one could take the same form and allow it to lead an angelic existence or a mortal one, depending on whether or not one "put it in matter". This sort of dissociation leads to a theory of matter and form that is lacking in adequate experiential support.

To summarize: it is the composite which ought properly be said to "have a C-potency" or to be the "ground" for C-potency. But the roles played by the matter-substrate and by form, relative to C-potency, are different. It is matter which has the capacity to "take on" different forms; in this sense, matter is basic to CP-potency, i.e. to the potency which makes the thing capable of being acted upon. The initial form is responsible for whether and how it will be acted upon by a given external cause. With CA-potency, the source of the mutability lies rather on the side of form, though any activity initiated comes, of course, from the composite as a whole.

Can a C-potency ever be "pure"? The answer would seem to be: no. There can be no spatio-temporal object capable of becoming anything else whatever (CP), nor can there be one capable of accomplishing anything whatever (CA). The limits on possible change come mainly from the side of form. Could one suggest, then, that in some broad sense primary matter has a pure C-potency, or "is" a pure C-potency? The 'pure' here has reference to the future, so the question can be rephrased: are the possible future states of a thing entirely indeterminate, as far as the primary matter of the thing is concerned? And the answer, of course, is: no. A mouse could not decay into a mountain, not even through a whole series of intermediate changes, because there are some fundamental quantitative laws which govern *all* changes, including unqualified changes. Since the substrate is by definition the only link binding the initial and final states, these laws have to be somehow "carried" by the substrate, not by the initial or final forms. Even where one "element" decays into another, it is still true that the substrate of the change must bear with it certain restrictions that limit the product that results.

A C-potency could be "pure" only in a secondary and improper sense. If primary matter be considered in abstraction from individual instances, it can be thought of as a sort of "fundamental possibility of changing" without any specification of the limits within which the change must take place. But this lack of specification, or "purity", comes not just from the primary matter itself, but from the conditions of abstraction. It is a kind of unqualified C-potency, not of the primary matter of a designated change, but of primary-matter-in-general, or more precisely, of the *concept* of primary matter. The "indeterminacy" of this concept (and consequently of the C-potency) is akin to the indeterminacy that a generic concept (*animal*) displays by comparison with one of its species (*zebra*).[27] The concept, *animal,*

---

[27] In his essay, Dr. Sellars makes a similar point by talking of the indeterminacy of the thing-kind (e.g. bronze) by contrast with the quantitative particularity of *instances* of this thing-kind (e.g. this chunk of bronze).

is "indeterminate" only in the sense that it leaves unspecified the various specific differences that can occur among its referents.

The "second-level" properties of a concept *qua* concept, cannot automatically be predicated of the referent of that concept. A zebra, for example, is not lacking in specificity just because the notion, *animal* (which is correctly predicated of it) is lacking in specificity. The C-potency of primary matter is indeterminate only if we abstract from concrete instances. The concrete C-potency of the matter-substrate of a designated real change is thus never entirely "pure".

Before leaving C-potency, it may be well to note that there is another notion somewhat akin to it, but differing in some important aspects. When a man who is at the moment seeing is said to have the "ability" to see, one is reminded of C-potency. The "ability" or "power", however, is not future-directed in this case, and does not necessarily involve privation, as C-potency does. It is essentially an ability to *do* something or to have something done to one. It is directed towards activity rather than towards a state of being, or future actuality. For X to have the "capacity" to become an oak, it is necessary that it at present not be an oak. But for X to have the "ability" to see, it is not necessary that X at present be not-seeing.

In this connection, Aristotle distinguishes between two types of activity, one which is directed towards a specific goal, the reaching of which signals the end of the activity, and one which contains no such built-in "cut-off".[28] Aristotle's examples of the latter: seeing and understanding; of the former: learning, healing and building. It should be noted that these last examples are ambiguous. As they stand, they do not exemplify "terminating" activities, as they purport to. One, having built, could still have the ability to build. To see them as "terminating", they must be *particularized* (building a particular house, learning a particular theorem . . .). Ordinarily, one would not, having built a particular house, still be said to have the ability to build *this* house. The activity here is directed towards a specific goal, and when it is achieved, the activity necessarily ceases. This is similar to the instances of C-potency above, and thus the ability to perform such "terminating" activities is similar to a C-potency. It is not quite equivalent, because one can have the ability to learn Pythagoras' theorem while one is learning the theorem, whereas a thing could not be said to have the ability to become an oak if it is an oak already. Nevertheless, "terminating" activities, as Aristotle stresses, involve potency rather than actuality; the actual performance has an incompleteness that makes it inappropriate to regard the activity itself here as an "actuality".

---

[28] *Meta.* 1048b 18–34.

Non-terminating activities like seeing, on the other hand, lie rather on the side of actuality, because there is no built-in term to limit them. Aristotle suggests that they are more correctly described as present actuality than as potency-to-movement. When someone is seeing, he is not losing the ability to see. Thus this sort of "ability" in nowise involves privation and is thus quite different from C-potency; the two are related to actuality in different ways. Since "ability" in this sense has no direct connection with *becoming*, it has no relevance for our discussion in this section, of the potency that is characteristic of the substrate of becoming, primary matter. So we can leave it aside.

§ 5 D-*Potency*

There is a second sense of 'potency' which is still Aristotelian in its roots, the sense in which the bronze of a statue is said to be "in potency" to the statue-form which presently determines it. This potency is directed to a present form, not a future one; it is not an explicit principle of change; it resides in the present *determinability* (hence D-potency) of the matter vis-à-vis the form. It is true that CP-potency involved determinability too: to say that a chunk of bronze *could* become a statue implies that the bronze-matter is capable of being determined by both the chunk-shape and the statue-shape. But CP-potency was dependent upon not only the general determinability of the bronze, but also upon the present chunk-shape as limiting the future shapes the bronze could take on.

CP-potency, as we saw, pertains properly to the composite matter-form thing as a whole. D-potency is referred to a "matter" which is relative to a "form" now determining or qualifying it; it rests upon the capacity of this "matter" to be so qualified or determined. Primary matter is frequently defined as that which is in D-potency to substantial form; the substantial composite can be in D-potency to the accidents which qualify it. But the substantial form of such a composite could not of itself be in D-potency to a further substantial form, i.e. it is incapable of being determined by another form in its own order, because both forms would then be co-present. (We are accepting in this treatment of potency the Aristotelian definitions of the philosophic notions involved; their validity and utility is not for the present up for discussion.) Now substantial form is the primary "actuality" of a thing, that from which its activity, considered as governed by a single goal, flows. Two substantial forms could not, by definition, co-exist in a single substance: either one of the forms is not substantial (i.e. not primary, not deciding the *telos* of the thing as a whole), or else there is more than one substance.

310

Does it follow, then, that the "matter" which is determined by substantial form is itself lacking in form? In one sense, it does: there are no other forms present "in actuality", i.e. present as independent principles. It follows from the Aristotelian notion of substance that the "matter" which is correlative to substantial form is "unqualified" or "unspecified", in the sense that it does not contain any formalities *in actu*. It could thus be called a "pure" D-potency, not as containing no specifications of *any* kind—the analysis of D-potency simply will not bear this weight—but as containing no formality of a sort which would limit the effectiveness, so to speak, of the controlling substantial form.

To summarize: if the central fact from which the philosophical analysis of nature begins is the unity of behavior in natural beings, and if the principle or ground of that unity in the being is called its "substantial form", then one can associate with this "form" a matter co-principle which is that in the being which is governed or directed by the form. This matter is called "primary" in the sense that there is no D-potency in the being more fundamental than it. It is called "pure" potency for the same reason, and also to indicate that it opposes no barrier, as a principle of *determinability,* to the form. But as to whether it is "indeterminate", "*nec quantum nec quale . . .*", this analysis does not decide. One is still free to admit or not admit the presence of "subsidiary forms", a point to which we shall return in the next section. This approach depends, of course, on the validity of the whole notion of D-potential analysis, i.e. on seeing in unit-things two factors, or aspects, one determining, the other determined, and on admitting the notion of "ground" or "principle" in the things for each of these aspects; these are then claimed to be really—because conceptually—irreducible to one another.[29]

§ 6 V-*Potency*

A form which is present in the "virtual" or "subsidiary" way discussed in §3 will be said to be in *V-potency* to the principal form which, so to speak, "commandeers" it. The oxygen molecule in the living cell is subordinated to the form or *telos* of that cell and the cell in turn to that of the living body as a whole. Yet the molecule is *there,* both as a spatial structure and through its customary power of action. It is not present in its full "actuality" as an independent agent; the contrast here is between actuality-autonomy and V-potency. Only a form can be said to be in V-potency. There is an analogy between V-potency and D-potency, between the way in which a form "de-

---

[29] This approach is discussed in "Matter as a Principle", elsewhere in this volume.

termines" matter and the way it "determines" or subordinates another form. V-potency is also related to C-potency: when something is V-potentially present in the living body, it may well be recoverable from the body as a terminus of some conceivable change. The living body has, thus, a C-potency to produce oxygen molecules, for instance. But it must be emphasized that V-potency does not *depend* on C-potency, on the recoverability of the subsidiary form, on the future "actualization" of the virtual form. It is descriptive only of the *present* status of the subsidiary form vis-à-vis the principal one; it can easily happen that a form, now in V-potency, is nevertheless not capable of separate actualization later on.

The pluralist and the Thomist will describe V-potency in quite different ways, as we have seen. The pluralist will speak of *subsidiary,* rather than *virtual,* forms, and will argue that they are "actually" present, though in a special way. The Thomist prefers to use the language of potency: only the principal form is "actually" present according to him. The two appear to be contradicting one another, but as is usual in such cases in philosophy, it is rather a matter of their attaching different meanings to the same terms ('actuality', 'form' . . .). To adjudicate between them, one would have to compare the two sets of concepts and see which of them gave a more supple and revealing way of describing the natural world as we experience it.[30] Fortunately, we do not have to make this comparison here: our V-potency is translatable either into the language of "subsidiarity" or of "virtuality".

Ought a form in V-potency be regarded as on the side of the principal form, or as pertaining to the "matter" which this latter form qualifies? It would seem at first sight to be on the side of form. Yet there is a difficulty. If a substantial change occurs, the principal form vanishes but the virtualities may persevere, presumably carried by the substratum since there is nothing else in which they can inhere. The matter-substratum must, then, be assumed to contain virtualities and thus some sort of organization, even though it does not at any time constitute a separate substance; in Father Luyten's phrase, it "brings with it the former acquisitions". These V-potencies are highly determinate. They do not inhere in the matter as accidents in a substance; the manner in which matter carries them cannot be described in terms of the ordinary Aristotelian categories of substance and accident. But this is scarcely unexpected, since these categories are not fashioned for contingencies of this sort, for the relating of a virtuality to an incomplete principle.

The textbook discussion of substantial change customarily points out: (1) by hypothesis, the original substance does not survive; (2) no accident

---

[30] This point is raised in more detail in my essay, "Cosmologia", *Philos. Studies* (Maynooth), *11*, 1961, 216–29, esp. pp. 223–25.

could survive either, because this would by definition make whatever it was in which the accident inhered a substance, and there would be no fundamental change. The conclusion drawn is that since no "actuality" survives, the substrate-survivor must be void of all specification of any sort. That the original and the final principal forms are different actualities, we can grant; it is also true that the substratum is of itself "*nec quantum nec quale*", in the precise sense that such adjectives properly apply only to substances. But this does *not* make the substratum "pure" where V-potency is concerned, i.e. void of all specific V-potencies. In any concrete change, the substratum may be full of virtualities of all kinds. It is thus not ontologically indeterminate, by any means.

The substrata which persist through changes as diverse as the death of a dog and the generation of a plant obviously carry with them very different V-potencies. It is quite misleading to describe both of these by the same phrase, 'primary matter', if this is taken to connote an ontological principle which is indeterminate in *every* conceivable respect. If this connotation were to be accepted, the death of a dog might just as easily give rise to an acorn as to a dog-corpse. The specificity of substantial changes can be understood and described only in terms of *specific* V-potencies carried in the substratum, and thus differentiating the substratum of one substantial change from that of another, not simply in terms of individuation or space-time location but in more formal terms of virtuality and structure.

If, then, primary matter be defined as the substratum of substantial change, it cannot be regarded as "pure" or void where V-potency is concerned, except perhaps where the change of one "element" (in Aristotle's sense) into another is concerned. And even here there would be quantitative conservation laws governing the V-potential aspects of the change.

§ 7 L-*Potency*

One last avenue remains to be explored. If primary matter be defined in terms of the scholastic adage: *actus non limitatur nisi per potentiam,* it will appear not as a principle of determinability (as it did in the Aristotelian D-potency of §5) but as a principle of limitation, which is not by any means the same thing. The adage claims that anything which limits an *actus* must be called a potency, an L-potency, let us say. An L-potency co-exists with the actuality to which it is correlative, unlike C-potency and like D-potency. In the context of hylemorphic composition, it pertains to the matter alone. The matter is said to "be" (not to "have") an L-potency, a principle of limitation and numerical differentiation of form.

The climate is now Platonic rather than Aristotelian. Primary matter is defined by an analysis not of change but of intelligibility. The criterion of actuality is the form taken by itself, not the composite. Matter is the source of restrictive, existential limits; these are non-formal, hence, non-intelligible. It is the source of instability of nature, of defect. More importantly, it is the source of that most radically non-formal of all physical features, individuality. It limits actuality-form to a particular career in time and space, subjects it to all the contingencies of history.

If this sort of analysis be accepted, then we may be in sight of a "pure" potency, at last. The principle of limitation is set over against actuality in a completely anonymous and formally indeterminate way. The primary matter of one cow is not existentially the "same" as that of another cow (or else they would be the same cow). But the difference between the "two matters" cannot be specified except in terms of limitation, of L-potency itself. Each is "pure" L-potency, undifferentiated capacity for limiting, but each differs from the other *totally* since they individuate two beings, totally different as individuals from one another. Calling primary matter "pure" in *this* context no longer sets up the paradoxes that it does for the other forms of potency. In the other cases, we have argued that if primary matter be "pure", there is no way of differentiating in its own terms between one instance of it and another. And this led in each instance to contradictions.

But here, 'pure' means something like: unqualified in its power to limit. The primary matter of one cow will limit the actuality, *cow,* to existence in one space-time career, while the primary matter of another will limit the same actuality to an entirely different career. The general function of the primary matter in the two different composites will be the same. Each is unqualified in its ability to limit the form, *cow;* each is entirely free of actuality or intelligibility on its own part. Each is in these senses "pure". The fact that the two cows are numerically different does not affect this, since the differentiation is ultimately outside the order of 'intelligibility, i.e. entirely within the order of L-potency itself.

With the other types of potency, it was necessary to differentiate between different instances of primary matter (i.e. different matter-form composites) by introducing some specification from outside the order of potency. The virtuality of the V-potency is specified by the actuality it would be in the absence of the form which here overrides it. C-potencies are differentiated by the very different actualities that different changes can lead to. The only way in which one can reach a "pure" primary matter relative to these two forms of potency is by an abstraction from the specifiable differences that distinguished concrete instances of such "primary matter" from one another. The "purity" is thus, as we have seen, no more than the "purity" of the concept or of the genus when differences are abstracted from, or left out of account. But with L-potency this difficulty does not arise, precisely because as L-potency, primary matter is *by definition* a principle of individuation, and no further agent of differentiation can be required.

We have now seen some of the principal senses in which the term 'potency' has been used in philosophy, and examined in particular the role it plays in discussions of primary matter. We have seen that the phrase 'pure potency' cannot be applied to primary matter in the offhand fashion that many traditional treatments of the problem assume. Much depends upon which sense of 'potency' one has in mind; 'pure' likewise will take on different senses. In the original Aristotelian sense of 'potency' (what we have called here C-potency), it is simply incorrect to describe the material co-principle of a given concrete being as a "pure potency".

A more serious problem lies behind these differences of sense, one that we cannot touch on here.[31] What guarantee is there that the "matter" which is defined in terms of C-potency or D-potency is the same as that defined through L-potency? The same word 'matter' is used, true. But then the same word 'potency' was used too, to cover senses that now clearly appear as different. Is there anything more than a loose, and ultimately misleading, analogy between the different senses of 'matter'? How can we show that primary matter defined and justified through an analysis of individuation is the same ontological principle as that which is called upon to provide continuity in substantial change? In searching for an answer to this question, the precisions provided by the analysis of potency above may turn out to be of considerable help.

University of Notre Dame

---

[31] See "Matter as a Principle".

PART THREE

From Matter to Mass

THE CONCEPT OF MATTER

IN FOURTEENTH CENTURY SCIENCE

James A. Weisheipl, O.P.

§1 *Introduction*

One of the fundamental principles of modern physics is the principle of the conservation of matter, more technically known as the conservation of mass. Simply expressed, it states that in all physical transformations the amount of matter involved remains constant in any given system, or, to put it in another way, in physical transformations no amount of matter is ever created or destroyed. Antoine Lavoisier expressed this in his *Traité élémentaire de chimie* in 1789 when he wrote:

> We must lay it down as an incontestable axiom that, in all the operations of art and nature, nothing is created; an equal quantity of matter exists both before and after the experiment. . . . Upon this principle the whole art of performing chemical experiments depends.[1]

This principle, commonly thought to have been a discovery of the seventeenth or eighteenth century, is actually a fundamental axiom in all natural science. Even the pre-Socratics who were concerned with transformations in the physical world, and even the Eleatics, who denied transformation, knew that nothing could come from nothing or be dissolved into nothing. Creation and annihilation are not "changes" as the natural scientist understands the word. The ingenerability and incorruptibility of matter were, in fact, explicitly taught by Plato and Aristotle. In order for matter itself to change it would have to be composed of potency and act; it would have to be "a form immersed in matter". But "primary matter" by definition is the first root, the ultimate potentiality, having no determination whatever, just as for Plato the receptacle had to be entirely free from all characteristics. Therefore, primary matter can neither be generated nor corrupted; it is rather the eternal root, the substratum and source of all generation and corruption. The scholastic philosophers of the Middle Ages unanimously recognized that in all natural changes the total amount of matter remains the same. Whether the change be fundamental, as when water is changed to air, or ac-

---

[1] A. Lavoisier, *Traité élémentaire de chimie*, I. c. 13, tr. by Robert Kerr in *Great Books of the Modern World*, 45, Chicago, 1952, p. 41b–c.

cidental, as in augmentation, condensation, rarefaction or mere locomotion, the quantity of matter involved was thought to remain constant.

There was never any serious doubt about the principle as a fact of nature. However, there has been considerable development in the understanding, or interpretation of this principle of conservation. For example, the principle is not understood today as it was in the seventeenth century. Today, because of the new concept of mass-energy transformation, the principle is extended to include the equivalence of mass and energy. It is commonly formulated as the conservation of mass-energy. In the seventeenth century, however, the principle was understood in terms of inertial mass, which meant the quantity of matter (*quantitas materiae*). Newton defined the "quantity of matter" as "the measure of the same [matter], arising from its density and bulk conjointly (*Quantitas materiae est mensura eiusdem orta ex illius densitate et magnitudine coniunctim*)".[2] It is this quantity of matter which, according to his own statement, Newton everywhere intends by the term 'body' or 'mass'. This quantity of matter, although really distinct from weight, "is known (*innotescit*) by the weight of each body, for it is proportional to the weight, as I have found by experiments on pendulums, very accurately made".[3] Similarly, the concept of mass employed in the seventeenth century was very different from the concept of undetermined "primary matter" discussed in the High Middle Ages. Thus, while no serious doubt was cast upon the conservation of matter as a principle of natural science, the meaning embodied in the statement depends upon the concept of matter intended.

The concept of matter, or mass, as the "quantity of matter", arising from its density and bulk conjointly, was actually developed in the fourteenth century by the Oxford Calculators who were to have considerable influence on the development of Western scientific thought. The concept of mass is still in need of serious historical and critical examination.[4] Here it is possible to examine only the concept as it developed in the fourteenth century against the background of Aristotelian physics and in the context of fourteenth century problems. Recently Prof. Philipp Frank has examined the "common sense" meaning of the principle and found it wanting for scientific usage.

If we use only the language and experience of "common sense," we believe that we understand fairly well the meaning of the statement that in a certain

---

[2] Isaac Newton, *Principia Mathematica Philosophiae Naturalis*, Def. I, rev. trans. by Florian Cajori, Berkeley, 1947, p. 1.

[3] *Ibid.*

[4] For some years Dr. Max Jammer of the Hebrew University, Jerusalem, has been working on a history, *Concepts of Mass in Classical and Modern Physics*, but at the time of this writing it has not yet appeared in print.

volume of a body there is a certain "quantity of matter." This concept seems to be very clear if we assume that "matter" consists of a great number of equal small particles (formerly called "atoms") and therefore we mean by "quantity of matter" in a certain volume just the number of these equal particles. This concept of "mass" as the number of "atoms" was familiar to the Greek atomists and Epicureans.[5]

Prof. Frank objects to this concept, which he believes to be that of Newton, because it does not describe the operations by which this quantity is measured. "Newton's definition is not an "operational definition" but refers to common sense conceptions".[6] This so-called common-sense conception of mass as the number of particles in a given volume may or may not represent the view of most modern physicists. It may even be a fair interpretation of what a Greek atomist might have imagined if he had thought of a certain "quantity of matter". But it is an erroneous interpretation of Newton's definition within the tradition in which it was developed. Much of the modern misunderstanding of this classical definition can be eliminated by a study of the tradition which formulated it and by a study of the philosophical problem involved, particularly in the writings of fourteenth-century theoreticians of science.

§2 *Aristotelian Background*

In Aristotelian physics there were two related problems which led to the late scholastic notion of *quantitas materiae*. (i) In substantial change, as when air is produced from water, the same amount of matter becomes something different and it occupies a greater volume without acquiring additional parts of matter. In connection with this problem the scholastics discussed not only the principles of change in general, but also the principle of individuation, which was eventually formulated as *materia signata quantitate*. (ii) In rarefaction, as when air expands, and in condensation the same amount of matter occupies a larger or smaller volume "not by the matter's acquiring anything new, but because the matter is in potency to both states".[7] In this context the scholastics frequently discussed the relation of quantity (the magnitude, bulk, or dimensions of a body) to matter.

Before one can discuss the meaning of the "same amount of matter" or the "quantity of matter" in scholastic physics, one must appreciate, at least to some extent, the purely potential character of "primary" matter in Aristotelian physics.

[5] Philipp Frank, *Philosophy of Science*, Englewood Cliffs, 1957, pp. 111–12.
[6] *Ibid.*, p. 112.
[7] Aristotle, *Phys.*, IV, 9. 217b 8–9.

Aristotle distinguished sharply between substantial and accidental changes occuring in nature. Accidental changes, or motion strictly defined as "the fulfilment of what exists potentially, in so far as it exists potentially" (*Phys.*, III, 1.201a 10–11), always presupposes an existent subject fully constituted in species. Changes such as growth and decrease in living things, alterations in sense qualities, and locomotion, do indeed depend upon the substantial nature of the individual, but they do not entail any change in the individuality or specific nature of the subject. All these changes Aristotle explained in terms of a subject called "matter" (potential principle), "form" (actualization) and "privation" of the form to be acquired. However, "matter" in the case of these accidental changes is a fully constituted and existing substance. The scholastics called this matter "second matter" or "body" (*corpus*). All the obvious characteristics of physical motion, namely its continuity, divisibility, temporality, magnitude and velocity, could be explained by the fact that physical substances are quantified, quantity being the first necessary accident of a physical body.

Substantial change, on the other hand, is the transformation of the very substance itself, that is, a radical transformation of the individual nature anterior to all its consequent accidents. Since the actual quantity of a natural body can be increased or decreased without substantial change, actual quantity was considered to be an accident distinct from the substance and consequent upon the actual constitution of a substantial being. Consequently substantial change could not have any of the quantitative characteristics of accidental change. In other words, it must be devoid of temporality, magnitude, continuity, divisibility and velocity. Aristotle had also explained substantial change in terms of matter, form and privation. But here 'form' means the first substantial actualization of matter; and 'matter' means the ultimate potential source of substantial change. The scholastics called this "primary matter". For Aristotle this primary matter was itself devoid not only of all accidental characteristics, such as quantity, color and place, but it was devoid of every substantial actualization. It is "that which in itself is neither a something, nor a so much (*quanta*), nor a such, nor any of those things by which being is determined" (*Metaph.*, Z, 3.1029a 19–21). In other words, since primary matter is postulated in the first place in order to explain the reality of substantial change, then in itself it can have no actuality at all, neither essential nor existential. The least actuality would render it substantial, and every subsequent act can only be accidental.

Usually when Aristotle discussed substantial change, he spoke in terms of the elements. His common examples are earth changing to water, water to air, air to fire, and fire again changing to earth. The elements were, of course, recognized by their peculiar combination of hot and cold, moist and dry. The ancients believed that the four elements were the ultimate natural bodies composing the universe, and into which all natural compounds could be reduced. Alterations in natural compounds were explained, in part, by changes in the proportion or status of the elementary parts. But any change of one element into another could not be explained by any prior natural bodies. Such an elementary change was as ultimate as one could find in nature. Consequently the potentiality for such change must be utterly devoid of all characteristics, that is, "matter" in this case is clearly a purely potential principle. Aristotle apparently considered the change of one element into another striking proof of "matter" as a purely potential principle in nature.

Not all scholastics of the thirteenth century, of course, appreciated the pure potentiality of primary matter. One of the major philosophical controversies of this century involved this precise point. Albertus Magnus and Thomas Aquinas, following Aristotle, insisted that the very first actualization of primary matter constitutes a complete substance, rendering all other forms accidental. From this it follows that there can be only one substantial form in every individual. Defenders of the plurality of substantial forms, on the other hand, followed the inspiration of Avicebron.[8] For them corporeal matter (as opposed to "spiritual matter") was itself constituted by a *forma corporeitatis*. Consequently, subsequent actualizations were considered to be just as substantial and essential as the intrinsic form of corporeal matter. The pluralists, particularly William de la Mare and John Peckham, had conceived primary corporeal matter as a complete entity, and they could see no reason why subsequent entities, such as the vegetative soul, sentient soul, and rational soul, could not be essential attributes. Apart from the authorities alleged, the pluralist position was fundamentally a surrender to human imagination, which cannot help but spatialize all images.

For Albertus Magnus and St. Thomas primary matter was so completely potential that it could not be known in itself, much less imagined. "Indeed", says St. Albert, "if matter is taken by itself, it is unknown; further, it is not a starting point for knowing anything else, nor is it apprehended or understood at all except by analogy to form".[9] Primary matter is called a material principle "not by any direct (*secundum se*) predication, but denominatively" from what is known of second matter.[10] St. Thomas was even more insistent than St. Albert on the pure potentiality and complete imperceptibility of primary matter in itself. He would not even allow for an incipient

---

[8] On this point see the excellent article by Daniel A. Callus O.P., "The Origin of the Problem of the Unity of Form", in *The Dignity of Science*, ed. by James A. Weisheipl O.P., Washington, D.C., 1961, pp. 121–49.

[9] St. Albert, *Lib. VII Metaph.*, tr. III, c. 5, ed. Borgnet, VI, p. 459a.

[10] *Ibid., c. 2, ed. cit.*, VI, p. 453b.

actuality, an *inchoatio formae*, in it, as Albert had done.[11] For Aquinas, since the root of all intelligibility is act, and since primary matter is completely devoid of all actuality, even that of existence, this matter had to be entirely unintelligible and imperceptible *secundum se*; it could be known only relative to its actualization.[12]

But if primary matter is conceived as pure potentiality, lacking every determination, how then could the schoolmen speak of the "quantity of matter" or the "same amount of matter" in substantial generation?[13] How could they designate "this matter" and consider such designated matter the root principle of individuality? The answer lies in what has already been said. First of all, primary matter can be discussed in two ways: in the abstract (*materia communis*) or in the concrete (*materia individualis* or *signata*).[14] As a universal reality, it is an abstraction. Species, such as *man* and *triangle,* exist individually in the world of nature, but they can justifiably be universalized as true predicates. Matter, on the other hand, is not like this. It is not its nature to be universalized and employed as a predicate. Rather it is already a "this" in nature, a subject of predication. But—to pursue the objection—it was this concrete matter which Albertus Magnus and Thomas Aquinas insisted was pure potentiality and unintelligible in itself! How could one speak of the "quantity of matter" or even of "this matter"? Albert and Thomas give the same answer: individual first matter is perceived and understood only in terms of its actualization. Every "principle" as such, is understood only in relation to what proceeds from it, as the dawn is understood as the beginning of the day. Primary matter as the purely potential principle of all material reality must be understood in terms of what follows, namely its actual realizations. The first actuality of this matter, as we have already observed, is the substantial composite called "second matter" by the Scholastics. More important, primary matter is the unique root

---

[11] St. Thomas, *In II Phys., lect.* 1, n. 3. See the detailed study by Bruno Nardi, "La Doctrina d'Alberto Magno sull' *Inchoatio formae"*, in *Studi di Filosofia Medievale*, Roma, 1960, pp. 69–101.

[12] St. Thomas, *Sum. theol.*, I, *q.* 86, *a.* 2 *ad* 1; *In I Phys., lect.* 13, n. 9; *In VIII Metaph., lect.* 1, n. 1687.

[13] The schoolmen following Aristotle (*Metaph.*, X, 5) distinguished various senses of the word 'same'. See, for example, St. Thomas, *In X Metaph., lect.* 4, nn. 2001–2012. For our purposes only three need be kept in mind. (i) Sameness in substance; technically this is designated by *idem*. (ii) Sameness in quality; technically this is designated by *similia*. (iii) Sameness in quantity; and technically this is designated by *equalia*.

[14] This distinction is frequently noted by St. Thomas, e.g. *Sum. theol.*, I, *q.* 75, *a.* 4; *q.* 85, *a.* 1 *ad* 2; *In VII Metaph., lect.* 9–12; *De verit., q.* 2, *a.* 6 *ad* 1.

principle of quantification, solidity, spatio-temporal relations, and other sensible phenomena. It is, in fact, by reason of primary matter—not substantial form—that bodies are individual, quantified, spatio-temporally situated, and perceptible in sense experience.[15] Consequently, it is primary matter precisely as potentially quantified (*potentia quanta*) that is the root principle of individuality and the primary (*primo*) subject of actual quantity, position and perceptibility.[16] The view of St. Thomas is no different from that of Albertus Magnus. For Aquinas "materia signata, quae est principium individuationis",[17] is the sole principle of individuation, and not a co-principle.[18] This "matter, which is the principle of individuation, is unknown in itself (*secundum se*), and it cannot be known except through form, from which the universal definition (*ratio*) of the thing is derived".[19] Nevertheless, this individual, potential principle is the unique source of corporeity, actual quantity and all quantitative attributes such as position in place, weight, velocity when moving, continuity and temporality, Hence, matter is designated "this" or "so much" or "the same amount" precisely as it is understood (*intellecta*) in reference to some determined quantity. The undetermined passive source is said to be a determined "this" precisely when "consideratur cum determinatione dimensionum, harum scilicet vel illarum".[20] "Hence, matter now taken as underlying corporeity and dimensions can be understood as distinguished into different parts",[21] even though primary matter, as such, has no parts. One might add parenthetically that it is psychologically impossible to understand "this matter" except "prout subest dimensionibus".[22]

---

[15] These characteristics of matter are most explicitly and succinctly presented by Albertus Magnus in *Lib. XI Metaph.*, tr. I, c. 7.

[16] *Ibid., ed. cit.*, VI, p. 590b.

[17] St. Thomas, *Sum. theol.*, I, q. 75, a. 4.

[18] Father M.-D. Roland-Gosselin believes that St. Thomas actually maintained two principles of individuality: matter conferring ontological unity and quantity conferring numerical unity (*Le "De Ente et Essentia" de s. Thomas d' Aquin*, Paris, 1948, pp. 94–99). This, however, assumes that for Aquinas concrete primary matter has an intelligibility apart from quantitative designations, which is denied by Aquinas. Only in speaking of the Eucharist, in which there is no primary matter, does St. Thomas call dimensive quantity a "quoddam individuationis principium" (*Sum. theol.*, III, q. 77, a. 2), but this does not mean that quantity is an independent source of individuality (cf. *Quodl.* I, q. 10, aa. 1–2; *Quodl.* VII, q. 4, a. 3; *De verit.*, q. 2, a. 6 ad 1).

[19] St. Thomas, *In VII Metaph., lect.* 10, n. 1496.

[20] St. Thomas, *De verit.*, q. 2, a. 6 ad 1.

[21] St. Thomas, *Sum. theol.*, I, q. 76, a. 6 ad 2.

[22] St. Thomas, *In Boeth. De trin.*, q. 4, a. 2; see also *De ente et essentia*, c. 2, ed. Roland-Gosselin, p. 11.

For the sake of clarity this Aristotelian view of the Schoolmen can be summarized briefly. First, primary matter is a purely passive and indetermined principle, unknowable in itself. Second, it can be perceived and understood only analogously, that is, in terms of the determined actualities which flow from the principle. Third, these determined actualities are principally the corporeal composite, actual quantity, position in place and time, and perceptibility in sense experience.

This brings us to the second problem in Aristotelian physics which prepared the way for fourteenth century developments, namely the problem of condensation and rarefaction. In condensation a given amount of matter comes to occupy less space, and it is said to be "dense". In rarefaction the same amount of matter, that is, the very same matter, comes to occupy greater space, and it is said to be "rare".[23] Aristotle, St. Albert and St. Thomas speak about this motion as "receiving greater dimensions" and "receiving smaller dimensions", because for them actual quantity consists in the visible dimensions a body happens to have at any given time. Thus without increase or decrease of matter, the potentiality of matter is simply actualized differently in the two states.[24] Nevertheless none of these thinkers considered condensation and rarefaction to be motion in the category of quantity. Rather these motions were universally thought to be alterations, belonging to the category of *quality*.

In the thirteenth century practically all Aristotelians were influenced in one way or another by the *De substantia orbis* of Averroes. In this important work Averroes tried to give meaning to the expression 'this matter', *haec materia*, considered prior to substantial form and variable actual quantity. For Averroes, only matter could be the root of individuality and plurality within a species. Just as division of the continuum produces the plurality of number, so divided matter produces the plurality of individuals. He rightly criticized Avicenna for considering only actual quantity, i.e., terminated, variable quantity, in his explanation of multiplicity within a species. Actual quantity is an accident posterior to corporeity; therefore, it cannot be the cause of many individual bodies. Averroes noted that many absurdities follow from Avicenna's view, "one of which is that form itself is not divided by the division of matter"; consequently there could be no plurality of forms

---

[23] Aristotle, *Phys.*, IV, 9. 217a 26–b 10; *De caelo*, III, 1. 299b 8–9. St. Thomas, *In IV Phys., lect.* 14, n. 13: "Rarum est ex hoc, quod materia recipit maiores dimensiones; densum autem ex hoc, quod materia recipit minores dimensiones; et sic si accipiantur diversa corpora aequalis quantitatis, unum rarum et aliud densum, densum habet plus de materia". See also *In I De gen., lect.* 14, n. 5; *In II Sent., dist.* 30, *q.* 2, *a.* 1; *Sum. theol.*, III, *q.* 77, *a.* 2. The distinction between the three senses of 'same' mentioned above in note 13 should be kept in mind.

[24] *Phys.*, IV, 9. 217b 8–9.

326

within a species.[25] Averroes suggested that there must be another kind of dimensionality prior to every divided form, by which primary matter would be divisible and actually divided from all other segments of itself. This antecedent dimensionality Averroes called *dimensiones interminatae*. This allowed him to explain stability in a given amount of primary matter and variability in actual terminated dimensions.[26]

Aristotelians such as Albertus Magnus and Thomas Aquinas refused to recognize *dimensiones interminatae* as anything more than a point of reference, a known quantitative latitude within which a given body may have this or that terminated quantity. Giles of Rome, on the other hand, developed Averroes' suggestion at great length, as Miss A. Maier has pointed out.[27] It seems, however, that in his early work, *Metaphysicales quaestiones,* Giles really misunderstood Averroes, and that he worked out his final view oblivious of the real position of Averroes. In discussing how *dimensiones indeterminatae* precede substantial form, Giles replied in his early work[28] that there are two such dimensions: those prior to all form, and those prior to the specific form. The latter type was supposedly discovered (*venatur*) by Averroes in his famous treatise; it allows the body to be in place, but without specific dimensions. The first type, however, Giles thinks was unknown to Averroes. This Aegidian discovery has two aspects: as *dimensiones* it makes primary matter to be "much or little", and as *indeterminatae* it allows matter to occupy a greater or less volume of space, "because the same amount of matter sometimes occupies a smaller place, as in a measure of earth, and sometimes a larger space as when from that measure of earth there is produced ten measures of air".

Later Giles of Rome abandoned this complicated view in favor of a simpler development of the Averroist position, although, as we have already noted, he seems to have been unaware of its Averroist heritage. In his *Theoremata de corpore Christi* (1276), and again in his *Commentary on the Physics* (1277), Giles expounded his famous doctrine of the *duplex quantitas*:

---

[25] Averroes, *De sub. orbis*, c. 1, ed. Venetiis, 1489 (no foliation). A concise presentation of this doctrine is found in the pseudo-Thomistic treatise *De natura materiae*, c. 2, ed. J. M. Wyss, Fribourg, 1953, pp. 94–95. Averroes undoubtedly influenced the view of William of Rothwell O.P., who strongly defended the divisibility of matter prior to the accident of quantity. See his *De principiis rerum naturalium*, MS Vat. lat. 11585, fol. 192*r–v et passim*.

[26] See the commentary of Alvaro de Toledo (c. 1290) on the *De substantia orbis* of Averroes, ed. by Manuel Alonso, S.J., Madrid, 1941, pp. 71–75 and 93–94.

[27] Anneliese Maier, "Das Problem der Quantitas Materiae", in *Studien* I: *Die Vorläufer Galileis im 14. Jahrhundert*, Roma, 1949, pp. 29–48.

[28] The emended text of *Metaphysicales quaestiones, lib.* VIII, *q.* 5, is published by A. Maier, *ibid.*, pp. 37–38, note 14.

one an indetermined quantity by which matter is "tanta et tanta, ut quod sit multa vel pauca", the other a determined quantity by which matter occupies "tantum et tantum locum, ut magnum vel parvum".[29] These two quantities, according to Giles, are not the same, for if air is generated from water, there is as much matter (indetermined quantity) in one measure of water (determined quantity) as there will be in ten measures (determined quantity) of air. Similarly in condensation and rarefaction there is as much matter in a small volume as there is in the large. In other words, an indetermined quantity belonging to primary matter was postulated to explain the constant "amount" of matter, while determined quantity, an accident, was taken to explain the variability of actual dimensions.

In the doctrine of Giles of Rome there are three points to notice. (i) The two types of quantity are presented as really distinct quantities, both of which are real.[30] (ii) The quantity by which matter occupies a given volume varies in condensation, rarefaction, and in elementary changes without loss or addition of material parts—and without atoms or pores. (iii) The quantity by which matter is "so much" remains constant in condensation, rarefaction and in all substantial changes, so that no natural agent can alter this quantity.[31] This constant quantity Giles calls *quantitas materiae*, a term he frequently employed in his *Quodlibet* IV, *q.*1, disputed and determined in 1289. Giles of Rome thus developed a clear distinction between a constant "quantity of matter" and the variable volume occupied by matter. But we are still a long way from the precise determination of this quantity developed in the fourteenth century and assumed in the seventeenth.

§3 *William of Ockham*

Despite the vicissitudes of 1277, 1284 and 1286 the view of Albertus Magnus and the *Doctor Communis* was recognized in the fourteenth century as the "common teaching" of the schools. This does not mean that the views of Albert and Thomas were unanimously accepted, or even that they were correctly understood. The intellectual scene of the fourteenth century is full of complexity, dissension, novelty and development. It would be a mistake to

---

[29] See Maier, *ibid.*, pp. 29–36.

[30] This point was particularly criticized. Thomas Sutton objected that two real quantities cannot exist at the same time, and that all change, including condensation and rarefaction, is no more than a reduction of potency to act (Maier, *ibid.*, pp. 43–44). The author of *Quodlibet* VIII, *q.* 10, attributed to Hervé Nédelec, also rejects the reality of two quantities (*ibid.*, p. 48, note 25). Giles' view was similarly rejected at Paris by his confrère, Gregory of Rimini, in his *Sentence* commentary of 1344 (*Sent.* II, *dist.* 12, *q.* 2, *a.* 1, ed. Venetiis 1522, fol. 78*vb*).

[31] Giles of Rome, *Theoremata*, prop. 44, quoted by A. Maier, *ibid.*, p. 33.

consider fourteenth century scholastics as reactionaries against Aristotelianism and the "common teaching". It would be just as erroneous to consider them as unoriginal, uncritical parrots of earlier views. The researches of Pierre Duhem, Constantine Michalski, Anneliese Maier and many others have directed attention to some of the vitality and originality of fourteenth century thinkers. These researches, however, have led some to view fourteenth century speculation as an effort "to overthrow Aristotle" and "to establish modern science". The individuality of medieval thinkers, the multiplicity of authoritative sources, and the basic respect for learning characteristic of medieval universities should be sufficient to warn a modern reader against such extravagant statements.

One of the most remarkable figures of the early fourteenth century was the English Franciscan, William of Ockham, who is considered by some today to be the "father of modern science". His claim to this title is variously presented, but underlying the various claims is the presumed modernity of his concept of matter. This is most frequently presented in the Cartesian manner of a simple identification of matter and extension—a clear, simple concept of mass. This interpretation, however, is an over-simplification, and it fails to consider the basic principles underlying his view.

By the time Ockham left Oxford in 1320, short of becoming a Master in Theology, he had developed the essential doctrines of his philosophy of nature. In his lectures on the *Sentences* (c. 1316–18) and in his two treatises *De sacramento altaris* (c. 1319), the "Venerable Inceptor" presented all the fundamental principles and characteristic views of his philosophy, which he insisted was the true doctrine of Aristotle. Later works, such as his commentaries on Aristotle's *Physics* and logic and his *Summa logicae* do not reveal any essential modification or addition.

The basic principle of Ockham's natural philosophy is that only individual *res absolutae* are existing realities; everything else is merely a name, a term. An "absolute thing" for Ockham is anything which can by the absolute power of God (*potentia absoluta Dei*) exist independently of any other thing. Since no change or action, for example, can exist independently of a subject even by God's absolute power, nouns and verbs commonly used to describe motion do not signify any reality or *res* over and above the individual subject. Every individual subject, being a substance, can by God's power exist without accidents, since whatever is prior can always exist without that which is posterior; it is a *res absoluta*. Material substances are composed of matter and form, each of which can be conceived without the other, according to Ockham. Being *res absolutae*, individual matter and individual form are the real existents designated by the various parts of speech. Were it not for the Eucharist, Ockham would have denied absolute reality to every accidént. But the Christian faith teaches that sensible qualities such as color, taste and weight, remain *per se subsistentia*[32] in the Eucharist without any subject. "Heaviness remains there with other accidents, but nothing there is heavy".[33] Consequently only individual matter, individual form and individual sense qualities can by divine power exist independently of everything else. Ordinarily these three distinct *res* exist together in nature, even though they can exist separately. In any case, these three, and only these three, can have real existence outside the mind. "Besides absolute things, namely substances and qualities, no thing (*res*) is imaginable either in act or in potency".[34]

From this principle follows Ockham's well-known thesis that motion, time, place and the like, are not realities over and above individual substances and qualities. Consequently, the multiplicity of nouns, verbs, adjectives and adverbs used in human speech to describe situations, universal natures and abstract ideas can designate, or refer to nothing other than individual substances and qualities. These and only these are the personal referent (*suppositio personalis*) of all parts of speech. The meaning, however, or significance (*suppositio simplex*) of these terms, namely abstract nouns, verbs adjectives and adverbs is to be found exclusively in the mind (*intentio animae*). Thus "the fiction of abstract nouns" derived from adverbs, conjunctions, prepositions, verbs and syncategorematic terms is considered by Ockham to be the cause of a great many difficulties and errors, since beginners in philosophy imagine that distinct nouns correspond to distinct realities in nature.[35] Such abstract nouns as 'motion', 'change', 'movement', 'action', 'passion', 'heating', 'freezing', and the like, which are derived from verbs, are used in human speech only "for the sake of brevity in speech or elegance in discourse".[36]

---

[32] Hugh of St. Victor (*Sum. sent., tr.* VI, *c.* 4. *PL 176*, 141), quoted by Peter Lombard in the *Sentences*, IV, *dist.* 12, *d.* 1, ed. Quaracchi 1916, p. 808.

[33] Anonymous gloss on *Decretum Gratiani, dist.* 2, *c.* 27, ed. Lugduni 1609, p. 1924; also quoted by Peter Lombard, *loc. cit.* Cf. Ockham, *Summa logicae*, P. I, *c.* 44, ed. P. Boehner, St. Bonaventure, N.Y., 1951, p. 124; *De sac. alt.* II, *c.* 21, ed. T. B. Birch, Iowa, 1930, pp. 266–78.

[34] Ockham, *Summa logicae*, P. I, *c.* 49, *ed. cit.*, p. 141. This fundamental Ockhamist doctrine was clearly recognized by Francis de Meyronnes in his *Quodlibet* disputed about 1322: "Et istis adiungitur avaritia mira quorumdam quod nullum ens reale volunt ponere nisi cogantur, et dicunt quod non possunt cogi nisi ad substantiam et qualitatem, omnibus aliis praedicamentis positis tantum secundum rationem." *Quodl., q.* 6, cd. Venetiis 1520, fol. 235, where the editors have noted in the margin: "Contra Occam et sequaces".

[35] Ockham, *Tract, de successivis*, ed. P. Boehner, St. Bonaventure, N.Y., 1944, p. 46; *De sac. alt.* I, *q.* 1, *ed. cit.*, pp. 52–66.

[36] *Tract, de successivis, ed. cit.*, p. 37.

What about quantity? What about the great number of terms used in natural science to signify quantity and the quantitative aspects of matter, sensible qualities, motion and time? For Ockham, quantity is not a *res absoluta*, for it cannot exist independently of substance or qualities; quantity cannot even be imagined without hypostasizing it, without rendering it substantial. Moreover, none of Ockham's authorities claimed the existence of quantity in the Eucharist independent of sense qualities. What then is "quantity"? Briefly, it is a noun, a term, referring to nothing over and above individual physical substances or individual sensible qualities; its meaning, or signification, is simply the non-simultaneity of a thing's parts, each of which is capable of moving spatially toward the other.

The source of Ockham's doctrine concerning quantity, as Miss Maier has shown,[37] is the French Franciscan, Peter John Olivi (†1298). Although Olivi did not openly attack the "common teaching" of the schools, it seems that he really held the view secretly that "quantitas non dicit rem absolutam aliam a substantiam".[38] He presents arguments on behalf of this view as "objections" to the common teaching, but he offers no refutation of these objections. In Ockham's systematic philosophy of nature, Olivi's "objections" become main arguments for the new view.

The earliest explicit defence by Ockham of the identification of quantity with substance and quality seems to be found in the *reportatio* of Book IV of the *Sentences*, q.4: "Whether the Body of Christ is really contained under the accidents of bread":

> First of all, one must ask, what is quantity? Here I say definitively that quantity refers to no absolute or relative thing (*res*) other than substance and quality. I say further that quantity is nothing but the extension of a thing having parts which can be moved spatially one toward the other. As was said in Book II concerning duration . . . so extension or quantity does not refer to anything absolute or relative beyond substance and qualities, but it is a kind of word (*vox*) or concept, principally signifying substance, namely matter or form or corporeal quality, and connoting many other things (if such exist) between which there can be locomotion.[39]

Ockham then gives two arguments to prove that quantity is not a form distinct from substance and quality. First, he argues, if quantity were a distinct form, it would have to inhere in some subject; but this subject could not be

[37] *Studien, IV: Metaphysische Hintergründe der spätscholastischen Naturphilosophie*, Roma, 1955, pp. 153–75.

[38] See Maier, *ibid.*, p .160; Peter John Olivi, II *Sent.*, q. 58, ed. B. Jansen, II, Quaracchi, 1922, pp. 440–49; *Tract. de quantitate*, in Venice edition of his *Quodlibeta*, n.d., fol. 49v–53.

[39] Ockham, *Sent.* IV, q. 4 G, ed. Lyons 1495, controlled by Oxford, Balliol College MS 299, fol. 180va (= IV, q. 1).

matter or form, since there is no more reason for inherence in one rather than the other, nor could that subject be the composite, since the immediate subject of every accident must be as simple as the accident itself. "Hoc nunc suppono, post probabitur et prius fuit probatum in tertio".[40] Second, Ockham argues, matter, form and quality are themselves *quantum et extensum sine omni extrinseco*, and therefore they do not need to be extended by a distinct accident called "quantity". He defends this statement with regard to matter for two reasons: (i) Matter existing under substantial form is already extended in place and position, since any part of matter could be annihilated without affecting the other parts. (ii) If quantity were an absolute thing posterior to substance, then God could annihilate it without affecting substance in the least; but supposing that God annihilated all quantity posterior to a definite piece of matter existing in Oxford or in Rome, that matter would still be in Oxford or in Rome. Therefore, matter of itself is a thing existing in place and position. This is the famous "argumentum theologicum" which, Ockham adds, can be applied to substantial form and to quality with the same result.[41]

The two treatises *De sacramento altaris*,[42] written at the earliest after the *reportatio* of the Fourth Book of the *Sentences*, are directed principally against the objections of a *quidam doctor modernus* who held that the identification of quantity with substance and quality is "contrary to Aristotle ... contrary to the common opinion of the doctors ... contrary to experience ... and also contrary to reason".[43] This *quidam doctor*, as Miss Maier has shown, [44] is none other than Richard of Mediavilla, O.F.M., who had raised these objections about twenty-five years earlier in his commentary on the *Sentences* (revised c.1295) against the teaching of Peter John Olivi. Richard not only cited eminent authorities against Olivi's position, but he raised

---

[40] These references are not necessarily part of the original text; certainly not if, as Maier suggests, the *reportatio* of Book IV is chronologically prior to Books II and III. The references may have been inserted later by Ockham or by a scribe. In any case the references are not at all clear. In *Sent.* III, *q.* 6 C, Ockham rejects the view (held by Thomas Wilton) that accidents are composed of matter and form as are substances, but here Ockham merely says, "quod suppono esse falsum ad praesens". (See also *De sac. alt.* I, *q.* 3, *ed. cit.*, p. 112, where no reason at all is given). The explanation given in the *Tractatus de principiis theologiae* attributed to Ockham (ed. L. Baudry, Paris, 1936, pp. 142–43) has not, as yet, been located in the *Sentences*.

[41] *Sent.*, IV, *q.* 4G.

[42] The chronological relation between these two treatises has not been conclusively established. For sake of convenience I call the "first treatise" that which is printed first in all the editions.

[43] *De sac. alt.* I, *q.* 3, *ed. cit.*, pp. 116–120; also II, *c.* 30, *ibid.*, pp. 354–58.

[44] A. Maier, "Zu einigen Problemen der Ockhamforschung", *AFH*, *46*, 1953, 178–81.

three major objections against it: (i) In a condensed body there is less quantity, but no loss of material parts; therefore, matter and quantity must be distinct. (ii) There is no quantitative difference between a measure of air and the same measure of water, even though their subjects are different; therefore there must be a difference between quantity and substance. (iii) If matter, form and qualities each had their own dimensions, then many solids would exist simultaneously in the same place; but this is absurd.

In reply, Ockham repeats his "theological argument" and adds what was to become his favorite argument, one drawn from condensation and rarefaction. In the natural phenomenon of condensation and rarefaction no amount of matter is lost or acquired. For Ockham this proves that no *res absoluta* is being generated or corrupted. Therefore, "quantity" cannot be a *res*. What, then, do we mean by condensation? Condensation means nothing more than that "the parts are moved locally so as to occupy a smaller place now than they did before, and one part now is less distant from another than previously".[45] In other words, what people call "quantity", "magnitude" or "dimensions" is not a distinct reality at all. These nouns signify that the parts of matter (a *res absoluta*) are not all together, not "totum simul" (an *ens rationis*). Not-being-all-together is a mental designation which cannot possibly have a real existence of its own. 'Quantity', therefore, is only a word used to designate really existing matter when its parts are more or less not all together. The same is true, according to Ockham, when the term 'quantity' and its linguistic variants are applied to substantial form and to sensible qualities.

Ockham is careful to observe that *normally* the parts of matter are distributed in place, that is, "quantified" in the sense explained. From condensation and rarefaction it is clear that this distribution can vary without the addition or loss of material parts. And there is no reason, Ockham argues, why God cannot by His absolute power so condense a body as to eliminate all spatial distribution completely, still preserving the reality of matter existing in Oxford or in Rome. This is actually what God has done in the Eucharist: the Body and the Blood of Christ exist in a definite place, but without their spatial dimensions.[46] Ockham goes on to say that God could by His infinite power make all the parts of the material universe exist all together at the same point of space without "extension", and still preserve the distinction of parts,[47] just as all the parts of Christ's Body and Blood are preserved in the Holy Eucharist without any "dimensions".

From this it is clear that Ockham did not identify matter and extension

---

[45] *De sac. alt.* I, *q.* 3, *ed. cit.*, p. 130; see also p. 136.
[46] *Sent.* III, *q.* 6 E; *Sent.* IV, *q.* 4 N; *De sac. alt.* II *c.* 6.
[47] *Sent.* IV, *q.* 4 H; also *q.* 6 J.

as Descartes did in the seventeenth century.[48] What Ockham did in effect was to deny the reality of what most people call "quantity". Instead of identifying extension and matter, he denied extension and gave matter the characteristic of "being in some place". Not-being-all-together in place is normal for matter, but not essential to it. Consequently, when Ockham speaks of "eadem quantitas numero", as he frequently does, the numerical identity of matter is dependent on identical position in place, and not on quantity. Hence, the expression 'the same quantity of matter' in the sense of *mass* can have no real meaning in the philosophy of Ockham; nor does he ever use the expression in this sense. Moreover, 'quantity', in the sense of a measurable volume or magnitude, has nothing whatever to do with matter or its intelligibility. As natural condensation proves, the size of a body is variable, uncertain and irrelevant; it is even possible that a body have no size or magnitude whatever. Finally, it is also clear that the "parts" which move in greater or less proximity are not to be understood as "atoms", but simply as undivided parts of primary matter.

At Paris, Ockham's view was immediately attacked by Francis de Marchia, O.F.M., the earliest known proponent of "impetus" to explain projectile motion. Marchia objected precisely because of the difficulty in explaining condensation and rarefaction.[49] It was likewise rejected by Walter Burley,[50] who was then teaching at Paris, Jean Buridan,[51] the foremost advocate of the "impetus" theory, and Nicole Oresme[52] as completely inadequate: it could not explain how the same *quantitas materiae* can remain when a body occupies various actual dimensions or magnitude in space. At Oxford, however, opposition to Ockham's view is considerably less patent, except for John Lutterell's inclusion of this thesis in his list of 56 articles submitted to the Holy See for censure.[53] Whatever may have been the reaction of Oxonians to Ockham's thesis, we know that after 1328 they turned their "Oxford subtleties" to questions of a very different sort.

---

[48] This point is urged more strongly in my article, "The Place of John Dumbleton in the Merton School", *Isis, 50,* 443–45.

[49] See A. Maier, *art. cit., AFH, 46,* 1953, 174–78; and *Studien,* IV, 200–209.

[50] Burley, *Expositio in libros Physicorum,* lib. I, text. 15, ed. Venetiis 1501, fol. 13rb–15va; *Tract. de formis,* MS London, Lambeth Palace 70, fol. 125–134v, esp. fol. 132va.

[51] See A. Maier, *art. cit., AFH, 46,* 1953, 174–77; *Studien,* IV, 209–216.

[52] A. Maier, *Studien,* IV, 218.

[53] "Duodecimus articulus: Quod tam quantitas continua quam discreta sunt ipsa substantia", ed. J. Koch, *RTAM, 7,* 1935, 375. Lutterell's reason for listing this article as erroneous (*ibid.,* p. 379) is most peculiar; and, in fact, it was not repeated by the theological commission, cf. *RTAM, 8,* 1936, 178.

§4 *The Oxford Calculators*

Thomas Bradwardine's treatise of 1328 was concerned with the proportion of velocities in moving bodies.[54] It attempted to formulate a mathematical law of dynamics universally valid for all changes of velocity in local motion in such a way that an increase or decrease in ratio of force to resistance
on the one hand would always beget a truly proportional increase or decrease of distance traversed in a given time on the other. In the traditional
formulation of the law, it was thought that twice the velocity would follow
simply from doubling the moving power or from halving the resistance—
which happens to be valid for a particular case. In Bradwardine's formulation, the velocity is increased (doubled, tripled, etc.) by a geometrical, not an
arithmetical increase in the proportion of moving force to resistance. That
is, in order to produce a proportionally double velocity, the proportion of
moving force to resistance has to be squared, not simply doubled. This was
simply expressed by Bradwardine and his followers by saying that "the velocity of motions follows from a geometrical proportion (*velocitas motuum
sequitur proportionem geometricam*)".

Authors after Bradwardine commonly divided discussions of motion into
two parts: *velocitas motuum penes causam,* or the relation of mover to
resistance (dynamics), and *velocitas motuum penes effectum*, or the relation
of distance to time (kinematics). The successors of Bradwardine were particularly intent on extending his concept to every type of motion, that is, to
changes of quality, condensation, rarefaction and the like. In local motion
the variables are easily discernible: distance and time on the one hand, moving force and resistance on the other. But in qualitative changes, such as condensation and rarefaction, the "distance" or "latitude" to be covered in a
given time is not easy to determine. What, for example, is the distance (*latitudo* or *spatium acquisitum*) of rarity and density? By what is this latitude
determined? This question was usually phrased as "penes quid raritas et
densitas attendantur". There seems never to have been any doubt that dynamically the velocity would follow Bradwardine's geometric proportion.
The problem, then, was a kinematic one.

The problem is discussed in an elementary way by Roger Swineshead in
his treatise *De motibus naturalibus*, which was "given at Oxford for the util-

---

[54] Ed. H. L. Crosby, Jr., *Thomas of Bradwardine, His Tractatus de proportionibus*,
Madison, 1955. A summary of this treatise can be found in A. Maier, *Studien*, I, 81–110;
Marshall Clagett, *The Science of Mechanics in the Middle Ages*, Madison, Wisconsin,
1959, pp. 437–40; James A. Weisheipl, O.P., *The Development of Physical Theory in
the Middle Ages*, New York, 1959, pp. 72–81.

ity of students" some time between 1328 and 1337.[55] Contrary to Ockham, Roger Swineshead believes quantity to be a *res* distinct from substance and quality,[56] and the position of material parts in place (actual magnitude or volume) to be a mode of quantity (*modus quantitatis*). Condensation and rarefaction for him involve a change in the mode of quantity, but apparently not in quantity itself. For Swineshead what remains constant in condensation and rarefaction, as well as in substantial changes, is the *massa elementaris*, as he calls it.[57] The *massa elementaris*, or *inanimalis*, signifies the inanimate bulk of matter which remains constant, despite the variation in volume and the variation in density. This "mass" differs from what he calls *massa humoralis* only in that the latter is animated and depends upon the humors in a living body. Death reduces "humoral mass" to a given amount of "elemental mass", which remains constant. Now, just as volume is taken to be a modality of quantity, so rarity and density are taken to be not *res*, but *modi positivi rerum* signifying the "situs partium in toto". Thus for Roger Swineshead density and rarity belong to the category of "position", rather than "quality".[58] Rarity and density, therefore, depend upon the proportion between volume and *massa elementaris*. Thus, the greater the proportion of magnitude to mass, the greater the density. Condensation and rarefaction are, of course, produced by the "primary sense qualities", namely hot and cold, wet and dry. But the latitude of rarity depends upon the proportion of magnitude, or volume to *massa elementaris*. The difficulty with Roger Swineshead's view is that "mass" itself is unknown. There is no way of determining the "quantity of matter".

In the *Logica* or *Regulae solvendi sophismata* of 1335, William Heytesbury is concerned only with determining the proportion of velocities in condensation and rarefaction, which, incidentally, he calls "augmentation".[59] The question is to determine a universal law by which one could describe

---

[55] MS Erfurt, Amplon. F. 135, fol. 25–47*v*.

[56] *Ibid.*, fol. 26*rb*.

[57] *Ibid.*, *diff.* 3, *c.* 2, *pars* 2, *q.* 3, MS fol. 31*rb*. The term 'massa' occurs frequently throughout this work in a more technical sense than is found in earlier writers, particularly theologians who commonly spoke of "the mass of human kind" or "the corrupted mass (*massa corrupta*) of fallen nature." For other ancient meanings of the term, see Albert Blaise, *Dictionnaire Latin-Français des auteurs chrétiens*, Paris, 1954, p. 517.

[58] "Pro quibus est sciendum quod densitas et raritas non res, sed modi rerum consistunt; sub praedicamentis enim 'positionis' collocantur, cum sint situs partium in toto". *loc. cit.*

[59] Ed. Venetiis 1494, fol. 45*ra*–49*va*, compared with MS Erfurt, Amplon. F. 135, fol. 14*vb*–16*ra*.

the relative velocities of rarefactions. After rejecting two opinions which hold that the greater velocity of rarefaction depends upon the degree (*latitudo*) of quantity acquired, he gives his own opinion, which is that the velocity depends upon the proportion of quantity acquired to the original volume in equal time.[60] That is to say, if two bodies of unequal volume acquire equal quantities in equal time, then that body which acquired *proportionally* the greater quantity would have rarefied more quickly. For Heytesbury motion consists essentially in a proportion. Thus, as the proportion acquired is greater, so is its velocity. In his consideration of the problem, Heytesbury neglects both the amount of matter and the degree of density in the original bodies.

John Dumbleton, a contemporary of Heytesbury at Merton, rejects this opinion in his *Summa logicae et philosophiae naturalis*[61] as does Richard Swineshead, a younger contemporary.[62] Like Heytesbury, Dumbleton considers condensation and rarefaction under the heading of augmentation and diminution, "because growth and decrease come about by rarefaction".[63] His own view is that "the velocity of augmentation is determined by the distance acquired, as it is in other motions". That is to say, the velocity of growth depends entirely upon the precise amount of quantity which is acquired in a given time "penes hoc quod precise acquirunt" without any reference to mass, whether they be equals or unequals.[64] In the course of the discussion, however, it becomes clear that Dumbleton does not intend to make velocity of rarefaction simply dependent upon volume acquired, but rather upon volume *respectu eiusdem materiae*. It is likewise evident in Richard Swineshead's discussion that he wishes only to modify Dumbleton's view: "pro ista materia potest corrigi positio".[65]

Richard Swineshead, known to later generations simply as "the Calculator", presents the clearest notion of *quantitas materiae*. Discussing rarity and density in the *Liber calculationum*,[66] he notes that there are only two reasonable opinions about their dependence on other factors:

> One holds that rarity depends upon the proportion of the quantity of a subject to its matter, and density upon the proportion of matter to quantity. The

---

[60] Here the reading in Amplon. MS F. 135, fol. 15*ra*, is better than the printed version.

[61] Dumbleton, *Summa*, P. III, *c*. 19. MS Vatican, Vat. lat. 6750, fol. 46*va*.

[62] Swineshead, *Calculationes*, *tr*. VI (De augmentatione), ed. Venetiis 1520, fol. 22*rb*.

[63] Dumbleton, *loc. cit.*, fol. 47*vb*.

[64] *Ibid.*, fol. 47*ra*.

[65] Swineshead, *Calculationes, loc. cit.*, fol. 24*vb*.

[66] *Ibid., tr*. V (De raritate et densitate), fol. 16*vb*–17*ra*.

second [opinion] holds that rarity depends upon quantity, not simply taken, but as it is in proportionate matter, or in comparision to matter.[67]

Both opinions, Swineshead observes, have this in common that they consider rarity and density to consist in a certain proportion between quantity and matter. Obviously rarity and density cannot be identical with mere magnitude, for then all equals in quantity would be equally dense. It is obvious that there is more matter (*plus de materia*) in a cubic foot of earth than there is in the same measure of air, otherwise earth would not be "more dense". Thus if fire is generated from earth, the magnitude of the whole is increased, and the whole is rendered more rare than it was before. But since no matter is lost or acquired, there must be more matter in earth than there will be in an equal measure of fire. Therefore, rarity and density must depend upon the proportion between magnitude (volume) and the amount of matter.

But the two opinions are different,[68] Swineshead explains, because the first holds that "just as the proportion of quantity of matter is greater, so is the rarity greater; thus if rarity were to be doubled, the proportion of quantity to matter would have to be doubled". The second opinion, however, holds that "proportionally just as the whole quantity is increased *manente materia eadem,* so rarity is increased; thus in order to double the rarity of any rare body, one would not double the *proportion* of quantity to matter, but one would simply double the quantity, as long as the matter remains the same". In other words, the first opinion would compare rarity in bodies merely according to the size of the proportion, without considering the amount of matter or the *degree* of density and rarity in those bodies. Against this formulation Swineshead objects that the law does not hold for all cases, and therefore it ought to be formulated more accurately, that is, with the "condition" as part of the law. Otherwise it would follow that all bodies of equal volume, increasing equally in volume, would rarefy with equal

---

[67] "Una ponit quod raritas attenditur penes proportionem quantitatis subiecti ad eius materiam et densitas attenditur penes proportionem materiae ad quantitatem. Secunda ponit quod raritas attenditur penes quantitatem non simpliciter, sed in materia proportionata vel in comparatione ad materiam." *Ibid.,* fol. 16*vb.*

[68] L. Thorndike notes these two opinions in his chapter on the Calculator (*A History of Magic and Experimental Science,* III, p. 379), but he is unable to understand the difference. A. Maier (*Studien,* I, p. 98 note 33) remarks that the first opinion assumes the Aristotelian function for the dependence of density on mass and volume, while the other assumes the Bradwardine function. Our own explanation, presented in the text, is that they have nothing to do with Bradwardine's problem; the truth of Bradwardine's function is taken for granted. Rather, the first opinion is simply a particular case, of which the second is a universal formulization. For this reason both opinions are "reasonable".

velocity; but this is not true in the case where bodies are unequally rare to begin with. Thus, provided that matter and density are the same in all bodies under consideration, then increase in rarity is proportioned to the increase in volume. This condition Swineshead includes in the law when he says "raritas attenditur penes quantitatem non simpliciter, sed in materia proportionata vel in comparatione ad materiam". Consequently, just as the rarity of a single body is increased merely by increasing the volume, *manente materia,* so—in a universal law—all rarefaction is proportional to increase of volume *in materia proportionata,* that is, given the same amount of matter in water as in air.[69]

The Calculator then proceeds to show the universality of his law by indicating the relative proportions between mass, magnitude and rarity in all possible cases, of which there are only four. Density, the converse of rarity, would involve the decrease of magnitude in the following laws, provided the amount of matter remained the same (*manente materia*). In these laws Swineshead clearly reveals his concept of mass as a definite "quantity of matter" derived from both magnitude and density conjointly:

1) If two bodies have equal mass (*equaliter habeant de materia*), as the matter of water compared to the matter of air generated from it, then proportionally as the volume of one is greater, so is its rarity.
2) If two bodies are equal in volume and equally rare, then they have equal mass (*equaliter habebunt de materia*).
3) If unequal in volume and equal in rarity, then proportionally as one is greater than the other, so it has greater mass (*ita plus habet de materia*). more rare, so it has less mass (*ita minus habet de materia*).

The question here is not whether the same amount of matter remains in
4) If equal in volume and unequal in rarity, then proportionally as one is condensation, rarefaction or in elementary change. Overtly it is a question of formulating in a universal manner the "latitude" of rarity and density in terms of some constant: "penes quid raritas et densitas attendantur". Implicitly, however, it is a question of determining the meaning of the "amount of matter", or the "quantity of matter": If two bodies are equal in volume and equally rare, then they have equal mass, *equaliter habebunt de materia.* In the last analysis it is a question of the experiential foundations of a meaningful concept of a certain "quantity of matter". The amount of matter which persists throughout all changes of the elements is not directly knowable. That the same quantity of matter remains constant throughout all changes can be taken as a fact of nature. However, the *tota massa primae materiae,* as Albert of Saxony calls it,[70] cannot be known to us by its magni-

---

[69] Swineshead, *Calculationes, loc. cit.,* fol. 17*ra.*
[70] See A. Maier, *Studien,* I, 49.

tude alone, that is by its volume or bulk alone, for this is manifestly variable. Nor can it be known by its density alone, for this too is variable, as ordinary experience testifies. Therefore, the quantity of matter, in order to have real meaning for us, must be a derivative of its density and magnitude conjointly.

In the Parisian discussions of impetus, Francis de Marchia, Jean Buridan, Albert of Saxony and others showed that a certain force must be impressed on the body itself in violent motion, and not on the medium, because the greater mass a body has, the farther it can be projected. Even here the meaning of 'mass' is relative to the density and magnitude of the body taken conjointly: "Because a stone has more matter and is more dense than a feather, it receives more of the moving force and retains it longer than a feather, and so it moves for a longer time than the feather".[71] The concept of mass, then, is a derivative measure of a given matter which cannot be directly perceived.

From this it should be clear that the concept of *mass* developed in the fourteenth century was a highly refined concept differing from the simpler concept of *primary matter* and from the physical dimensions traditionally classified in the category of quantity. When the philosophers of antiquity and the schoolmen of the Middle Ages acknowledged the conservation of matter as a law of nature, they meant that "primary matter" remains the same in all transformations. Here 'same' was taken in the sense of a substantial identity, since there is no creation or annihilation of such matter. In the new principle of the conservation of mass, however, the quantity of matter, or mass, is said to be the same before and after transformation. Here 'same' is taken in the sense of a quantitative equality, that is, quantitatively the same.[72] Technically, therefore, the two masses are said to be *equal*, rather than the 'same'. However, as we have seen, this quantity is not the simple magnitude belonging to the Aristotelian category of quantity. Rather, it is a complex quantity derived from magnitude and density conjointly.

This concept of mass had become common property when Newton defined *quantitas materiae* as "the measure of the same arising from its density and magnitude conjointly (*orta ex illius densitate et magnitudine coniunctim*)". This definition seems to be as true today as it was for Newton; and it was as true in Newton's time as it was for Richard Swineshead. It took experiments on pendulums "very accurately made" to show that this mass is "proportional to weight". However, one should add the condition, provided that the altitude and other conditions remain constant, for weight itself can change without any change of mass. Once it is known that mass

---

[71] Albert of Saxony, *Expositio in libros Physicorum, lib.* VIII, *q.* 13.
[72] See the different senses of 'same' discussed in note 13 above.

is proportional to the weight, then for practical purposes weight can be used to measure concretely the mass of a body. This, of course, is only an expedient. Our concept of mass as a certain quantity of matter remaining constant in all changes cannot be derived from weight. At best, weight can be only an approximation. But more important, our understanding of *quantitas materiae,* as historical and philosophical analysis shows, is always relative to a body's density in a given magnitude, that is, it is derived from characteristics known in sense experience, namely its density and magnitude conjointly.

In this paper we have tried to examine the historical and philosophical foundations of our concept of static, inertial mass. The concept of gravitational mass is an entirely different problem, the setting for which is far beyond the fourteenth century.

Albertus Magnus Lyceum
River Forest, Illinois

COMMENT

THERE IS ONE MINOR POINT IN FATHER WEISHEIPL'S EXCELLENT PAPER THAT I would take exception to, namely his interpretation of Ockham's so-called "nominalism" or what the late Father Boehner more appropriately referred to as his "realistic conceptualism". The author seems to have fallen into the all too common error of confusing the ontological problem of the real distinction with the semantical problem of real signification. While the mistake is minor from the standpoint of its bearing on the general argument of the paper, it can lead to a serious misrepresentation of Ockham's philosophy in general.

To say, for example, "The basic principle of Ockham's natural philosophy is that only individual *res absolutae* are existing realities; everything else is merely a name, a term" is certainly misleading, as are such subsequent remarks to the effect that only such really distinct things as individual matter, individual form and certain absolute qualities such as thought, knowledge, etc. "can have real existence outside the mind" or the conclusions he draws from Ockham's theory of supposition.

What the author's analysis overlooks or ignores is the semantical function of connotative terms in the context of a proposition. To say that a given body has a certain quantity or extension at one time which it may not have at another, or that an individual piece of brass has now this form, now that, is to assert a *real fact* about real things, as any careful reading of Ockham reveals. And this is true, even though the "form" of brass or the "quantity" of the body are not "things" really distinct from the brass which *is* formed or the body which *is* extended. For by Ockham's stipulated definition, two things are really distinct, if and only if, the entity of one is so totally other than that of the second that to assume that either exists in isolation from the other does not involve a contradiction. But the *way* in which such really distinct things exist in the objective world, viz. as having such and such a size, configuration, etc. or as being substantially united as matter and form in a living organism, is certainly not to Ockham's mind a mere subjective state of affairs, a situation created by the mind. His only contention is that this state of affairs, this way things really are, is not itself a "thing" really distinct from the things which are this way or exist in such and such a state.

To put the problem in a contemporary context, I submit that the point made by Ockham is not greatly different from that made by Russell and Wittgenstein when they insisted that the world of reality, which at any given moment consists of the totality of "what is the case" (or for Ockham, "what is true") consists of *facts,* not *things*. That is to say, objective events, or real situations (which

342

the proposition both signifies and asserts either to be the case or not to be the case) cannot be adequately described, or accounted for by enumerating or naming the individuals (Russell), the simple objects (Wittgenstein) or the *res absolutae* (Ockham) involved therein. What is further required is some descriptive phrase or statement which expresses, and to that extent signifies, the *way* in which such things exist, or the real context in which they occur. As Ockham is careful to note in explaining the way in which connotative terms (like 'quantity', or 'white') signify, their signification is not exhausted by the fact that are always referred to some *res absoluta* and to that extent, in the context of a significant proposition, personally supposit or point to such things. They also signify some factual context in which the thing pointed to occurs, and their signification is the same as a descriptive phrase or series of phrases which define or describe that context. The "meaning" of such terms includes both sense and reference (to use Frege's terminology), and in the context of a proposition such a term designates not only the thing (for which it supposits personally) but also the objective or extramental situation in which that thing is said to occur or to be. Hence it is inaccurate to state, as the author does, that such terms as are "used to describe situations . . . designate nothing other than individual substances and qualities . . . The meaning, however, or significance (*suppositio simplex*) of these terms . . . is to be found exclusively in the mind (*intentio animae*) . . ."

When, therefore, Ockham adds a warning to beginners in philosophy about the philosophical difficulties and errors that have their source in the *fictio nominum abstractorum,* he is anticipating the contention of Russell and others that the grammatical form of a proposition does not always reflect the "logical form" of the fact. Thus the two grammatically similar statements: "This body has such and such a quantity" and "this body has such and such a soul" assert —according to Ockham—two radically different facts or states of affairs. Unlike 'a quantity', 'a soul' is an absolute, not a connotative term. It denotes or names some thing really distinct from the body. 'A quantity', while seemingly performing the same semantical function, does not—according to Ockham's ontological theory—denote such a really distinct thing. When used in personal supposition, it denotes some thing (a body, or a quality) *but it also connotes an objective fact* about that thing, viz. that its integral or substantial parts are spatially distributed.

Allan B. Wolter, O.F.M.
St. Bonaventure University

MATTER IN

SEVENTEENTH CENTURY SCIENCE

Marie Boas Hall

§1 *Introduction*

The new theories of matter promulgated by seventeenth century scientists were many, varied and complex; they all shared a profound conviction that the previously accepted Aristotelian view of matter was philosophically false and scientifically sterile. Natural philosophers sought for new concepts that could aid them in their attempts to understand nature. Although in the end there never was any firm agreement as to what, exactly, matter was, there was universal agreement about what a theory of matter ought to be able to do in explaining the world, and in what terms this explanation should be expressed. The mechanical philosophy gradually came to be an integral part of seventeenth century scientific thought, susceptible of many interpretations but widely agreed to be a necessary ingredient in any scientific theory or explanation.

Early in the seventeenth century it became apparent that, in fact, there must be more involved in a useful theory of matter than a mere definition of what the stuff which made up the physical world might be. There was indeed much useful discussion of the construction of matter in terms not entirely alien to pre-Socratic thought, and a universal conclusion that matter was not continuous, but physically discontinuous; that there was no *Aristotelian* plenum, though there might be no true vacuum; and that the world was made up of very small, discrete, individual bodies. Had this been all that was required there would be little to discuss here, for the conclusion is not difficult to reach or to understand, nor need it alter the pattern of one's general scientific thought, as many early proponents of particulate theories (Daniel Sennert[1] for example) unconsciously or consciously demonstrated. But in fact such new theories of matter only assumed scientific importance when use was made of the particles they envisaged in trying to explain natural phenomena and when the Aristotelian theory of forms (developed

---

[1] Sennert (1572–1637) in *De Chymicorum cum Aristotelicis et Galenicis Consensu ac Dissensu*, (1619).

over the centuries) was replaced by the mechanical philosophy. For thereby the properties of bodies were subjected to a new and rigid examination which utterly changed men's attitude towards the external world and profoundly affected the development of science. Though it was the philosophers who gave this point of view real sophistication, it was the scientists who introduced it into general discussion and proved its usefulness.

§2 *The Rise and Fall of Ancient Atomism*

It is tempting to assume that scientists, rebelling against accepted Aristotelian doctrines, would naturally turn to anti-Aristotelian notions already in existence: the atomic theories of Graeco-Roman antiquity. In fact, this did happen—had already happened before the seventeenth century—but it provided no real solution to the problems that theories of matter were now to be called upon to face. Democritus, Epicurus and Lucretius were much read, as innumerable editions of *De rerum natura* testify, but they had relatively little to offer seventeenth century natural philosophers, whatever they offered thinkers like Bruno or Gassendi. Partly because every seventeenth century scientist had read Aristotle, who was the only real source for Democritean atomism, the arguments against ancient atomism prejudiced men in advance. Added to this were the repeated discussions of many generations' disputing and redisputing about minima, least particles, infinite divisibility and so on, as well as the incisive discussions by mathematicians, all of which tended to show that the concept of an indivisible atom was very nearly untenable.

More important was the unfortunate fact that ancient atomic theories were scientifically out of date. Democritus's views on the physical universe were more primitive than those of Aristotle; Epicurus was no scientist and did not even understand the nature of sound; Lucretius had not attempted to subsume later Greek physics in his cosmology. Something could be salvaged from the views of Hero of Alexandria and the Alexandrian school of physicists and physicians on whom later Greek commentators on Aristotle had leaned heavily, but this was more suggestive than constructive and provided no complete system. No wonder then that the works and even the names of those who tried to rescue ancient atomism and transfer it unchanged to the seventeenth century world have an unfamiliar ring. Nicholas Hill's *Philosophia Epicurea* (1601), Sebastian Basso's *Philosophia naturalis adversus Aristotelem* (1621); J. C. Magnen's *Democritus reviviscens sive de atomis* (1646) all are deservedly forgotten, and merely served to prove that neither Epicurus nor Plato nor Democritus could live again in the seventeenth century.[2] Even Gassendi's great work on Epicureanism is scientifically a magnificent failure which survived because of its literary and philosophic influence. No scientist could take seriously Gassendi's elaborate, turgid and prolix attempt to introduce Democritean atoms into the physics of the mid-seventeenth century—though his success in Christianizing atomist cosmology deprived anti-atomists of one of their most fatal weapons. It is impossible to find any real influence of Gassendi's work on later scientists who already had other, more cogent theories of matter to choose from; for it must not be forgotten that Gassendi's *Philosophiae Epicuri Syntagma* of 1649 was only a small collection of atomic texts, and the real doctrine of Gassendi's interpretation had to wait for posthumous publication (as *Syntagma philosophicum*) until 1658, too late to be of importance to science.[3]

The reason why atomic theories of antiquity found themselves too out of date for acceptance was not only because of the positive advance of physical science, though this was naturally important, since it is difficult for a scientist to take seriously a theory propounded by someone ignorant of what to him are "simple facts". Sixteenth century science had, as it happens, not added many new discoveries which needed to be interpreted by a theory of matter; on the other hand, the experimental and mystic sciences of natural magic and alchemy had added many new phenomena, and scientists were increasingly inclined to feel that science should have something to say in these matters. Natural magic included magnetism, which Gilbert investigated in an experimental fashion, though he was unable to offer any useful or interesting explanation of the origin of the phenomena he discovered and extended. The use of lenses in telescopes and microscopes outdid the illusions of the conjurer; the suction pump was as mysterious in its operation as any pneumatic toy described in della Porta's *Natural Magick*; surely these lay in the province of natural philosophy, which ought to be able to explain their origin. Alchemy, rapidly becoming either technological, or medical

---

[2] Of course, the names, and even the existence, of ancient atomists were frequently invoked to give sanction to contemporary acceptance of scientific corpuscularianism, and "Moschus the Phoenician" (mentioned by Strabo) became Moses to give theological support. But this kind of reasoning was commoner to philosophers and divines than to scientists. (Cf., e.g., Cudworth's *True Intellectual System of the Universe*). Walter Charlton's *Physiologia Epicuro-Gassendo-Charltoniana* (1654) was Charlton's own work, much modified from Epicureanism by adjustment to contemporary science. Charlton was a physician, and later F.R.S.

[3] The publication of Bernier's French abridgement in 1675 introduced Gassendi's ideas to the literary and general public; it could not reach the scientist. Even Robert Boyle, still a young man in 1658, never read Gassendi's work in its entirety; he refers several times to Gassendi's *Syntagma*, but always as a "little" work. This could only mean that he knew the 1649 work, not that of 1658.

chemistry, offered a host of mysterious phenomena which also needed explanation: some substances when mixed together gave off heat; certain salts added to water produced cold; some colorless solutions turned from blue to either green or red, others to yellow or white when appropriate colorless substances were added; some liquids mixed to produce solids; some solids dissolved in liquids and permanently lost their solidity; shapes, odors, tastes, colors, solids, liquids, heat, cold, came and went in bewildering confusion. The philosophically minded chemist could offer no explanation but that of forms: through the chemical art he was able to impress or withdraw forms and qualities to any extent. He did not yet quite know how this was done; but one day the secret of complete command would appear. Then the forms. of yellowness, density, malleability, incorruptibleness, perfection and so on would be mastered by the chemist, and then it would be easy to impress them on a base metal and prepare true gold. Though the natural philosopher could hardly concern himself with the dream, the properties of heat, cold, color, fluidity and so on were real, and the natural philosopher could not ignore the need to include them in his concept of the physical world.

Ancient atomism could not help very much. It could explain density, solidity, transparency and coherence by arguing that substances varied in the amount of vacuum between the atoms,[4] but even so it was incapable of coping with the host of forms and qualities now forcing their attention on the seventeenth century natural philosopher. A new approach was needed: and this was supplied by a new kind of theory of matter, at once non-atomic and anti-Aristotelian, which offered immense possibilities for scientific explanation and investigation. It derives from ancient atomism in a very limited sense only, for the actual concept *atom*, is irrelevant to its development. Yet ancient atomism had some influence; inadequate though it was to deal with seventeenth century science, it appeared to be closer to the truth than the Aristotelian way. Ancient atomists had "explained" the observed properties of matter by attributing appropriate characteristics to individual atoms, which was very much simpler than assuming that properties arose from extraneous "forms". Its disadvantage was that it merely pushed the explanation back a stage, from gross matter to its component atoms. (And indeed the ancient atomists had never gone so far as to consider general properties like heat, dryness or color). The atomic theories of antiquity suggested to seventeenth century thinkers that matter might have certain simple and fundamental characteristics which would account for a large number of observed phenomena. That is, every macroscopic property might not require an individual microscopic cause; but variations in some state or configura-

---

[4] This was particularly stressed by Hero, in the preface to his *Pneumatica*.

tion of the small parts of matter might produce different effects in gross matter.[5] More specifically, the new theories were to suggest that not only were the size and shape of the component units of matter relevant, but their *motion* might play an important—even a critical—role. It should be noted that in this approach motion was no longer related to form: velocity, impetus, acceleration, momentum, inertia were all totally divorced from the concepts of fourteenth century mathematical physics and were regarded as states subject to mathematical and quantitative treatment and requiring no analysis of their nature.

§3 *Matter and Motion*

This typically seventeenth century attention to dynamics appears almost simultaneously about 1620 in the work of three very different men: an English lawyer, an Italian scientist and a Dutch schoolmaster, Bacon, Galileo and Isaac Beeckmann. Beeckmann's theory, developed mainly between 1616 and 1620, comes closest to ancient theories, for he believed in real atoms. In fact he asserted the existence of four kinds or shapes of atoms, one corresponding to each of the four elements. The essences or properties of substances derived, he held, directly from the atoms. But motion, as well as shape and size of the atoms determined the properties of the component body. Motion, shape and size were to him equally important and all must be considered for a satisfactory explanation. For example, fire particles, small, subtle, pervasive and most apt for motion, caused bodies to become hot by setting the component atoms in motion; and cold was mere absence of heat.[6] Though Beeckmann's theory is now known only through his diary, his influence upon Descartes is obvious, and well known.

In 1620 appeared Bacon's *Novum Organum*, a work which has often baffled philosophers by the conflict between its expressed aim and its achievement. Bacon's persistent attempt to illustrate his inductive method by its application to what he called "the discovery of forms" has aroused much criticism, not least from his nineteenth century editors. Seventeenth century English scientists found Bacon's discussion both plain and suggestive, because they found it easy to divest it of its incrustation of logic and consider it only in relation to theory of matter. Unlike Beeckmann, Bacon

---

[5] This suggests a certain indefiniteness in explanation which was, indeed, characteristic of seventeenth century mechanical philosophies. It was an inevitable result of the method of explanation employed, but one worth risking for the sake of manifold advantages.

[6] *Journal*, ed. Cornelis de Waard, 3 vols., La Haye, 1939–45, *1*, 25, 152–53, 216; *2*, 96, 198; *3*, 138 *et passim*.

was not an atomist; on the contrary, he thought men could waste as much time mentally analyzing matter into atoms as they could in spinning webs of metaphysics.[7] Yet the atomic point of view was, he thought, far superior to the Aristotelian doctrine of forms because it was more useful.[8] It fell short to chiefly not repudiating the notion that matter was inert; for motion, so he believed, was the clue to the understanding of forms. It may be worth repeating here as a reminder Bacon's quasi-legal definition:

> For though in nature nothing really exists besides individual bodies, performing pure individual acts according to a fixed law, yet in philosophy this very law, and the investigation, discovery, and explanation of it, is the foundation as well of knowledge as of operation. And it is this law, with its clauses, that I mean when I speak of *Forms*.[9]

Surely Bacon was trying, clumsily, to express the need for general principles to explain the properties of bodies; and indeed he managed to be at once more general and simpler than Beeckmann. Bacon's theory needed no atoms or special kinds of matter; only particles—literally small bits of matter—and motion. Bacon stressed motion even more than did Beeckmann, insisting that it was the real key to the understanding of the properties of matter. His definition of heat, almost too well known to quote, amply illustrates this: "Heat is a motion, expansive, restrained, and acting in its strife upon the smaller particles of bodies."[10] Less familiar is his prediction that many other properties, including specifically color, whiteness and chemical action, would also prove to be the result of the motion of "the smaller particles of bodies", a guess that was to prove influential later.

It is surprising to find Bacon so deeply influenced by contemporary mechanical thought; he is indeed the only early protagonist of the mechanical philosophy who had not worked on dynamical problems. It is, on the other hand, only to be expected that Galileo should have considered the role of motion in the small parts of matter, as well as in gross matter. More especially since he was well read in the classics of ancient atomism and seems to have adopted the theory espoused by Hero of Alexandria as a basis. (As, for example, in his discussion of cohesion in the First Day of *The Two New Sciences,* and its application to the problem of the strange limitation on the ability of a suction pump to raise water). Galileo's most complete and important discussion—on heat—arose from the exigencies of polemic in *The*

---

[7] *Novum Organum*, Book I, Aph. lxvi; cf. Book II, aph. viii.

[8] Cf. *Novum Organum*, Book I, aph. lxiii; also *Cogitationes de natura rerum*, and the Fable of Cupid.

[9] *Novum Organum*, Book II, aph. ii.

[10] *Ibid,* aph. xx.

Assayer (Il Saggiatore).[11] He wished to give a philosophic basis to his contention that comets (even if they had been solid bodies, which he thought they were not) could no more grow hot as a result of rapid motion through the atmosphere than an egg could be cooked by anyone (except an ancient Babylonian) by whirling it on a sling. Digressing briefly to consider the nature of heat, Galileo placed heat in the same category as taste, odor, color and other "qualities" which only became manifest through the action of the senses. These he described as "mere names . . . residing only in the consciousness". Yet this was not the case with all properties; as he put it:

> Now I say that whenever I conceive any material or corporeal substance, I immediately feel the need to think of it as bounded, and as having this or that shape; as being large or small in relation to other things, and in some specific place at any given time; as being in motion or at rest; as touching or not touching some other body; and as being one in number, or few, or many. From these conditions I cannot separate such a substance by any stretch of my imagination.

Heat was emphatically not to be classed with these fundamental properties, but rather with those which required the action of the senses to acquire full reality: it was the result of "nothing . . . except shapes, numbers, and slow or rapid movements" (of the small parts of matter). So odor arises when small particles impinge upon our noses, taste when small particles strike our tongues. In each case three things are requisite (for obviously not all bodies can produce each of these sensations): particles of a certain kind (fire, in the case of heat), motion of these particles, and an organ of sensation.

§4 *Descartes*

Galileo, so much at home in macroscopic dynamics, never tried to apply the same methods to microscopic dynamics, no doubt realizing the magnitude of the task. Gravity thus remained a property whose action he could describe, but for which he never tried to find an explanation. It was thus that he laid himself open to Descartes's rebuke:

> All that he says of the celerity of bodies falling in a vacuum &c is without foundation; for he ought to have determined beforehand what weight is; and

---

[11] For the passages cited see *Discoveries and Opinions of Galileo*, tr. Stillman Drake (New York, 1957), pp. 272–78, or *The Controversy on the Comets of 1618* (Philadelphia, 1960), tr. Drake and C. D. O'Malley, pp. 300–314. Attention was first drawn to these in a classic discussion by E. A. Burtt, *The Metaphysical Foundations of Modern Physical Science*, chapter III, sec. C (pp. 73–80 of the revised edition, London, 1949).

if he had truly understood its nature, he would have known that there is none in a vacuum.[12]

Descartes's rebuke was perfectly fair: for he himself did not dream of ignoring the necessity of explaining such a fundamental property of matter. Where previous discussions of the mechanical philosophy had dealt with description and possibilities, Descartes made his version of it an integral part of his philosophy, and labored to render it perfectly general. He showed none of the vagueness of the first progenitors of the mechanical philosophy, but was complete and precise in every detail of his theory of matter, which he discussed in connection with every branch of science.

The general outlines of his theory are too well known for detailed exposition here. That matter and extension are one, so that there is no empty space; that motion has divided matter into particles, mathematically though not physically divisible to an indefinite extent; that these particles are of three kinds, distinct yet mutually transmutable; that motion (necessarily by impact) is imparted to terrestrial matter by the "subtle matter" or "aether" —to say this is to outline his theory without explaining either its purpose or its importance. For what was important about Descartes's theory is less its details than the conviction that this theory was adequate to explain the whole physical universe, since from matter so conceived and from motion one could mentally construct the whole universe. And the universe so conceived would at least approximate the world around us, which demonstrated the correctness of the approach. As he wrote at the end of the *Principles of Philosophy*:

> Being certain that every body which we perceive is composed of other bodies so small that we cannot perceive them: I think no one who uses his reason can deny that it is better philosophy to judge what happens among these little bodies (which only their minuteness prevents us from perceiving) in the light of what we see happen among those bodies which we do perceive, and to account by these means for everything in Nature—as I have tried to do in this treatise—than to explain the same things by inventing I don't know what others which bear no relation to what we perceive—first matter, substantial forms, and all that grand apparatus of qualities which many are in the habit of imagining, each one of which may be more difficult to know, than the things which are to be explained by them.[13]

[12] Letter 146 to Mersenne, 11 October 1638 (*Oeuvres*, Adam-Tannery edition, II, 385).

[13] *Principia Philosophiae*, Book IV, art. 101. I have taken this and subsequent quotations from the French translation, using the edition of 1659. The Latin version, from which many English translations are derived, is less explicit, but as Descartes saw and approved the French text, it seems reasonable to assume that this represents his meaning accurately.

An important characteristic of Descartes's theory was that relatively few properties of gross matter were dependent on the nature of the particles themselves; what mattered was rather motion. The size, shape, and so on of particles determined the nature of the substance of which they were parts; the properties exhibited by this substance resulted from variations in the motion of the particles caused by the action of the subtle matter or aether. Thus, it was the characteristics of the particles of water which determined the fact that the substance they composed was water, rather than some other fluid; but its fluidity was caused by the fact that the particles were perpetually moving among themselves; if their relative motion stopped, the substance of which they were parts ceased to be a fluid, and became a solid; which is what happened when water solidified to ice. This was a great advance, because it reduced the number of causes required for known properties, and at the same time simplified them. Not that Descartes entirely escaped the excessive elaboration of detail characteristic of ancient atomism; for example, he wrote: "I suppose that the little particles of which water is composed are long, smooth and slippery, like little needles."[14] It was true that to him fluidity resulted from motion; but he still felt it essential to explain why the particles of water could move so easily under the action of the aether. The idea of considering the relative rest or motion of particles was of great generalizing value, for it related the various states of matter in such a way as to explain how it was possible for solids and liquids to be converted one into another; what the peculiar fluidity was which characterized both air and fire; how rarefaction and condensation were possible. Further, the action of the aether in producing motion of the particles caused the body to grow hot; light was the result of nothing but motion in the aether; gravity arose from the peculiar motion characteristic of aether. And from the nature of light Descartes was able to explain such phenomena as the tails of comets.[15] Descartes even tried—at length, but not very clearly—to explain such mysterious and occult problems as the nature of certain chemicals and the cause of magnetism (which he found to consist of the action of the aether on specially shaped particles).

As is so often true of Descartes, the scientific details fall far short of the philosophic concept. The notion of the subtle matter as responsible for all motion, and of motion in turn as responsible for very many of the secondary qualities of matter, was well conceived. It offered a simple and satisfactory explanation for many diverse phenomena, and effected enormous simplification of detail. For the sake of this advantage, many Cartesians were prepared to overlook or minimize such naive and contradictory details as the

[14] "Meteores" in *Oeuvres*, Adam-Tannery ed., *6*, 233.
[15] *Principia Philosophiae*, Book III, arts. 133, 135.

"screwed" magnetic particles, the transmutation of the elements (now beginning to be regarded as an "occult" concept), and the strange small, flexible, shapeless particles which existed to fill up the interstices between other particles and thereby prevent the otherwise inevitable yet impossible vacuum. The enormous logic of the Cartesian system overbore such relatively minor considerations (as they were felt to be), more especially since the system was so conceived that it could be called "mathematical" in an age when that was the pinnacle of rationalist praise—though one did not need to understand geometry in order to read Descartes's *Principles of Philosophy*.

§5 *Cartesianism*

Even for experimental scientists the Cartesian system was useful and acceptable, for it had sufficient flexibility to permit the inclusion of facts unknown to its inventor. New discoveries added to its strength, when it appeared that Descartes had left principles whereby the new discoveries could be explained. The puzzling "vacuum" in the Torricellian tube or the receiver of Boyle's air pump was difficult for true atomists to explain, for it was not a real vacuum; at least, one could hardly call it "empty space" when it admitted light, magnetism and perhaps fire. The Cartesian had no such difficulty: it was empty only of air, and still filled with the aether which naturally transmitted the observed light, magnetism and so on, quite unaffected by the presence or absence of air. New discoveries in optics—diffraction, the double refraction of Iceland spar, the color of thin films—called forth new theories on the nature of light by, for example, such scientists as Hooke and Huygens. Both were Cartesians in that they accepted the general premises of Descartes's theory of matter; both evolved their own theories of light, different from that of Descartes but conceived within the framework of the Cartesian system. Hooke's theory of pulsed vibrations was intended to explain colors—which it did, though not in such a way as to withstand the assault of Newton's experimental evidence and alternative, non-Cartesian theory. Huygen's theory—precise, detailed and truly mathematical—had more stamina. Light, he held, certainly "consists in the motion of some sort of matter" since it is produced by fire which has the property of disuniting the particles of bodies, which "is assuredly the mark of motion, at least in the true Philosophy, in which one conceives the causes of all natural effects in terms of mechanical motions".[16] In fact, Huygens maintained, light consists in the interaction between particles of luminous bodies and the aether (supposedly an elastic fluid) which in turn sets up wave fronts similar to those of sound in air. A whole series of wave fronts is generated,

---

[16] *Treatise on Light*, tr. Sylvanus P. Thompson, Chicago, 1945, Chapter I.

whose generation and propagation are susceptible of mathematical treatment. By this concept Huygens was able to explain reflection, refraction, diffraction and (in part) the double refraction of Iceland spar. There was indeed only one drawback to his theory: he could not explain the production of colors; but he thought himself excused because that was a difficult subject "in which no one until now can boast of having succeeded".[17]

§6 *Experimental Corpuscularianism*

Huygens's work showed once again how far one could proceed in explaining the properties of bodies on purely rational grounds. This indeed seemed to Cartesians the only reasonable way, especially when dealing with invisible particles; to such thinkers it seemed absurd to try to "prove" details of structure by means of experiment. Experiment might find out new phenomena to explain, but it could never demonstrate anything, nor was it really necessary to confirm obvious (that is, ratiocinative) truths. Hence the ambiguous attitude displayed by many Cartesians towards the work of Robert Boyle. They rightly took him to be the exemplar of the ideals of the Royal Society; yet while valuing highly his pneumatic discoveries—which none could forestall, though many could enjoy repeating—most Cartesians thought the very notion of an experimentally based corpuscular philosophy childishly and unnecessarily empirical. For what, they argued, could Boyle hope to achieve, except to demonstrate with immense labor what they knew to be true already by the surer and swifter method of reason? And in addition there was Boyle's strange addiction to chemistry, a science most physicists, especially on the Continent, neither understood nor wished to understand.

In actual fact, Boyle's "corpuscular philosophy" (as he preferred to call it) was original in conception and in the method he chose for its demonstration. In spite of an informal style and a pretense of eclecticism, Boyle had developed a carefully thought out and well constructed theory of matter. He was not an atomist, recognizing with the best scientists of his time that any particle was, as he put it, "mentally, and by divine Omnipotence divisible"; but he believed that the ultimate or least particles were sufficiently small and solid so that "nature doth scarce ever actually divide (them) . . . and these may in this sense be called *minima or prima naturalia*". These least particles in turn combined into "primitive concretions or clusters" which "though not absolutely indivisible by nature into the *prima naturalia* . . . yet . . . they very rarely happen to be actually dissolved or broken, but remain entire in great variety of sensible bodies, and under various

---

[17] *Ibid.*, Preface.

forms or disguises".[18] These were the smallest particles detectable, the corpuscles directly responsible for stimulating the senses. The size and shape of both *prima naturalia* and the corpuscles formed by their association affected the nature and properties of the matter they composed. Even more important, however, was the motion of these two kinds of corpuscles, for motion alone was responsible for the innumerable changes in properties which every theory of matter had to explain. Motion "altered the texture" as Boyle said, and thereby altered the properties. The source of the motion did not make any difference; its existence was enough. So Boyle instanced the change from water to ice as an example of loss of motion; the rubbing of two sticks of wood together to produce, successively, heat, flame and charcoal, as an example of gain in motion; and the turning of milk into butter and whey, the fermentation of apples after bruising and similar domestic mechanical actions, as examples of what should be explored scientifically and carefully.

Granted that God had made the universe out of what Boyle called "those two grand and most Catholic principles, matter and motion", how was one to discover the relations between the structure of matter, its changes of motion and the properties which were the result of this structure and motion? Boyle was no Cartesian, to frame what he regarded as *a priori* hypotheses; at least he would frame no more than need be. He took his inspiration direct from Bacon, and insisted that the key to an understanding of nature must be experiment. And a more profound innovation was his belief that for the "discovery of forms" no kind of experiment was better than chemical experiment. For it was, Boyle thought, through chemistry that the corpuscles composed of *prima naturalia* were revealed as having independent and permanent existence. Thus he instanced the fact that liquid mercury

> may be turned into a red powder (mercuric oxide) or a fusible and malleable body (a metallic alloy) or a fugitive smoke (the vapor), and disguised I know not how many other ways, and yet remain true and recoverable mercury.[19]

One of his most famous early experiments to demonstrate that changes of properties need not mean the loss of existence for a well-defined corpuscle was that on the "redintegration of nitre" (saltpeter).[20] He decomposed

---

[18] This view of the structure of matter is most clearly expressed in *The Origin of Forms and Qualities* (*Works*, ed. T. Birch, 6 vols., London, 1772, *3*, 29–31). There is a very similar discussion in the "Propositions" of the *Sceptical Chymist* (*ibid.*, *1*, 474–75).

[19] *Origin of Forms and Qualities, loc. cit.*, p. 29.

[20] "A Physico-Chymical Essay, containing an Experiment with some Considerations touching the differing Parts and Redintegration of Salt-Petre", in *Certain Physiological Essays.*

saltpeter (potassium nitrate) with a glowing piece of charcoal (which he thought to be pure fire) and found he had volatile niter, which could be dissolved in water to give spirit of niter (nitric acid) and fixed niter (actually potassium carbonate because the potassium combined with the carbon of the coal and oxygen from the air); since these could be recombined to form saltpeter again, Boyle argued that he had shown that this familiar salt was composed of two permanent corpuscles, temporarily joined. This was to have applications in chemistry; his primary purpose here was to further the corpuscular philosophy. In the preface he declared that his purpose was in large part "to beget a good understanding betwixt the chemists and the corpuscular philosophers"[21] both by showing chemists that natural philosophy could teach them to understand the processes which they undertook in the laboratory and by showing the natural philosophers that chemistry, which dealt with finely divided matter and its properties, could be of assistance in demonstrating their theories of the structure of matter. But he also intended, as he told Spinoza,

> to explain how the common doctrine of substantial forms and qualities, accepted in the schools, rests on a weak foundation, and that what they call the specific differences of things can be reduced to magnitude, motion, rest and position of the particles.[22]

If he could successfully demonstrate this, he thought he could convince men that the explanation by means of forms was sterile, and should be replaced by an explanation in terms of matter and motion.

This, in fact, was what he set himself to, do; and there poured from the press a long series of works dealing with various physical and chemical properties and their mechanical explanation. The elasticity of air, the nature of fluidity and firmness, the origin of colors, the nature of cold, the mechanical origin of heat, taste, odor, volatility, fixedness, corrosiveness, magnetism, acidity were nearly all explored in individual essays or treatises, along with others. The list is almost oppressively long, especially since it was interspersed with general treatises on the corpuscular philosophy.

To understand the use Boyle made of his theory of matter it is necessary to consider some specific examples of his method and success. One of his

---

[21] "Some Specimens of an Attempt to make Chymical Experiments Usefull to Illustrate the Notions of the Corpuscular Philosophy".

[22] Oldenburg to Spinoza, 3 April 1663, printed in A. Wolf, *The Correspondence of Spinoza*, (New York, n.d.), pp. 110–115. This is a reply to a very long letter of criticism which Spinoza wrote in the spring of 1662, after reading the Latin edition of *Certain Physiological Essays*, sent by Oldenburg. Spinoza certainly misunderstood both Boyle's purpose and his argument; in particular he understood nothing of chemistry, insisting that niter and spirit of niter differed only as ice and water.

most interesting works is *The Experimental History of Colour* (1664) which is crammed with novel and fascinating experiments, and in which he tried, for the first time, to explain color mechanically. He was convinced that color was a secondary quality and therefore amenable to explanation in terms of matter and motion. That it *was* a secondary quality he argued from the fact that one can see color without light (just as one can feel heat without fire): that is, if the organ of sight is stimulated either by a blow, or by the imagination (as in dreams) one believes that one sees color. *The Experimental History of Colour* begins with a brilliant investigation of whiteness and blackness. Boyle concluded that whiteness and blackness were the result of the arrangement of the particles on the surface of the body: a white body's particles were so arranged as to act almost like a mirror to reflect a very high proportion of the incident light; in a black body, on the other hand, the particles were so arranged as to absorb almost all the incident light, reflecting very little. To demonstrate this he pointed out how it is easy to set black paper alight with a burning glass, difficult to set white paper alight in this way; that if a tile painted half white and half black were exposed to the sun, the black half became very hot while the white was still cool; that a room hung with black hangings was darker than one hung with white hangings and so on.[23] A century later Benjamin Franklin could do no more.[24] Armed with these successful and accurate conclusions, Boyle naturally proceeded to investigate color along the same lines; in this (more difficult) case with mixed success. He made some interesting discoveries: he noted the colors of soap bubbles (Newton's rings); he explored the changing colors of a solution of *lignum nephriticum,* a yellow solution with a blue opalescence which it loses, as Boyle found, upon the addition of acid—the first detailed discussion of its optical properties; he investigated the manner in which blue vegetable solutions were turned red by acids, green by alkalies, and showed that this was a reliable test for acidity and alkalinity (which therefore were the result of the texture and motion of the particles); he tried endless combinations of chemical solutions to produce an enormous variety of color changes. All this was intended to demonstrate that the "forms" of colors were the result of nothing but the action of matter and motion. Aside from his own success, Boyle by his work provided inspiration for the investigations of Hooke (trained in Boyle's own laboratory) and Newton (an indefatigable student of Boyle's work); both approached the problem of color in quite a different way from Boyle, considering changes in color as a result of

---

[23] *Works*, I, 721–22.
[24] I. Bernard Cohen, "Franklin, Boerhaave, Newton, Boyle & the Absorption of Heat in Relation to Color", *Isis, 46*, 1955, 99–104.

changes in light itself, rather than in the structure of the colored body. Yet without Boyle's work, neither might have been familiar with the facts of color which their theories had to explain.

To us it seems only natural to consider "light and colors" together, as Newton was to do ten years after the publication of Boyle's work. To Boyle it was more reasonable to consider light in connection with fire, and hence with heat. Like all mechanical philosophers, he took heat to be the effect of the agitation of the particles; he pointed out many times that it could be produced by mechanical action (like hammering a piece of metal) as well as by chemical activity and, of course, by fire.[25] Indeed, if a hammer struck a nail on the head, the resultant blow could produce *either* motion of the whole nail (into a block of wood) *or*, if this were impossible, motion of the particles of the nailhead, which would then grow hot. Even *in vacuo* friction alone would produce heat, though not flame.[26] Yet flame was closely related to heat; Boyle at first wondered whether it might not be merely a state of matter, that is, matter in a special kind of motion; he finally concluded:

> flame is little or nothing else than an aggregate of those corpuscles, which before lay upon the upper superficies of the candle, and by the violent heat were divided into minute particles, vehemently agitated and brought from lying as it were upon a flat, to beat off one another.[27]

Flame (and fire) then consisted of bodies heated hot enough to shine. Hence fire was certainly material, a conclusion with two important consequences: first, that no occult forms were required to explain either its existence or its action on other bodies (both the result of vehement agitation of the particles); and second, that it ought to be possible to demonstrate this by experiment. Hence Boyle's *New Experiments to Make Fire and Flame Stable and Ponderable,* in which he described the elaborate and quantitative series of calcination experiments on metals and various "minerals" like sulphur, whose invariable gain in weight he attributed to the addition of fire particles: hardly a surprising conclusion in view of the state of knowledge about the chemical structure of air. Boyle's experiments appeared to prove his point amply: fire was manifestly a mechanical agent, not an occult force. Light appeared to Boyle closely related to fire; he planned a series of experiments on calcination by means of a burning glass, but was defeated by

---

[25] Cf. "A Discourse about the Absolute Rest in Bodies" (*Works, 1,* 446), and "The Mechanical Origin and Production of Heat" (*Works, 4,* 223, 249–50).

[26] *A Continuation of New Experiments Physico-Mechanical* (1669), *Works, 3,* 265–66.

[27] *A Defense against Hobbes and Linus* (part II, ch. 2), *Works, 1,* 142.

the English weather. But he had once more opened up a new area of scientific investigation; Hooke, for one, pursued it by examining under a microscope the sparks struck off flint and steel, and showing them to be glowing bits of metal.[28]

Boyle's boldest attempt at a mechanical explanation of occult properties arose from his investigations into the causes of magnetism and electricity. Seizing on Gilbert's observation that bars of iron left standing upright over a period of time became magnetized, and that a bar of iron laid north and south on an anvil could be magnetized by hammering, Boyle concluded that magnetism must result merely from a peculiar arrangement of the iron corpuscles. As he put it:

> if there be introduced a fit disposition into the internal parts of the metal by the action of the loadstone, the metal, continuing of the same species it was before, will need nothing, save the continuance of that acquired disposition, to be capable of performing magnetical operations.[29]

That it *was* merely a rearrangement of the corpuscles which caused the change from non-magnetic to magnetic iron was further demonstrated by the fact that if a bar of iron were heated before standing it upright, or hammering it, the resultant motion of the particles made it receive "the magnetic disposition" more quickly. This was a truly mechanical explanation; unfortunately, it failed in this case to stimulate further investigation. About electricity Boyle was less clear, though he hazarded a guess that it too had a mechanical origin, arising from "electric effluvia": he thought that the friction necessary to render an electrical body attracting rubbed off material, non-aetherial particles. Not enough work had yet done on electricity to provide him with experiments to suggest other sorts of mechanism; he intended to investigate the matter himself, as a brief paper entitled "Enquiry and Experiments about Electricall Bodys" shows, but never did so.

From the examples above it hould be clear that Boyle found no physical property too complex for experimental investigation and mechanical explanation. The most important aspect of his explanation was that it not merely supplanted prevailing explanations which relied on forms and occult forces, but proved beneficial to the advance of science by suggesting new fields in need of experimental exploration and mechanical interpretation. This stimulus was equally active in his use of the corpuscular philosophy in chemistry, though there the problem was far more complex, since, before Boyle, few physicists or chemists thought of chemistry as a physical sci-

---

[28] *Micrographia*, observation VIII; facsimile in R. T. Gunther, *Early Science in Oxford, 13*.

[29] "Mechanical Origin and Production of Magnetism", *Works, 4*, 340–45.

ence.[30] Boyle, having made original contributions to natural philosophy, could afford to dabble in the quasi-esoteric science of chemistry; at the same time interest in chemical experiment never led him to abandon physical, mechanical reasoning. He believed, as indicated above, that complex corpuscles were the units of chemical reaction, since they, and they alone, could survive unchanged through a long series of reactions, to reappear unchanged at the end of the process. Only these corpuscles, and the more complex substances made by joining corpuscles together, appeared to Boyle to have chemical validity. As a consequence he utterly rejected the doctrine of elements or chemical principles, denying the existence of any set of substances out of which all other substances were made and into which all other substances could be decomposed or analyzed. For both logically and experimentally, he insisted, corpuscles and *prima naturalia,* and they alone, were the true elements.[31]

Having rejected the concept of elements and principles—of earth, air, fire and water, or salt, sulphur and mercury, or oil, phlegm, spirit, &c.—as the chemical basis of matter, Boyle was free to treat all chemistry from a corpuscularian point of view. This was important less for itself—it is not certain that chemistry always benefits from being treated like physics— than because it led Boyle to useful conclusions. He concentrated on what he believed to be permanent corpuscles, that is to say, on those which could undergo transformation in the course of a chemical reaction and yet, after further reaction, be recovered again unchanged. As a result he built up a large group of simple chemical substances whose properties he studied carefully and whose identities he was sure of. He was the first to devise detailed identification tests for individual substances: indicator tests for acids and alkalies; crystal shape for salts; flame tests for copper; characteristic reactions for various substances. Thereby he simplified the chemical picture,

---

[30] Thus Fontenelle, comparing Boyle (after his death) with the now rightly forgotten chemist Samuel Du Clos, who spent all his time as a member of the *Académie royale des Sciences* analyzing plants into salts, spirits, phlegms and oils, found Boyle's attempt to apply the corpuscular philosophy to chemistry too simple and clear to be true chemistry. (Section for *Chymi,* 1669, in *Histoire de l'Académie Royale des Sciences,* 1666–1698).

[31] This is the conclusion of the *Sceptical Chymist.* Misled by a partial and hasty reading of Boyle's definition of an element (and ignoring the fact that he said he was trying to give a definition acceptable to all contemporary chemists), modern historians have blamed Boyle for being too much of a physicist and for neglecting the now-useful concept of an element. But the "element" of the 17th century was not just a substance impossible to analyze further; it was a substance universally present in all bodies and hence *always* a product of analysis. This misinterpretation is a conspicuous defect in the otherwise admirable paper by Thomas S. Kuhn, "Robert Boyle and Structural Chemistry in the Seventeenth Century", *Isis, 43,* 1952, 12–36.

showing the identity of many common substances known under a wide assortment of names, and gaining at least partial knowledge of the composition of many more substances. This showed chemists a new side to their subject, and directed their major activities away from the futile and repetitious analysis of organic materials (which obligingly yielded the supposed elements of each chemist) into more fruitful lines towards the understanding of the nature, composition and preparation of inorganic substances.[32] It is possible to imagine that Boyle's corpuscular emphasis was not necessary for this kind of chemical thinking; it is however a fact that Boyle, who always kept the corpuscularian philosophy in mind and applied it to every chemical operation, was the only chemist to achieve this changed point of view. The success of his approach is witnessed by the usefulness of the chemical experiments he described in stimulating the work of other chemists, and the fact that particles remained a part of chemical explanation, though not so obtrusively as with Boyle.

§7 *Newton*

Boyle showed that matter and motion alone could explain a vast number of chemical and physical properties, when such an explanation was combined with experimental investigation and confirmation. Newton, influenced strongly by Boyle, showed that an experimentally based theory of matter could explain the world, and thereby outdid Descartes. Newton was stirred to emulate Descartes precisely because he found Descartes's theory of matter totally unpalatable, both in principle and detail. To Newton, Descartes's famous first assumption about matter, that it was identical with extension, was unacceptable, so that he could never be a Cartesian. To equate matter with extension was philosophical nonsense as far as Newton was concerned, since he had no difficulty in postulating a vacuum; worse, it was theologically unsound, since it placed an unwarranted limitation upon God's omnipotence and was nearly atheistic.

> If we say with Descartes that extension is body, do we not offer a path to Atheism, both because extension is not created but has existed eternally, and because we have an absolute idea of it without any relationship to God?[33]

Matter differed from extension precisely as it had attributes impressed upon it by God. (Newton's theory of matter ineluctably led him to a discussion of

---

[32] For a fuller development of these points, see Marie Boas, *Robert Boyle and Seventeenth Century Chemistry*, Cambridge, 1958.

[33] *De Gravitatione et aequipondio fluidorum*, Cambridge University Library Ms. Add. 4003.

the relation of God to His universe, because "the main business of natural Philosophy is to . . . deduce Causes from Effects, till we come to the very first cause, which is certainly not mechanical".[34]) Boyle's corpuscular theory was, basically, more acceptable to Newton than Descartes's theory of matter; but it failed in not being mathematical. Boyle could explain changes in properties as being the result of changes in motion, but he could not characterize the changes in motion in any rigorous way. No one as yet had devised a dynamics of particles comparable to that developed for the macroscopic world. Only Newton seriously attempted it.[35]

A clear understanding of what Newton really thought about the nature of matter and the proper explanation of its properties has always been (in his own phrase) "pressed with difficulties." Is one to accept the apparent mathematical austerity of the *Principia* with its refusal to say what the cause of gravity might be (though there was more to Newton's theory of matter than an explanation of gravity) and its insistence on *"hypotheses non fingo"* (though, as Professor Koyré has shown, Newton made use of hypotheses here as well as elsewhere)?[36] Or should one lay more stress on the speculative, experimental attitude manifested in the Quaeries to *Opticks?* What should one make of the aetherial hypotheses discussed in Newton's early papers and letters, like those on light and colors, and the famous letter to Boyle?[37] Did Newton, as he hinted, really frame these hypotheses only to please his correspondents? Did he, indeed, care at all about a mechanical philosophy? If he did (and in fact there is abundant evidence that he did) was he a firm proponent of an aetherial theory or not? Fortunately, Newton's unpublished manuscripts, of which he was a zealous hoarder, provide a clearer picture, and show that the connection which one might suppose to exist between the discussions of matter scattered through the *Principia* and the more speculative discussions in *Opticks* is a real connection. The manuscripts reveal as well both why Newton devoted so much time to aetherial speculations and why in the end he remained too unsatisfied to proclaim them as doctrine.[38]

To understand thoroughly the nature of matter and to derive from

---

[34] *Opticks*, Quaery 28.

[35] For a fuller discussion of this point, see Marie Boas and Rupert Hall, "Newton's Mechanical Principles", *Journal of the History of Ideas*, 20, 1959, 167–78, and A. Rupert Hall and Marie Hall, "Newton's Theory of Matter", *Isis, 51,* 1960, 131–44.

[36] A Koyré in *Revue d'Histoire des Sciences*, 8, 1955, 19–37, and in *Bulletin de la Société Francaise de Philosophie*, Avril-Juin 1956, 59–79.

[37] These are all conveniently available in *Isaac Newton's Papers & Letters on Natural Philosophy*, ed. I. B. Cohen, Cambridge, Mass., 1958.

[38] The relevant documents are to be published in A.R. & M.B. Hall, *Unpublished Scientific Papers of Sir Isaac Newton*, Cambridge, 1962.

thence the properties of bodies was an early ambition of Newton's. Steeped as he was in the "new philosophy" of the 1660's, he could hardly fail to be aware of the importance of the mechanical philosophy. And he quickly found such contemporary accounts as those of Descartes, Hooke and Boyle deficient in the extent of their explanation. They could and did explain much; but not all that Newton thought could and should be explained. And, unlike his predecessors, he sought for explanation which should belong to mathematical as well as to experimental physics. Very early in his work he began to grapple with attraction and repulsion which he recognized as omnipresent forces, tiresomely occult, yet at the same time susceptible of mathematical expression. Descartes had explained apparent cases of attraction as the effect of impulse of the aether; Boyle, without an aether, had to assume that only the fortuitous concourse of corpuscles was involved, as when he defined hygroscopic salts as those which "happened" to have pores the right size and shape to admit particles of water casually brought into contact with the salt particles by the ordinary motion of the atmosphere in which the water particles were dissolved. Newton found this cumbersome, and too remote from the world of mathematical law. After his early investigations of gravity he seems to have become convinced that attraction and repulsion were such common forces in nature that it was impossible to ignore them; it was imperative to try to fit them into mathematical physics. Newton's discussions of his theory of matter, therefore, nearly all are extensively concerned with the problem of how these forces, once their universal existence has been demonstrated, may be characterized and explained.

Underlying all Newton's writing on science is a profound belief in the particulate structure of matter: it is embedded in the structure of the *Principia* no less than that of his writings on optics. As he wrote in the Preface to the first edition of the *Principia:* "the whole burden of philosophy seems to consist in this—from the phenomena of motions to investigate the forces of nature, and then from these forces to demonstrate the other phenomena." Further, the phenomena of motions should be universally applicable; it was obviously applicable to larger bodies, but it equally certainly was applicable as well to the lesser particles of which bodies were composed. It is indeed the purpose of the third of the "Rules of Reasoning in Philosophy" with which Book III opens to relate the behavior and motion of particles to those of large bodies.[39] So

---

[39] "The Qualities of bodies, which admit neither intensification nor remission of degrees, and which are found to belong to all bodies within the reach of our experiments, are to be esteemed the universal qualities of all bodies whatsoever."

the extension, hardness, impenetrability, mobility, and inertia of the whole, result from the extension, hardness, impenetrability, mobility, and inertia of the parts; and hence we conclude the least particles of all bodies to be also extended, and hard and impenetrable, and movable, and endowed with their proper inertia. And this is the foundation of all philosophy.

As for the parts themselves, Newton was very nearly an atomist—more so certainly than was Descartes. He readily admitted that the least parts could be divided mathematically and imaginatively; whether they could be divided "by the powers of Nature" was a more difficult question. On the whole he thought not; in *Opticks* he wrote,

> All these things being consider'd, it seems probable to me, that God in the Beginning form'd Matter in solid, massy, hard, impenetrable, moveable Particles, of such Sizes and Figures, and with such other Properties, and in such Proportion to Space, as most conduced to the End for which he form'd them; and that these primitive Particles being Solids, are incomparably harder than any porous Bodies compounded of them; even so very hard, as never to wear or break in pieces; no ordinary Power being able to divide what God himself made one in the first Creation.[40]

With all mechanical philosophers, Newton assumed that the properties of matter—heat, magnetism, color, gravity—resulted from the motion of the least particles. The peculiarity of the Newtonian explanation lies in the fact that he so often explained the motion as caused by forces of attraction or repulsion. All mechanical explanations involve, ultimately, an arbitrary limit to causative argument; at some point the mechanical philosopher must stop, and assume that he has explained far enough. So Descartes found that the motion of ordinary particles needed explanation, but not the motion of the aetherial particles. Boyle, seeing that this was no great advantage, inquired no further than the changes in motion of the particles themselves; this eliminated the suppositious aether, but left many forces (including those of chemical action) unexplained except in terms of chance. Newton was obsessed with the need to find out the laws governing the universe, which he felt must exist even in the regulation of the properties of matter. He was able to treat gravity mathematically, by assuming a force of attraction; no wonder he extended the concept of a force of attraction (with its converse, repulsion) to other properties. So he argued that attraction and repulsion operated on light to produce reflection, refraction and diffraction; on metals, acids and other chemicals to produce observed chemical reaction; on rubbed bodies to produce electricity. It was an enormous economy to be able to interpret so many properties of bodies as being the result of a single force (for repulsion was only negative attraction); and it eliminated

---

[40] Quaery 31.

the loose action of chance necessitated by Boyle's explanations. Further, it was potentially subject to treatment in mathematical terms.[41]

But Newton was too much a product of his age not to wonder whether forces of attraction and repulsion were suitable ingredients of a mechanical philosophy. They sounded suspiciously occult. Sometimes, however, Newton was content to treat these forces as self-sufficient, without trying to offer a causal explanation of their existence. In some of his early papers, in the first edition of the *Principia,* in the *Conclusion* which he planned as part of that edition, but later suppressed, in the Preface (in several versions) he was content to develop and explore various examples of the connection between attractive and repelling forces and the particles of bodies as the cause of observed properties. This remained always the heart of his doctrine; for if this much were granted his explanations were self-sufficient. Yet he could not help speculating on the possible cause of these forces, which he was reluctant to regard as inherent in matter.

The only possible cause of these forces lay, to seventeenth century thought, in some kind of aetherial hypothesis. Newton firmly rejected the dense aether of Descartes, which he proved to be cosmologically impossible. But he could not resist trying to find a possible aether, which would explain the forces of attraction and repulsion and avoid the difficulties of occult forces. In many (but not all) of his optical papers, in his Letter to Boyle, in some manuscript versions of the General Scholium (introduced into the second edition of the *Principia*), and in many of the Quaeries to *Opticks,* Newton tried out various versions of a possible aetherial hypothesis. He had no difficulty in devising such an hypothesis, one that would (as he hinted in the final paragraph of the printed version of the General Scholium) explain the action of light, gravity, chemical action, sensation, electricity, all by means of an electric "spirit" (elastic fluid). The difficulty was, as he ruefully concluded:

> these are things that cannot be explained in few words, nor are we furnished with that sufficiency of experiment which is required to an accurate determination and demonstration of the laws by which this electric and elastic spirit operates.

So it remained an hypothesis, not to be treated on the same level as his mathematical and experimental demonstrations.

But because Newton failed to find an explanation for his forces of at-

---

[41] It is fairly clear that this was what Newton had in mind from the textual evidence; a suppressed version of the General Scholium, and some annotations by Newton have made it quite plain. See A. Rupert and M. B. Hall, "Newton's Electric Spirit: Four Oddities", *Isis, 50,* 1959, 473–76, and A. Koyré and I. B. Cohen, "Newton's "Electric & Elastic Spirit" ", *Isis, 51,* 1960, 337.

traction and repulsion this by no means makes his theory of matter a failure. The mechanical philosophy as he applied it had led him to many grand discoveries: to his understanding of light and color, to his optical theories, to an understanding of gravity, to the Newtonian system of the world. Hence his conviction that this, and this alone, was the proper method of reasoning in natural science. As he wrote in the Preface to the *Principia*

> I wish we could derive the rest of the phenomena of nature by the same kind of reasoning from mechanical principles, for I am induced by many reasons to suspect that they may all depend upon certain forces by which the particles of bodies, by some causes hitherto unknown, are either mutually impelled towards one another, and cohere in regular figures, or are repelled and recede from one another. These forces being unknown, philosophers have hitherto attempted the search of nature in vain; but I hope the principles here laid down will afford some light either to this or some truer method of philosophy.

It was a justifiable boast; and Newton had excellent precepts to leave to his disciples. His true disciples were not those who devised elaborate theories of matter (like Boscovich) but those who tried to find out more about the properties of matter, and to explain them rigorously.

§8 *Conclusion*

The seventeenth century approach to the study of matter differs markedly from the modern approach. Its most striking difference lies in its strict utilitarianism. Convinced that there was no way of finding out what the least particles of matter were really like, mechanical philosophers concentrated on explaining the properties of matter in the most economical manner possible, with the general assumption of the existence of mobile particles. While the original progenitors of the mechanical philosophy all stressed motion as an important cause of properties, they all retained the need to consider the size and shape of the particles for a complete explanation, even though these could only be discovered imaginatively. Descartes's introduction of an aetherial mechanism to account for motion solved certain philosophic problems, and introduced some simplicity, but did not eliminate all need for speculation about size and shape of particles, and added a necessarily inexplicable aether. Boyle, rejecting the aether, achieved considerable simplicity, but at the cost of denying the existence of forces, supposed occult, and handing back the world to chance, except for the omnipresent supervision of God, which could be perceived rationally, but hardly experimentally. Newton's introduction of the forces of attraction and repulsion further simplified the number of explanations required to account for the properties of matter: the size and shape of the particles was even less important to him than to Boyle, and properties were now considered subject to mathematical law. Boyle had showed how corpuscularian notions might be used in chemistry; Newton showed how the force of attraction between particles was similar, perhaps identical with that between gross bodies, so that chemical action was related to the now non-mysterious gravity. It is perhaps not surprising that the chemist's atom was the first to be stabilized on an empirical basis by Dalton's ingenious conception of *weight* (an experimentally detectable property) as the key to the differences between particles of different kinds of matter. Physics had to wait longer to see the introduction of an atom which could be treated with the mathematical rigor which evaded Newton, and which could be explored directly through experiment.

Indiana University

COMMENT

IN THE DEFT AND MASTERFUL MANNER WE HAVE COME TO EXPECT FROM HER, DR. Hall has given us in this paper a superb summary of the "corupscular philosophy" of matter proposed in the seventeeenth century. To this summary, I can add nothing of significance. If I tried to add anything new, I would only find that she has already mentioned it elsewhere in her authoritative writings on the corpuscular philosophy. It need not trouble us that she does not discuss Leibniz or other non-corpuscular views. The corpuscular philosophy in some form or other was, indeed, the prevailing philosophical interpretation of nature in the seventeeth century.

I have only two short comments to make on the paper. The second is more provocative. The first is simply that her consistent distinction between philosophers and scientists in the seventeeth century seems to me to be terribly anachronistic. Of course, she is not the only one to assume such a distinction. It is to be found in our current histories of science and in all our histories of philosophy since the nineteenth century. Today such a distinction is taken for granted, even when we talk about the relation between philosophy and science. But is there any reason for perpetuating this distinction when we talk about the seventeeth century? Why should we go on calling Galileo, Huygens, Boyle and Newton mere "scientists", when they considered themselves to be philosophers cultivating the "true philosophy"? And why should we insist on calling Bacon, Descartes and Leibniz "philosophers", when they thought of themselves as true scientists? The seventeenth century thinkers did distinguish mere technicians, artisans and "an astronomer merely arithmetical", as Galileo put it, on the one hand, and natural philosophers, scientists and "the astronomer philosophical" on the other. But they did not distinguish between true philosophy and true science. Such a distinction was not envisaged by them, and I for one do not see any advantage in imposing such a distinction anachronistically upon them.

My second comment concerns interpretation. First, we can all admit, I think, that the new philosophies of matter in the seventeenth century were pointedly anti-Aristotelian, at least before the time of Newton. They were, as Dr. Hall points out, a reaction to such "occult qualities" as the Aristotelian first matter, substantial forms, accidental forms, final causes and the like, all of which were still taught in the schools with varying accuracy and seriousness. But the new, reactionary theories of matter could not be, according to her, a simple return to the atomic theories of Graeco-Roman antiquity (i) because every scientist of the seventeenth century knew Aristotle's objections to Democritus' atomism, and (ii) because those Graeco-Roman theories were scientifically out of date. Obviously there could be no *simple* return to Greek atomism in the sense of accepting the world as Democritus or Lucretius knew it. Too much had happened since then, as Bruno and Gassendi themselves fully realized. But that the new theories of matter—the corpuscular philosophy of Boyle as well as the atomic theory of Beeckman—were in *fact* a return to the atomism rejected by Aristotle can, I think, be validly and profitably shown.

Dr. Hall is certainly correct in saying that the new theory of matter, despite minor differences of detail among authors, was fundamentally mechanistic. Descartes, Huygens, Boyle and others recognized no other criterion for "the true philosophy, in which", to use the words of Huygens, "one conceives the causes of all natural effects in terms of mechanical motions". This mechanical philosophy tried to explain all observable properties by the motion, shape, and size of the particles of matter, as Dr. Hall has clearly shown. She is also correct, as I have said, in calling this approach anti-Aristotelian. But when she calls this approach "non-atomic", the word 'atom' must be taken in its narrow etymological sense of 'indivisible'. Possibly this sense of the term is sufficient to classify seventeenth century scientists into atomists and anti-atomists. But there were many who were uncertain about the natural divisibility of ultimate particles, and even the best scientists recognized that any material particle was, in the words of Boyle, "mentally, and by divine Omnipotence divisible".

In the last analysis it is really irrelevant to seventeenth century thought whether the particles of matter are absolutely indivisible, as Beeckman, Gassendi and Democritus would have it, or not. It is even irrelevant whether the vacuum exists in nature, or whether space is really empty, or whether the universe is a plenum. By "irrelevant", I do not mean that seventeenth century scientists were indifferent to these questions. Indeed there was much controversy over atoms and the vacuum, and this must be recognized in order to appreciate the differences of approach. Nevertheless, whatever those particles may be, whether atoms, little bodies, corpuscles, small parts of matter, or *prima naturalia*, they all had this in common: their motions were strictly mechanical, and they themselves were ingenerable and incorruptible. It is this basic assumption which brings seventeenth century theories of matter back to the view of Democritus and the objections of Aristotle.

It is true that Democritus and Leucippus proposed to explain all natural phenomena in terms of atoms and the void. But their attempt must be understood as an answer to the Eleatic problem. Parmenides of Elea had denied the reality of change (*genesis*) because for him change is inexplicable. As he saw it, the admission of change landed one in the following dilemma:

> What comes to be must do so either from what is or from what is not, both of which are impossible. For what *is* cannot come to be, because it *is* already; and from what *is not* nothing could have come to be, because what *is not* cannot exist as a substratum. (*Phys.*, I, 8; 191a 29–32)

In other words, since the non-real cannot exist, nothing can come from it; and since the real already exists, there can be no coming-to-be, or *genesis* of the real.

Further, since the non-real (nothingness) cannot exist, there cannot even be locomotion, for every place is full. Therefore Parmenides had to deny the multiplicity and mutability obvious to the senses. In other words, for Parmenides the truth of the matter is that all reality is one solid mass devoid of change, although the opinion of mankind maintains multiplicity and change. It was in order to avoid the Eleatic dilemma and at the same time to account for multiplicity and mutability that Leucippus, the teacher of Democritus, said "that *what is* is no more real than *what is not*, and that both are alike causes of the things that come into being." (Theophrastus, *Physic. Opiniones*, I, fr. 8. 19–21) Thus Leucippus conceived the non-real, or emptiness (the void) to be as real as the solid, hard realities in nature, which he called atoms. This little concession of admitting the reality of non-being made all the difference in the world, for Leucippus could explain multiplicity by recognizing a void between individuals. He could also explain locomotion by recognizing a void into which individuals could move. This void, of course, was not the atmospheric air, for Empedocles had shown air to be a corporeal substance. It was simply non-being, emptiness, nothingness, which Leucippus and Democritus maintained existed just as much as physical bodies. This conception of non-being having physical existence is philosophically very strange, but it is very similar to our conception of empty space existing in reality.

There are two important points, it seems to me, to notice about this atomism of antiquity. First, it was unable to answer the objection of Parmenides to the reality of *genesis*, or the coming-to-be of atoms. The void, indeed, made movement in place intelligible, but it could not account for any intrinsic mutability of the atom. If an atom really changed intrinsically, the new atom would have to come from atom, which is no change at all, or it would have to come from nothing, which is impossible. Consequently Leucippus had to concede the impossibility of intrinsic change, or *genesis* and *olethros*. In fact Leucippus gave his atoms the character of the Parmenidean One, except that he allowed for many such ones. The second point to notice is that the only motion provided for was mechanical motion, i.e., an external force exerted on an atom allowed it to move spatially from one place to another. In such a view the appearance of becoming is nothing but the composition of atoms, and perishing is nothing but the separation of atoms. Growth is really nothing but addition of more atoms, while so-called qualitative changes are really nothing but the locomotion of atoms. There is no need here to mention anything about the size, shape or density of the various particles recognized by the ancients. Nor is there any need to mention the eternal vortex (*diné*) in which all bodies are whirled (Diog. IX, 31–34). We already have the two essential elements of a purely mechanistic philosophy of matter. These two are the denial of intrinsic *genesis*, or *fieri*, and the exclusive recognition of locomotion mechanistically produced as the only real motion in nature. It was precisely against these two assumptions that Aristotle directed his strongest objections, not only in the *De generatione et corruptione*, but also in the *Physics*.

If the seventeenth century scientists knew Aristotle's objections to Democritus' atomism, as Dr. Hall claims, then we must go on to say that they paid little attention to them. In fact, the seventeenth century scientists accepted all the consequences of Democritean atomism, viz. denial of the substantial unity of things, the intrinsic mutability and spontaneity of nature, the reality of sensible qualities such as color, heat, odor and sweetness, the reality of teleological operations, the stability of species, and the reality of all movements other than loco-motion. Thus, the seventeenth century "mechanical philosophy" was in fact a return to the mechanistic theories of antiquity. However, the seventeenth century scientists did succeed in bringing the anti-Aristotelian mechanical theory "up to date". In this sense the new theory of matter was not *simply* a return to the atomic theories of Graeco-Roman antiquity.

James A. Weisheipl O.P.
Albertus Magnus Lyceum

ACTION AT A DISTANCE

Mary B. Hesse

⛢ The question whether matter can act at a distance across empty space or whether some medium of contact, or ether, is required, is one which has constantly recurred in physics, and has been thought to raise philosophical as well as purely scientific issues. Stated thus baldly, the problem lacks definiteness, and requires careful analysis of what is meant by 'matter', by 'act', by 'empty space', and by 'ether'. Many would now hold that the answer to the question of action at a distance depends essentially on our concept of matter and is relative to the existing state of science, rather than that our concept of matter must be framed in accordance with an *a priori* decision about action at a distance. But this has not always been so, and it is clear that, historically at least, metaphysical convictions about possible types of interaction have often been related to the acceptability of certain kinds of physical theory. This essay attempts to trace the historical relation between the action-at-a-distance problem and the progress of science, and to assess the permanent conceptual issues that seem to be involved.

§1 *Definition of the Problem*

Things may influence or act upon other things in many different ways: they may collide with each other; they may react chemically; they may attract or repel like two magnets, or on the other hand like two human beings; they may communicate at a distance by shooting particles at each other, or by transmitting a disturbance in a medium; they may, if they are human beings, speak to one another, or even (perhaps) communicate telepathically. All these and many other processes have been used as models for fundamental interactions in the history of physics. It will be noticed that those which involve only non-intelligent bodies, tend to be actions by contact (with the significant exception of the magnet), while those which are, superficially at least, actions at a distance, usually involve human beings. This general feature of physical interaction is already enough to explain the widespread preference for contact-action theories in physics, and the intuitive suspicion that action at a distance must retain overtones of anthropomorphism.

Two questions have to be distinguished here. There is first the conceptual or methodological question of whether interaction at a distance can be understood or explained at all without postulating a medium of *some kind;* and there is secondly the empirical question of whether, if a medium is postulated or "discovered", it is a substance similar to or different from ordinary observable matter. The first question can be made independent of whatever concept of matter may be accepted, so long as one is sufficiently liberal in one's understanding of what a "medium" can be (even empty space could be said in a sense to be a medium), but the second question cannot even be formulated until the concept of matter is more or less clearly defined. As a matter of historical fact, it does not seem that the first question has ever been put in the absence of *some* conception of what would count as a "material" medium, but sometimes a negative answer to it has forced natural philosophers to conceive of "immaterial" media as conceptual necessities.

Since it was the Greeks who first explicitly studied the concept of matter, it is to them that we must look for the first statements of the problem of action at a distance. Two streams of thought in Greek philosophy combined in the view that there is no action at a distance, and that all action is by contact of parts of matter. The first was Atomism, which attempted to solve the dilemma of the Parmenidean changeless "Being" by postulating atoms moving in the "Not-Being", or void. This meant that the atoms were, like Parmenides' Being, imperishable, homogeneous, and without intrinsic qualities, but the possibility of motion and change was saved by distinguishing atoms from void, and hence by endowing atoms with geometrical shape. Thus, chiefly as a consequence of the metaphysical impasse created by Parmenides, the notion of primary and secondary qualities of matter first entered philosophy; the primary qualities being mechanical and geometrical, and the secondary qualities being definable or constructible in terms of these. There was no suggestion that the atoms could act at a distance, for this would have meant that they were endowed with powers or qualities other than those necessary to define pure Being: moreover any such action would have to take place, not merely across empty space in any modern sense, but across "non-existence". Being could affect Being only by coming into contact with it.

A second characteristic of Greek thought, more practical in application, led to the same conclusion. This was the widespread use of mechanical analogues in scientific explanations, both among the Presocratic cosmologists, and among the Hippocratic medical writers before and during the time of Aristotle. Increased familiarity with mechanical techniques and inventions led to comparisons between the mechanisms of the body and such gadgets as pumps, bellows and levers, and between the movements of bodily fluids and irrigation channels, boiling liquids, differential deposition of solid matter in centrifuges, and so on. Some such mechanical processes appear to involve action at a distance, or at least attractive as opposed to impact forces: for example the "suction" of a vacuum, and the behaviour of magnets. But it is clear even in Plato and Aristotle that such apparent exceptions to the general rule of mechanical action by impact or pressure were not regarded as fundamental, and attempts were made to explain them in terms of the circular motions of the air or other "emanations", everting pressure rather than attraction. According to Plato and Aristotle and their schools, there are no "pulls" but only "pushes" in nature.

It is not clear that this conviction was based on any consistent metaphysics, and even Aristotle's remarks about it read like rationalizations after the event. But Aristotle, unlike the Atomists, left open the possibility of diversity of kinds of material substance. Since there is no void for Aristotle, his "matter" is ubiquitous, and in itself qualityless, and therefore when Aristotle insists that every motion and change has a mover in contact with it, he may be understood to be saying no more than that matter is informed by power of *some* kind at places adjacent to a body in forced motion. This would not commit him to any particular mechanism for the transmission of this power from agent to distant patient, and the many kinds of immaterial emanation and substantial form which were later postulated to account for it could rightly be claimed to be consistent with Aristotelian teaching. There is here the ambiguity which runs right through the history of concepts of action at a distance, namely that if the medium of transmission is not defined too closely, the assertion that action must be continuous through the medium may be no more than a directive to look for some continuity of qualities, no matter what, and the search is almost always successful, although the result may be quite unlike matter with the qualities we know from experience of gross bodies.

§2 *The Mechanisation of Physics*

For this reason, the problem of action at a distance became much sharper with the successful mechanisation of physics in the seventeenth century. Cartesianism and Atomism, though to some extent rivals, both presupposed a concept of matter involving only the "primary", geometrical and mechanical, qualities. One of the most revolutionary features of this period of scientific revolution was the elimination from physical theory of the quasi-material, quasi-animistic, substances which had been postulated in Renaissance philosophy to account for the transmission of physical action. It was not so much Aristotle's mechanism that was rejected in the seventeenth

century as the self-moving souls, substantial forms, sympathies and antip-
athies, *horror vacui,* multiplication of species, and the rest, which pervaded
later Aristotelianism. Thus it was not enough for Descartes to seek to
explain, for example, magnetic attraction, by some kind of emanation "laying hold of" pieces of iron and drawing them to the magnet, like, as Gassendi put it, a chameleon darting out its tongue to catch a fly. Descartes
rather sought a vortex mechanism in terms of subtle particles forced
through the pores of the magnet, and drawing particles towards the magnet
by the pressure of circular thrust. As with Aristotle, there are no pulls but
only pushes in nature.

The programme of the corpuscular philosophy, accepted by almost all
seventeenth-century philosophers, was to explain all physical, and even
biological, processes in terms of mechanical particles in motion. A subsidiary point of disagreement between Atomists and Cartesians was the question whether or not there is void, but both parties agreed that there is in
any case no action across void—for the Atomists, particles can only affect
one another by colliding. The mechanistic programme, however, caused
scientific difficulties. How could it be made to account for those obvious
phenomena which seem to require forces of attraction, and even forces
acting at a distance—for example, the cohesion of solid bodies, the rise of
liquids in thin tubes, the expansion and contraction of gases, the motion of
heavy bodies towards the earth, the action of the moon on the tides, the
behaviour of magnets? Cartesian vortex mechanisms invented to account
for these were ingenious but unconvincing, especially as the behaviour of
bodies came to be described in more detail and in quantitative and mathematical terms. The stage was set for Newton's fundamental physical synthesis, and at the level of the concept of matter, this synthesis implied one
significant addition to the furniture of the world allowed by the mechanical
philosophers: namely the mutual attraction and repulsion of bodies at a
distance.

The first significant appearance of attractive forces was in Newton's
theory of gravitation, although Newton himself was reluctant to regard
this attractive power of bodies as an ultimate property, and sought some
mechanical explanation in terms of pressures in a fluid ether pervading all
space. But he would not allow such speculations to affect his mathematical
presentation of the theory in the *Principia Mathematica,* and insisted there
that a merely *phenomenal* description of the motions of the heavens implied that bodies have an acceleration towards each other defined by the
inverse-square law, no matter what *cause* of this acceleration may be
imagined. In his later discussions of other physical phenomena, however,
chiefly in the *Optics,* he seems to accept as fundamental, at least provi-

375

sionally, attractive and repulsive forces acting at a distance in order to account for cohesion, elasticity of gases, the behaviour of magnets and electric bodies, certain chemical reactions, and reflection and refraction of light corpuscles, as well as the phenomena of gravitation.

For the more conservative mechanists, this seemed like a reversion to all the immaterial influences, sympathies, and occult qualities which had been banished from physics so recently and with so much difficulty. One of the best accounts of the points at issue between the Newtonians and their critics is to be found in the Leibniz-Clarke correspondence. This was initiated by Leibniz in 1716 in a letter in which he asserted that the philosophy of Newton was contributing to the decay of natural religion in England. Clarke replied on behalf of Newton, and the correspondence continued until Leibniz's death, ranging widely over Leibniz's metaphysical principles and over scientific topics such as the nature of space and time, the existence of vacuum, and the theory of gravitation.

Leibniz argues on grounds of continuity and sufficient reason that there is no void, and asserts that the vacua apparently produced in the barometer tube and in air pumps are void only of gross matter and not absolutely empty. The space contains rays of light "which are not devoid of some subtle matter", and "the effluvia of the load-stone, and other very thin fluids may go through" the glass. Clarke objects that if these were material they would exert resistance, and there is no resistance to bodies moving in a vacuum. But he is prepared to admit that immaterial substances may be present in void space: "God is certainly present, and possibly many other substances which are not matter; being neither tangible, nor objects of any of our senses". As for action at a distance, Clarke agrees with Leibniz that it is impossible. In reply to Leibniz's assertion that an attraction causing a free body to move in a curved line would be a miracle, he says:

> That one body should attract another without any intermediate means is indeed not a miracle, but a contradiction: for 'tis supposing something to act where it is not. But the means by which two bodies attract each other, may be invisible and intangible, and of a different nature from mechanism; and yet, acting regularly and constantly, may well be called natural; being much less wonderful than animal-motion; which is never called a miracle.[1]

But Leibniz will not have any talk of

> . . . some immaterial substances, or some spiritual rays, or some accident without a substance, or some kind of *species intentionalis*, or some other I know not what . . . That means of communication (says [Clarke]) is invisi-

---

[1] *The Leibniz-Clarke Correspondence,* ed. H. G. Alexander, Manchester, 1956, p. 53.

ble, intangible, not mechanical. He might as well have added, inexplicable, unintelligible, precarious, groundless and unexampled.[2]

Clarke replies that attraction is only the name of an empirical fact, whatever may be its explanation, and therefore it should not be called occult, even if its efficient cause is not yet discovered. If Leibniz or anyone else can explain these phenomena by the laws of mechanism he will "have the abundant thanks of the learned world". But elsewhere Clarke is doubtful of the possibility of explaining gravitation by impulse, since it depends on quantity and not surface area of matter; hence he thinks it must be due to something "immaterial" which penetrates matter.

The argument is the same as that which runs through the whole history of theories of interaction. If there is continuity of causes transmitting actions from one part of space to another, what is the nature of these causes? Leibniz holds the comparatively "modern" view of Cartesian mechanism, asserting that matter can act upon matter only by contact and according to the laws of mechanics, and that soul or spirit cannot act upon matter at all, for if it did it would violate the natural conservation of *vis viva*. Clarke holds the traditional view that immaterial spirit may act upon body, remarking that this is as easy to conceive as cohesion "which no mechanism can account for", and he maintains in particular that God is substantially present everywhere and may intervene by acting directly upon matter. For Leibniz the activity of God is of another order, and from the scientific point of view he was no doubt right, in 1716, to question Clarke's immaterial substances and non-mechanical explanations, for the time had not come when these could be made sufficiently precise to be acceptable in a scientific theory. There is no disagreement between them about the facts, the disagreement lies in the question of what kinds of theory are to be admitted in explanation of the facts, and Leibniz shows a less empirical spirit than Clarke in insisting that theories must conform to certain *a priori* conceptions of interaction.

Leibniz's arguments were in fact ignored by most eighteenth-century physicists, who accepted Newton's matter endowed with attractive and repulsive powers, and used it in particular in various fluid theories to account for the phenomena of heat, electricity and magnetism, and chemical reactions. Leibniz had, however, one professed disciple: Boscovich, who published in 1758 a universal physics, the *Theoria Philosophiae Naturalis,* ostensibly based on Leibnizian principles. But in fact Boscovich had turned Leibniz inside out—instead of rejecting the void in the interests of continuity, he effectively rejected the extension of matter on the same grounds.

[2] *Ibid.,* p. 94.

For Boscovich "matter" exists in the form of point particles carrying inertia, but interacting by means of distance-forces of attraction and repulsion whose magnitude depends on the distance between the particles. It was this theory which later influenced Faraday at a crucial point in nineteenth-century physics, and led to the notion of force-fields rather than "matter" as the fundamental physical entities. To this development we now turn.

§3 *Field Theories*

In the early nineteenth century three modes of transmission of physical action were recognized:

(i) Action by impact of ultimate atomic particles, as described by Newton's mechanics.

(ii) Action at a distance by attractive and repulsive forces, including repulsive forces exerted at short distance between parts of gases and other elastic fluids, and gravitational attraction apparently exerted over long distances through empty space.

(iii) Action in a continuous medium, described by the extension of Newton's mechanics of point particles to the mechanics of continuous fluids by Euler, and extended later to the mechanics of continuous elastic solids.

This third type of interaction theory was at first of mathematical rather than physical significance, and had in fact been developed by ignoring the fundamental physical problem of the nature of the elementary parts of matter and its forces. But it provided the first mathematical models for later field theory. From the purely mathematical point of view, a *field* in physics may be defined as a region of space in which each point (with possibly isolated exceptions) is characterised by some quantity or quantities which are functions of the space coordinates and of time, the nature of the quantities depending on the physical theory in which they occur. Euler created a field theory in this sense for hydrodynamics, by characterising the field of motion of a fluid by functions of the space coordinates, such as the velocity of the fluid and its pressure at each point. In this purely mathematical sense, however, it might be said that the formulation of the theory of gravitation in terms of a potential function defined at all points of a space containing gravitating bodies, is also a field theory. But there is clearly a physical difference between a gravitational potential of this kind and the velocity-field of a fluid. The fluid field is a continuous material medium having properties other than velocity, but the gravitational "field" has apparently no properties other than the potentiality for exerting attractive force on masses introduced into it.

It was Faraday who first made explicit some of the conditions under which one can speak of physical interaction through a "real" field, as opposed to pure action at a distance. His criteria for "physical reality" are interesting in showing how the conception of "reality" is, as it were, made anew with each physical theory. It is precisely because Faraday does not accept the definitions of mechanical and chemical "matter" as the sole criteria of reality that he is able to introduce what Maxwell later called "quite a new conception of action at a distance" in which real physical processes are going on in the medium, although in the mechanical sense the space is "empty".

In a letter of 1844, published in the *Philosophical Magazine* and entitled "A speculation touching Electrical Conduction and the Nature of Matter", Faraday characterises the current view of the atomic constitution of matter: atoms have a certain volume and are endowed with powers which hold them together in groups, but chemical experiments show that they do not touch, therefore only space is continuous throughout matter considered as an aggregate of atoms. But this leads to a paradoxical consequence in regard to electric insulators and conductors, for the space between the atoms of an insulator must be an insulator, and space between the atoms of a conductor must be a conductor. This contradiction leads Faraday to the view, which he ascribes to Boscovich, that an atom is a *point* with "an atmosphere of force grouped around it". The properties of a body, such as conduction, relation to light or magnetism, solidity, hardness, specific gravity, must then belong, not to a "nucleus" abstracted from its powers (for this is in any case inconceivable), but to the forces themselves.

> But then surely the *m* [the atmosphere of force] is the *matter* of the potassium, for where is there the least ground (except in a gratuitous assumption) for imagining a difference in kind between the nature of that space midway between the centres of two contiguous atoms and any other spot between these centres? A difference in degree, or even in the nature of the power consistent with the law of continuity, I can admit, but the difference between a supposed little hard particle and the powers around it, I cannot imagine.

It follows, in contrast to the orthodox view, that "matter" is everywhere continuous and that "atoms" are highly elastic and deformable, is mutually penetrable, and that

> matter fills all space, or, at least, all space to which gravitation extends ... for gravitation is a property of matter dependent on a certain force, and it is this force which constitutes the matter. ... This, at first sight, seems to fall in very harmoniously with ... the old adage, "matter cannot act where it is not".

This paper seems to mark a decisive transition from the conception of mechanical action to that of continuous action in terms of forces filling space.

Here *all* physical forces are regarded in this way, but in other papers, of 1851 and 1852, Faraday does not make the transition in the case of gravitation, but explicitly distinguishes action at a distance from the new conception of action in a real medium by means of three questions about gravity, radiation, and electric and magnetic force:

(i) Can transmission of action be affected by changes in the intervening medium, as regards, for instance, a bending of the lines of force, or polarity effects? If the answer is Yes, as in the cases of electric and magnetic induction but unlike gravitation, this is an indication of a real process going on in the medium.

(ii) Does the transmission take time? Again an affirmative answer indicates the presence of a real medium.

(iii) Does the transmission depend upon a "receiving" end? An affirmative answer here indicates an action at a distance, as in the case of gravitation, but not of radiation. This, however, is not a decisive criterion, because electric and magnetic effects, like gravitation, do seem to depend on *two* poles of the interaction, and yet Faraday wishes to regard them as actions in a medium, on the strength of the answer to (i). After investigating experimental answers to the three questions, Faraday's conclusions are that gravitation seems to be a pure action at a distance, whereas radiation is clearly action in a medium, and electric and magnetic effects are also actions in a medium, although the physical nature of this medium is still obscure.

The question of the nature of the media, both of light radiation and of electric and magnetic phenomena, brings us to the nineteenth-century theories of the ether. Early mathematical investigation of optics, following Fresnel's mathematical wave theory of diffraction, refraction and polarisation, had been content to derive Fresnel's equations from the most general principles of mechanics, namely Lagrange's equations or the principle of least action, without attempting to describe an actual etherial mechanism which would account for the phenomena of light propagation. There were, indeed, extreme difficulties in imagining any satisfactory material mechanism, since the light ether had to be at once subtle, to allow passage of bodies through it with negligible resistance, and also of great rigidity, to allow transmission of light at great speed. These and other difficulties gave rise to the invention of bizarre mechanical models of the ether, both as a medium for light and of electromagnetism, but these were generally intended merely as aids to imagination and calculation, rather than as literal descriptions of a physical reality. It has occasionally been the fashion to scoff at the workshop-full of gadgets invoked by Kelvin, and in his earlier papers by Maxwell, to provide such models, but it should be noticed that none of the mathematical physicists who put forward these models seriously intended them as descriptions of a real material ether. They were sometimes considered to be necessities of thought, but only in the sense of making the mathematical formalisms more intelligible, and sometimes as checks on their internal consistency.

In the third of his great papers on the electromagnetic theory of light, in 1864, Maxwell explicitly abandoned such models as *hypotheses* of the ether, but at the same time made clear that he did not thereby withdraw from his adherence to Faraday's conception of the real field:

> I have on a former occasion attempted to describe a particular kind of motion and a particular kind of strain, so arranged as to account for the phenomena. In the present paper I avoid any hypothesis of this kind; and in using such words as electric momentum and electric elasticity in reference to the known phenomena . . . I wish merely to direct the mind of the reader to mechanical phenomena which will assist him in understanding the electrical ones. All such phrases in the present paper are to be considered as illustrative, not as explanatory.
> In speaking of the Energy of the field, however, I wish to be understood literally.[3]

Energy had now become the fundamental physical quantity defining the field, and since it obeyed a conservation law it came to be regarded as a substance in its own right, rather than as a mere property of substantial matter. Also, Faraday's conception of a real medium had been vindicated by Maxwell's mathematical synthesis of optics and electromagnetism, in which energy was present in the intervening space as well as in material bodies. As a criterion for the reality of the field, transmission of action in a finite time now took precedence over Faraday's other criteria, for, combined with the principle of the conservation of energy, it implied that energy must be present in the medium during the time taken for action to pass from one material point to another. *How* the action passed in a mechanical sense was a question which began to lose its meaning—it was the energy of stress and motion in the field which became fundamental: the field was not to be explained in terms of matter, matter was rather a particular modification of the field. From this point of view the assimilation of mass and energy in the mass-energy of relativity theory, was only the last stage in a conceptual development initiated in classical field-theory by the treatment of energy as a fluid-like substance. Also, the abandonment of the material ether in relativity theory, as a consequence of the absence of any absolute material standard of rest, was not new, but only the culmination of the classical re-interpretation of the medium in terms of energy-flow.

---

[3] "A Dynamical Theory of the Electromagnetic Field", *Scientific Papers*, I, p. 563.

§4 *Illustrations of a Conceptual Dispute*

The field view did not, however, lack critics. Some physicists, particularly in France and Germany, refused to make the distinction Maxwell had made between imaginative mechanical models, and the conception of a real physical field. They wished, rather, to confine the scientific content of Maxwell's theory to Maxwell's equations, and to accept the field-functions such as energy and displacement-current only as implicitly defined by these equations, and not as "real" entities in a physical field regarded as more fundamental than matter. This type of "mathematical phenomenalism" has gained many adherents among physicists during the present century, since it has become progressively more difficult to give coherent and mutually consistent pictures of what Maxwell would have regarded as the real physical events underlying observable phenomena.

The issue between Maxwell and these Continental physicists was not, however, wholly one of rival philosophies of scientific theory. The Continental school had consistently maintained, throughout the nineteenth century, an action-at-a-distance conception of electric and magnetic phenomena, stemming from the attracting and repelling particle theories of the previous century. At any given point of development, it was generally possible to say that the empirical facts were explained as well by this action-at-a-distance theory as by the British fields, and even that the two theories were essentially the same, since each could be derived from the other by mere mathematical transformation. Thus Hertz asserted:

> Maxwell's theory is Maxwell's system of equations. Every theory which leads to the same system of equations, and therefore comprises the same possible phenomena, I would consider as being a form or special case of Maxwell's theory; every theory which leads to different equations, and therefore different possible phenomena, is a different theory. . . .

> If we wish to lend more colour to the theory, there is nothing to prevent us from supplementing all this and aiding our powers of imagination by concrete representations of the various conceptions as to the nature of electric polarisation, the electric current, etc. But scientific accuracy requires of us that we should in no wise confuse the simple and homely figure, as it is presented to us by nature, with the gay garment which we use to clothe it.[4]

But closer study of the development of the two types of theory shows that the question is not as simple as Hertz supposed, and it provides an excellent case-history in support of the proposition that there is a real scientific difference between what is asserted in theories employing different representa-

---

[4] *Electric Waves*, (Eng. trans. 1893), pp. 21, 28.

tions of their respective formalisms, even though they may be empirically equivalent in Hertz's sense. This question is crucial to the problem of whether there is any real difference between theories of action at a distance and those employing continuous action in a medium, and hence whether action at a distance is a real philosophical issue, or only a matter of convenience in theoretical formulation.

Comparison between the field and action-at-a-distance methods in nineteenth-century physics can be made from two points of view: that of the particulate nature of electricity, and that of the finite velocity of transmission of electromagnetic effects. The Continental methods go back to Ampère's investigation in the 1820's of the law of force between current elements, which he expressed in terms of attractions and repulsions acting instantaneously along the line joining the elements. During the century this law of force went through many *ad hoc* modifications designed to make it consistent, first, with the conservation of energy, and second with the propagation of action at a finite speed as required by Maxwell's equations. Two of the assumptions made by Ampère had to be discarded, namely the central direction of the forces (along the line joining the current elements), and the instantaneous propagation of action. Maxwell's continuous-action theory had led by natural and obvious deductive steps to the finite speed of propagation, but the acceptance of Maxwell's formal equations by the Continental school did not carry this same plausibility into their action-at-a-distance theory, where the finite velocity had to be injected *ad hoc* at the cost of some conceptual awkwardness. On the other hand, Maxwell's theory by itself was not sufficient for a solution of the problem of the law of force between current elements, towards which some progress had been made by the Continentals. In Maxwell's theory there are no independent current *elements*, since *all* currents are continuous circuits, a "material" current being completed if necessary by a non-material displacement-current in the "ether". Maxwell's theory was in fact not suited to the expression of any phenomena which depended on the discrete and atomic, as opposed to the continuous, and for this purpose the Continental theories were far more suitable. After the discovery of electron emission and transmission in high vacua by J. J. Thomson, the problem of the law of force between discrete moving electric bodies again became urgent, and was solved more easily as an extension of Ampère's formula than of Maxwell's equations.

Thus, although all the phenomena could in principle be accommodated in both types of theory, some phenomena found easier expression in one than the other, and this fact seems to show that the two theories were *not* equivalent for all scientific purposes. Theories in science are sometimes rejected, not on grounds of inconsistency with empirical facts, but on grounds of complexity, incoherence, and lack of predictive power. Now it does not *follow* from this that theories rejected on these grounds are empirically false, but if there are two theories which both lead deductively to the same empirical facts, but are inconsistent with each other, it is natural to extend the criteria of falsity to include grounds of rejection other than empirical falsification, for these are the grounds that enable us to choose between the theories. In this sense, for example, the Ptolemaic system is *false*, even though it can be made to account for the actual motions of the solar system, because it is complex, lacks predictive power, and is not coherent with the general theory of gravitation from which the Copernican (or rather Keplerian) system follows.

The nineteenth-century case-histories in electromagnetism seem to indicate that the issue between medium theories and action-at-a-distance theories was then a real scientific issue, unless we adopt a wholly positivist attitude to theories and regard all "unobservables" as mere pictorial devices denoting nothing in reality. But although the issue was a real one, its resolution was not as definite as in the case of Ptolemy versus Copernicus. In terms of nineteenth-century physics both types of theory had some justification, with a bias at the end of the century towards field theory. Twentieth-century developments have placed the issue still more in doubt, since the dualism and latent contradictions in classical physics between atomicity and continuity have become explicit and apparently insurmountable.

§5 *Interaction in Modern Physics*

Before the development of the general theory of relativity, gravitation had remained outside the synthesis of classical physics, and had been almost universally regarded as a pure action at a distance, for the sorts of reasons outlined by Faraday. Since a finite velocity of propagation was regarded as one of the chief criteria for a real field, a decisive step in favour of field theories throughout physics was taken within special relativity by the proof that neither gravitation nor any other physical process could be propagated at a speed greater than that of light.

It is important to analyse the status of this consequence of the special theory, because if it is true, it follows either that there is no action at a distance, and hence that what has been taken to be a philosophical problem has an empirical solution, or that action at a distance must be radically re-interpreted. The proof that the velocity of light in vacuum is the maximum velocity for any physical process, depends on some immediate consequences of the Lorentz transformation of space-time frameworks, of which the most important is the following: it can be shown that if any causal action were propagated with a velocity greater than light in some reference frame, then the temporal order of cause and effect would be reversed in some other frames. That is to say, if the causal action between A and B were propagated faster than light in some frames, it would always be possible to find other frames in which B precedes A; but we imply by the causal relation: "A causes B" that B never precedes A; thus causal action as generally understood cannot be propagated faster than light. This argument cannot, of course, legislate for the world. Even if the special theory of relativity is accepted as a valid description of the world, there is nothing logically inconsistent in holding that for some processes our usual notions of cause and effect are inapplicable. What the arguments do show is that we cannot retain those notions and at the same time postulate actions propagated with velocities greater than c. Common-sense ideas about causality are more fundamental to science than the notion of processes travelling faster than light, and there is nothing in the context of special relativity to induce us to abandon the former rather than the latter, so it may be concluded that if the special theory is accepted, then there is no detectable propagation of action exceeding the velocity of light.

In relativity theory, then, gravitation satisfies at least one of the classical conditions for a real physical field. In general relativity, gravitational potentials, and momentum and energy densities, are defined, and conservation laws of momentum and energy in space are shown to hold. Thus gravitational field theory satisfies another of the conditions for a real field, namely the presence of energy at space-time points remote from matter. There is no material medium in the sense of an ether, but space itself becomes the medium. This gravitational theory is indeed conceptually further from the notion of action at a distance even than the electromagnetic field theory, for here it is not the presence of the field sources which causes a field to appear in previously empty Euclidean space, but rather the geometrical properties of space itself are determined by the presence of matter, since the gravitational potentials specify the variable curvature of the non-Euclidean space. For the geometrician accustomed to thinking in terms of abstract spaces, the difference between the two models is very great: in one case geometry itself is the model, whereas in the electromagnetic case the model is still a refined version of fluid flow. The mathematical advantages of the geometrical model have led to various attempts, upon which Einstein was engaged until the end of his life, to incorporate electromagnetism and quantum theory with gravitation in a unified field theory of the geometrical type, but so far no fully satisfactory theory of this kind has been produced.

From the scientific point of view, however, relativity theory has not said the final word on action at a distance. Even if that theory is accepted, there are still two ways of avoiding the conclusion that action at a distance is a physical impossibility. One is to re-interpret action at a distance in such a way that it becomes consistent with a finite velocity of propagation: and the other is to remark that even instantaneous action at a distance might be postulated in a *theory*, so long as it is in principle impossible actually to *observe* the resulting causal anomalies. This second method depends upon the fact that causal anomalies are not self-contradictory, but merely contradictory with our normally accepted notions of causality, and these notions need not be affected in practice by unobservable violations of normal causality in a theory. The possibility of this way of escape for action at a distance was opened up by quantum theory.

The question of modes of action in quantum mechanics is closely connected with the uncertainty principle. In the first place, if this principle is expressed in terms of the complementary variables energy and time, it is clear that detection of a finite amount of energy requires a finite time-interval. Thus no action involving passage of energy from one point to another distant from it can be *observed* to be instantaneous. On the other hand, it is conceivable that instantaneous action at a distance might be postulated theoretically, as it were within the uncertainty limits, in such a way that the causal anomalies resulting from the special theory of relativity could not in principle be observed. Thus quantum theory opens a way, at least on the small scale, which appeared to have been closed by relativity theory, but so far suggestions of such instantaneous action or action faster than light have not passed beyond the speculative stage.

Continuous action on the small scale however does not fare any better. It is universally agreed that there is at present no consistent continuous-action interpretation of quantum theory analogous to that of classical theory, either in terms of particles, or waves, or fields, and it is argued by many that there cannot in principle be any such interpretation within the framework of the present theory. The most commonly accepted interpretation of the theory has been what Reichenbach calls *restrictive*, that is to say, it is held that quantum theory makes no statements at all about "real" unobservable events occurring between observations, but only about *states* which are functions of observables produced by measurements on the system. The theory speaks merely about systems passing from one state into another when measurements are made. The transitions are discontinuous, and describable neither as action at a distance nor action by contact in the classical sense. The "quantum jump" of an electron, for example, from one energy level to another, with emission or absorption of radiation, now appears as a successive occupation of energy states, with corresponding creation or annihilation of photons. There is no causal action of one state on the other; the transition is detected in a single experimental operation, that is, there is no separate description of a particle leaving one state and then entering another, so that it is meaningless, within the restrictive interpretation, to speak of the duration or any other property of the transition. This is neither a continuous action nor an action at a distance—it is not an action at all.

It does not follow, however, that continuous-action descriptions may not be possible on the macroscopic scale where the quantum of action is negligible. Indeed quantised field theories approximating to classical theories on the large scale have been developed, and these are able to some extent both to describe the interaction of particles with radiation, and to assimilate quantum theory with the special theory of relativity. Such theories have had some success in rationalizing the experimental results obtained in nuclear and other high-energy reactions, by interpreting these in terms of particle creations and annihilations. Since these creations and annihilations can occur randomly even in "vacuum", this theory in a sense re-introduces the notion of a material "ether" pervading all space, but in a relativistically-invariant way, so that this ether cannot be regarded, as the nineteenth-century ether was, as an absolute standard of rest.

The development of quantum field theory is, however, seriously hampered by the occurrence of infinite self-energy terms in its equations. Such divergence difficulties have been one of the motives for recent attempts by Wheeler and Feynman to reintroduce the conception of action at a distance on the large scale. Since it can no longer be maintained that this takes place instantaneously, action at a distance must now be understood to mean direct particle-interaction involving no independent field with its own energy and momentum. It has been assumed by most physicists that such action would violate the conservation principles, but Wheeler and Feynman have been able to show for classical electrodynamics that this is not so if the advanced as well as retarded solutions of Maxwell's equations are taken into account. This leads to the apparently paradoxical result that one event affects another at a distance r at a time r/c seconds *before* it occurs, as well as r/c seconds afterwards. It is of course contrary to all ideas of normal causality that an event should have an effect *before* it takes place, and such a notion is open to the objection that we might be able to intervene to prevent the cause occurring as soon as we had observed its prior effect, but if we did this successfully, then the prior effect which did occur should not have occurred. This paradox has in fact been urged by philosophers as a general and decisive refutation of any theory involving temporal reversal of cause and effect. Just in the case of quantum theory, however, there seems to be an escape from this paradox. If action at a distance of the Wheeler and Feynman type were incorporated into quantum field theory in such a way that the advanced effects always occurred within the uncertainty limits, it would never in principle be possible for a macromechanism (including a human agent) to detect them in time to prevent the later occurrence of the "cause".

On the whole, then, the most commonly accepted interpretation of quantum theory is agnostic about the nature of small-scale interactions, and even denies that either continuous action, or action at a distance, can be significantly postulated within the uncertainty limits. And on the large scale, quantised field theory is more analogous to classical field theory than to action-at-a-distance theory. The suggestions that have been made regarding the re-introduction of action at a distance are still speculative, but they are sufficient to show that the uncertainty principle *might* be used to confer considerable freedom upon the forms of theory, and that therefore different modes of action in future theories cannot be excluded, even within the general framework of relativistic and quantum physics.

§6 *Conclusion*

Finally, we may return to the two questions with which we began. First, the conceptual question: is it conceptually or methodologically necessary to retain an ether or medium of contact *of some kind* in theories of interaction? And secondly, the empirical question: given the fundamental concept of "matter" or "substance" in a particular physical theory, is there in fact an ether of *this* kind, or of some other kind, or does action take place across empty space?

The second question may not always be easy to answer in the case of a particular physical theory of matter, because the critical experiments may not have been performed, or their interpretations may be in doubt. But from a philosophical point of view the question seems easy to understand—we know what sort of experiences would lead to a positive or negative answer. On the other hand, fundamental theories of matter are not static, and the attempt to answer the second question often raises the first, and often involves that progressive withdrawal from empirical positions as soon as they are falsified which indicates that the question has become a metaphysical one. Thus, it is at first believed that matter acts only by contact; then faced with matter attracting at a distance with no apparent medium, subtle matter of dubious status and properties has to be postulated. All attempts to describe these precisely are refuted. So the medium is described in terms of stresses and tensions, in such a way that energy is the only material property which is located in it; then energy is itself regarded as substantial, and this is said to show that action is after all continuous. Again, although it is shown as conclusively as is possible in science that action can only be propagated with a finite velocity, this is not taken as a final refutation of action at a distance, for the antithesis turns up again within the framework of finite velocities, and presumably it will continue indefinitely to take new shapes as new theories are developed. Clearly no single or simple assertion of any kind, metaphysical or empirical, is being made when it is said that matter can, or cannot, act at a distance.

Is it, however, conceptually or methodologically necessary to postulate a medium? The preference for action-by-contact theories in physics was historically connected with the objectification and depersonalisation of nature, and the desire to eliminate from scientific explanations all "psychological" or animistic models, in favour of the model of mechanism; and it was a fact that most familiar mechanical devices acted by contact. Such consideration may help to explain the deep-seated intuition of what is possible, which forms a climate of thought favourable to continuous action. But this intuition has seldom been translated into cogent metaphysical arguments, even by those who, like Aristotle and Leibniz, held it most strongly. It has more often in fact functioned as a regulative principle, a directive to look for, or perhaps merely to postulate, a medium which is material in some sense, whenever action appears to make jumps.

The conceptual question then becomes a methodological rather than a metaphysical one. There is no doubt that apparent assertions about action at a distance and continuous action are used as regulative principles from time to time in physics, in the form "Do not postulate unobservable intermediate entities" by Newton (in the *Principia*), and by most subsequent positivists down to the restrictivists in quantum theory; and on the other hand "Always look for continuously acting causes", by the Atomists, Descartes, Newton (not in the *Principia*), Faraday, and the quantum theorists like Bohm who oppose the restrictive interpretation. At first sight it looks as though the second directive will encourage the construction of more fruitful models, because models conforming to it will have to contain descriptions of intermediate unobserved events as well as observables, and in general (in theories not governed by the uncertainty principle at least) it is eventually possible to devise further experiments to detect the intermediate events predicted. Continuous action therefore appears to be more powerful as a predictive model, and to make more claims upon the facts, and this would seem to explain why action at a distance has usually been associated with positivist views of theory, where it is desired to assert no more than is already justified by experiment. But further consideration of historical examples suggests that this is too simple a view of the matter. It does not explain why the model of attractions and repulsions at a distance was useful throughout the eighteenth century, nor why the recent theory of Wheeler and Feynman is fertile in revolutionary suggestions, even though these may turn out to be unacceptable. There is no simple equation between action at a distance and positivism, and action-at-a-distance theories do not always lack the content which makes good models.

Action at a distance and contact-action form one of those pairs of apparently contradictory principles which continually reappear in the history of science: atomicity and continuity, mechanism and vitalism, determinism and freedom, causation and teleology, body and mind. Unlike some of these, however, the dispute about action at a distance does not now raise extra-physical problems bearing on the nature of life and mind, although, as we have seen, this has not always been the case, for prior to the eighteenth century the problem was closely associated with some of these other antitheses, and was itself a dispute about the place of animistic explanations in physics. And it may be that its obvious connection with the ostensible phenomena of extra-sensory perception will in the near future raise all these problems again, but in a more extreme form, for these phenomena, if veridical, seem to involve not only "jumps" across space and time of regular and determinate amounts, but also a certain *independence* of space and time. Since existing physical theories, of continuous and distance action alike, have always depended on *regular* variation in space and time, this is one of the features of para-normal phenomena which makes their theoretical expression exceptionally difficult. But if the history of physics is any guide, it seems that if *some* theoretical explanation is available, its agreement with pre-conceived notions of matter and action is less important than its intrinsic simplicity, predictive power, and correspondence with the facts. It would therefore be rash to conclude that para-normal phenomena or any other distance actions, do not occur, *merely* on *a priori* grounds.

Meanwhile, with regard to physics, it must be concluded that continuous-action formulations while not conceptually *necessary* are at least conceptually convenient, and, with our present concept of matter and energy, seem to accord best with the empirical facts.

University of Cambridge

PART FOUR

*The Concept of Matter
in Modern Philosophy*

MATTER AND

INDIVIDUATION IN LEIBNIZ

Edward Manier

A complete investigation of the role of the concept of matter within the philosophy of Leibniz would necessarily involve the consideration of many problems and the employment of many perspectives falling outside the boundaries of philosophy narrowly considered.[1] For the purposes of this short comment, however, attention will be confined to a problem which haunts all attempts to achieve reconciliation of a Platonic metaphysics of Ideal Forms and a Socratic ethic of concern for the individual soul. In the Platonic tradition, "bastard", "image", or "shadow" status is assigned to body and to sensation because of the characteristics of subjectivity, incommunicability, mutability, etc.; the realm of true being, in contrast, is absolute, communicable, unchanging. But can there be, in this latter realm, any place for the ineradicable individuality of the human spirit? If room is made by admitting that the really real includes elements of subjectivity and mutability, are not the grounds for assigning inferior, symbolic status to body gradually eroded?

A famous passage from the *Principles of Nature and Grace* makes clear that Leibniz understands the notion of individual substance to include the notion of expressiveness or imagery:

> Each monad is a living mirror, or endowed with internal activity, representative according to its point of view of the universe, and as regulated as the universe itself.[2]

---

[1] S. Russo, "The Concept of Matter in Leibniz," *Philosophical Review, 47,* 1938, 275–92, provides a helpful classification of the various usages of the term 'matter', as well as a discussion of the historical and systematic forces which influence Leibniz's employment of this concept. N. Rescher, "Monads and Matter", *Modern Schoolman, 32,* 1955, 172–75, discusses the concept of *vinculum substantiale* as a link between the monadic and mechanical contexts in which the concept of matter is used. For earlier discussions of the relation of Leibniz's dynamics to his metaphysics, generally critical of the view that his philosophy should be understood as developing from his mechanical studies, see B. Russell, *A Critical Exposition of the Philosophy of Leibniz,* London, 2nd ed., 1937, p. 89; and L. Couturat, "Sur la Métaphysique de Leibniz", *Révue de Métaphysique et de Morale, 10,* 1902, 21.

[2] *Principles of Nature and Grace,* §3, in *Leibniz Selections,* trans. by P. P. Wiener, New York, 1951, pp. 523–24.

The universe is a plenum in the sense that the slightest change at any point inexorably works its effects upon every other situated substance. A paradox familiar to all readers of Leibniz is his combination of this plenary theory of causality, and its explicit denial of isolated or isolable systems within the universe, with the dictum that the monads have no windows, i.e., that there is "no way of explaining how a monad can be altered or changed in its inner being by any other creature. . . ."[3]

These quasi-paradoxical positions are both rooted in a single, central aspect of the Leibnizian metaphysics: to each substance there corresponds a concept so complete that its analysis reveals all the predicates which can ever be truly applied to the substance as subject:

> This is the nature of an individual substance or of a complete being, namely, to afford a conception so complete that the concept shall be sufficient for the understanding of it and for the deduction of all the predicates of which the substance is or may become the subject.[4]

It is inferred from this thesis that if a true proposition can be formulated linking any two events, there must be a foundation for it in the natures of the substances involved: hence the causal plenum. Leibniz also infers that inasmuch as the complete concept of the substance enables the deduction of all the predicates of which the substance "may become" the subject, nothing new ever enters the substance from the outside; i.e. the monad has no windows.

Inevitably, a metaphysics constructed on this foundation appears as an extreme type of rationalism, a philosophy of pure form, with no room for a principle of matter, at least insofar as the latter is understood to be a "dark, irrational source of chance and luck".[5] Two interesting questions thus present themselves. First, to what extent is the Leibnizian philosophy characterized by a denial or minimization of the role of the concept of matter? Secondly, do any notable difficulties arise in the Leibnizian system as a direct result of such alteration in the role of matter as an explanatory concept?

The discovery of a philosophical system lacking a recognizable analogue for the concept of matter would certainly clarify the role of the concept in systems actually employing it. However, as we will see in the discussion to follow, Leibniz does not simply exclude the concept of matter from his philosophy. On the other hand, his distinctive, rationalistic, "predicate-in-

---

[3] *Monadology*, §4, Wiener trans., p. 533.

[4] *Discourse on Metaphysics*, §8, Wiener trans., p. 300. Also: *First Truths*, in *Leibniz: Philosophical Papers and Letters*, edited and translated by L. E. Loemker, Chicago, 1956, *1*, 414.

[5] L. Eslick ("The Two Cratyluses: the Problem of Identity of Indiscernibles", *Atti del XII Congresso Internazionale di Filosofia*, 2, 1958, 83) has described Leibniz as eliminating this role for the concept of matter.

notion" theory of truth does create special difficulties for the explication of this concept. These difficulties become prominent at a number of points in his system: the identification of the ultimate subject of predication and the discussion of the simplicity of the primitive concepts; the employment of the concept of infinity in the analysis of the related problems of individuation and contingency; the link between matter understood as a principle of non-extended monads and matter as the root of the bodily characteristics of inertia and impenetrability. It is quite likely that no one of these problems can be satisfactorily discussed in isolation from the others. However, it may be possible to suggest the character of Leibniz's predicament as a "complete" or pure rationalist seeking to find room in his system for the concept of matter by briefly discussing some of his difficulties in arriving at a theory of individuation.

Certain Leibnizian texts deny that matter, understood as *extension*, can function as a principle of individuation:

> There is no corporeal substance in which there is nothing but extension, or magnitude, figure, and their variations. For otherwise there could exist two corporeal substances perfectly similar to each other, which is absurd.[6]

Leibniz here contests the Cartesian theory of bodily substance, the view that extension and its modes suffice for the characterization of one of the types of finite substance. From Leibniz's point of view, the real attributes of any substance must be grounded in its nature and the corresponding complete concept. However, the uniqueness of each of two congruent triangles, for example, depends upon nothing but their location on an extrinsic ground or field, and nothing in the concept of the triangle determines its location in this field. Hence, the real individuality of a merely extended substance would lack an internal foundation, a scandal from the perspective of Leibniz's complete concept theory of concrete substance, although it is completely valid in the abstract discussions of mathematics.[7]

It follows that there must be some non-geometrical principle of the real individuality of concrete substances. Leibniz suggests that this principle is that traditionally known as *form* or *soul*, and thereby appears to imply that *form* must be understood as the principle of individuation. But this sug-

---

[6] *First Truths*, Loemker trans., *1*, 416. Also: *Discourse on Metaphysics*, §12, Wiener trans., p. 304; *New Essays concerning Human Understanding*, *2*, 27, trans. by A. G. Langley, Illinois, 2nd ed., 1916, pp. 241–42.

[7] "Though continuity is something ideal and there is never anything in nature with perfectly uniform parts, the real, in turn never ceases to be governed by the ideal and the abstract. . . . This is because everything is governed by reason; otherwise there could be no science and no rule, and this would not at all conform with the nature of the sovereign principle." Letter of February 2, 1702, to Varignon, Loemker trans., *2*, 883–84.

gestion can only be adequately understood in the context of his own distinctive theory of substance, and hasty decisions concerning its accuracy must be avoided.

In one of his few explicit statements concerning the principle of individuation, Leibniz appeals to the notion of infinity:

> Individuality includes infinity, and only he who is capable of comprehending it can have the knowledge of the principle of individuation of this or that thing.[8]

The analysis of any natural event, for example, my writing at this time, leads to the discovery of an infinity of mechanical and psychological causes or conditions. It is in this infinity that Leibniz locates the inscrutable uniqueness of the individual. But a closer examination of this position is required to determine whether or not the irreducibility of the individual may not be, as with Spinoza, no more than a function of man's limited powers of comprehension, with the consequence that, from the point of view of a clear and distinct idea of God, all things would be understood to be one. This problem is emphasized by the fact that Leibniz clearly regards certain aspects of our human characterization of the world as confused, i.e., as falling short of the stature of the "primitive concepts" through which God understands the world.

> Those are confused, though clear, which are perceived through themselves, such as color, because we can only explain them to someone else by showing them to him. For though the nature of color is analyzable, since it has a cause, we cannot sufficiently describe or recognize it by any concepts that are separately explained; it is known only confusedly and hence cannot be given a nominal definition. . . . If we proceed to seek the elements of the elements, we shall come at last to primitive concepts which have no elements at all, or none which we can explain to a sufficient degree.[9]

Starting from the complexity of concrete experience, it is impossible for the human mind to attain the primitive concepts; however our concepts of numbers approach them closely, and it is possible for us to reason about them in spite of our incapacity for their intuitive comprehension.

In this way, Leibniz argues that the perfections or attributes expressed by these concepts are identical with the divine attributes, and that they are all compossible in God.[10] However, although the divine nature and its attri-

---

[8] *New Essays*, 3, 3, Langley trans., pp. 309–313. Also: *Monadology*, §36, Wiener trans., p. 540.

[9] *On Universal Analysis and Synthesis*, Loemker trans., *1*, 353. Also: *Meditations on Knowledge, Truth, and Ideas*, Loemker trans., *1*, 451; *New Essays*, 2, 4, Langley trans., pp. 445–46.

[10] *Discourse on Metaphysics*, §1, Wiener trans., pp. 290–91; *That a Most Perfect Being Exists*, Loemker trans., *1*, p. 259.

butes are identified as the reflective and creative sources of the possible and actual worlds, he denies both that the various possible worlds are compossible and that the derivative concepts which characterize concrete events can all be truly applied to the same event. The ground of this apparently inconsistent denial is to be found in his explication of the distinction between God and the world in terms of two types of infinity.[11] The infinity of God is simple and absolute; his perfections admit of no limitation or dilution. On the other hand, while the various worlds—and through the principle of plenitude, each of the substantial inhabitants of these worlds—are also infinitely complex, they are not absolutely perfect, and their infinity is compatible with limitations of the perfection with which they express the various primitive concepts. It is this variability in the perfection of their expressiveness which limits or distinguishes the individual concrete substances.

It is a fact that throughout his mature career, from the *Discourse on Metaphysics* in 1686 to the *Monadology* in 1714, Leibniz understood the individuation of concrete substances in terms of an analogue for the concept of matter. The analogue is not understood as a "dark, irrational source of chance and luck", but as a dyad of more or less.[12]

> A substance, which is of an infinite extension insofar as it expresses all, becomes limited in proportion to its more or less perfect manner of expression. It is thus then that we may conceive of substances as interfering with and limiting one another, and here we are able to say that in this sense they act upon one another, and that they, so to speak, accommodate themselves to one another.[13]

Although all substances are comprised of similar, infinitely complex formal elements, they differ from each other with respect to the degree of perfection with which these elements are expressed in each of them individually. The most basic function of the concept of matter in this system is to provide for the possibility of relations of more and less, of duration and extent, which both connect and distinguish a plurality of individual substances.

Clearly it is impossible to speak of Leibniz's as a philosophy of pure form in the face of these considerations and such texts as the following:

> If there were only spirits, they would be without the required connexion, without the order of time and place. This order demands matter, movement and its laws. As soon as there is a mixture of confused thoughts, there is

---

[11] *New Essays*, 2, 17, Langley trans., pp. 161–62; Letter of September 1, 1706, to Des Bosses, Loemker trans., *1*, 53.

[12] L. Eslick, *op. cit.*, p. 87, supplies the contrast of Aristotelian and Platonic conceptions of matter, but his paper implies that Leibniz lacks any analogue for either of the two classical conceptions of matter.

[13] *Discourse on Metaphysics*, §15, Wiener trans., p. 311.

sense, there is matter. For these confused thoughts come from the relation of all things one to the other by way of duration and extent. Thus it is that in my philosophy there is no rational creature without some organic body, and there is no created spirit entirely detached from matter.[14]

However, if matter is understood as the root of the relation of all things one to the other by way of duration and extent, it need not be an "irrational" principle. In fact, Leibniz considers the development of mathematical theories of situation adequate for the formal expression of the relations in question. But surely this is a thinly veiled equivalent to the Cartesian position rejected earlier. Moreover, Leibniz's criticism of the Cartesian theory of extended substances, that formal expression is abstract, aloof from the concrete uniqueness of the individual, must retain its relevance in opposition to his own views.

Some attempt is made to solve this problem by appealing to the "divine spectator". Instead of being distinguished and related by an abstract and extrinsic scheme of relations of duration and extent, finite substances are considered as presenting their unique natures to the divine intellect. Thus a substance is active insofar as a particular characteristic is known distinctly in it; passive insofar as some other characteristic is only confusedly expressed by it. However, such a device does not avoid the implication of an external scale of comparison. What is confusedly known in a Leibnizian substance cannot be absolutely confused; it must be confused only in relation to some more distinct expression of the same formal perfection in another substance. To say otherwise is to deny the principle of sufficient reason: the predicate or consequent always inheres in the subject or antecedent. A confused predicate is one which is neither primitive nor open to analysis, but the location of such a predicate in the subject concept could never be established.

Our tentative conclusion after these brief remarks is that Leibniz fails to achieve a reconciliation of the communicable Platonic Forms and the irreducible value of the individual within his system. Insofar as he employs matter as an internal principle of individuation, the result is the implication of some absolutely confused predicates and resultant tension with the doctrine that the individual nature affords a complete, communicable concept. Insofar as he stresses the possibility of expressing individual differences within an abstract mathematical or logical framework, he minimizes or overlooks entirely his concern for an internal ground for the uniqueness of the individual.

University of Notre Dame

---

[14] *Theodicy*, §§121, 124, trans. by E. M. Huggard, New Haven, 1952, pp. 192, 198 *Monadology*, §52, Wiener trans., p. 543.

KANT'S DOCTRINE OF MATTER

John E. Smith

It might be thought that a philosopher like Kant who had so much to do with the founding of an idealist tradition, would have laid little emphasis on matter. The facts do not bear out the supposition. Kant had much to say about the concept of matter and it plays a major, even if not always unambiguous, role in his thought. Matter is, for example, employed by Kant as a principle which guarantees a real, external object for knowledge and he urges it against what he takes to be the erroneous idealism of Berkeley. On the other hand, when Kant is called upon to give his own view of the status of matter we find him interpreting it as appearance (*Erscheinung*) in contrast with the thing in itself. After a century and a half of discussion we are used to the problems and difficulties surrounding all attempts to understand Kant's ideas. Achieving clarity about his doctrine of matter proves to be no exception to the general pattern. Unfortunately, many of the things Kant had to say about matter are bound up with certain other doctrines of the critical philosophy and a fully adequate account would require a full scale interpretation of the entire theory of knowledge. Kant, for example, characterizes matter rather consistently as the representation of something as *outer* and in order to grasp what this means we would need to settle certain difficult points in the doctrine of outer sense. But a full development of the critical theory of knowledge is beyond our present purpose. A working paper on Kant's doctrine of matter must be confined to more modest limits. Ideas basic to his theory must be set forth as far as possible without raising the many questions about his analysis of knowledge which long discussion has shown to be unavoidable. The chief sources of information here are the first *Critique* and the *Metaphysische Anfangsgründe der Naturwissenschaft*.[1]

These writings point to the two basic contexts in which matter figures in Kant's thought. On the one hand, Kant refers to matter and to material content repeatedly throughout the argument supporting his epistemological theory. And, on the other, the concept of matter is the most fundamental no-

---

[1] This work, the title of which I would translate as *The Basic Elements of Natural Science*, has never been satisfactorily translated. The work, moreover, has been unduly neglected, which is unfortunate because it not only throws light on Kant's own views regarding the science of nature, but it provides some clues to the interpretation of his account of empirical cognition in the *Critique*.

tion in his philosophy of nature and natural science. It belongs as much to his account of science as to his theory of knowledge. Its dual status in the *Critique* as substantial material content in space on one side and as phenomenal appearance on the other, reflects the same duality to be found in Kant's claim that his theory is an empirical realism and a transcendtal idealism at the same time. In the *Critique* the concept of matter appears at many different points in the argument, a fact which points to ambiguities but also helps to explain inconsistencies, real or apparent, in Kant's views as well. The *Anfangsgründe* presents fewer problems in this regard because matter is the key concept in the analysis, and the entire theory is built around it. The arrangement, however, is without complication; matter is defined in terms of motion and then considered in accordance with the four categoreal headings, quantity, quality, relation and modality. The fourth section, which Kant calls "Phenomenology" throws light on his view of the connection between matter and the object of knowledge.

§1 *The Doctrine of Matter in the* Critique of Pure Reason

Kant treats matter (*Materie*) in many places in the *Critique* and it is of the utmost importance to identify the particular context within which his statements occur. As is made clear in the Appendix on the "Concepts of Reflection" (B 316–B 324), matter may be taken in a logical sense as given concepts or material for judgment; it may be understood in an empirical or existential sense as the essential constituents of something; it also figures in a further and difficult-to-name sense according to which it means unlimited reality or the possibility of things in general.

Matter (*Materie*) is referred to by Kant as material content in contrast with form in the case both of concepts and judgments. In B 322, 'matter' means material for judgment, or the subject matter. In B 10, Kant speaks of matter as the content of the concept in distinction from its form. The final relation between conception and judgment need not be decided; in either case matter means that which is thought or arranged as distinct from form which is the manner of its arrangement.

Matter is further described as the material of knowledge, both in the sense of something given without which empirical cognition would not be possible and in the sense of the ultimate subject matter of the understanding. In A 223 (= B 270), sensation is equated with "matter of experience", and in many places (B 34; B 60; B 119; B 207–8), matter is identified with that in appearance (*Erscheinung*) which corresponds to sensation. In so far as sensation for Kant always means the immediate presence of the sensible content to the knowing subject (e.g. A 19 = B 34), matter must be presumed to be immediately apprehended. Kant makes the point explicitly in the First Edition version of the Paralogisms (see esp. A 371), where he maintains that matter, as constituent of appearance and as itself appearance, has "a reality which does not admit of being inferred, but is immediately perceived". As bound up with sensation, matter always belongs to the *given* and is, as Kant points out in the Anticipations of Perception, that element in the total appearance which *cannot* be anticipated (esp. A 167 = B 209). This means that matter must always be encountered; it cannot be constructed. When it is received, it is present to the perceiver.

In addition to his identification of matter with sensible content, Kant assigns to it a special status in the theory of *objective* cognition. The concept of an *object* is, of course, central to Kant's epistemology. Although there are many passages in which he writes uncritically as though objects are "given", it is clear that the central problem of the *Critique* is to isolate and justify the conditions under which representations alone may be said to possess objective validity, i.e. possess a real object. 'Object' always means "object of knowledge" for Kant and it carries with it a pejorative sense; when representations are validly said to have an object, it is because they stand under the constraint of certain conditions derivative from understanding and reason. From the Transcendental Deduction and, even more, from the Second Analogy (esp. A 197–8 = B 242–3), we learn that for representations to acquire "relation to an object" they need to be connected in accordance with necessary rules ultimately derivative from the rational faculties. Emphasis upon this side of Kant's theory has led to the supposition that his doctrine of knowledge and of truth is one of rational coherence alone. But the coherence interpretation explicitly contradicts Kant's repeated claim that empirical cognition is not possible on the basis of form alone without content. Despite the priority which Kant's theory gives to the *a priori* or necessary conditions of experience—forms of intuition, categories and principles—the fact remains that knowledge is never possible without material content which can be given only through sensation. In many passages (B 88; B 207–8; B 440; B 748; B 751), Kant makes a point of saying that matter is an essential element if we are to have an *object* as the referent of our concept. In B 88 he even identifies the two; the entire passage is instructive:

> But since it is very tempting to use these pure modes of knowledge of the understanding and these principles by themselves, and even beyond the limits of experience, which alone can yield the matter (objects) to which those pure concepts of understanding can be applied, the understanding is led to incur the risk of making, with a mere show of rationality, a material use of its pure and merely formal principles, and of passing judgments upon objects without distinction—upon objects which are not given to us, nay, perhaps, cannot in any way be given.

In B 646 (= A 618), matter is said to constitute "what is real in appearance" and in the *Anfangsgründe* Kant is even more explicit in defining matter as the *object* which is meant by or referred to in the concept. In the "Discipline of Pure Reason" (B 748), reference is made to "the matter of appearances whereby (*wodurch*) *things* are given in space and time". Regardless of Kant's tendency at the heart of his argument to place the ground of objectivity in the *a priori* conditions, i.e. on the side of form, the fact is that matter or content given in sensation also figures among the conditions necessary for having a real object. The only concept which represents the material element *a priori* is the concept of a thing or object in general. But this concept can never be more than a rule of synthesis of representations; it is not the concept of a real, i.e. determinate object. For that, matter is required.[2]

In other passages, Kant characterizes matter more directly and not merely in terms of its status in the matter-form distinction. Matter is defined further as "substance in the world" (A 627 = B 655), as "the physical" (B 751) or the constituents of things (*Gehalt* and *Inhalt*), as the substance and existence of things in distinction from their states or accidents (B 663–4), as the *substantia phenomenon* (B 333) known through the space it occupies and the effects it can produce. Matter as substance or the permanent in time bears further consideration. In several passages (e.g. A 618 = B 646) Kant cites *extension* and *impenetrability* as the distinguishing characteristics of matter in the sense of the real thing or object. The meaning of extension is given along with Kant's theory of space; the meaning of impenetrability derives from Kant's so-called dynamic conception of matter and it marks one of his distinctive ideas. It is more fully developed in the *Anfangsgründe*, but seeds of the doctrine are to be found in the *Critique*. Matter does not occupy space by "mere bulk"—the apt expression of Kemp-Smith—but rather in its force of attraction in bringing other objects to it or in repulsion which means resisting penetration by other objects. Kant seems to have thought of matter as *substantia phenomenon* (cf. B 321; B 333; B 663–4)—a permanent in

---

[2] The question of ultimate consistency in Kant's position is not raised here. As against every thorough-going rationalism which would find all the necessary conditions for knowledge in understanding alone, Kant stresses the need for given material which cannot be constructed or anticipated. On the other hand that very material is frequently interpreted by him in a way which comes perilously close to reducing it to form. In B 341 (= A 285), he holds that all we can know of matter is external *relations* some of which are self-subsistent and permanent. And, he claims, it is these relations which alone give us a determinate object. As long as these relations are thought of as *spatial* and thus as determined through outer sense, the material pole is preserved. But if the spatial or intuitional element is ignored and the relations in question are taken as expressable through concepts alone, the material or given element is lost.

time, as expressed in the First Analogy (A 182 ff. = B 224 ff.)—which is known through action and the effects produced on the senses. Here as always Kant denies that we can have a wholly intelligible grasp of matter independently of its appearance to sense.

In the *Anfangsgründe,* Kant identifies matter with motion in its various aspects. The stress laid upon motion, force and permanence may seem to reduce extension to a minor role. This is only apparently the case. Kant repeatedly argues that in so far as matter means the content of a real object, it must be represented as *outer*, i.e. as being in space and sharing the characteristics of space. Thus, for example, insofar as matter has parts, these parts are outside each other as the parts of space.

The relation of matter to space is important and it brings with it questions concerning the role of outer sense in empirical knowledge. Kant, on the one hand, relies heavily on the idea that material content is given and that it affects the senses as a basis of the claim that we have a real existent object of knowledge. On the other hand, there are many passages where he claims that this same matter is "outer" only in so far as it is represented as such through outer sense. The two aspects can be combined if we recall the doctrine of empirical realism and transcendental idealism. In relation to a reality considered *in itself*, i.e. considered as the object of a purely intelligible knowledge in which the appearance of an object to the senses plays no part, all of our experience is *appearance* (*Erscheinung*) and thus transcendentally ideal. But in relation to a reality considered as knowable by human beings only in accordance with the conditions imposed by human capacities, experience as empirical cognition is empirically real, i.e. it is genuine knowledge of objects through the effect of material upon outer sense when the sensible material thus received is represented as in space and is judged in accordance with the necessary forms and principles for objective knowledge.

Kant was not unaware of the difficulties and he often spoke of his position as "paradoxical". His doctrine of space illustrates the point. The ultimate status of space as a form of intuition means that space is "in us" (A 370 and many other places), i.e. as a form of sensibility, and is transcendentally ideal. As such it is neither a real being in itself, nor a set of logical or purely conceptual relations. But, Kant repeatedly argued, the assigning of this ultimate status to space is not inconsistent with granting to it and to its content an empirically real status. He believed that our representations of things can be of what is external, i.e. material, not because we have a power of immediately knowing things in themselves, but because our perceptions are related to a space in which *all things are external to each other*. The distinction between what has genuine external existence in space, i.e. matter, and what is represented only as inner, is never for Kant a distinction between what is appearance and what is in itself, but *a distinction within appearance*. Matter is therefore, not the thing in itself, but the appearance as external.

The doctrine of matter is not left unaffected by Kant's doctrine of appearance as the solution to the problems raised in the antinomies. Both versions of the Paralogisms make this clear. The arguments differ considerably in the two editions, but there is a most important point of agreement between them. In the first edition (A 359 ff.), Kant places emphasis upon the idea that matter is but appearance and that nothing of it is known apart from the senses. He attempts to overcome the heterogeneity existing between soul or self and matter by interpreting the latter as a "species of representations". Soul and body are not two heterogeneous substances but rather representations of two different sorts. Matter is that representation which is external or outer and which corresponds to a something in space. Matter is *not* a kind of substance in this argument (see esp. A 385), but only the representation of something as outer. Kant goes so far as to say that matter, not being a thing in itself but only the appearance to outer sense, may very well, in itself, be simple and appear as composite only in virtue of its effect upon outer sense. The question of the nature of matter as it appears in experience is shifted from that of its inner nature as substance to that of the conditions which lead us to regard some representations as corresponding to *outer* objects. The answer is found in outer sense; matter becomes the representation of something as external made possible by the outer sense and its form of intuition.

In the second edition (B 368 ff.), Kant is concerned to show the impossibility of our knowing a substantial ego in empirical terms. Less emphasis falls upon finding a way of closing the gap between body (matter) and the self or thinking substance. Kant, however, returns (B 427–28) in the conclusion to his former point that since we do not know reality in itself, we cannot be sure that the heterogeneity of matter and mind as normally understood represents any final truth. The assumed heterogeneity, he says, between the object of inner sense (the soul) and the objects of the outer senses has always constituted a major problem. His proposal is to say that the two differ not inwardly (i.e. in their substantial character) but "only in so far as one *appears* outwardly to the other" (B 428). It may be, says Kant, that "what, as thing in itself, underlies the appearance of matter" (*was der Erscheinung der Materie, als Ding an sich selbst, zum Grunde liegt*) may not be so different from the soul. But since no final resolution of the essentially speculative problem is possible, we are forced to remain within the sphere of appearance and its distinctions. Matter, in both statements of the Paralogisms, takes on the status of a *kind of representation* with appearance or experience, i.e. the representation of a something as outer.

Kant's discussion of matter and form as concepts of transcendental reflection (B 316 ff.) provides a brief summary of the basic senses in which matter figures in the *Critique*. Concepts of reflection, for Kant, express the relations in which concepts stand to one another, depending upon the faculty in which they originate. Matter and form are said to underlie all other reflection because of their generality. Matter is understood as the *determinable* in general and form as *determination*. In the logical context, matter means "given concepts" or material for judgment; in the empirical or existential context, matter means the constituent elements (*essentialia*) of a thing; in the metaphysical context, matter means unlimited reality or the material of all possibility. Considered in relation to understanding and sensibility as separate faculties, the relation of matter to form undergoes a change. With regard to understanding, *matter is prior to form* in the sense that judgment always presupposes something as given, and this means for Kant ultimately "given to the senses". With regard to sensibility, *form is prior to matter* because sensibility is a faculty with its own structure (i.e. it is not for Kant as it was for Leibniz merely a confused form of representation or an inferior form of understanding) and no perception of material content can be had without the forms of space and time. The given element, matter, is prior to judgment, but to be given in the first instance the same material element is subject to form as a condition of perception (and, we should add, sensation as well).

As should be clear enough from the foregoing, the concept of matter figures in so many contexts in the *Critique* that no single formula will suffice to express its full meaning. Kant wanted to retain a doctrine of matter as given material of sensation which cannot be constructed but but must be encountered and he wanted this doctrine in order to have a genuine, outer object of knowledge. He shared the view of common sense to that extent; ordinary experience and refined knowledge are about "real" things. On the other hand, it is equally clear that his transcendental idealism prevented him from identifying matter with a thing in itself and led him to assign to it the status of appearance, i.e. of reality as essentially conditioned by human faculties, especially the fact of its appearance to sensibility. As appearance, however, matter is known only as outer representation (i.e., as in space or object of outer sense) and our principal access to it is through the effects which it produces. Matter takes on the character of a way of representing while the ground of the outer representation remains unknown. There is, nevertheless, no possibility of going wrong in interpreting Kant if we consistently identify matter with the *given* in any context; it represents, even if this characterization is at a formal level, what can never be anticipated as content or constructed *a priori* in determinate fashion.

405

§2 *The Doctrine of Matter in the* Metaphysische Anfangsgründe

The *Anfangsgründe*[3] treats the "general conception of matter as such". In accordance with his view that a general science of nature cannot be built up in disregard of the general principles of understanding and experience, Kant proposes to analyze the concept of matter under the four headings of his table of categories—quantity, quality, relation and modality. The work thus divides into four sections according to an architectonic principle. Each section is to consider the concept of matter in one of its aspects and each is said to add "a new determination" (366) to it. Kant's description of the fundamental characteristics of matter represents a return to the *Critique* and shows at the same time that "phenomenological" considerations, although they appear to be confined to but one section of the *Anfangsgründe* (Section IV is entitled, "*Phenomenologie*"), actually determine the whole discussion. In defining matter in its basic sense, Kant says: "the fundamental characteristic of a Something as an object of outer senses (*äusserer Sinne*) must be motion, because only through motion can these senses be affected" (366). Motion is fundamental and all other predicates of matter are said to find their ground in it; the doctrine of matter is said to be a *Bewegungslehre*. The subject matter of the four sections is determined accordingly. In Section I (*Phoronomie*), matter is considered as pure quantum of motion, or more accurately, motion is considered as pure quantum; in Section II (*Dynamik*), matter is considered as having the quality of an original power of motion; in Section III (*Mechanik*), matter is considered as having the quality treated in the previous section in relation to another; in Section IV (*Phenomenologie*), matter is seen as having motion or rest relative to a mode of representation, i.e. as appearance of outer sense.

It is important to notice Kant's identification of matter with the outer or with the object as falling beyond the concept. In the Preface to the work (362), he refers to matter as that which makes it possible for a concept to have "its own object" and he refers to the subsidiary concepts of motion, inertia and the filling of space as conditions for applying concepts to "outer experience" (*äussere Erfahrung*). Matter is here in its familiar role as the guarantor of an existing object in space. The curious fact is that Kant speaks of "outer senses" in the plural—not his usual practice—rather than the representation of something as outer through "outer sense" as form of intuition. Although this issue cannot be discussed here, it is noteworthy that mat-

---

[3] Citations are to Hartenstein's edition of the *Sammtliche Werke*, 1867, *4*; all translated material is my own.

ter appears as having to do with the external and with the securing of an object for a concept.

The most elemental definition of matter in the *Anfangsgründe* is as follows: "Matter is that which is movable in space" (369). The force of the term *"Das Bewegliche"* is that of a something which is capable of moving or of being moved; it embraces both the fact of the motion and a "that which" moves. In relation to the cognitive faculty, matter means an object of outer senses (the plural persists in this work) and in contrast to form it means the "object of sensation" (*Gegenstand der Empfindung*). Once again, matter is said to constitute what is "real" in experience, i.e. that it is experience of an existing object. Rest belongs as much to matter as motion does; Kant understood rest (*Ruhe*) as the existence of something in the same place throughout a time. Rest means duration (374).

Under the heading of "Dynamics", matter is analyzed as pure quality of motion or power and in this connection Kant introduces the concept of filling a space. This is one of the distinctive features of his theory. To fill a space means the power (*das Vermögen*, 387) to resist penetration. The initial proposition of the section is most explicit on the point: "Matter occupies a space, not through its bare existence, but through a specific moving force" (388). Kant's argument is that the occupancy of space by a body means the capacity of that body to alter—obstruct or redirect—the motion of another body. Matter is thus a cause of motion in the sense of being able to alter motion by occupying space with intensity. Kant calls the cause of motion "moving force" (*bewegende Kraft*) and holds that this property and not mere occupancy of space defines what we mean by matter filling a space.

The doctrine of power or force is put forward by Kant in explicit opposition to the view that the occupancy of space means primarily the "solidity" of matter. He is arguing against certain of his contemporaries who held that, according to the principle of contradiction, it is inconsistent for the same space to be occupied by two different things at once. In accord with his doctrine that the principle of contradiction is not sufficient to determine questions of material content, Kant says: "All by itself the principle of contradiction does not exclude any material which approaches and seeks to penetrate a space in which something is already to be found" (389). In so far as there is any contradiction involved, it would have to find its ground or explanation in the more basic fact that for something to assume a position in space means that it has the power to exclude all movable things external to it. It is contradictory to say that something is in a space which is at the same time penetrated by something else. Kant goes on to analyze other aspects of the occupancy of space by matter—repulsion, elasticity etc.—in terms of his dynamic conception. One of the principal features of his theory is that impenetrability, and indeed force in general, is subject to degrees. Occupancy of space, though it becomes a matter of degree, is not definable in mathematical terms alone but has a physical basis.

Kant assigns to impenetrability the status of the fundamental property of matter whereby it "reveals itself to our outer senses as something real in space" (400). But by itself this property is insufficient to account for an object. A second, fundamental force is required; the force of attraction. Kant argues that in so far as matter consists in or maintains itself through repelling —via the force which is at the root of impenetrability—other forces, in the absence of such forces it would have no cohesion; it would be infinitely distributed and we could not explain the consistency of matter occupying a given space. If repulsion were the only force, space would be empty of matter; it follows that in addition we need an intensive (*zusammendrück-end*) force which is opposed to extension. All matter (Kant speaks here of the "possibility of matter") must have, as an original property, a force of attraction or cohesion.

In a most revealing comment about the force of attraction (401–2), Kant asks why impenetrability or the principle of repulsion is made fundamental or a matter of immediate apprehension while attraction is assigned the status of an inference. Although the question put is clearer than the answer, Kant's chief point is that, since matter must appear to sense, the property of filling a space is the most immediate we apprehend whereas for attraction we have no immediate sensation and we do not readily refer it to an object in experience.[4]

In the third section, "Mechanics", Kant characterizes matter as having its force in relation to other bodies. In the previous section, matter was considered only as occupying a space, i.e. as possessing force in its original constitution without regard to anything else. Mechanics, however, is concerned with the imparting of motion and with the formulation of laws which are based on the *relation between many bodies* or parts of matter. Such concepts as quantity of motion, mass, velocity, quantity of matter etc., are defined and determined through the relations between bodies in space.

In the final section, "Phenomenology", matter is defined in its modal characteristic; it is described as that which has motion (*das Bewegliche*) in so far as it can appear as an object of experience (450). The main theme is the relation of matter to the human faculties. The opening passages are most explicit in identifying matter with the *object* of experience (451). This sec-

---

[4] The distinction in this passage between a predicate connected directly to a subject concept and one which is connected only through some other predicate is at the heart of Kant's distinction between analytic and synthetic judgments. The passage reflects exactly the same position Kant adopted in his reply to Eberhard in the *Streitschrift*.

tion is of the utmost importance for Kant's conception of space and especially his contention that motion and rest as properties of matter can never be thought absolutely but only relatively. Matter in space can be related to matter in space, but not to space itself. Space cannot be perceived, but must be intuited. What can be perceived is matter in space and such perception is always a necessary condition for empirical cognition purporting to be true of a real object.

§3 *Epilogue*

A most satisfactory way of understanding Kant's view of matter and the material world is to view it against the background of positions held by his contemporaries. On the one hand there were the adherents of the Cartesian tradition according to which the material world is characterized primarily by extension understood as a mathematical property capable of being expressed in a purely conceptual way. It is important to notice that on this view, extension means not so much the *visible* spread or bulk of something appearing to sense, as *mathematical* property which can be directly grasped by the mind and expressed through geometry. In addition to extension the Cartesian tradition stressed the purely mechanical nature of matter, especially its complete otherness from the world of mind and feeling.

Against this position Kant had two principal objections. He refused to accept a view of knowledge which excluded the contribution of the senses. Human beings are incapable of attaining purely conceptual knowledge of the world; appearance to sense is always a necessary condition. Consequently, he rejected the Cartesian mathematical extension as the essence of material substance. In addition, he was opposed to the purely "materialist" conception of matter according to which all qualitative changes and characteristics are functions of quantity of matter. In this regard, Kant was closer to Leibniz and the Leibnizians. Like them, he wanted a place for power and what he called intensive magnitude.

The Leibnizian view, on the other hand, presented other problems; Leibniz, following in the Aristotelian tradition, would not acquiesce in the banishing of the forms of things from the real world. He wanted, moreover, to retain the concepts of potentiality and possibility, something which seemed impossible on the Cartesian view. Kant was on the side of Leibniz in his "dynamic" view of matter and in his refusal to allow that all of its characteristics can be deduced from extension. On the other hand, Kant placed Leibniz in the same camp as Descartes on the issue of purely intelligible knowledge. Kant repeatedly criticized Leibniz for trying to reduce the sensible component in knowledge to a mere form of confused conception.

To Kant this meant the attempt to construe the world in exclusively mathematical and conceptual terms. As against this view, Kant was the empiricist in every respect. Knowledge demands that the world appear to the senses; we have no power of grasping it directly by means of the understanding and the reason. Mathematics is important, but in addition to the fact that (on Kant's view, of course) it is not a purely conceptual instrument, we can never construe the world completely *a priori* since it contains a material element which cannot be anticipated.

In addition, Kant was uneasy about Leibniz' ontological idealism, especially his attempt to identify the ultimate nature of things with monads or points of force. Apart from Kant's general objections to a naive (because not preceded by criticism) ontological theory, he regarded the Leibnizian view as not sufficiently empirical. For Kant matter is more brute in character than can be described in terms of monads. And indeed Kant stressed this point the more it became necessary for him to have a genuine "outer" object as a contrast to inner sense or self consciousness.

The ultimate tension in Kant's theory of material existence stems from his attempt to maintain his empirical realism with a genuine outer material object and also to solve the antinomies of reason through the doctrine of appearance at the same time. As against some forms of idealism, he urged the reality of a material pole. As against the materialist interpretation of the physical world he urged that matter is appearance and is known, in so far as it is known at all, only as object of outer sense.

There is also a something-less-than-perfect integration in Kant's view between his doctrine of matter as it figures in the theory of knowledge and as it occurs in his theory of science and cosmology. In the former, it appears as a limiting concept the meaning of which is determined by the nature of our knowing equipment. Matter, that is to say, is understood only in so far as it figures among the necessary conditions of experience. In the *Anfangsgründe,* on the other hand, *matter* is treated more directly as an essential concept in the interpretation of the natural world. We discover what matter is more directly in its own right and not only through its role in the cognitive process. Even when we say this, however, and further note that in the four-fold treatment of matter in the *Anfangsgründe,* considerations of Phenomenology are confined to but one part, the fact remains that at the outset of the discussion Kant defined matter in terms of its having to affect the senses. His primary characterization of matter as motion is said to be dependent upon the fact that it must exert an influence upon us in order to be known. The long arm of epistemology was difficult to avoid.

In the subsequent history of the philosophy of nature and of science, Kant's influence is seen chiefly in his having established the *reflective ap-*

proach. The older cosmology and the philosophy of nature gave way, under the impact of positions influenced by him, to the study of the structure of our knowledge of nature. We speak not so much of matter as of the concept of matter and not so much of levels or forms in nature as of the role played by principles in theory construction. In this regard the "critical" philosophy is still very much alive.

APPENDIX

A check list of important passages in *The Critique of Pure Reason* upon which an account of Kant's theory of matter must be based.

A 6 = B 10	B 88	A 618 = B 646
A 20 = B 34	B 321	A 627 = B 655
A 86 = B 119	B 322–23	B 663–4
A 185	B 333	B 748
A 223	B 341 = A 285	B 751
B 207–8		

In addition to the above, sections such as the First Analogy; the Anticipations of Perception; the Paralogisms; the Refutation of Idealism and the Second Analogy should be consulted as a whole.

Yale University

MATTER IN

THE IDEALIST TRADITION

A. R. Caponigri

⚏ "Matter", Hegel writes in the *Encyclopedia of the Philosophical Sciences,* "is the abstract form, the existence reflected in itself, as abstract denominations, of that which is the essence of body" (126, 127). This characterization of matter places it in the realm of nature; and it further assigns to it in that realm the status of an abstraction. Abstraction, in its turn, is for Hegel, and for idealism in general, a negation. In this aspect, therefore, matter appears as a reflection twice removed, in the mirror chamber of negation. For nature itself is in its essence a negation; and matter, as the abstract form of the essence of body is a negation within a negation. Notice, it is not said, the negation of a negation. Nature is the idea of the form of being as other. It is the process by which the idea becomes other to itself, the negation of itself and hence external to itself. From the point of view of the idea, this otherness, this negation, this externality is relative; but not so with respect to nature. With respect to nature, this externality is absolute, for it is the denomination of nature as nature, as Hegel writes in the same work (245–247). The first form of this exteriority, that is the primitive denomination of exteriority itself, is space; which is, in a sense, exteriority as the pure idea of otherness in its static multiplicity. The second form of this exteriority which is nature, is time; this is exteriority in its pure dynamic aspect as otherness, pure negation, that is, and destructive force. For whatever time encounters it devours; and what it devours, does not return. Time is, therefore, the pure form of natural becoming; which is not to be confused with ideal becoming. And the difference lies in this, that natural becoming, according to time, does not conserve that which it transcends, but destroys it; so that in this order that which formerly was, now is not. Thus we can understand the aphorisms to which Hegel gives voice: time is nothing else than the pure form of corruption, that is, becoming without conservation, annihilation and not transcendence; in another context, death. The concrete dialectic of time and space yield a movement and place, the primitive denominations of body as body. The analysis of place and movement yields, in their dialectical relation, those specific and concrete properties by which body is designated. And

412

finally, of these denominations, matter is the abstract form, that is, the abstract unity of these denominations as abstracted from the concreteness of body and projected as abstract denominations.

Thus, in the quest of the meaning of matter in the idealist tradition, are we led deep into the labyrinthine mirror palace of idealism; into the seemingly endless corridors of negation opening upon negation. And when finally we come upon it, this matter seems a thing of little importance; the name of a name perhaps, but nothing more. Our task, however, is neither to eulogize or denigrate; it is, to continue the simile, to pick up the Ariadne's thread and by its guidance find our way back to the idea. That is to say, it is our task to come to understand the terms in which matter is thus characterized, and more importantly still, why and how idealism, which is after all, the greatest identifiable speculative tradition in the West, is led to characterize matter in this fashion and what function this negation of a negation, this substance of an illusion called "matter", plays in the mighty system of the idea. In order to do this, we shall propose to ourselves the following questions: 1) What, in the briefest characterization, is the idealist enterprise? 2) What, in the system of the idea, is the positive role of negation? 3) What is the operation by which nature, as matter, is returned to the unity of the idea and endowed with its intelligibility?

§1 *Idealism*

Much ink is wasted in what might be called the "dualistic" characterizations of idealism, that is, those which characterize it in opposition to something else, for example in opposition to materialism, with Bakewell, or to realism, with Ewing and Carlini. Far more profitable would it be to seek at once a positive characterization of idealism, in terms of what idealism seeks to do. (It is needless, we assume, to notice that this is a speculative undertaking; yet not perhaps entirely needless, when one reflects that a host of objections commonly brought against idealism indicate a considerable deterioration of the appreciation of what 'speculative' means in the Western philosophical tradition.) What is the speculative undertaking which passes by this name, 'idealism'? Any simple answer to this question must remain inadequate; but it is an inadequacy which must be risked.

Idealism seeks to answer the question: how is it possible that the real should constitute an intelligible system, when the conditions which must be fulfilled stand in seeming contradiction to each other? It will at once be pointed out that idealism makes a grand assumption; and this is conceded immediately, for no one has ever alleged anything about idealism which was not in the grand manner. This assumption is, that the real is an intelligible system; and even further, that to be real means to be intelligible; and further still, that to be intelligible means to be a system, in a system, or for a system. This again is immediately conceded; but not entirely. Not entirely, because the assumption is only seemingly such; it will disappear, as the undertaking advances, and if its advance is successful. It will then have acquired the status of a principle. For in the last analysis, and at the risk of paradox, it may be said that the measure of success of the idealist undertaking is pragmatic. Its success will be its greatest proof, if it be successful.

What are the seemingly contradictory conditions which the real as an intelligible system must meet? These conditions were enunciated long ago with the very birth of philosophy in Greece. On the one hand, all existence is of the concrete and the particular; indeed, 'to exist' comes to mean, independently of the manner in which it is grasped by a knowing agent, precisely: to be in a particular and concrete manner. But what so exists (i.e. the particular and the concrete) cannot be understood, is not intelligible, in its concreteness and particularity. That is not to say that such cannot be known in any manner whatsoever; on the contrary they can be known in many ways under these characteristics; and even further, there are senses of the term known in which this precise particularity, concreteness and even uniqueness is placed in the position of emphasis. A simple example of this kind of knowing is not far to seek; thus if one "knows" a painting of Modigliani, the kind of knowing is wholly oriented to the concrete and particular, and this is always true of art. The idealists wish to point out that the particular is not intelligible as particular.

This intelligibility has many aspects, as Western thought has developed it. Only two of these aspects are relevant here, however, and need detain us. The first is that it is not a manner of being known, and therefore has nothing to do essentially with a mind; although, eventually it is the intelligibility of the real which accounts for minds. This intelligibility of the real is a measure for certain kinds of knowing; specifically that kind of knowing which classical thought called *science*; but this intelligibility is in nowise dependent upon any kind of knowledge as an event. In itself, it is a dimension of the real and of being. The reason why the particular cannot be intelligible in itself lies precisely in its particularity. When examined, this particularity offers itself either as a pure presence or as a consequence. As a pure presence it is independent of all relations; we know of such pure presences when we turn to works of art; they are pure presences, for in their character of art they are independent of all relations, no matter what relations the sociologist, the psychologist, and others may seek to force upon them. Now it is perfectly possible to say that all particulars are such *presences*; in this case they would not be intelligible nor would one ask that they be intelligible.

Each would have the status of an epiphany, as does every true work of art and before each, one would stand in awe or wonder, as Adam did on the first day. It is further possible to say that the real is such a presence; and if this is said, one is dispensed from asking that the real be intelligible. Or the particular presents itself as a consequence. In this case to ask of it "intelligibility", is to ask: of what is it the consequence? 'Intelligibility', therefore, means essentially: to belong to some kind of system. But this consequence itself may be of diverse kinds. In the first place, there is the kind of consequence by which one event is said to be "consequent" upon another. The peculiarity of this kind of consequence is that it links particular to particular even into a kind of system, of which cosmogonies were examples. Yet such a system, although it yields a kind of intelligibility, does not yield the kind which the philosopher seeks. For the system which may thus be constructed is itself a particular, and is therefore *in its own character* a particular. If the real is a system, it must be one in which indeed such limited systems are possible but it cannot have the characteristics of any of these. The kind of consequence which the particular involves for the philosopher is not an eventual consequence but a consequence of reason. This reason must be such as to determine every aspect of the particular, i.e. place that particular under every aspect in a system of relations, while not itself adding a fresh dimension of particularity to that system. (Parenthetically, this is the reason why theism has always been a problem to the philosopher, for it seems to introduce a fresh particular as the reason for the system.) Aristotle made the inestimable contribution of suggesting that this reason is the *end*; that the real is a system by reason of its end. Although modern scientific thought has relinquished this insight, it cannot be said that speculative thought has done so. Certainly the idealist has not. He is prepared to say that the real is an intelligible system because all elements of particularity are relatable to each other, and, equally important, each to itself, and all to the whole through the notion of the end. But this is not all. The idealist takes a very particular view of *end*.

Nothing could be less true of the idealist than to say (as Stace does of Hegel) that his philosophy is a form of development or evolution. To say this is to give a false notion of end, as it informs the real as an intelligible system. For in every such system of development (which appears to be but the futuristic form of that eventual consequence which we mentioned above), there lingers an element of transcendence which the idealist, responsive to the basic logical demands of his insight, is concerned to remove. The modern idealist is thoroughly immanentistic; and this immanence is the clue to his conception of the end which is the intelligible ground of the real. He represents this immanence by the image of the circle which he takes to be the perfect form. In this form, end and beginning are identified;

or if they are differentiated, it is as aspects of the whole, not as termini of a process. This, I think, is what Hegel intended when he spoke of "implicit" and "explicit", which he conceived in the form of a logical and not a processive relation. The end, which is the reason of the intelligibility of the real, is the explicit, the whole as explicited; which is not something different from, but wholly identical with the whole, the idea of which it is the explication. The nature of the end is that it brings to explication the implicit character of the whole; but while in this aspect it grounds the intelligibility of the whole, it does not do so to the exclusion of that beginning, but only by explicit reference to it; for it is only by reference to the implicit dimension of the real that the explicit itself enters into and founds the system of intelligibility; and the explicit returns to the implicit as to its own ground. So it becomes clear that the end really is not the explicit, but the implicit; by way of the explicit it finds its way back to itself. The real is an intelligible system or simply intelligible, therefore, only on the condition that it constitute an immanent circular movement the path of which, as explication, passes through the realm of particular existence, necessarily, to return to the implicit ground. This immanent circular logical movement is the idea; and the world is its career in existence. In this movement, it is to be noted, explication is the ground of particularity; the return to implication constitutes the ideal dissolution of the particularity; at the same time, however, since it is a logical and not a natural becoming (as Hegel notes), the return enriches the implicit state of the system. This is an idea of which Croce makes great use; it is not, on any grounds, to be confused with an idea of development.

But where, in this movement, is there room for matter? There is a broad sense in which the implicit is referred to as the "matter"; but this is obviously not what we must account for. What we must try to account for is the sort of characterization of matter Hegel gave in the quotation offered at the beginning of these remarks. To come to closer grips with matter in this sense, we must look more closely into the inner mechanics of that circular movement of the idea through existence. Specifically we must inquire into the status of the negation in that process, and more precisely still, into the positive status of the negation.

§2 *Negation and Positivity*

The circular movement of the real has a single point of departure and of arrival; this point is identity. *Identity*, however, is a complex concept. Idealism distinguishes immediately between abstract and concrete identity. Abstract identity is identity without difference; it is the kind of identity which results from the operation of intellect. Abstract identity is not *simply* (that is, without mediation) opposed to the concrete identity from which it is distinguished. On the contrary, the relation between them is rather one of inclusion; that is to say, abstract identity is a moment within concrete identity. As such, it is a moment of negation. The identity of the real, of the idea as indicating the real in its totality, is not abstract but concrete.

Concrete identity differs from abstract identity in this that it does not exclude, but includes difference. Abstract identity is reached by the process of excluding differences. Concrete identity includes difference and is relative to it. Moreover it involves difference in two ways: implicitly and explicitly. Since all difference involves non-being and negation, to say that concrete identity involves difference is to say that it involves non-being and negation, and this in the two ways mentioned above, i.e. implicitly and explicitly. The identity of the idea, that is, of the real, includes non-being and difference. The movement of the idea, of the real, in the process of realizing itself, lies between these two terms, the implicit and explicit involvement of non-being and negation in the structure of the real. It is not to be supposed, however, that this movement is linear between these terms. It has already been said that the movement of the idea is circular. The rhythm is not only from the implicit to the explicit, but from the explicit to the implicit as well. The second phase of this movement becomes, as we shall see, the basis for the spiral movement which is superimposed on the circular movement of the idea; for the movement from the explicit to the implicit is always in the context of the explicit, as the movement to the explicit is always within the context of the implicit. In other words, the explicit status of the idea is dissolved in the direction of implications which transcend the order of implications from which the movement to the explicit had taken its point of departure. This is the enrichment of the idea of the real upon itself, of which the idealist speaks.

The important point, however, is that this movement, both in its pure circularity and in its spiral structure, and both as it departs from the implicit to the explicit and as it returns from the explicit to the implicit (or rather, more accurately, advances from the plane of the explicit to a higher range of the implicit) moves by way of non-being and negation. This consideration, consequently, reveals in its widest sense, the function of negation in the movement of the real. It is, so to say, the true motive principle. For without it the idea would never depart from that status of purely implicit differentiation toward the concrete identity by way of the explication and transcendence of difference. Being, therefore, is not a plenum; its basic law is not the law of abstract identity. Being is a process, and the basic law of being is identity, concrete identity, through explication of difference through negation, to the reaffirmation of concrete identity through the mediation of explicated differences, which takes place through a higher negation, as the implications of the concrete identity of the explicit are revealed. Negation, therefore, while a moment of non-being in the process of the real, is wholly positive in the function which it performs in that process. Unless the seed go into the ground and die, there will burgeon no tree and no flower or fruit.

§3 *Negation, Nature and Positivity*

The concrete identity of the idea as pure implication is pure internality. This is not internality to a subject; but the internality of the real to itself upon which subjectivity itself is based and of which, in its various degrees, it is a mode. That is to say, the real and its intelligibility are absolutely coterminous as pure implication. The absolute implication of the idea is its own actuality and thence its own intelligibility, and both are grounded absolutely in the idea itself and have no ultimate foundation beyond the idea in any other actuality than the actuality which is implicit to the idea as its own reality. But the basic implication of the idea as pure internality and pure implication, as a whole, that is, and not in terms of any specification of implication which may subsequently appear, is simply the "naught" of the idea as pure internality, that is, the idea as pure other to itself, as pure exteriority. The primitive negation of the dialectic of the idea is therefore that negation whereby the idea is posited as pure exteriority, as pure explication, as nature. The initial stage of this negation establishing nature as the pure other of the idea pauses in an abstract identity of nature in which it excludes that fundamental difference in and to itself which is the idea. There is, then, as the nadir of this primitive negation a moment of abstract confrontation of two abstract identities, pure idea and pure nature. But this confrontation cannot abide, or can at most be only artificially maintained; for when attention reverts to the inclusive process of which the two identities are constitutive moments, they are related concretely and the abstract confrontation is over. This, however, is the initial moment of spirit. The philosophy of nature, on the contrary, and hence ultimately the identity of matter, depends precisely upon the artificial maintenance of this moment of abstract confrontation. It is made possible by the effort, which, interestingly enough, is the effort of thought, that is, of the idea, to fix nature as the purely other. Even more, this fixation of nature in exteriority as the pure other, means positing it as a pure identity, though abstract; therefore as a pure and seamless same. The pure form of this otherness is pure exteriority; but it is clearly a purely artificial purity, which is, as we have already said, maintained by an energy of the idea, that is the totality of its negation as pure implication. Hence the abstract positivity of the order of nature as pure otherness and exteriority.

This artificial character is rendered complete, however, only when its artificiality is completely disguised, and its negativity taken as a complete positivity, when, that is, thought or idea takes the stance of being confronted by the other simply as other and as opaque, that is, as containing its principle of reality and intelligibility not in the idea and its return to the idea but in itself and in its own categories. But what is the positive function of the pure and primitive negation which is nature? For every negation must have a positive function in the total career of the real, as we have noted. The answer is: the function of this absolute negation is to render explicit as pure differences all the absolute and basic implications of the idea as pure internality; for it is only by this total explication as pure exteriority and otherness, that the total reintegration of these implications as the authentic explication of the idea is ultimately possible. If that exteriority were not rendered complete, there would remain at the heart of the real an unexplicated residue of implication; hence a residue of the intelligible and hence of the unreal. In other words, the idea must totally pour itself out into nature and the primitive categories of nature before it can begin the process of reintegration of the real as explicit idea. This indicates the absolute positivity of nature, which in itself is pure negation, in the total economy of the real and the idea; and why nature, when the real or the idea is correctly seen as pure process and not as a spurious development, can never be absolutely transcended as forms of existential spiritualism try to do.

The basic category of form of nature as pure exteriority or as body and hence as the pure positivity of the other, which is the status of nature as the same, is *space*. [Space, whether described as extension or as that solidity and impenetrability of which Locke speaks, has the pure form of exteriority because not only is every discernible and indiscernible difference in space as space outside of every other such discernible, but space as space is exterior to space; as evidenced by its mathematical divisibility, contrary to the opinion of Berkeley.] Magnitude and number are the pure form of exteriority as space. The second category of nature as pure exteriority is time. Time is based itself upon a negation within space. This is the negation born of the infinite divisibility of space; for every actual division of space is finite. Time arises in the interstices between this mathematical infinite divisibility and the finite character of every actual division. Or, in a second consideration, it may be placed within the interstices of these actual divisions which must be successive and be generated the one on the negation of the other. Hence we can grasp the rationale of Hegel's designation of time as the pure form of corruption, that is, corruption or change which is unredeemable by any movement of transcendence or synthesis. Both time and space, therefore, are modes of explication of the implicit, and in the dialectic of time and

419

space which generates movement this process of explication of the implica- ·
tion of being as pure other is realized. Death, therefore, that is, corruption
whose form is time, is the pure form of nature in process; but a death which
is the ground of an eternal birth, for movement is a constant, though the subjects of movement come to be and pass away, in nature, absolutely.

We come then to matter. What is matter? We have already cited the
definition of Hegel; and it cannot be improved upon, though to a degree
it too must be negated in order to reveal its positive meaning. If space, time,
movement, birth and death, generation and corruption, are the pure forms
of exteriority or nature taken as concrete (though, as we have seen, this
concreteness is spurious, since it is taken as other to idea), matter is the
abstract actuality of these modifications or categories of body. It is therefore
a negation of a negation. And it must be admitted that Hegel would seem
to leave it suspended there. But this is not entirely the case. There is in the
process of the real no pure negativity. The positivity of matter consists in
this, that by its very status as the abstract projection of the concrete existence
of body as pure exteriority of the idea, it opens the path back to the concrete
integration of body and idea. For as pure abstraction, it is related to body
only by way of the idea. Thus the dialectic which will eventuate in the concrete explicit identity of the idea is begun here, with the concept of matter,
at the nadir of the process of exteriorization of which nature is the pure form.

University of Notre Dame

COMMENT

'ABYSS' IS A WORD HEGEL SOMETIMES USES TO DESCRIBE THE PREDICAMENT OF philosophers who divide the real asunder by abstractions. A commentator on an interpretation of Hegel's conception of matter moves along the edges of abysses. The abyss seems deeper when the discussion of "pure matter" follows an examination of "primary matter", for the commentator might be tempted to separate "pure matter" from "predicateless Absolute" as he would separate "primary matter" from "Prime Mover". I am saved from the involuted perils of dialectical rock-climbing by Mr. Caponigri's excellent presentation of Hegel's position. I shall not refine or quibble: the Hegel I shall talk about is the Hegel expounded. My objective as commentator will be to try to place Hegel's conception of matter in the context of other views of matter which have emerged in our discussion. The need to take variant meanings into account became urgent when we turned our attention to Kant and Hegel. Yet the basic assumptions of these radically different analyses of matter have already appeared in our discussion. I shall, first, sketch a schematism of conceptions of matter and, second, raise three questions, in the framework of that schematism, concerning the significance of matter and the properties attributed to it in the idealistic tradition.

Our discussion of "matter", to begin with, has had two points of reference or fixity: (1) "matter" as what is conceived to underlie change or motion in "physical" inquiry and (2) "matter" as what is preconceived or postulated in any conception of change in "philosophical" inquiry. We have found analyses of matter in which the philosophical principle is identical with the physical substrate; others in which the philosophical conception of "matter" is broader than the "matter" which undergoes physical change, and in which the substrate of local motion is one variety of matter; and others in which physical matter is generic, and the scientific analysis of changes consists in reducing them to physical motion. 'Matter' is defined differently in these different approaches. Yet, for all their differences, the different conceptions of "matter" are applied to a common set of problems. The conceptions are related analogically rather than equivocally. They are held together by the commonplace that matter accounts for continuity and individuation in change. Physical matter is characterized in the investigation of things in motion; the philosophical problems of matter are considered in the investigation of what is conceived to be changing, and what is conceived to be, in continuity and individuality.

Let me take the Aristotelian conception of matter first, since we have discussed it in some detail. Matter is a substrate which persists, or a potentiality which is actualized, in change. The analysis of kinds of change and motion requires the differentiation of primary matter from proximate matters. Aristotle was the first philosopher to give matter a technical meaning, but he attributes to Democritus the notion of a "common body" which is "a source of all things, differing from part to part in size and shape",[1] which may be examined as a second conception of matter. It was to become widely influential since it is the conception of matter associated with most forms of "materialism". Philosophical and physical matter coincide, for matter is being and the void is non-being. Matter is substance, reality, the stuff that occupies space; its properties account for motion; according to the atomists it consists of indivisible parts or atoms. The oppositions of these two conceptions of matter raise philosophic problems which have had long histories, such as, is matter to be conceived as a potentiality or as an actuality? does its operation require an active or a passive power? do the "elements" of matter change one into another or are they unchangeable least parts? A third conception of matter is based, not on analysis of the processes of change or of the motions of bodies, but on the conditions of appearances or phenomena. Such a conception of matter has appeared in Mr. Smith's presentation of Kant and in Mr. Sayre's account of *Phenomenalism without Paradox*, but I should like to treat it in the ancient formulation which I brought into the discussion yesterday. In appearances, matter is flux rather than substrate or body; it is possibility rather than potentiality or force. Protagoras holds that "matter is in a state of flux in such a way, however, that as it fluctuates things are formed continuously by additions which make up for losses, and the sensations are transformed and modified according to age and other bodily conditions"; he also says that "the intelligible principles (*logoi*) of all appearances (*phainomena*) are inherent in matter because *matter in its essential nature is all those things which it appears to be to everybody*".[2] Matter is neither potentiality nor actuality but flux, and forms are imbedded in matter.

Hegel's conception of matter seems a whimsical perversity against the background of an assured common-sense materialism, but it loses its strangeness when it is treated as a fourth conception in the context of the three conceptions thus far outlined. The idealistic conception has familiar antecedents in the Neoplatonic tradition. Plotinus treated matter as negation and non-being. He argued that matter is not corporeal, and yet it is not incorporeal since it is not soul, intelligence, life, intelligible principle (*logos*), limit (*peras*), or power (*dunamis*), and he concluded therefore that it is not properly called "being". "It would be more plausible to say that it is non-being, and not in the sense in which it is said that motion and rest are non-being, but rather it is true non-being, an image and phantasm of corporeal mass, an aspiration to existence".[3] The Latin writers of the Middle Ages learned to call matter *close to nothing* (*prope nihil*) from St. Augustine. The deep and the darkness upon the deep

---

[1] Aristotle, *Physics* III; 203a33–203b1.

[2] Diels, H. *Die Fragmente der Vorsokratiker*, 80A 14; 5th ed., Berlin, 1935, *2*, p. 258.

[3] Plotinus, *Enneades 3, 6; 7*.

which were first created were unformed and invisible. "That whole, however, was close to nothing (*prope nihil*), because it was as yet altogether unformed, but now it was something that could be formed. For you, Lord, made the world of unformed matter (*materia informis*), which, being almost nothing (*paene nulla res*), you made of nothing, whence you would make the great things which we sons of men wonder at."[4] If being is identified with idea rather than with matter, matter is not potentiality, nor force, nor flux, but negation of the power which Plato identified with being and found in material things in the degree that they approximate intelligible forms or formulae.

Philosophical analyses of change and motion employ these and like conceptions of matter—potentiality, subject, extension, force, flux, and negation—and the analogical connecting links among them are rooted in the problems of change which are treated. Matter is also to be treated as mass, law, and as density in a field. We have already found in our discussion of the concept of matter in the fourteenth century that attention to the problems of generation and corruption (as contrasted to the problems of motion), or rarefaction and condensation, and of velocity initiated examination of the "mass of matter" and the "quantity of matter" (and altered the conceptions and uses of the "quantities" of time and space). Sixteenth and seventeenth century theories will elaborate these conceptions of matter in physical and in philosophical inquiry. We have found in Kant an influential reformulation of the conception of matter as appearance and as the given in every experience and judgment in his critical philosophy, and of the complementary conception of matter as that which is movable in space as one of the principles of physical science. Idealistic philosophies will elaborate the consequences of this reformulation during the nineteenth century, and in the course of elaborating the conception of matter as flux they will move to other conceptions of matter.

A. O. Lovejoy has recently published a series of lectures in which he expounds the reaction to Kant which stressed the importance of Reason as opposed to Understanding and which criticized Kant for treating the ideas of reason in terms of the categories of understanding. Under the influence of Jacobi, Fichte, and Schelling, "intuition of reason" or "intellectual intuition" provided true philosophic insight into principles free from the forms of time and space and the categories of the understanding.[5] Hegel exhibits some of the marks of this tradition when he praises Kant for developing a dynamic concept of matter as attraction and repulsion but criticizes him for giving matter a status underlying appearance and independent of concept.[6] Nonetheless, Hegel rejects intellectual intuition and accommodates the Kantian philosophy of understanding. Intellectual intuition operates in the night in which all cows are black; it is like a pistol shot in Schelling's hands. Hegel therefore uses the under-

---

[4] St. Augustine. *Confessions*, *12*, 8. Cf. *ibid*. 6: "Citius enim non esse censebam, quod omni forma privaretur, quam cogitabam quiddam inter formam et nihil, nec formatum nec nihil, *informe prope nihil*."

[5] *The Reason, the Understanding, and Time,* Baltimore, 1961, pp. 1–22.

[6] *Encyclopädie de Philosophischen Wissenschaften in Grundrisse,* 262.

standing as "method" and exhibits its self-transcendence to attain to unity of contraries, the Absolute with all its differentiations. As the Absolute is implicit (potential) in the finite, so the finite is "sublated" (*aufgehoben*) in the Absolute: the Absolute transcends the finite only in virtue of the potentiality (*an sich sein*) which is its Immanence in the finite.

The questions which I wish to ask Mr. Caponigri are concerned with what has happened to the concept of matter in the contexts of assumptions and of problems in which Hegel treats it. In particular, I should like to discuss how this interpretation of matter affects the interpretation of natural laws, but to raise that question it is necessary to discuss also how matter functions as a principle of natural philosophy and how it functions as a stage of phenomenological inquiry. It is to be expected that Hegelian matter is a beginning point, an end point, and a coincidence of beginning and end; that it is positive, negative, and a combination of positive and negative. Mr. Caponigri has laid the foundations for answers to these questions in his examination of the relations between matter and negation. But it may also be expected, apart from the peculiarities of the Hegelian dialectic, that this conception of matter will be reflected in the interpretation of laws of science, system of philosophy, and grounds of experience. The sequence of my questions will lead up to the laws of science: (1) the implications of the Hegelian concept of matter in philosophy, (2) its place in the phenomenology of the relation of processes of thought and processes of becoming, and (3) its consequences in the structure and sequence of laws of nature.

First, the philosophical conception of matter has undergone profound changes. As in other philosophical analyses, "matter" is needed to account for persistence through change and for individuality. But being itself is now process; externality is a development of internality; identity is both abstract and concrete; and space and time are categories of nature conceived as pure externality; it is "Mind" in the form of being-other. On the first level, nature is what is spread out in space. In a philosophy of nature to which the "Logic" is prior, however, the transition is from self-consciousness in which mind, as knowledge, is its own object to self-knowledge in which, as immanence in nature, mind becomes object. In the place of hierarchies of potential and actual, such as we found in the Aristotelian tradition, we encounter moments of negative and objective, but despite some similarities there are important differences between ordered potentialities and serial negations, such as the difference between first matter as potentiality and matter as pure negation. What philosophical consequences follow from the fact that "matter" is a first principle of being and motion in one theory while it is a last abstraction in the other?

Second, in spirit matter is positive as well as negative; nature and mind are united and *aufgehoben* (negated and sublated) in a world of absolute self-knowledge. Kant's phenomenological approach led him to consider matter relative to a mode of representation, appearance of outer sense, and consequently as the given. Hegel considers matter in the *Phenomenology of Spirit* as the meeting-point of abstraction and thought, of negation and being. "Matter is really pure abstraction; and, being so, we have here the pure essential nature of thought, or pure thought itself, as the Absolute without predicates, undetermined, having no distinctions within it."[7] How does this conception of the relation of the processes of thought to the processes of change affect our conception of investigation and proof in philosophy and science?

Third, the investigations of motions in the natural sciences have no direct dependence on pure negation or predicateless Absolute, yet the concept of matter affects the definitions of motion, space, and time and the interpretation of physical laws. This is apparent, for example, in the preference Hegel expresses for the organic form of Kepler's statement of the laws of planetary motion over the form of Newton's statement which expresses causes as external pushes and forces. Matter in space and time is other than itself. No material body can be "simply located". (1) The self-externality of separate bodies is first "negated" in their physical *inter-relation,* and the whole process of development in nature is the progressive overcoming of this external otherness (mechanism). (2) In chemical combinations (chemism), matter constitutes its unity by combining differences, each of which, in separation, has its property only by its affinities to the others. (3) In life (teleology), the material has become an organic whole, the parts of which have no independent reality at all—they are only by virtue of the whole. The functioning of the whole is not confined to the limits of its bodily parts; reactions and responses are describable in the way in which the organism appropriates its world. Self-externality has been overcome in the life of the organism, but its material manifestation is still subject to it. Self-externality is negation, which *qua* otherness, is "negated" and "taken up" in life into the *self* of the organism. The life of the organism becomes a thorough unity of self and other, a *reflection into self.* This is "absolute negativity", that is, the cancelling or negating of the negativity of externality, that is, the very form of mind, being in and for itself. Can these differences be stated in terms of consequent differences in conception of physical law and of the nature and objective of natural science?

My three questions, thus, have to do with the basic principles of philosophy, the grounds and warrant of scientific inquiry, and the interpretation and structure of physical laws, as they are influenced by Hegel's conception of matter.

Richard P. McKeon
University of Chicago

---

[7] *The Phenomenology of Mind,* trans. J. B. Baillie, VI B, 2 b; 2nd ed., London, 1931, p. 592.

DISCUSSION

Caponigri: If you take matter in its positive character then you can construct a philosophy of nature, mechanics and dynamics, and here negation plays, as Professor McKeon suggested, a role analogous to that which potency has played in the systems we have previously examined. But then the other conception of matter that I have tried to emphasize here, which I think is really more important for the understanding of Hegel's total system as an idealistic system, is the movement *out* from the Idea. This is not the movement of Spirit but the movement of the Idea; the necessity for the Idea to "other" itself as matter is grounded in its necessity to integrate itself through differentiation. In negation, the process of constituting the other as other to itself then becomes the ground for many of the categories given, say, by Aristotle among the accidents, such as movement, corruption, and generation. But I think also very important for an adequate reply to the questions proposed is the distinction in Hegel between change and natural change. What intrigued me in my own readings of this is to ask if he can relate these two. Actually the process of negation which the Idea must go through as establishing itself as other to itself in order to reintegrate itself as differentiated, is both a logical and a natural movement, and he does not, so far as I can see, completely correlate these, because the properties that belong to the kind of natural transformation which you would study at the level of nature are not proper to the system of the Idea as a whole. The system of the Idea does not undergo the kind of corruption and generation or the kind of multiplication that you can study at what I call the "fringe" level. But the necessity for the movement into nature and into negation and into matter is itself justified ultimately on the ground that the Idea will always be other to itself in the mode of identity which is undifferentiated, which is a mode of otherness unless it goes through the total process of differentiation and reintegration. The real positive function of matter is that it becomes the kind of nadir which Idea must reach in order to begin the return to its own token integration. In the total system of the Idea and not as making the basis of a philosophy of nature, this is the real function of matter. It is almost like putting your foot on the ground in order to take the next step.

Smith: (Written comment) The point with regard to Hegel seems to be this: The drive towards complete intelligibility characteristic of rationalistic idealism meant a denial of the brute character of matter and a tendency to play down its being as an extended "being-there" of things. Hegel was worried about spatial spread-outness and he seems to have felt that the idea is alien to being spread-out, so to speak. The more he understood nature after the fashion of a system

426

of categories intelligently connected, the more nature tended to lose its external character as extended in space. It is interesting that Kant always held on to that element, which is one of the considerations behind his thesis that space is not a general concept. The question therefore can be raised as to whether any view which reduces space to a purely logical relation, as Leibniz and Hegel ultimately do, must not also have trouble preserving the extendedness of things.

Caponigri: I wouldn't be too sympathetic to that because I don't think it properly represents what I understand Hegel's motivation to be, since he would never concede space to be purely logical: there are no *purely* logical relations in Hegel, unless I misunderstood him. All the relations that Hegel elaborates are both logical and real, and consequently I don't see what it would mean to say that space for him is reducible. To say so seems to miss what I conceive to be his positive point, namely, that spread-outness is not alien to spiritual idea at all but is a necessary moment in the total history, or shall I say, "career" of spirit, which itself is not a career in time but is an absolute or eternal "career". Multiplicity is in Hegel's total system a moment of negation because the total positive moment is unity and unity through differentiation. But the necessity of multiplication through matter is a positive necessity of the total career of spirit; this accounts for his notion of time as involving total destruction, death, and so on, because you need only the multiplication that distributes them over a numerable system but also the *path* of the substitution of one for the other, the death-process which is another kind of multiplication, the multiplication through successive generations. These are both necessary and both effectuated, as he sees it, through matter, and they are not at all things that he is trying to eliminate, but they are necessary moments, phases, through which the total reintegration of the idea will take place.

Mc Mullin: Would it be possible to put what you have just said in this way: The principle of multiplicity for Hegel is matter but matter is not an ultimate principle, since it itself is a moment in the career of Spirit and therefore finds its ground in Spirit. Would that be correct?

Caponigri: Yes, I certainly don't think matter is ultimate because negation is not ultimate. The Idea is totally possible. Maybe I could put this more positively in terms of your question—Yes, Hegel would say that matter accounts for the fact that there are many; many may be necessary in order that the kind of unity or identity which constitutes the Idea will be effectuated, because this unity is of the kind that involves the sort of differentiation which multiplication is. One type of multiplication is completed by way of generation where one replaces the other in some kind of succession which is like death; this justifies the generations of men, each individual in the generation is a man, and they are all part of the Idea. While this may sound very archaic, I think that's what he means.

Mc Mullin: What I'm trying to see is just how archaic—in the best sense of the term—it is. Would it be correct to say that the ultimate ground for multiplicity is to be found not in matter but in Spirit?

Caponigri: Yes, or more accurately, in the Idea . . .

Mc Mullin: So that one could contrast this with systems in which matter appears as a separate principle, as I think it does in the Aristotelean system?

Caponigri: Hegel really thought that he was healing—I think that's his own term—the breach there, that he was really an Aristotelean, that he had no quarrel with Aristotle whatever, but that he was completing this process by showing that it was not an ultimate one but belonged to the total system. He thought that so long as you were dealing with two principles which were not reconciled, not reduced, that your system lacked something in total intelligibility or rationality. So that I think he would differ with Aristotle only in that he would not take matter as being ultimate. But then I have to qualify that: he *would* take it as ultimate in a restricted sense, if one were constructing a philosophy of nature. But that is for him an abstract member of the encyclopedia of philosophy; it's not a concrete member; it can't really be understood unless its relationship with the total process of philosophy is understood. Unless I'm very much mistaken, I think that's what he means.

Hanson: I don't have the foggiest conception of what the expression 'the process of negation' means, when some relation is suggested between logic and motion . . . It seems to me that if one takes the context in which in logic one negates a proposition, this is something to which process-talk doesn't seem at all appropriate. I mean, the idea that a person should be half-finished negating p, or three-quarters finished negating p, now this sounds a bit difficult to understand unless you mean by this that he's half-through writing the negation of p. If the analogy here is with something like subtraction, taking away properties from, then I can see that this is certainly something one *does*. But is this a good analogy? . . .

McKeon: Couldn't we ask another question? We've been talking about Nature and we have been making a series of assumptions, such as that there are individual things which undergo changes and that some of these things might not undergo changes. For Hegel, the supposition we are asked to make in this connection is that our beginning is something that Whitehead would call an "organic universe", that is a whole which is complete without this possibility and therefore the first problem would be precisely to ask: how do you get the otherness that you want to talk about when you engage in physics? You get paradoxical results from this question. One of these paradoxes is that in precisely the region in which some of his predecessors wanted to find concreteness, Hegel finds only abstraction. The terms that are concrete terms become abstract terms, but the paradoxes, although beguiling, don't seem to be nearly as important in this approach. If our orientation is from a cosmology which is unified and if our attempt is to place our dynamics within that cosmology, then what was matter becomes necessarily a series of negations of that initial unifying principle. You can lay your differences out then, and from this point onwards the Newtonian physics proceeds. Dr. Caponigri pointed out that Hegel thought that he was continuing Aristotle; he was doing it, of course, by wedding Aristotle and Plato in order to continue them, but he also thought that he was continuing Newton. And if we could focus on what happens to a Newtonian system

428

(which among its principles includes absolute space, absolute time, absolute motion, and talks of hard, massive, particles) when it is carried over into a system which begins from an "organic universe", we would then find it worth-while to ask: what has happened to matter?

Or perhaps we could formulate it from another standpoint: what advantage would Hegel's conception of matter have as opposed to the ones that we have been discussing on previous days? We could then put Hegelian "matter" within the scheme in terms that would not require a discussion of the entire Hegelian philosophy.

Caponigri: I'm afraid I couldn't contribute any enlightenment on that point since I have always been persuaded that that was the weakest part of Hegel, his attempt to construct a philosophy of nature.

Cohen: Does Hegelian "matter" persist through Hegelian "time?" Unless I know the answer to that I can't place this concept of matter with relation to the others we have been talking about.

McKeon: I think that the reason that this is a difficult question is that in many respects the reason why physics is abstract is precisely a need to separate out and arrange ideas. Matter becomes abstract. Motion is not a movement from here to there in the Aristotelean sense. This involves at one extreme non-being and at the other extreme the Idea. You can squeeze this broad idea of motion down to apply it to any concrete motion that you have experienced but your explanation of it would then be a theoretic science, that is, it would be an abstract explanation. But if matter is negation, then matter must be there in order to differentiate the objects that you were going to examine in the laboratory; without these matter-negations they wouldn't exist. But I don't know what the persistence of a negation would mean.

Cohen: Yet the way you describe it makes it suspiciously like prime matter. (*McKeon*: Oh, Yes.) Which somehow should persist; yet I see no basis for it to persist . . .

MATERIALISM AND MATTER
IN MARXISM-LENINISM

N. Lobkowicz

⚛ According to the recently published Soviet *Philosophical Encyclopedia*,[1] the Marxist-Leninist world-outlook considers the problem of the relation of consciousness to matter as:

> the central question of philosophy, i.e. as the starting-point for the solution of all other questions of philosophy in general and of Dialectical Materialism in particular. This problem has always been and still is at the very core of philosophical thought. All philosophical trends, of the past as well as of the present, fall into two fundamental and irreconcilable groups, according to the way in which they solve this central question of philosophy: *materialism* and *idealism*.[2]

And in the (quasi-official) textbook, *The Principles of Marxist Philosophy*,[3] first published in 1958, it is said:

> The question of the relation of thought to being, of Spirit to Nature, is the central question of world-outlook. Which is primary and primordial: Nature (being, matter) or Spirit (reason, consciousness, idea)? In other words: does matter precede consciousness or, on the contrary, does consciousness precede matter? Do being and matter determine thinking and consciousness or is it the opposite that is true? ... According to the solution they offer, philosophical doctrines divide into two fundamental trends: materialism and idealism. Those philosophers who acknowledge matter as primary, are called materialists; they hold that nobody created the world surrounding us, that nature exists eternally ... Idealists, on the contrary, consider thinking or "Spirit" to be fundamental. They maintain that Spirit existed before Nature and independently of it.[4]

---

[1] *Filosofskaya Entsiklopediya*, ed. by F. V. Konstantinov, Izd. "Sovetskaya Entsiklopediya", Moskva, 1960, *1*. Abbreviation: *FE*. This first volume of the *Philosophical Encyclopaedia* was signed for print on August 15, 1960; three other volumes are to be expected in the course of 1962/63.

[2] *FE*, p. 483/b ff.

[3] *Osnovy marksistskoy filosofii*, Moskva 1959. This is the 2nd edn. of a work, first published in 1958; see the summary by J. M. Bocheński, *Die dogmatischen Grundlagen der sowjetischen Philosophie*, Dordrecht-Holland, 1959. It is, however, not expressly characterized as 2nd edn., and slight changes have been introduced after the XXI Congress of the C.P.S.U. Signed for print on October 19, 1959 (1st edn.: August 7, 1958). Abbr.: *OMF*.

[4] *OMF*, p. 11.

It is well known that the interpretation, the concepts of *materialism* and *idealism,* as indicated in the texts quoted above, originates from F. Engels. In his pamphlet *Ludwig Feuerbach and the End of Classical German Philosophy,* published in 1888, Engels points out that "the great basic question of all philosophy is that concerning the relation of thinking and being":

> The question of the relation of thinking to being, the relation of Spirit to Nature—the paramount question of all philosophy . . . which is primary, Spirit or Nature?—that question, in relation to the church, was sharpened into this: did God create the world or has the world been in existence eternally? According as this question was answered this way or that, philosophers divided into two great camps. Those who asserted the primacy of Spirit to Nature and, therefore, in the last instance, assumed world creation in some form or other . . . comprised the camp of idealism. The others, who regarded Nature as primary, belong to the various schools of materialism. This and no other is the original meaning of the two expressions: idealism and materialism.[5]

This strange identification of two quite heterogeneous problems, that of the relation of thinking and being and that of the relation of Spirit and Matter, has had a decisive effect on all later Soviet handling of the two concepts, *materialism* and *idealism.* Thus Lenin, who explicitly refers to the passage in *Ludwig Feuerbach,*[6] declares:

> The existence of something reflected that is independent of the reflectants (i.e. the independence of the outer world of consciousness) is the fundamental premise of materialism;[7] matter is a philosophical category for the denotation of objective reality which is given to man in his perceptions, and which is copied, photographed and reflected by our perceptions, while existing independently of them;[8] the *sole* "property" of matter with whose recognition philosophical materialism is bound up is the property of *being objective reality,* of existing outside our consciousness.[9]

---

[5] F. Engels, *Ludwig Feuerbach und der Ausgang der klassischen deutschen Philosophie,* Stuttgart, 1888, p. 15 ff.

[6] V. I. Lenin, *Materializm i empiriokrititsizm,* Moskva, 1909, in V. I. Lenin, *Sochineniya,* 4th edn., Moskva, 1941 ff., *14,* p. 87 ff. Abbr.: *ME.*

[7] *ME,* p. 111.

[8] *ME,* p. 117.

[9] *ME,* p. 247. It is interesting to note that as Stalin did not refer to this famous Leninist definition of matter, it is reported neither in the *Short Philosophical Dictionary* of M. M. Rozental' and P. Yudin (1939; 4th edn. 1955) nor in G. F. Aleksandrov's textbook, *Dialectical Materialism* (1953). It is, however, literally quoted in the first edn. of the *Bol'shaya Sovetskaya Entsiklopediya,* Moskva, *22,* 1935, p. 133, and it reappears again in the 2nd edn., Moskva, *36,* 1954, p. 522/a. We find it in *OMF* (1st edn., p. 119; 2nd edn., p. 115), in *FE,* p. 482, etc.

In Stalin too, we find the same identification; whereas the first of his famous "principal features" of Marxist philosophical materialism is that "the world is by its very nature material", the second feature is that:

> contrary to idealism . . . Marxist philosophical materialism supposes that matter, Nature, being, is an objective reality existing outside and independent of our consciousness, that matter is primary, since it is the source of perceptions, representations, consciousness, and that consciousness is secondary, derivative, since it is a reflection of matter, a reflection of being.[10]

In other words: whereas in the Western usage 'materialism' and 'idealism' denote an ontological and an epistemological theory respectively, i.e., two philosophical theories of entirely different orders, Marxism-Leninism uses 'materialism' as connoting realism and similarly 'idealism' as connoting any negation of materialism.[11] This idiomatic peculiarity seems to originate from the following misunderstanding. It seems at least probable that, as ontological materialism entails epistemological realism and epistemological idealism entails some kind of spiritualism, ontological materialism and epistemological idealism are incompatible. But Marxism-Leninism mistakes this entailment for an equivalence and argues, moreover, that any epistemological realism entails ontological materialism[12] and that any ontological position other than materialism entails epistemological idealism. Finally this alleged equivalence is claimed to be a simple identity: a non-materialistic realism is but a hidden idealism, therefore there is no difference between materialism and realism—both are "materialism"; anybody who asserts a primacy of Spirit to Nature is a disguised idealist, therefore ideal-

---

[10] I. Stalin, *O dialekticheskom i istoricheskom materializme*, contained both in *Istoriya Vsesoyuznoy Kommunisticheskoy Partii (bol'shevikov). Kratky kurs*, Moskva, 1953, pp. 99–127; here p. 106 ff., and in I. Stalin, *Voprosy Leninizma*, 11th edn., Moskva, 1952, pp. 574–602; here p. 580 ff. Abbr.: *DHM*, with references to both editions.

[11] Some examples: according to Lenin's *Philosophical Notebooks*, Aristotle wavered between idealism and materialism, which is repeated by *FE*, p. 91/b. According to *FE*, 448/b, "Descartes' idealism is complicated by the religious presuppositions of his system". Compared with older works, however, *FE* is unusually gentle in this respect; thus to the authors of the *Short Philosophical Dictionary*, philosophers like Plato, Hume, Comte, Spencer and Dewey are all idealists, whereas F. Bacon, Spinoza, Hobbes, Locke and even Darwin are materialists. The decision as to whether a philosopher is to be classified as materialist or idealist often depends upon some rather incidental text in the "classics".

[12] Most recent Soviet sources have begun to realize that there is something wrong. Thus, e.g. *FE*, p. 210/a, admits that the acceptance of the "objectivity of being" does not by itself characterize sufficiently a materialist position. "It can get along together with objective idealism, with the religious philosophy of Neo-Thomism, such as, for example, in the work of Bocheński, Sciacca, and others."

ism and any negation of materialism are one and the same—they are both "idealism".

But whether this Marxist-Leninist idiom be based upon a fatal misunderstanding[13] or rather, as all communist philosophers would claim, upon a profound philosophical insight,[14] in any case it decidedly calls for an examination as to what Marxism-Leninism does claim by characterizing itself as "materialism". As we cannot, however, discuss all aspects of Marxist-Leninist materialism, we may restrict ourselves to an examination of the following problem: what exactly does Marxism-Leninism claim by saying that the world is by its very nature material or, to use another formula of Stalin, that all the "multifold phenomena of the world constitute different forms of matter in motion"?[15]

Before we, however, approach this problem, the following three introductory remarks may be useful:

(1) Contrary to most other contemporary philosophies, Marxism-Leninism is an ideology, i.e., a system of thought thoroughly ordered towards political action. Most of its ontological theories have to be understood as extrapolations of a social theory which, in its turn, is used as an "ideological weapon" by the Communist Party, whose history, then, must be regarded as "the visible incarnation of the ideas of Marxism-Leninism".[16] It is, therefore, always to some extent questionable to discuss Marxist-Leninist ontological or epistemological theories in themselves, leaving out of account their ideological and political background; for at a purely theoretical level the

---

[13] See G. A. Wetter, *Der dialektische Materialismus*, 4th edn., Freiburg i. Br., 1958, p. 330 ff.; English translation *Dialectical Materialism*, transl. by P. Heath, New York, 1958, p. 281 ff.; J. M. Bocheński, *Der sowjetrussische dialektische Materialismus,* Bern, 1950, p. 89 ff.; and especially J. de Vries, *Die Erkenntnistheorie des dialektischen Materialismus,* München, 1958, p. 92 ff.

[14] This "insight" has, most obviously, a Hegelian background. If one presupposes with Hegel that Nature and the absolute Spirit are related to one another like a thinking and its immanent *Setzung*, and if one identifies, moreover, the human mind with the Absolute Spirit, the identification of idealism with any recognition of a "creating" Spirit seems to be a logical consequence.

[15] *DHM*, p.106/p.580.

[16] "Za tvorcheskoe izuchenie marksistsko-leninskoy teorii", *Kommunist, 14,* 1954, p. 6, quoted by Wetter, *op. cit.*, p. 319. A good example of the dependence of ontological on social and political theories is the recent theory of "gradualness" (*postepennost'*). In 1950, as a help in arguing for the non-revolutionary character of the passage from socialism to communism, Stalin introduced the concept of a gradual revolutionary leap, see I. Stalin, *Marksizm i voprosy yazykoznaniya*, Moskva, 1950, p. 58 ff.; some years later, B. M. Kedrov wrote an article that described "gradualness" as an ontological category, see *Voprosy Filosofii* (Abbr.: *VF*), 2, 1954, p. 50 ff. See also my article "Sowjetideologie und Volksdemokratie", *Wort und Wahrheit* (Wien), *11,* 1960, p. 709 ff.

rigidity and the dogmatism of Marxism-Leninism (which may seem acceptable as long as one considers it mainly as an instruction for political action) easily comes to appear not only intolerable, but entirely unintelligible.

(2) This does not mean, however, that there exist no true Marxist-Leninist philosophers. The widely accepted opinion that no true philosophy is possible as long as there is no absolute freedom of thought does not seem to be altogether correct; the Christian and the Moslem philosophies of the Middle Ages are probably the best counter-instances. The basic tenets of such thinkers may be grounded in dogma; but within such a frame, no matter how inhuman and narrow, one may always find serious attempts to philosophize. One must, however, avoid applying the high critical standards of contemporary Western philosophy to Marxism-Leninism; up to now at least, communist philosophy is of interest less to the philosopher properly speaking than to the historian of philosophy.

(3) Although it would be hardly correct to speak of a decisive liberalization of Soviet philosophy since Stalin's death[17], in the last four or five years so many original contributions have been published that it would be simply inexcusable to discuss a problem like ours mainly on the strength of texts written before 1953. For this reason, much more weight will be given in this essay to more recent Soviet works, on the assumption that these are, on the whole, more competent and more revelatory than those written under Stalin's rule.

§1 *Materialism*

At first sight it might seem that materialism is a highly unequivocal position. Any materialist philosophy will deny the existence of supernatural forces as well as of spiritual beings and try to reduce everything knowable to matter. The question might, of course, arise as to how such a position can possibly be proved; as to the meaning of the basic tenets, however, there seems to be little to ask.

And yet it is easy to show that this first impression is treacherous. There are, indeed, several ways in which the materialist contention that everything is material and that nothing but matter exists is fundamentally ambiguous.

(a) If someone claims that nothing but matter exists, we can under-

---

[17] It is often overlooked that the decisive liberalization of Soviet philosophy was stimulated by Stalin himself. His authoritative decision on linguistics of June/July 1950 that declared language not to be class-conditioned, made possible all later discussions on logic, on philosophical questions of physics, etc. None of the later changes, e.g. the reintroduction of certain "laws of dialectics" omitted by Stalin, is as important as the earlier one.

stand him as saying either that *matter* is the most general category, or that there are no other than material existents (substances, individuals). As can easily be seen, these two assertions are not strictly equivalent; for if I say that there are no other than material existents, I can still maintain that some of their properties are not to be described as material (provided that 'material' does not simply mean *property of material existents*) and thus avoid at least an intensional identification of the two concepts: *matter* and *being*. One could argue, for example, that *matter* and *material* can be predicated only of existing individuals and not of their properties; or again, one could admit that all properties of material individuals are themselves material, without necessarily allowing that properties of such properties could be said to be material. In other words: any materialist will maintain that *matter* is a transcendental concept; yet it might be only an extensionally transcendental concept that cannot, without further ceremony, be identified with the intensionally transcendental concept of being.[18] On the other hand, someone might want to claim that there are entities which are neither existing individuals nor their properties, things which, therefore, cannot be called material. Thus e.g. the Stoics who denied the existence of non-material individuals and are, therefore, usually considered as materialists, nevertheless held that the true ($\alpha\lambda\eta\theta\epsilon\varsigma$) is incorporeal, since it is neither an individual nor one of its properties, only an ideal being, a $\lambda\epsilon\kappa\tau\delta\nu$[19]. We may, therefore, distinguish between *matter* as a radically extensionally transcendental concept (in a materialist system that denies any non-material entities at all, although it still may admit non-material properties of material entities) and an extensionally transcendental concept of matter which embraces only real being, even though ideal entities like meaning, propositions or even Platonic ideas are admitted in the system. (Though there might be some doubt as to whether such a system would still be truly materialistic.)

Thus we get a whole scale of possible materialist positions. We might speak of a "maximalist" materialism that takes *matter* to be an intensionally transcendental concept and thus identifies it with *being;* of a "minimalist" materialism that denies spiritual individuals and, of course, supernatural forces, but admits ideal entities and non-material properties of material existents; and of several intermediary positions.

(b) This is, however, by no means the only ambiguity of the basic

---

[18] 'Extensional' and 'intensional' are used here in a special sense. An "extensionally" transcendental concept is one which applies to all individuals, but not to the properties of these individuals. An "intensionally" transcendental concept is one which would apply to both.

[19] See Sextus Empiricus, *Adv. Mathem.*, 7, 38 ff.; Sexti Empirici *Opera*, Lipsiae, 1912 ff., B 81.

materialist tenet. For a materialist not only denies the existence of a certain kind of entities, individuals or properties, he maintains moreover that the actually existing things are such and such, namely, material. Once again, this might seem a thoroughly unequivocal assertion: whatever exists, is material, i.e. it is of the same kind as the palpable objects we usually call "material"—stones, water, fire and the like. Such statements might help us to know what exists and what does not exist; they yield, however, very little information as to how and what the actually existing things are. In other words: if whatever exists, is material, what does this tell us of what exists? If nothing but matter exists, what are, then, the properties of whatever exists? It is easy to see that these questions can be answered in several different ways. Someone might want to claim that matter is to be defined as that which really exists and whose existence can be "scientifically" acknowledged; this is, of course, the least satisfactory of all possible answers. Another might want to say that matter is what can be known through the senses; or: what is in space and time; or: what is changeable; etc.

(c) Finally, there is a third ambiguity which is probably the most important of all and, unfortunately, at the same time, the least easy to describe. If we inquire into the exact meaning of assertions like "the world is by its very nature material" or "nothing but matter exists", we are interested not only in the common attributes of material things (like *knowable through senses, existing in space and time,* etc.), but, moreover, in the semantics of the expression 'matter', especially insofar as it reveals, so to speak, the "ontological function" of matter.

Someone might want to claim that 'matter' is a generic term for material things like stones, trees and dogs; another might want to go so far as to add that properties of such things are matter, too. In this case, the semantics of 'matter' will be similar to that of 'a (subsistent) being' and 'being' respectively.[20] This is, however, neither the only possible nor even the usual interpretation. Matter, conceivably, might also be understood as something things are made or consist of. Thus one could suggest, for example, that 'matter' designates anything of which some other thing consists: flesh and bones are the "matter" of animals, chemical compounds the "matter" of flesh and bones, atoms the "matter" of chemical compounds, etc. Or again, one could lay down the convention that only those things *everything* consists of, like elementary particles, are to be called "matter". Finally, someone might want to say that 'matter' designates not a thing at all, but a metaphysical principle of all material things; and in that case it might be something things consist of, for example, or a "radical subject", a "substratum", a "substance" or whatever else might be denoted by such ambiguous expressions.

---

[20] The German distinction between *'Seiendes'* and *'Sein'* and the French terminology introduced by Sartre (*'étant'*, *'être'*) would be more appropriate.

These preliminary reflections indicate that the basic materialist tenet of the thorough materiality of the world is susceptive of many different interpretations. The concept of matter can be transcendental in several different ways; material things can be characterized this way or that; and the ontological function of "matter" will differ from system to system. There are probably still other such sets of ambiguities; for the purpose of our inquiry, however, the three forementioned will be sufficient. As it is somewhat difficult to keep asunder the second and the third group of problems, we shall treat them jointly; and as the transcendentality of the concept of matter will largely depend upon the definition of matter itself, we shall invert the order followed up to now and dispose our essay according to the following two questions:

a) By what attributes does Marxism-Leninism define matter and which ontological function does it impute to it?

b) Are there, according to Marxism-Leninism, any entities or properties not to be qualified as "material"?

As to both questions, we shall try to point out by what kind of proofs Marxism-Leninism usually substantiates the respective answers; we shall, however, not discuss such proofs in detail, since their hidden logical structure cannot be made intelligible without entering into the highly complex matter of Soviet philosophical methodology.[21]

§2 The Marxist-Leninist Definition of 'Matter'

In order to understand how the Marxist-Leninist concept of matter arose, one has to remember the complications and difficulties in which classical materialism was entangled by the developments taking place in physics during the closing years of the last century. Because of the discovery of radioactivity, the previously simple concept of matter suddenly became obscure. Many of the properties, previously ascribed to matter, like compactness, impenetrability or even extension, seemed no longer acceptable; the new discoveries showed that atoms are neither unchangeable nor indivisible; the disappearance of matter in radioactive decay, in particular, came as a considerable shock. In a word, it seemed no longer possible to give an exact and authoritative definition of matter; many philosophizing scientists, like L. Houllevigue, H. Poincaré and A. Righi, simply spoke of an abandonment of the traditional concept of matter.

In order to evade the difficulties arising from such discussions, Lenin decided to define matter in purely epistemological terms as "objective reality given to us in sensation".[22] There is, of course, the famous passage in which

---

[21] See T. J. Blakeley, *Soviet Scholasticism*, Dordrecht-Holland, 1961.

[22] E.g. *ME*, p. 254.

Lenin maintains that "the *sole* "property" of matter with whose recognition philosophical materialism is bound up is the property of *being objective reality,* of existing outside our consciousness",[23] and no Soviet philosophical textbook has ever omitted to quote or at least to paraphrase this "classical definition of matter".[24] It is, however, obvious that the contention that matter is objective reality, though it may inform us that matter exists, tells us neither what it is nor, consequently, what actually does exist; and, in particular, it does not exclude spiritual beings, since everybody who maintains that such beings exist, obviously takes them to be objective reality. It seems, therefore, beyond question that Lenin had in mind objective reality which is knowable through the senses; the severe criticisms of the Leninist definition of matter as objective reality without qualification, which have by now become usual in the West, hit the letter rather than the spirit of Marxism-Leninism. One might add that many Soviet textbooks quote the definition of matter as "objective reality given to us in sensation" as well; and at least one of them, published in 1958, says explicitly:

> According to the Leninist definition, matter is the philosophic category for the denotation of objective reality which exists outside of man; matter is that which, acting on our organs of sense, produces sensation. This definition of matter makes reference to its most essential traits: objective existence and ability to act on the sense organ.[25]

It seems, moreover, that Lenin was quite aware of the sensualism entailed by his definition of matter: he accuses E. Mach, B. Petzold as well as the Russian V. M. Tshernov of trusting too little in the testimony of our sense-organs, of being "inconsistent in the carrying through of sensualism",[26] and some pages later he explicitly approves the following definition in A. Franck's *Dictionnaire des sciences philosophiques,* published in 1875:

> Objective sensualism is materialism, for matter and bodies are, according to materialists, the only objects that can reach our senses.[27]

Since Marxism-Leninism is, however, by no means a consistent empiricism—it recognizes the importance, for example, of abstractions and abstract theories[28]—it takes everything for material that can be known either directly

---

[23] *ME*, p. 247.
[24] I. D. Pantskhava, *Dialektichesky materializm,* Moskva, 1958, p. 133.
[25] *Ibid.*
[26] *ME*, p. 116.
[27] *ME*, p. 118.
[28] Thus e.g. *FE* criticizes the positivist "principle of verification", and tries to show that all basic questions of philosophy would become meaningless if one were to presuppose it; see p. 242/a.

by our senses or through abstraction and inferences from our sense-experience, i.e. again simply everything that can be acknowledged as "objectively real". It might seem, therefore, in spite of what we just said, that it is Lenin's definition of matter as objective reality without qualification that Marxism-Leninism is mainly relying upon.

It is, indeed, true that Marxist-Leninists, when trying to show that something is material, often simply prove that it really does exist. Thus, in 1953, the philosophizing physicist S. G. Suvorov advanced the following "proof" of the materiality of the electromagnetic field: it undergoes influences of compact matter, therefore it is not simply a formal device for calculation, but reality—and no other proof for its materiality is needed.[29] On the other hand, however, no Marxist-Leninist would admit a proof of the objective reality, for example, of God; he would argue that God cannot be objective reality, since he is not material. But one cannot, obviously, consistently prove the materiality of A by proving its existence and, at the same time, reject a proof of the existence of B on the grounds that B is not material—especially, if the contention that only material things exist (which may perhaps be presupposed as a sort of axiom) amounts to saying that only objective reality exists.

Thus only the following interpretation seems possible. According to Marxism-Leninism, matter is to be defined as objective reality which is either knowable through the senses or at least can be conceived in analogy to things knowable through the senses. Thus the magnetic field, for example, although it can be neither seen nor heard, is an objective reality detected by methods which can be understood as a sort of enlargement of direct sense-knowledge (or, at least, its "being objective reality" is detected by such methods); it can, therefore, be conceived as analogous to customary material things. Vague as such a definition may sound, in any case it seems to exclude spiritual as well as ideal entities. There still remain, of course, serious difficulties, especially concerning the matters discussed by Marxist-Leninist political economy. Thus, according to G. F. Aleksandrov, the value of goods (Marx' *"Warenwert"*) is something real and, consequently, material—a "social relation that arises from the production process and is revealed during the process of exchange";[30] yet it seems difficult to admit that phenomena like values are objects of sense-knowledge, no matter how the latter be "enlarged". It might be, however, possible to understand such phenomena as properties of material things, an interpretation which would attenuate the difficulty considerably.

---

[29] S. G. Suvorov in *Uspekhi Fizicheskikh Nauk*, *1*, 1953, p. 135, quoted by S. Müller-Markus, *Einstein und die Sowjetphilosophie*, Dordrecht-Holland, 1960, p. 372.

[30] *Dialektichesky materializm*, ed. by G. F. Aleksandrov, Moskva, 1953, p. 390.

The epistemological definition of matter just described strongly suggests a distinction between two different concepts of matter: a philosophical and a scientific. It was, indeed, Lenin himself who distinguished sharply between the "matter" concerning which materialism and idealism differ in their respective answers and "the question of the structure of matter, of atoms and electrons" which, according to him, "concerns only this "physical world" ".[31] Regarding the latter, Lenin had recognized that no physical interpretation of the structure of matter may be considered as definitive:

> The "essence" of things, or "substance", is also relative; it expresses only the deepening of man's knowledge of objects; and if yesterday the profundity of this knowledge did not go beyond the atom, and today does not go beyond the electron and ether, Dialectical Materialism insists on the temporal, relative, approximate character of all these *milestones* in the knowledge of Nature gained by the progressing science of man. The electron is as inexhaustible as the atom; Nature is infinite. . . .[32]

Yet this distinction was not without its drawbacks. First, it encouraged an emancipation of the sciences from their ideological tutelage; and secondly, there was the disturbing possibility that, by using a more technical and therefore narrower concept of matter, scientists might discover that besides or even beyond matter there is something different from matter, e.g. energy or the field. Therefore, in 1951, at a meeting of the Institute of Philosophy of the Soviet Academy of Sciences, this very distinction between a philosophical and a scientific concept of matter was rejected; while hitherto it had been described as "a necessary presupposition for the consistent maintaining of a materialistic line in philosophy",[33] now suddenly it became "totally opposed to scientific philosophy, to Dialectical Materialism".[34] From now on, only the philosophical concept of matter was to be used, by philosophers as well as by scientists; according to F. T. Arkhiptsev, this philosophical concept of matter:

> embraces the whole objective world, everything that existed, exists or will in the future be produced by Nature. The concept of matter embraces all known and unknown kinds of Nature; it is the all-embracing, absolutely universal concept. And as it was elaborated by philosophy, it is called a philosophical concept.[35]

This condemnation[36] of a probably quite useful distinction throws an

---

[31] *ME*, p. 246 ff.

[32] *ME*, p. 249.

[33] *Bol'shaya Sovetskaya Entsiklopediya*, 22, 1935, p. 134.

[34] S. G. Suvorov, *loc. cit.*, quoted by S. Müller-Markus, *op. cit.*, p. 370.

[35] F. T. Arkhiptsev in *VF*, 6, 1951, p. 52.

[36] More recent Soviet textbooks seem to tend to revive the old distinction between

interesting light on Soviet philosophic method. On the one hand, Marxism-Leninism claims that materialism is daily confirmed by all the sciences; as one of the authors puts it: "the entire path of the development of science in the last half-century is a triumphant confirmation of Dialectical Materialism".[37] Yet on the other hand its own exceedingly broad definition of matter is said to be the only scientific one,[38] and it is declared obligatory for all sciences. In other words: since all conceivable accesses to scientific falsification are barricaded by a concept of matter broad enough to permit the recognition of *any* scientifically discoverable reality as material, by definition sciences cannot falsify the basic Marxist-Leninist tenet. Yet if a falsification is strictly inconceivable, the statement about the "triumphant confirmation" through science is not very meaningful either; for the possibility of proof seems to depend upon, at least, the conceptual possibility of disproof.

One might be tempted to add that if *matter* is an all-embracing, absolutely universal concept, then the statement "everything is material" cannot be proven or meaningfully confirmed anyway, since it is analytic or tautologous. There is, however, at least one instance wherein this observation would not hold true. Suppose that A's, B's and C's be the only conceivable beings; and suppose, moreover, that it be proved that neither B's nor C's, although being conceivable, actually can exist. In this case, then, A will be, in a sense at least, a transcendental concept (one might call it a *"quoad se"* transcendental concept, since, in that case, the statement 'only A's exist' will be, so to speak, analytic or tautologous only *quoad se,* not *quoad nos*); and yet it will be correct to say that the statement 'only A's exist' has been proven. This point is of some relevance, since Soviet thinkers seem constantly to presuppose that the existence of entities other than material ones has been, once for all, disproved by their "classics". It is on this assumption that the concept of matter is said to be all-embracing and absolutely universal; and the constant recurrence to sciences is a self-satisfied applause rather than a verification. To put it more bluntly: like any other believer, a Marxist-Leninist enjoys the "corroborations" and, as regards negative cases, he will try to exclude them by an appropriate re-interpretation. There is, of course, a difference between a Marxist-Leninist and any other believer: whereas religious believers usually claim that God told them what to believe,

---

a philosophical and a scientific concept of matter. See for example *Osnovy marksistskoy filosofii. Popularny uchebnik*, Moskva, 1960 (not to be confounded with *OMF*): "The philosophical concept of matter has to be distinguished from the way in which natural sciences describe the world (*ot estestvennonauchnoy kartiny mira*), i.e. from those ideas on the structure . . . of concrete forms of matter which arise in the development of science." p. 51.

[37] N. M. Sisakyan in *VF*, 2, 1959, p. 89.

[38] See e.g. F. T. Arkhiptsev, *loc. cit.*

Marxists-Leninists maintain that their basic tenets, the so-called "principles of Marxism-Leninism", have been scientifically proven by the "classics". In the last resort, however, this difference is rather verbal: for these "principles" are being accepted not so much on the ground of their respective proofs as because they have been promulgated by the "classics"; as has been recently shown by T. Blakeley, a reference to a "classical" text is usually considered to be a sufficient proof.[39] The question as to whether the "classics" actually *did* prove their point is of little relevance; Soviet thinkers are satisfied simply with a claim in this respect. It is highly significant of the Soviet philosophic atmosphere that, since 1931, there are only three cases in which a proposition of a "classic" has been called in question (one of the three critics being, by the way, a "classic" himself).[40]

Up to now, we have heard about only two attributes of matter: it is objective reality, existing outside our consciousness, and it is, usually at least, knowable through the senses. Both are characteristic of Lenin's conception of matter in purely epistemological terms: objective reality as opposed to pure impressions, Kantian "phenomena" and the like, and knowableness through senses as opposed to any kind of intellectual intuition or mystical experience. There are, however, according to Marxism-Leninism, several other attributes of matter, although Soviet thinkers seem not to be inclined to introduce them into a definition of matter; since Lenin maintained that the *sole* property of matter with whose recognition philosophical materialism is bound up is the property of being objective reality, all other properties of matter (except, usually, the sensuous perceptibility which is often only indirectly alluded to) are treated independently of the definition. And yet it was Lenin himself who asserted (only about ten pages later, by the way) that:

> a Dialectical Materialist considers motion as an *inseparable property of matter*.[41]

Once again, therefore, it would seem that there is not just one property of matter with whose recognition Dialectical Materialism is bound up;[42] be-

---

[39] T. Blakeley, *op. cit.*, especially p. 13 ff.

[40] *Ibid.*, p. 18 ff.; also my work *Das Widerspruchsprinzip in der neueren sowjetischen Philosophie*, Dordrecht-Holland, 1960, p. 5 ff. The "classic" in question is Stalin who, sometime around 1947, criticized a small passage in Engels' *External Politics of Russian Tsarism;* the two other criticisms, by E. A. Asratyan (1955) and A. Kol'man (1958), concern passages in Engels, too.

[41] *ME*, p. 257. Our italics.

[42] This statement, contrary to what H. Dahm, "Der Streit um die Materie des Diamat", *Ost-Probleme* (Bonn), 27, 1956, pp. 290 ff., thinks, must not be understood to contradict Lenin's statement about the "*sole* property". For in the latter passage, Lenin speaks of "philosophical materialism" in general, whereas in the former he is concerned with Dialectical Materialism.

sides being objective reality given to us in sensation, matter is always and necessarily in motion. Although emphasizing (against energeticists like W. Ostwald) that there never can be motion without matter, Lenin does not shrink from asserting that:

> whether we say the world is moving matter, or that the world is material motion, makes no difference whatever.[43] This assertion does, however, not entail any denial of bodies at rest; rest is said to be a limiting case of motion, a "relative equilibrium" that "only has meaning in relation to one or other definite form of motion".[44]

Matter without motion, therefore, is "just as unthinkable as motion without matter"; according to Engels, motion is the "mode of existence of matter (*Daseinsweise der Materie*)".[45] More recent Soviet sources, however, usually reserve this latter definition (*sposob ili forma sushchestvovaniya materii*) to space and time, and speak of motion as of the "form of being of matter (*forma bytiya materii*)";[46] according to the *Philosophical Encyclopaedia* (which, incidentally, uses the older definition of Engels), motion is "an inseparable property (of matter), an attribute belonging to matter intrinsically (*vnutrenne*)".[47]

But as matter "cannot move otherwise than in space and time",[48] there are still two more properties of matter, both of which are said to be "basic forms of the existence of matter".[49] "A being outside of time makes as little sense as a being outside of space".[50] As the essence of space and time consists in motion,[51] matter, motion, space and time are absolutely inseparable.[52] We are told that real space is three-dimensional, and time one-dimensional

---

[43] *Ibid.*

[44] F. Engels, *Herrn Eugen Dührings Umwälzung der Wissenschaft ("Anti-Dühring")*, 11th edn., Berlin, 1958, p. 70.

[45] *Ibid.*, also F. Engels, *Dialektik der Natur*, 3rd edn., Berlin, 1958, p. 61.

[46] This was first observed by H. Dahm, *art. cit.*, p. 921 ff. The difference between these two formulae is often overlooked, thus e.g. by G. A. Wetter, *op. cit.*, p. 346 ff.; and by Bocheński, *op. cit.*, p. 8. It would seem, however, that even Soviet philosophers do not stress this difference very much. Thus, contrary to *BSE*, *14*, 1952, p. 291, or to *OMF*, p. 122, more recent works use the classical formula of Engels: the popular version of *OMF*, p. 54 ff.; I. D. Andreev, *Dialektichesky Materializm*, Moskva, 1960, p. 118 ff.; etc.

[47] *FE*, p. 433.

[48] *ME*, p. 162.

[49] *OMF*, p. 132; *FE*, p. 298/b; I. D. Andreev, *op. cit.*, p. 125 ff., etc. H. Dahm points out that the *Great Soviet Encyclopedia* (Abbr.: *BSE*) defines space as a *universal* and time as *one of the basic* forms of existence of matter; see *BSE*, *9*, 1951, p. 272, and *35*, 1955, p. 105.

[50] F. Engels, *Anti-Dühring*, p. 61; also *Dialektik der Natur*, p. 25.

[51] This queer contention goes back to Lenin's *Philosophical Notebooks* (V. I. Lenin, *Filosofskie Tetradi*, Moskva, 1947, p. 241).

[52] See e.g. *BSE*, *9*, 1951, p. 273.

and irreversible,[53] but their exact relationship to matter remains somewhat in the dark, as no Soviet source risks discussing the crucial question of the exact kind of distinction that holds between matter and its "attributes". It is even difficult to say whether, according to Marxism-Leninism, space and time are really properties of matter or rather aspects of its motion;[54] the *Philosophical Encyclopaedia* evades this problem simply by saying that space and time are "forms of the existence of matter in motion".[55]

Last but not least, matter is said to be infinite; some texts prefer the pleonasm "eternal, infinite and boundless".[56] Infinity is said to be "the most universal qualitative characteristic of matter in motion"; accordingly, the world is:

> infinite as to space, infinite as to time and infinitely multiform as to its properties, as to those concrete forms in which matter is in motion. Whereas infinity in space and time concerns the world as a whole, the infinity of properties characterizes not only the world as a whole, but each separate material object, too. From the point of view of Logic, the infinity of the material world might, in all three of its aspects, be understood as a consequence of the substantial character of matter. As matter is a unique substance which is *causa sui*, its evolution and motion cannot be limited by anything whatsoever.[57]

These last two sentences and, indeed, the whole passage, call our attention to the difficult problem as to what "ontological function" Marxism-Leninism imputes to matter. Strictly speaking, there are at least two different, though closely connected questions involved: in what sense is matter said to be unique? and: is matter a thing or rather some metaphysical principle of things?

We may begin by pointing to a certain disparity between the attributes which Marxism-Leninism ascribes to matter. As we have seen, there are at least five such attributes: matter is "objective reality", it is knowable through the senses, it is in motion, it is spatio-temporal, and it is infinite; as regards infinity, it is infinite as to space and time, and, moreover, infinitely multiform as to its properties. The disparity that we have in mind is simply the following. Each material thing, taken separately, is a sensuously perceptible objective reality which moves in space and time and is infinitely multiform as to its properties. It would, however, be absurd to maintain that each material thing is infinite as to space and time; these two attributes "con-

---

[53] G. F. Aleksandrov, *op. cit.*, p. 307 ff.; *OMF*, p. 136 ff.; *FE*, p. 298/b; etc.

[54] For more details, see G. A. Wetter, *op. cit.*, p. 357 ff.

[55] *FE*, p. 437/b.

[56] *OMF*, p. 121.

[57] *FE*, p. 154/a.

cern the world as a whole", i.e. the spatio-temporal *totality* of material things. The *Principles of Marxist Philosophy* is definite on this point:

> No material thing is unchangeable, all material things are finite. Yet wherever one thing disappears, another thing comes to be and replaces it, and this in such a way that not a single particle of matter disappears without trace or turns into nothing . . . Where the limits of one material object come to an end, the limits of another object begin, and there is no end as to this boundless interchange and interaction of material objects. Matter . . . is eternal, endless and boundless.[58]

There is, of course, nothing to object to in a distinction between properties of "separate material objects" and properties of the "material world as a whole"; yet it is somewhat difficult to see how *both* kinds of properties could be attributes of "one and the same" matter. It would be of no great help, either, to say that, in the last resort, as it were, *all* attributes of matter are properties of the "world as a whole". For though we might disregard the oddity of such an assertion, it seems impossible to consider the knowableness through senses, at least, as a property of the totality of all material things (nobody ever saw all material things). Moreover, it seems beyond question that Soviet thinkers consider all attributes of matter, except, precisely, infinity as to space and time, as properties of material things, taken separately.

This ambiguity, if an ambiguity it is, seems to originate from Engels. According to this "classic" of Marxism-Leninism, "matter as such is a creation of thought and an abstraction":

> We disregard qualitative differences of things by comprehending them under the concept of matter (*indem wir sie unter dem Begriff Materie zusammenfassen*). Unlike definite existing matters, matter as such is, therefore, nothing sensuously perceptible and existing (*nichts Sinnlich-Existierendes*). When natural science goes in search of a uniform (*einheitliche*) matter as such . . . it acts as if, instead of asking for cherries, pears or apples, it would like to see the fruit as such; or, instead of cats, dogs, sheep, and the like, the mammal as such; or the gas as such, the metal as such, the stone as such, the chemical compound as such, motion as such.[59]

Except for the somewhat queer terminology (and in spite of the fact that Engels paraphrases Hegel here),[60] this passage is unequivocal. There exists no matter as such, since it is nothing more than a generic concept which embraces all kinds of "definite existing matters". There exists no matter as such, only this quantity of a definite chemical compound or that piece of stone. Another passage seems to point in the same direction:

---

[58] *OMF*, p. 121.

[59] F. Engels, *Dialektik der Natur*, p. 271 ff.

[60] See G. W. F. Hegel, *Sämtliche Werke*, Stuttgart, 1932 ff., *8*, p. 59.

Nobody has ever seen or experienced matter as such or motion as such, only the different actually existing stuffs and forms of motion. Stuff, matter is nothing but the totality of stuffs (*die Gesamtheit der Stoffe*), from which this concept is abstracted, and motion as such is nothing but the totality of all sensuously perceptible motions; words like 'matter' and 'motion' are nothing but *abbreviations* in which we comprehend many different sensuously perceptible things according to their common properties (*nach ihren gemeinsamen Eigenschaften*). Matter and motion *cannot*, therefore, be known otherwise than by studying the single stuffs and forms of motion; through knowing the latter, we know *pro tanto* matter and motion *as such*, too.[61]

Again, except for the expression 'totality', it seems clear what Engels has in mind: 'matter' is a sort of generic term for all the different materials like water, wood or chemical compounds. There is, however, one major ambiguity indicated by the expression '*totality* of material things'. It is, to begin with, a highly unusual contention that matter should be the totality, i.e. the sum of all material things, since terms of this semantic type rarely if ever are used in a collective sense. Secondly, it seems that 'matter' cannot, at one and the same time, be a generic term for all kinds of stuff, i.e. be predicable of *any* quantity of *any* stuff, *and* designate *all* quantity of *all* stuffs, *taken together*. In the latter case, namely, 'matter' seems to be less a generic term than the name of a sort of vague, but necessarily unique individual. In other words: as unequivocal as the passage just quoted might seem, there are at least two ways in which it can be understood. We might disregard the expression 'totality', and then we may say that *anything* endowed with certain properties is matter; 'matter', then, is an abbreviation for *any* objective reality that is knowable through the senses and moves in space and time, whether it consists of gold, water or flesh and bones. We might, however, stress the expression 'totality', and then we may say that, strictly speaking, only the totality of *all* material things and stuffs deserves to be called 'matter'; 'matter', then, would be a sort of collective term, or else the name of a sort of unity of which the individual things that consist of definite stuffs would be sections or "appearances".

Although it seems highly probable that Engels had in mind the first rather than the second alternative, Soviet philosophers do not appear to be able to decide for one of them. Very often, they prefer to speak of matter as if it were a sort of totality, for example, when they argue that "the moving and eternally developing matter is the substance, i.e. essence, the ground of the world".[62] Taken literally, this statement would seem to suggest that there is but one Matter with a capital 'M', a sort of materialist *élan vital* which eternally develops and of which concrete things are but appearances.

---

[61] F. Engels, *Dialektik der Natur*, p. 251.

[62] M. Rozental', P. Yudin, *Kratky filosofsky slovar*, 4th edn., Moskva, 1954, p. 467.

As regards the expression 'substance', one has to remember that Lenin himself disliked it and maintained that only pompous professors would use it instead of the "clear and exact expression, matter";[63] if today Soviet philosophers sometimes do use it, they have in mind not so much the Aristotelian οὐσία as the infinite and thoroughly independent *substantia* of Spinoza. Most of all, however, Marxist-Leninist matter is reminiscent of Hegel's eternally evolving and self-differentiating "Spirit" translated into materialistic terms. Thus, occasionally, we meet statements like the following:

> The world is the motion of matter according to law (*zakonomernoe dvizhenie materii*);[64] matter is cause of itself, and hence nothing can act upon it, since there is nothing in the universe apart from self-moving matter and its forms of appearance.[65]

On the other hand, however, Marxism-Leninism is much more conscious of the existence of distinct individual things than either Spinoza or Hegel ever was; we might even say that it contains a considerable dash of "Aristotelian" (as opposed to "Hegelian") mentality.[66] Hegel and all Hegelians start from the "whole" which is itself conceived as a sort of individual, and reduce individual things to parts, aspects or appearances of this very "whole"; only the latter really does exist, whereas individuals are subordinated to it, they exist only in virtue of the totality. Consequently, Hegelians are used to thinking in terms of a universal drift, of motion and of relations, but not of things. On the contrary, Aristotle and, by the same token, all materialists not influenced by Hegel, start from individual things, ask what properties they have in common and subsume them under the appropriate concepts; according to them, what really does exist are things like individual cows and definite pieces of stone in comparison to which any commonness of properties and any being related to one another is a highly secondary affair. It is well enough known that Marxism-Leninism has inherited quite a lot from the Hegelian totality-thinking; yet there are, as we have just said, many "Aristotelian" elements, too. As regards the problem of matter, such an "Aristotelian" mentality turns up whenever Marxist-Leninists, instead of speaking of matter in general (of the "unique substance of the world"), begin to discuss the structure of concrete material

---

[63] *ME*, 157.

[64] *ME*, 156.

[65] I. B. Novik in *VF, 3*, 1954, p. 142.

[66] The distinction between a "Hegelian" and an "Aristotelian" trend among Soviet philosophers has been introduced by J. M. Bocheński, "Einführung in die sowjetische Philosophie der Gegenwart", *Aus Politik und Zeitgeschichte. Beilage zu "Das Parlament"*, 45, 1959, p. 608 ff. By "Aristotelian trend", here, is meant a naturalist Aristotelianism, like that of Alexander of Aphrodisias or, more recently, of Randall.

things. Thus they will distinguish between different types of matter, for example, between compact matter (*veshchestvo*) and fields, both of which are said to possess mass as well as energy[67]—and treat them as though they were some kind of individual substances. According to the *Principles of Marxist Philosophy:*

> matter exists in the form of an infinite variety of bodies and objects which, quantitatively and qualitatively, are different from each another . . . The different types of matter differ by a greater or smaller complexity and are objects of investigation of different sciences: physics, chemistry, biology, etc. The "elementary" particles of matter are relatively simple: photons, electrons, positrons, mesons, protons, anti-protons, neutrons, anti-neutrons, etc. More complicated forms are atoms and molecules. The next degree of complexity is represented by gases, liquids and solid bodies . . . and by the heavenly bodies too: planets, stars and the starry systems. Considerably more complicated are the bodies of organic Nature and, especially, its highest product, man. A special material object is human society . . .[68]

Occasionally, they will even quote Marx' statement that matter is the subject (*sub'ekt*) of all changes,[69] and they do not seem to have in mind a unique universal subject (like Spinoza's *substantia*), but rather *any material thing*. Here, once again, 'matter' seems to become a generic term that designates individual material things, i.e. any individual that exists outside our consciousness, is knowable through the senses and moves in space and time. As, however, this individual is neither infinite as to space and time, nor *causa sui,* nor the unique substance of the world, nor anything of that kind, we can, it seems, conclude that Marxism-Leninism tries to combine two thoroughly different conceptions of matter and that, consequently, its materialism is anything but uniform and consistent.

Yet before drawing such a conclusion we should consider whether we have not overlooked an interpretation which might remove at least some of the above-mentioned ambiguities. We have been presupposing that, except for the expression 'totality', passages in Engels indicate that he understood 'matter' as a generic term for material things. Actually, however, Engels does not speak of material things alone, but of "stuffs" as well. We must, therefore, consider the following possibility: do not Marxist-Leninists consider matter as a sort of "stuff" of which all material things consist? It is obvious that there are many arguments which seem to support this interpretation. First of all, it would seem much more natural to take 'matter' as a stuff-term (like 'gold' or 'wood'), instead of considering it as

---

[67] See e.g. G. F. Aleksandrov, *op. cit.*, p. 293; the popular version of *OMF*, p. 52; I. D. Andreev, *op. cit.*, p. 110. Not to be found in *OMF* itself.

[68] *OMF*, p. 121 ff.

[69] G. F. Aleksandrov, *op. cit.*, p. 282.

a generic term for material things (like 'body' or 'tree'), not to speak of the queer contention that it is a name for the totality of material things. In this event, the disparity of the properties of matter mentioned above would seem to disappear: there is no difficulty in saying that one and the same stuff is knowable through the senses as well as infinite in space and time; it seems easy to admit that a stuff might exist everywhere and always (though there are some difficulties as to what exactly this *does* mean). Besides, a stuff-term has as referent neither individual things, taken separately, nor all things, taken together, but rather a component of any of them; and as, by "adding" stuff to stuff, we never get anything other than again the same stuff (for example: water plus water is still water, whereas a body plus another body is not again a body), it would seem that the difference between 'taken separately' and 'taken together' does not matter. Last but not least, we have ourselves admitted that Engels, when speaking of matter, has in mind stuffs rather than material things.

In spite of all these arguments which probably might still be multiplied, the interpretation of Marxist-Leninist "matter" as some kind of "stuff" is untenable. First of all, so far as we know, Marxist-Leninists never actually do say that things *consist* of matter; occasionally, they seem to have a stuff in mind, but they will never use other expressions than 'things and nature are material', 'the phenomena of the world are different forms of moving matter', and the like. Secondly, when speaking about matter, they never use stuff-terms. When giving examples of "types of matter", they do not mention chemical elements or compounds, but "things" like elementary particles, atoms, living cells, organisms, animals and society. Thirdly, a materialism for which matter is a stuff of which things consist, cannot consistently say that there is nothing in the universe apart from self moving matter; for the definition of matter as of a stuff of which things consist entails that there exist, at least, the things that consist of it. Besides, if things really consist of matter, they cannot, in the last resort, consist of matter alone, since, in that case, they would *be* matter and not *consist* of it; yet the only co-principle that comes into question is motion—and, once again, Marxist-Leninists never say that man, for example, consists of matter and motion. He *is* "matter in motion", in the same way as this *is* an animal and that *is* a tree, and everything *is* a being. Finally, it seems somewhat difficult to see how motion and, indeed, *all* motion should be an "intrinsic" property of a stuff; for it would seem that things themselves, rather than anything of which they consist, change. It would be odd to maintain that if an animal dies, it is the stuff of which it consists that undergoes the change in question; though the stuff may change, too, it is most obvious that it is the animal, not the stuff it consists of, that dies. If an animal *is* a stuff, or if it *is* matter (it

449

would be more appropriate to say: if it is a quantity of a stuff), then, of course, this stuff, this matter (this quantity of a stuff) "dies"; yet even in this case, it is not the stuff of which the animal *consists* that dies, but, at best, the stuff which it *is*.

This last remark shows that there is, after all, a sense, in which Marxist-Leninist matter might be understood as a sort of "stuff". Provided that "stuff" be not defined as something another thing consists of (as a bed, for example, consists of the "stuff", wood), but rather as something which "another" thing *is* (as wood might be said to "consist" of the "stuff" wood, taking 'consist' as equivalent to 'is identical with') there is no reason why Marxist-Leninist matter should not be described as a sort of "stuff". Yet it is easy to see that if "stuff" is to be defined as something that material things *are*, 'stuff' is a generic term for material things. 'Matter', therefore, designates here not something things *consist of* (in the ordinary sense of the phrase) but things themselves. Thus we may return to our original contention that, although Marxist-Leninist matter is a sort of materialist *élan vital,* material things are called "matter", too. The inconsistency of this conception of matter might, however, be somewhat attenuated by saying that matter, though being a sort of universal drift, actually never exists otherwise than in the form of a number of distinct, though closely interconnected, individual things; though it seems difficult to say what exactly such a statement might mean, it does not seem to be inconsistent. Another way, and probably a more appropriate one, to describe the situation in question would be as follows. It is well-known that some metaphysicians and, in particular, some Neo-Scholastics, when speaking of "being", have in mind individual beings as well as a sort of all-embracing Being with a capital 'B', the latter being neither God nor a pure concept, but rather a sort of universal bond. The similarity of such a "being" to Marxist-Leninist matter is patent; and as earlier Soviet thinkers often treated 'matter' exactly like Scholastics treat 'being' (we shall see this later), one might even say that the ambiguity of the Marxist-Leninist concept of matter gives form to a sort of materialist "problem of being". Yet we have to hasten to add that such reflections are far beyond the intellectual frame of contemporary Marxism-Leninism; the heights of metaphysics are—for the moment at least—out of reach for most Soviet thinkers.

There still remains a minor question to be considered, namely, whether Marxist-Leninist matter is truly a "subject of change"; the reader will remember that it was Marx himself who has used this expression ('subject of all changes'). This question may be considered in order to compensate, as it were, for the fact that we cannot anymore meaningfully ask whether matter is to be taken as a thing or as a "metaphysical principle". To a

Hegelian the problem is not very meaningful anyway; and as far as the materialist component of Marxism-Leninism (which we have called "Aristotelian") is concerned, 'matter' designates things.

It would go far beyond the scope of this essay to analyse in detail the Marxist-Leninist theory of change; it is as interesting as it is inconsistent, since most Soviet thinkers are prepared to allow, in this context at least, a violation of the principle of non-contradiction. We should like only to point out that Marxism-Leninism is very definite in saying that matter "is nothing inert to which motion has to be added . . . no unaffected "subject" (*podlezhashchee*[70]) for the predicate 'it moves '";[71] any "unchanging substance of things" is most emphatically denied.[72] Consequently, matter has to be considered as a "subject" that undergoes change not so much as to its accidents or "forms" as in itself. The definition of motion as of a "form of *being* of matter" seems to point in the same direction: materiality and motion are, so to speak, only two aspects of one and the same reality.

This denial of any unchanging subject of change has its counterpart in the thesis that matter is "throughout infinite in depth".[73]

> Just as the relation between things, and their modes of change, are endless, so too is the number of stages leading *into the depth* of things, *into the depth* of their being . . . However simple and elementary a given particle of matter may appear to us, in reality it can never be absolutely simple, absolutely elementary, there can never be any sort of ultimate building-stone, any sort of mythical *materia prima*, from which the whole world might seem to be built up.[74]

It is, therefore, impossible to say that, even if matter and change are not really distinct, there might still be some element of matter which is the last subject of change. When going "into the depth" of matter, we shall never find anything other than some kind of material things which are intrinsically in motion.

It would, however, be too simple to say that, in this case, matter would not be much more than a sort of subsistent motion; in any case, Marxist-

---

[70] '*Podlezhashchee*' is the technical term for 'grammatical subject'; although it uses the present participle instead of the perfect participle, the expression is a literal translation of the Latin '*subiectum*'. FE, p. 92/a, describes the Aristotelian material cause as "*materiya i podlezhashchee (substrat)*", as "matter and subject (substratum)".

[71] *FE*, 435/b. The passage, however, admits that matter is the "universal bearer" ('*nositel*') of motion; yet it is not clear what 'bearer' might mean, especially as opposed to 'subject'. *BSE, 30*, 1954, p. 191/a, treats under '*nositel*' only 'bearers for catalysers" in chemistry.

[72] See e.g. M. Rozental', P. Yudin, *op. cit.*, p. 467.

[73] V. I. Lenin, *Filosofskie tetradi*, p. 86.

[74] B. M. Kedrov in *Bol'shevik*, 2, 1948, p. 45, quoted by G. A. Wetter, *op. cit.*, p. 342.

Leninists are not Hegelian enough to say anything of that kind. Similarly, it would not seem appropriate to say that matter and motion are related to one another, say, like prime matter and substantial form.[75] Such interpretations seem inevitable only as long as one adheres to the schema "subject-form" which our everyday language suggests. Though Marxist-Leninists never brought forward any other schema, it is highly probable that they never permit the correlating of matter and motion in the same way that Scholastics and, in a sense, everybody except Hegelians, would do, namely, as a subject to its properties, "forms" or the changes that it undergoes. If they were forced to produce a schema, they probably would grasp at a picture and say that matter is "soaked through" with motion, or that motion is at the very "heart" of matter. "Whether we say the world is moving matter, or that the world is material motion, makes no difference whatever".[76]

§3 Matter, Being and Consciousness

We have seen that, except for matter as "universal drift" which we shall disregard from now on, 'matter' designates material things, i.e. any subsistent entity[77] which exists outside our consciousness, is knowable through senses and moves in space and time. There remains, however, the question as to the materiality of *properties*. It is, of course, obvious that if all things are material, all properties are material, too, in the sense that they precisely are properties of material things. Yet there is still another meaning of 'material' whose recognition might permit one to say that there exist non-material properties of material things. Suppose that we define material properties by saying that they exist outside our consciousness, are knowable through senses and change in space and time; in that case, if there are any properties of material things which, for example, are neither sensuously perceptible nor spatio-temporal, such properties will be "non-material".

This remark is of some interest, since many Soviet thinkers deny that consciousness, though being the property of a type of matter, is material. Before, however, treating the special case of consciousness, we should like to say some words on the type of transcendentality that Marxist-Leninists ascribe to the concept of matter.

Earlier Soviet thinkers unquestionably tend simply to identify *matter* with *being*. Thus e.g. the Deborinist B. Bykhovsky in his *Outlines of a Philosophy of Dialectical Materialism*, from 1930, speaks about matter in terms that a Thomist would use when speaking about being:

---

[75] This has been suggested by H. Dahm, *art. cit.*, p. 924 ff.

[76] *ME*, p. 257.

[77] Not 'any individual', since society is a form of matter, too.

Matter is everything that is, the most general concept, the genus of all genera. Whatever is, is a kind of matter; but matter itself cannot possibly be defined as a special case of some genus. If whatever exists is matter, then it is preposterous to consider matter as a characteristic differentiating anything from anything else, for such a something else cannot be but non-existent, i.e. it cannot be.[78]

A similar mode of expression is to be found in a textbook of Dialectical Materialism, from 1933, edited by M. B. Mitin:

Matter is the entire world existing independently of us. The concept of matter is the most general of all concepts. Everything that exists is matter in one form or other, though matter itself cannot be defined as falling under any other class.[79] (According to Mitin, too, it is simply impossible to assign a specific difference to the concept of matter.)

Although neither of these texts (which could easily be multiplied) mentions anything about properties, they seem to suggest that *matter* is an intensionally transcendental concept. As, however, philosophers of the early Stalinist period, especially some like M. B. Mitin, rarely used to think, it is possible and, indeed, highly probable, that they simply forget to think about properties. Mitin knew as well as any contemporary Soviet philosopher that, according to the official teaching, there exists a "subjective reality" too; if, therefore, only what exists "independently of us" is matter, *matter* cannot be the "most general of all concepts".

In any case, more recent texts hardly ever use such terminology. It is, however, very difficult to discover exactly which kind of transcendentality they ascribe to *matter*. The only texts which touch upon this problem are those which discuss the relation of *matter* to *being;* but although it would seem that today Soviet philosophers are inclined to count *being* among the so-called "philosophical categories",[80] there are very few texts which treat this kind of problem. In 1931, the otherwise little known Deborinist Gonikman proposed a "closed system" of categories which was to begin as

---

[78] B. Bykhovsky, *Ocherk filosofii dialekticheskago materializma*, Moskva, 1930, p. 78, quoted by N. Lossky, *Dialektichesky materializm v SSSR*, Paris, 1934, p. 27. Lossky quotes also a passage from A. M. Deborin's introduction to Hegel's complete works, 2nd edn., *1*, 1929, p. xvi: "being is by its very essence a material category".

[79] M. B. Mitin-I. Razumovsky, ed., *Dialektichesky i istorichesky materializm*, part I, *Dialektichesky materializm*, ed. by M. B. Mitin, Moskva, 1933, p. 107, quoted by G. A. Wetter, *op. cit.*, p. 343.

[80] The "philosophical categories" are generally defined as concepts designating the "most general objects, properties, aspects and connections in reality"; see e.g. V. P. Tugarinov, *Sootnoshenie kategory dialekticheskago materializma,* Leningrad, 1956, p. 4; also H. Fleischer: "On Categories in Soviet Philosophy—A Survey", *Studies in Soviet Thought, 1,* Dordrecht-Holland 1961, p. 64 ff. *FE*, p. 207, describes *being* as such a "philosophical category".

well as to end in the category of being;[81] yet this point of view has been explicitly rejected. The notion of *being* has always, in fact, been relegated entirely to the background in comparison with the central category of *matter;* thus the second edition of the *Great Soviet Encyclopaedia* treats *being* in half a page, for example, mentioning first the opposition between materialism and idealism and then proceeding immediately to a discussion of "social being".[82]

The recent *Philosophical Encyclopaedia,* however, devotes nearly seven pages to this subject, treating successively the concept of being in Buddhism, in ancient Chinese thought, in Greek, medieval and modern philosophy, and ending with a section on the Marxist-Leninist interpretation. Yet although the "historical" section distinguishes at the end no less than eleven fundamental meanings of 'being' (among them *matter, existence, essence, substance* and *idea*),[83] from the "systematical" section we learn little about the properly Marxist-Leninist concept of being. Being is said to be the "infinite subsistence (*sushchestvovanie*) of matter that is independent of consciousness", whereas non-being is said to be neither emptiness nor absolute disappearance, but rather the "conversion of matter from one form of being to another, i.e. the formation of a new form of being of matter".[84] As for the relation of *being* to *matter,* we are told that "there is no "being as such" without substance, without matter":

> As it denies the infinity of matter and immediately leads to idealism,[85] the very assumption that being precedes matter is a failure . . . Only matter subsists and its *being* is proved by the law of conservation and transformation of energy.[86]

Yet this does not mean that being and matter are simply one and the same, though it would seem that 'being' designates only the "epiphenomenon" of the existence of matter (an epiphenomenon, since matter exists by definition, as it were). We are referred to a passage in Engel's *Anti-Dühring,* according to which:

> the unity of the world does not consist in its being, although its being is a prerequisite of its unity, since it first must *be* in order to be *one* . . . The real

---

[81] See G. A. Wetter, *op. cit.,* p. 428.

[82] *BSE, 6,* 1951, p. 432/b ff.

[83] *FE,* p. 209/b.

[84] *Ibid.* This strange definition of *non-being* is confirmed by what is said on 'annihilation', p. 69/a: "an interaction of particles and anti-particles of such a kind that they disappear and change into other particles. The expression 'annihilation' is inexact. In the phenomenon in question there happens . . . exclusively a transformation of one form of matter into another."

[85] The idea seems to be as follows: if being is prior to matter, then matter proceeds from something non-material.

[86] *FE,* p. 209/b.

unity of the world consists in its materiality, and this is proved . . . by a long and protracted development of philosophy and natural science.[87]

From this text which in itself is queer enough, the *Philosophical Encyclopaedia* concludes to the still odder result that the "coincidence and identity" of being and matter "presuppose a distinction and are relative":

> The relativity of the coincidence of the notions of being and matter is easy to discover, since matter, not being, is the substance of the world, and the unity of the world does not consist in its being, but in its materiality.[88]

It is difficult to decide what such expressions could possibly mean; and, in any case, it does not help us much to answer the question as to the type of transcendentality of *matter*. The only conclusion that we might draw is that Marxism-Leninism probably would not be prepared to admit the existence of ideal entities, since they hardly are a being "with substance, with matter". Yet as we shall see in a moment, not all Soviet philosophers agree on this point, though most of them tend to reduce meanings, propositions, and the like to "subjective reality", i.e. to activities of human mind.

The only relatively well-reasoned essay on our problem that we know of was published by the Slovak philosophical quarterly in 1958.[89] F. Cízek, the author, starts from the observation that the category of *reality* which simply states the fact of being, is wider than the categories of *objective reality* and of *matter*:

> A phenomenon can be objective as well as subjective, ideal as well as material, . . . but if it exists, it is reality. The category of reality implies, indeed, not only objective, but also subjective phenomena, and not only material, but also ideal events.[90]

Thus, taken purely as such, the category of *reality* is in a sense neutral and "can equally well be used by a materialist as abused by an idealist". Marxism-Leninism does not, according to Cízek, deny that there are subjective and ideal realities; yet contrary to all forms of idealism it does not reduce objective and material reality to ideal products of any consciousness (which, according to *all* Marxist-Leninist authors, would be the case, if matter were to have been created by God). Marxism-Leninism tries rather to distinguish as clearly as possible "the problem of the objectivity of the existence of reality and the problem of the objectivity of our knowledge of

---

[87] F. Engels, *Anti-Dühring*, p. 51.

[88] *FE*, p. 210/a.

[89] F. Cízek, "Poznámky k materialistickému pojetí kategorie reality", *Slovensky Filozoficky Casopis* (Bratislava), 4, 1958, pp. 401–408. See also my book *Marxismus-Leninismus in der CSR. Die tschechoslowakische Philosophie seit 1945*, Dordrecht-Holland 1961, p. 134 f.

[90] *Ibid.*, p. 405.

it".[91] All things that exist independently of our mind and, consequently, independently of any mind at all, are objective reality, i. e. "certain specific forms of existence of matter in motion"; but psychic events are subjective, not objective realities, at least for the subject that experiences them. Finally, though the results of such psychic events, i.e. our ideas, are neither objective nor material, they are still realities.

According to this analysis, then, there would be at least one kind of reality that is not material: our ideas and thoughts on matter, i.e. material realities as reflected by our mind; as Cízek points out, the most Utopian ideas are, philosophically speaking, as "real"[92] as the ideas of Marx and Lenin, for example. As to the "subjective reality", i.e. the psychic events, they are neither explicitly classified as material, nor is their materiality explicitly denied. Some passages, however, indicate that they may be understood to differ from properly material realities:

> Subjective reality has its own relative independence. That the objective is reflected by the subjective does not entail any identity of the objective and the subjective . . . If, therefore, we emphasize the unity and the "identity" of objective and subjective reality as to their content, we may not forget their relative difference and independence as to their form.[93]

This analysis is remarkable for several reasons. First of all, it is the only essay of which we know that discusses the relation of *matter* and *being* (or, to use Cízek's terminology, of *objective reality* and of *reality* without qualification) in terms of their transcendentality. Secondly, it is unusually unequivocal as to the distinction between *subjective* and *ideal* reality, i.e. between psychic events and their intramental object-correlates; as we shall see, Soviet thinkers often confuse them. Finally, it seems to suggest that Marxist-Leninists, some of them at least, might be prepared to admit that their concept of matter is only partially extensionally transcendental (see §1, (a)). As regards this last point, however, we have to be careful. For the recognition of truly ideal entities seems to be bound up with the acceptance of entities which are neither material things nor, in particular, their properties; yet Cízek does not explicitly say that ideal reality is not a sort of qualitative determination of "thinking matter". Nevertheless, it is now clear that some Marxist-Leninist thinkers would deny that *matter* is an intensionally transcendental concept like *being* or *reality*.

The last paragraphs may have indicated that the crucial point of the

---

[91] Notice the ambiguity of the expression 'objectivity' which is common in Marxism-Leninism. "Objectivity of existence" is given, when something actually does *exist;* "objectivity of knowledge", when we *recognize* the former.

[92] 'Real', here, embraces also ideal phenomena.

[93] *Ibid.*, p. 406.

Marxist-Leninist conception of material properties is its interpretation of consciousness. It is, however, interesting to note that the discussion about whether consciousness is material or not, never even touches the problem as to the exact meaning of 'material'. In other words: one would expect that the decision as to whether consciousness is material or not would depend upon whether 'material property' means *property of a material thing* or, for example, *spatio-temporal and sensuously perceptible property;* and if it means the latter, we would expect that Marxist-Leninists would discuss whether consciousness is spatio-temporal and sensuously perceptible or not. This is not, however, what happens. Instead, all Marxist-Leninists refer to a passage in Lenin, according to which it is incorrect to call thought 'material', and then they try to adjust the meaning of 'non-material property' to the requirements of materialism and, in particular, of Dialectical Materialism as opposed to "vulgar materialism" of nineteenth-century philosophers like L. Büchner, J. Moleschott and K. Vogt.

The passage in Lenin in question criticizes J. Dietzgen for having said that:

> the non-sensual idea (*die unsinnliche Vorstellung*) is not only sensual, but also material, i.e. real (*wirklich*) . . . Spirit is not more different from a table, the light or a sound than those things are different each from another.[94]

Whereon Lenin:

> This is, obviously, incorrect. Rather it is correct that both thought and matter are "real", i.e. that they exist. But to call thought material is to make a wrong step towards a confusion of materialism and idealism.[95]

Yet besides the authority of Lenin, there is another and, indeed, equally important reason why Marxism-Leninism does not dare simply to identify consciousness with matter. This reason might be best described by reporting the following event. In 1954, the editors of the Soviet philosophical journal *Voprosy Filosofii* received from seven students of the University of Leningrad a letter submitting the following question: "Is it correct to assert that consciousness is material?". In the name of the whole editorial board, V. N. Kol'banovsky answered decidedly in the negative:

> No, it is not correct. Those who maintain it, confuse the material base of consciousness with the very essence of consciousness and thinking which are not material.[96]

---

[94] J. Dietzgen, *Das Wesen der menschlichen Kopfarbeit, dargestellt von einem Handarbeiter. Eine abermalige Kritik der reinen und praktischen Vernunft*, Hamburg, 1869; reedn. Berlin, 1955, p. 82 ff.

[95] *ME*, p. 231 ff.

[96] V. N. Kol'banovsky, "Pravilno li utverzhdat', chto soznanie material'no?" *VF*, 4, 1954, p. 236.

Some lines later the reason we alluded to crops up:

> Those comrades who argue for the materiality of consciousness have, obviously, forgotten that the conflict of materialism and idealism on the question of the relation of matter and consciousness is the very basis of all history of philosophy. What meaning would all this struggle have if consciousness were to be material? If, from the point of view of Logic, it were necessary to argue (*esli logicheski posledovatel'no*) for the materiality of consciousness, then it would be equally necessary to arrive at a denial of the fundamental question of philosophy, at the conclusion that all philosophy is needless . . . It is, therefore, wrong to include thought in the concept of matter.[97]

It is easy to see the point: if the question of the relation of thought to matter, of Spirit to Nature, is the "central question of world-outlook", then matter and thought simply cannot be one and the same, for otherwise the whole question would be meaningless. One might even suggest that this was what Lenin had in mind when he said that to call thought "material" is "to make a wrong step towards a confusion of materialism and idealism"; for all Marxist-Leninists agree that to deny the importance of the "central question of world-outlook" is a typical feature of idealism.

Yet on the other hand it was Lenin himself who agreed with Dietzgen's assertion that thought is "a function of the brain, just as to write is a function of the hand",[98] and who says in another passage:

> To be sure, the opposition of matter and consciousness has absolute significance only within a very limited field, in our case exclusively within the limits of the fundamental epistemological question, namely, what is to be acknowledged as primary and what as secondary. Outside such limits the relativity of this opposition is beyond all question.[99]

Accordingly, most Soviet philosophers maintain that the opposition of matter and consciousness is only "relative". Thus, e.g. M. B. Mitin who, as we know, described *matter* as nearly an intensionally transcendental concept, speaks of a purely epistemological opposition:

> We distinguish matter from consciousness, oppose them one to another; but this opposition is nonetheless relative, and is meaningful only in relation to the "epistemological" problem . . . The contrast between knowledge and being is a contrast between knowing matter and known matter, and nothing more. The wholly proper and legitimate contrast between subject and object loses its meaning outside the theory of knowledge. If we were to begin contrasting matter, from the scientific point of view, with Spirit, this would amount to a betrayal of materialistic monism.[100]

---

[97] *Ibid.*

[98] J. Dietzgen, *op. cit.*, p. 81.

[99] *ME*, p. 231.

[100] M. B. Mitin, *op. cit.*, p. 107, quoted by G. A. Wetter, *op. cit.*, p. 343.

Similarly, B. Bykhovsky tries to describe the relation of matter to consciousness in a way that reminds one of G. T. Fechner's *"Zweiseitentheorie"*, according to which the mental and the physical would be related one to another as the concave and convex aspects of the circumference of a circle:

> Physical and mental are one and the same process, only seen from two different sides . . . That which is seen from the outer, objective side as a physical process is equally perceived from within, by the material being itself, as a phenomenon of will or sensation, as mental in character.[101]

This amounts to saying that it is but a "being experienced from within" that gives to an otherwise thoroughly material process its "non-material" character. The expression 'subjective reality' which is constantly being used by all Marxist-Leninists, points in the same direction: the "non-materiality" of a psychical act is but subjective, i.e. it appears only from within. This interpretation (which, incidentally, was adopted by Stalin)[102] is followed by many Soviet philosophers up to this day. It contains, however, a serious inconvenience. No Marxist-Leninist will maintain that the "non-materiality" of mental events is subjective in the sense that, strictly speaking, we are wrong in maintaining it; though it appears only "from within", it is, in a sense at least, "objective". This being presupposed, one might admit that if matter experiences itself, the object of this experience is material; yet though the "spirituality" of a mental act might consist only in its being experienced, the experiencing itself has to be explained, too. Either it is again material "objective reality", and then there seems nowhere to be a "subjective reality"; or it is not material, and then this non-materiality cannot be purely "subjective" and "epistemological", but must have some objectivity, too.

Such considerations compel Soviet thinkers to look out for new interpretations. Thus Kol'banovsky, for example, distinguishes between a "material base" of consciousness and the very essence of consciouness itself:

> The material base of thinking and consciousness are the nervous processes that happen in man's brain; but the very essence of understanding and awareness that gives to man the possibility of abstracting from concrete objects and phenomena, the possibility to universalize them, to analyse and to synthesize, to discover complex connections of the multiform phenomena of reality . . . this essence of thinking and consciousness consists in an ideal reflection of the objective world.[103]

To the decisive question of how Marxism-Leninism understands the "essence of the ideal reflection of reality", Kol'banovsky has, however, no

---

[101] B. Bykhovsky, *op. cit.*, p. 83 ff., quoted by N. Lossky, *op. cit.*, p. 44.
[102] See J. V. Stalin, *Sochineniya*, Moskva, 1946 ff., *1* (1906/07), p. 312.
[103] V. N. Kol'banovsky, *loc. cit.*, p. 237/b.

other answer to offer than the classical formula of Marx, namely, that the ideal is nothing more than the material, transplanted in man's head and transformed in it. One finds the same lack of clarity in A. G. Spirkin's article on *Consciousness* in the *Great Soviet Encyclopaedia* (1956). Spirkin explicitly stresses that consciousness does not, in essence, consist of the material events that occur in the brain; yet he too has no other explanation to offer than the queer "epistemological distinction":

> Dialectical materialism proceeds from the assertion that material objects, phenomena and events ... that are reflected by our consciousness, exist in the latter as pictures, as thoughts on bodies and phenomena, not in a material, but in an ideal form ... The nervous stimulations and physiological events make up the necessary basis of the subjective picture, but not the picture itself ... Consciousness is an ideal, i.e. subjective picture of the objective world. From the point of view of epistemology, consciousness is an ideal phenomenon and as such opposed to matter; but this opposition is relative.[104]

This text, besides explaining very little, suffers from a fundamental obscurity which is common in Marxism-Leninism. It confuses, namely, the "subjective" and the "ideal", i.e. mental activities and their intra-mental object-correlates, the "pictures". This is apparent, too, from Spirkin's definition of consciousness:

> a singular and unique process of reflection of reality that includes all forms of man's psychic activities: sensations, representations, thinking, awareness, emotion and will.[105]

It is difficult to see in what sense psychic events, especially those of emotion and will, could reflect anything at all; and, in any case, such mental activities are most obviously not the "things transposed in our head", although it may be possible to qualify ideas in such a way. Yet this confusion in a way explains why Marxism-Leninism maintains that the opposition of matter and consciousness is "purely epistemological"; for it seems, at least, conceivable that mental acts and their "ideal" object-correlates, ontologically speaking, are one and the same reality, though from the point of view of subjective experience and of epistemology they have to be distinguished. Yet what, in that case, are opposed are by no means consciousness and its material basis, but rather the "content" of consciousness and consciousness itself. In other words: if someone can show that conscious matter reflects not in a material, but in an ideal way, he has not proved that consciousness is not material; he has only pointed out that the "content" of consciousness is not the material object itself, but rather its ideal copy. If, therefore,

---

[104] *BSE*, *39*, 1956, p. 658/b.
[105] *Ibid.*, p. 656/b.

Marxism-Leninism wants to maintain that it differs from all forms of "vulgar materialism", it has to prove that the mental "operation" of thinking itself, and not only the material thing as thought (the "picture" or "copy") is different from material (physiological) events.

We must, therefore, focus our attention on the question as to whether Marxist-Leninists are prepared to admit that consciousness is not only epistemologically, but also in some fundamental ontological sense different from matter, and, consequently, in some sense non-material. So far as they admit it, we shall then be able to say that the Marxist-Leninist concept of matter is extensionally rather than intensionally transcendental; if, however, they do not admit it, we shall have to say that only an "epistemological attitude" (whatever that may be) allows them to keep asunder the two concepts of *matter* and *being,* and, consequently, to distinguish Dialectical Materialism from a form of "vulgar materialism".

If we restrict ourselves to more recent contributions, it seems that we can distinguish at least three different groups among Soviet philosophers:

(1) Those who defend the materiality of consciousness, although admitting that, "epistemologically speaking", thought is ideal, not material. This, in a sense classical, point of view has recently been again advocated by N. V. Medvedev who emphatically denies that his position could be qualified as mechanism or vulgar materialism. According to Medvedev, vulgar materialism simply identifies consciousness with matter, whereas Dialectical Materialism calls consciousness only "material" insofar as it is a motion and thus a mode of existence of matter:

> Any motion whatsoever is inseparable from matter, has a material subject—and is in this sense material. Yet motion is a mode of existence of matter and not matter itself.[106]

It is easy to see that this position evades the problem. Nobody questions the fact that if man is matter, consciousness is a material property in the sense that it is the property, or motion, or "mode of existence", of a material thing. The real problem, however, concerns the materiality of the property itself.

(2) Those who hold that consciousness cannot be considered as material, either from an epistemological or from a properly ontological point of view. This interpretation was defended by F. I. Georgiev in the beginning of 1959:

> Psychic events appear to be ideal, not material, both considered in their relation to the brain and in their relation to objective reality . . . How can psychic events be at one and the same time, though from different points of view, both ideal and material? . . . To say that the epistemological character-

---

[106] N. V. Medvedev, "K voprosu ob otrazhatel'noy rabote mozga", *VF*, 6, 1960, p. 109.

istic determines the "ontological" characteristic of psychic events is to turn the whole problem head over heels and to be overreached by idealism.[107]

(3) Finally those who try to overcome the dilemma by maintaining that consciousness is neither material nor non-material, since neither 'material' and 'non-material' can be properly predicated of consciousness. As a matter of fact, we do not know of any Soviet philosopher who has maintained such an "intermediary" position; it was, however, explicitly proposed by G. Klaus, professor at the Karl Marx University in East Berlin, in his polemics against G. A. Wetter. Whereas in the first edition of his book, *Jesuits, God and Matter,* he had defended a position similar to that of Medvedev,[108] the second edition offers the following quite original analysis. According to Klaus, it is not altogether correct to say that consciousness is a property of matter; rather it is a property of the movement (*Bewegungsvorgänge*) of the brain and thus a property of a property of matter. But a property of a property of a thing is, "contrary to what Aristotle believed", not necessarily a property of the thing itself; thus e.g. the pendulum of a wall-clock has the property of being in motion, and this motion again the property of being periodical—and yet we cannot say that the pendulum is periodical. In a similar way, according to Klaus, neither of the two expressions 'material' and 'non-material' can be predicated of a property of a property of matter, although matter has still to be considered as the last subject of the property, consciousness.[109] In spite of its originality, however, this analysis does not seem to lead out of the dilemma. For if someone maintains that there be properties that cannot be described either as f or as non-f (in a qualified sense), he has, it seems, to admit that there exist properties of such a kind that they cannot be qualified as f, i.e. those properties which are described as non-f (in an unqualified sense); if, therefore, somebody maintains that there are things which are neither material nor spiritual (or neither material nor ideal), he has to admit that not everything is material.

It would seem, therefore, that only two alternatives are open for Marxism-Leninism: consciousness is to be described ontologically either as material or as non-material. Both alternatives lead to serious difficulties. Those who maintain that consciousness is material probably cannot escape some kind of "vulgar materialism" which reduces everything to matter and to which the question as to the priority of Matter to Spirit is hardly meaningful. It is

---

[107] F. I. Georgiev, "V. I. Lenin o vzaimootnoshenii psikhicheskogo i fiziologicheskogo", *Nauchnye doklady vysshey shkoly. Filosofskie Nauki* (Moskva), *1*, 1959, p. 22 ff.

[108] G. Klaus, *Jesuiten, Gott, Materie. Des Jesuitenpaters Wetter Revolte wider Vernunft und Wissenschaft,* Berlin, 1957; 2nd edn., Berlin, 1958, p. 138 ff.

[109] *Ibid.,* p. 356 ff. (added in the 2nd edn.).

of little help to maintain that this alternative still permits an "epistemologi-cal" distinction between matter and consciousness; for in this case "vulgar materialism" will be only "epistemologically" and "subjectively" mistaken, whereas, ontologically speaking, it would be correct to say with K. Vogt that thought stands in the same relation to the brain as the bile to the liver —which all Soviet philosophers violently deny. Yet the second position has not a much easier stand; for how can matter have truly non-material proper-ties? It is not by chance that, beginning with Aristotle, the Occidental phil-osophical tradition always maintained that from non-material activities or properties of a seemingly material object we have to conclude to a relative non-materiality of this object itself, to a relative "independence of its form from matter", or the like. Even admitting the basic assumption of Marxism-Leninism that consciousness genetically arises from matter as a late product of its historical development, we have to ask whether such a production of something non-material does not require in matter itself a certain trans-materiality, or else a radical change that has to be described as a sort of "dematerialisation". When F. I. Khaskhachikh, the late specialist for epistemological questions of the Stalinist period, says that:

> inorganic matter contains the possibility of sensitive and later on of thinking beings; but this possibility becomes actual only at a definite stage in the his-torical development of matter[110]

we have, it seems, to conclude to a basic homogeneity of matter, sensation and consciousness, or else to assume that at a definite stage of its develop-ment "matter" by a "dialectical leap" became sufficiently non-material[111] to produce non-material results like sensation or consciousness. Thus the second of the two positions would seem to break through the fundamental framework of Marxist-Leninist materialism. We cannot, therefore, but agree with G. A. Wetter who points out that:

> the view of Soviet philosophers would be bound, logically, to lead either to acceptance of the soul, or to vulgar materialism, if the problems involved were to be rationally thought out to a conclusion . . . The very conditions imposed upon the enterprise of Soviet philosophers, namely, the construction of a psychology devoid of a psyche . . . , without at the same time reducing the mental to the physiological, compel them to enter a blind alley from which there is no escape.[112]

We conclude this essay by pointing out that the dilemma that we have just been describing, is but a counter-part to the inconsistencies of the con-

---

[110] F. I. Khaskhachikh, *Materiya i soznanie*, Moskva, 1951, p. 47 ff.

[111] It would not seem sufficient to say "sufficiently complex", or the like. For if the "matter", man, for example, is only more *complex* than other matters, its properties may be more complex, too, yet they never will be *less material*.

[112] G. A. Wetter, *op. cit.*, pp. 552, 556.

cept of matter mentioned above. All such inconsistencies and dilemmas are, in the last resort, due to the basic paradox of Marxism-Leninism, namely, that it wants to be a materialism without leaving the heights of Occidental metaphysics which, to Soviet philosophers, is exemplified in Hegel. As has been often pointed out, such syntheses are hardly possible; and the synthesis of an extreme idealism with materialism, this most threadbare of all philosophical positions, can amount, to use a favourite expression of Lenin's, only to *"galimat'ya"* (rubbish).

University of Notre Dame

PHENOMENALISM WITHOUT PARADOX

Kenneth Sayre

§1 *Obscurities in Formulation*

Refuting Phenomenalism has become a fashionable exercise among philosophers in recent years, one result of which has been to point up a rather wide variety of theses which the Phenomenalist ought not to hold if in fact he were ever tempted to do so. Another result has been to obscure those aspects of Phenomenalism which make the effort to refute it worthwhile. Thus, however unfashionable it may be to take the Phenomenalist's part, it is not inopportune at this time to attempt to clarify some of the issues involved in this controversy, and to show that the Phenomenalist need not always come out second-best. My purpose in this paper is to formulate Phenomenalism in a way which avoids the usual traps and snares, and which at the same time preserves what I take to be the heart of the Phenomenalist's traditional contribution to the conceptual analysis of matter.

Not all the blame for obscurity in the Phenomenalistic thesis lies with the critics, for Phenomenalists themselves often have been content with a paradoxical manner of expressing their insights. Berkeley's Philonous, for example, confronts the bewildered Hylas with the assertion that "a cherry is nothing but a congeries of sensible impressions".[1] Mill speaks of that which we call by the names 'ice' and 'log' as "Permanent Possibilities of Sensation".[2] And Mach writes that "thing, body, matter, are nothing apart from their complexes of color, sounds, and so forth . . ."[3] More recently, Russell has suggested that "the thing" of common sense may in fact be identical with the whole class of its appearances";[4] the sun, for instance, is "a whole assemblage of particulars, existing at different times, spread out from the centre with the velocity of light, and containing among their number all those visual data which are seen by people who are now looking

---

[1] *Three Dialogues between Hylas and Philonous*, George Berkeley, LaSalle, Illinois, 1947, p. 81.

[2] *An Examination of Sir William Hamilton's Philosophy*, John Stuart Mill, 1872, p. 257.

[3] *The Analysis of Sensations*, Ernst Mach, Chicago, 1914, p. 6.

[4] *Mysticism and Logic*, Bertrand Russell, London, 1953, p. 147.

at the sun".[5] And Price, although himself not a Phenomenalist, understands that theory to assert that "a *system* of sense-data is a material thing".[6]

The main drawback of these traditional formulations, apart from their hyperbole, is that they tend to suggest that Phenomenalism has implications in areas where the Phenomenalist would do well to leave himself uncommitted. The correct and often repeated objection to the doctrine that material objects are composed of sense-data is that it makes material objects out to be much too flimsy. If sense-data, or sensible impressions, are entities of any sort at all, then surely they are not entities substantial enough to compete with electrons or quanta for the role of basic building block of the material world.

Wishing to avoid any apparent conflict with physical theory, Phenomenalists recently have proposed a variety of alternative formulations. Russell makes it clear that he considers material objects to be "logically constructed" and not physically constructed out of sense-data. In Russell's sense, for a thing of type A to be logically constructed out of things of type B is for any statement about things of type A to be replaceable without change in truth value by statements about things of type B.[7] As Ayer remarks, "those who assert that material things are "logical constructions" out of sense-data must be understood to claim . . . that a proposition which is expressed by a sentence referring to a material thing can equally well be expressed by an entirely different set of sentences, which refer only to sense-data."[8] It is now customary among Phenomenalists to present their thesis as an assertion about the meaning of statements about material objects. But this formulation has its own weaknesses. Not only is it unclear what sense of 'meaning' is involved in this assertion, but moreover no Phenomenalist has been able to produce a set of sense-datum statements which comes close to being able to do the job of the material-object statement it might be considered to replace. The Phenomenalist seems to have committed himself to a thesis in semantics which he is either unable or unwilling to pursue in any practical detail.

The formulation of Phenomenalism which I wish to present is intended to avoid these apparant entanglements with physics and semantics. I believe that it retains nonetheless the central insight which Phenomenalists of the traditional stripe have attempted to convey. It was at least part of the claim of the traditional Phenomenalists that we have no empirical evidence that

---

[5] *Mysticism and Logic*, p. 130–31. Russell in this work defends the Selective Theory, which differs from Phenomenalism primarily in sanctioning unsensed sense-data.

[6] *Perception*, H. H. Price, London, 1932, p. 282.

[7] *Mysticism and Logic*, p. 149.

[8] *The Foundations of Empirical Knowledge*, A. J. Ayer, London, 1953, p. 233.

there is anything in what we call a material object beyond that which possibly could be presented to us in ordinary experience. Thus any assertion that there is more to an object than can possibly appear to an observer is a speculative hypothesis for which we have no empirical evidence. As Berkeley suggests, what we mean in non-theoretical contexts by saying "that an orange tree exists is that we perceive it by our senses".[9] Mill writes that all changes of the sort involved in the combustion of a log and in the melting of ice are "intelligible without supposing the wood, the ice, or the water, to be anything underneath or beyond the Permanent Possibilities of Sensation".[10]

Insofar as we have empirical evidence for an assertion about a material object, that assertion cannot entail that there is more to the object than can be disclosed in sensory observation. The emphasis is on the evidential status of material-object statements in Russell's assertion that if we can state the law by which appearances of a thing vary, "we can state all that is empirically verifiable; the assumption that there is a constant entity (which "has" these appearances) is a piece of gratuitous metaphysics".[11] And Ayer remarks that the purpose of the Phenomenalistic analysis is to elucidate "the meaning of statements about material objects by showing what is the kind of evidence by which they may be verified".[12]

The thesis I shall defend is that any assertion about material objects which can be completely warranted on the basis of ordinary sensory experience can be expressed with reference exclusively to sense-data. This is weaker than the claim that all statements about material objects can be expressed in sense-datum statements, for it allows that there may be material object statements, for which we do not have complete empirical justification, which may not be warrantable on the basis of sense-data alone, and which therefore cannot be expressed in sense-datum statements.

A corollary of this thesis which is of particular relevance to the present topic of discussion is that no statement which asserts a distinction between matter and form as fundamental components of material objects can be wholly warranted on the basis of ordinary sensory experience. On this basis it may be maintained that in analyzing what we can say about material objects without exceeding the warrant of sensory observation no need arises for introducing the concept of matter as a principle apart from the sensible appearances of material things.

---

[9] *Three Dialogues*, p. 66.
[10] *Hamilton*, p. 251.
[11] *Our Knowledge of the External World*, London, 1914, p. 111–12.
[12] *Foundations*, p. 235.

Before expanding this thesis, it will be helpful to examine certain objections to the more traditional formulations of Phenomenalism, and to attempt in the process to secure a defensible definition of the term 'sense-datum'.

§2 *Phenomenalism Is Not Descriptive*

Persons whose acquaintance with Phenomenalism is second-hand seem to protest most against the notion that material objects might be made up of sensations. But it is clear that material objects are not composed of sensations, in any ordinary sense of these terms, and insofar as the traditional Phenomenalists have suggested that this is the case they have exhibited a bad sense of public relations. Our best information is that material objects are made up of atoms, which in turn are made up of elementary particles which can be described only in terms of scientific theory. It is not the part of the Phenomenalist to suggest anything to the contrary, and it is to the discredit of the traditional authors that their formulation did not make this clear. It is all too easy to find reason in Berkeley, Mill, and Mach to think that they conceived sense-data to be much too concrete. And the price of this manner of speaking is still being paid in misunderstanding and lack of sympathy. Even in recent literature we find critics professing to be unable to find sense-data with characteristics which would enable them literally to be parts of material objects, and pronouncing the downfall of Phenomenalism (or "The Sense-Datum Theory") on that basis.[13]

Another understandable misreading which, like this one, construes talk about sense-data as talk about entities in some sense present in the external world, is the notion that Phenomenalism is a theory about the phenomenological character of perceptual experience. It is then objected that Phenomenalism carries with it a false phenomenology and consequently is incorrect. Critics who take this tack cite with glee Lewis' remark in *Mind and the World Order:*

> It is indeed the thick experience of the world of things, not the thin given of immediacy, which constitutes the datum for philosophical reflection. We do not see patches of color, but trees and houses; we hear, not indescribable sound, but voices and violins. What we most certainly know are objects and full-bodied facts about them which could be stated in propositions.[14]

---

[13] For an example, see "The Myth of Sense-Data", W. H. F. Barnes, in *Proceedings of the Aristotelian Society, 45*, 1944–45, pp. 89–118.
[14] *Mind and the World Order*, C. I. Lewis, New York, 1929, p. 54.

Wild, for example, approves of this statement, but criticizes Lewis for going on to abandon "the aim of classic philosophy to describe the *thick* experience of the world of things *as it is given*" in favor of "the procedure of modern empiricism [which] . . . singles out a certain portion of the given as peculiarly accessible or *given* in some special sense".[15] Stout, for another example, maintains that the question what it is that we perceive "is one of fact and cannot . . . be answered on *a priori* grounds. It can only be answered by an analysis of the process of sense perception as it actually occurs in particular instances."[16] Stout's analysis concludes that there is an element in perception which draws our attention to actual physical objects as distinct merely from their sensible appearances. It would seem to follow that this element cannot be described in terms of sense-data alone.

Criticism of this sort may emphasize noteworthy aspects of perceptual experience. Its effect on the Phenomenalist, however, has never been what the critics hope for. The Phenomenalist in fact may explicitly subscribe to the proposition that material objects and not sense-data are presented in perceptual experience. No Phenomenalist in this century, as far as I know, has proposed an analysis of the phenomenological character of perception which would conflict with any of the analyses mentioned above. The Phenomenalist is concerned not with describing how things appear but rather with the problem how what is given in sense-perception (however described) can furnish evidence for statements about the material world. Phenomenalism entails no specific phenomenology, and hence cannot be criticized legitimately for a false phenomenology.

Objections of this sort have had the worthwhile effect of showing the Phenomenalist what he should not commit himself to, and of encouraging him to seek formulations of his position which make his commitments more explicit. Thus in recent years Phenomenalism has been presented almost exclusively in what, following Carnap, is called the "formal mode" of speech. In this formulation, Phenomenalism is made out to be a thesis about the meaning of material object statements instead of about the constitution of the material world. In order to give a just hearing to this formulation it will be helpful to make the concept of sense-datum more precise. This is appropriate for other reasons as well, for some critics seem to think that a difficulty common to *all* forms of Phenomenalism is its reliance upon an indefensible notion of sense-data, and I would like to exempt in advance

---

[15] "The Concept of *The Given* in Contemporary Philosophy", *Philosophy and Phenomenological Research*, *1*, 1940, pp. 70–71.

[16] "Phenomenalism", G. F. Stout, *Proceedings of the Aristotelian Society*, *39*, 1938–39, p. 7.

from this difficulty the formulation of Phenomenalism which I propose below.

§3 *In Defense of 'Sense-datum'*

It has been suggested at one time or another that sense-data are entities characterized 1) by being unaltered by mental attitudes,[17] 2) by being indubitable,[18] or 3) by being in no sense inferred.[19] Philosophers who have maintained that sense-data possess one or more of these characteristics have maintained moreover that they belong to sense-data uniquely, and hence that sense-data can be defined by the possession of these characteristics. Another approach to the problem of defining 'sense-datum' has been by use of technical verbs of perception, such as 'to be aware of' or 'to see' in a special sense of the word 'see'. Broad once suggested that 'sense-data' be used to refer to objects of which we are "directly aware".[20] And Ayer has used 'sense-datum' to designate what we see (or feel, etc.) in a sense of these verbs which entails that what is seen (or felt, etc.) really has the properties it seems to have.[21] As an example of a third approach, we have Russell's attempt to define 'sense-datum' in terms of a special sort of knowledge: "Let us give the name of 'sense-datum' to the things that are immediately known in sensation: such things as colours, sounds, smells, hardnesses, roughnesses, and so on."[22]

Each of these approaches has been roundly criticized in recent years. Barnes has pointed out that if sense-data are entities at all they are entities of a very queer sort, such that they fail to possess determinate characteristics which can be re-examined to settle questions about their nature.[23] Ryle has contended that the identification of sense-data with sensations results from the "logical howler" of assimilating the concept of sensation to the concept of observation.[24] The mistake allegedly is in thinking of sense-datum terms as objects of verbs which properly take as objects only terms which refer to phyiscal objects. And the attempt to identify sense-data as objects of a special sort of knowledge has been criticized in detail by Prichard, who claims that the mistake in this procedure stems from the erroneous notion

---

[17] Lewis, in *Mind and the World Order*, p. 66.
[18] Price, in *Perception*, p. 3.
[19] Russell, in *Our Knowledge of the External World*, pp. 75–78.
[20] *Scientific Thought*, C. D. Broad, London, 1923, pp. 234–40.
[21] *Foundations*, p. 24.
[22] *The Problems of Philosophy*, Bertrand Russell, London, 1946, p. 12.
[23] "The Myth of Sense-Data".
[24] *The Concept of Mind*, Gilbert Ryle, New York, 1949, p. 213.

that perception is a form of knowing.[25] These are samples of a large body of literature critical of sense-data.

As well taken as these points may be, I cannot see that they in any way affect the Phenomenalist's thesis about the relation between sense-datum statements and statements about material objects. The Phenomenalist is responsible for making clear his use of the expression 'sense-datum statement', a task to which we return shortly. But if he can do so without assuming that sense-data are *entities* of any sort, it is not germane to his thesis to point out that sensing is not knowing, that sense-data are not objects, or that they do not possess determinate characteristics. What is germane, and what the Phenomenalist cannot afford to ignore, are questions about the evidential status of sense-datum statements in respect to statements about material objects.

It is part of the traditional concept of sense-data that they are in some sense indubitable and in no sense inferential. Let us consider some of the difficulties involved in these notions, and see whether they still can be put to good use. To avoid issues connected with the charge of inventing entities, however, let us speak of sense-datum statements instead of sense-data. Thus we shall ask: "Is there any sense of 'dubitable' in which sense-datum statements are less dubitable than all material object statements?"; and "What is meant by the claim that sense-datum statements are non-inferential in a sense not characteristic of other statements?"

Russell once wrote that "a man possessed of intellectual prudence will avoid such rash credulity as is involved in saying "there's a dog!" "[26] The grounds for the prudent man's avoidance would be the fact that artificial stimulation of the optic nerves, hypnosis, a clever technicolor projector, or perhaps drugs, could induce the sort of experience a person has when confident he is seeing a dog. The possibility that his experience originates in one of these anomalous ways renders the belief of the prudent man less than certain even when he has every other reason to believe he actually is seeing a dog. What is certain is what can be expressed in the proposition: "There is a canoid [sic] patch of colour".[27] There is also allegedly a sense in which the belief that this is a dog is inferred from other beliefs. If one had never seen a dog before (or had never learned about dogs from other people), his experience on this occasion would not lead him to state that this is a dog. Moreover, at best one does not see a *whole* dog, but only part (one side) of one. Yet the belief that this is a dog includes the belief that there is more to this dog than the side which happens to be seen. Belief that this is a dog,

---

[25] *Knowledge and Perception*, H. A. Prichard, Oxford, 1950, pp. 45–46.
[26] *An Inquiry into Meaning and Truth*, London, 1940, p. 151.
[27] *Inquiry*, p. 139.

then, seems to depend at least partially on prior information, and in some sense may be said to be inferred from this information. Belief that there is a dog-like patch of color, however, is dependent for its veracity only upon the experience of the moment (disregarding the verbal facility needed to express it), and hence is in no sense inferential.

Now we may well agree that it is possible that the experience in question could be induced by hypnosis, drugs, or the like: and certainly it is true that we commonly believe there is more to dogs than what we actually see of them at a given moment. But the conclusions Russell draws from these facts are not equally obvious. First, in what sense am I called upon to doubt the statement: "There is a dog", in circumstances under which normally I would say confidently and deliberately that I am seeing a dog? It would be irrational flatly to *disbelieve* this proposition, for this would be to believe the proposition "There is no dog", and there is far more evidence for the former than for the latter. Nor would it be rational to suspend belief in the matter, especially if the dog shows signs of unfriendliness. However, the sense in which I am to doubt there is a dog is not a practical, but supposedly a philosophical or logical sense of 'doubt'. To doubt in this case involves admission of the logical possibility that my belief that there is a dog might be mistaken. If this is what Russell meant by doubting that there is a dog, then certainly he is right in maintaining the dubiety of this proposition. We do doubt in this sense, for this is no more than to admit that the denial of the proposition "There is a dog" is not contradictory.

But plainly speaking, our admission that the denial of a belief is not contradictory is not to doubt that belief at all. If Russell means by 'doubt' only admission of the logical possibility that one *might* be wrong, then no philosophical clarity results from giving it that name. For to call this admission 'philosophical doubt' only leads one to seek pointless explanations of how he can doubt when actually he does not doubt at all.

Nor is it easy to find a sense of 'inference' in which my belief that this is a dog is inferred from other beliefs. It may be true that this belief would not have arisen had I no previous experience with dogs. And certainly it is true that one does not see *all* there is to see of a dog at any one glance. But there is nothing in these facts to require our admission that the proposition that there is a dog is inferred, in any clear sense of the term 'infer', from other beliefs or propositions. It is not *deductively* inferred, for the denial that there is a dog is in no way inconsistent with any proposition about dogs which I entertain currently or have entertained. Nor is the proposition that this is a dog *inductively* inferred from previous information about dogs, for the denial of any part of my previous information about dogs seems in no way to weaken my present claim that this is a dog. There is no proof in these remarks that beliefs like the belief that this is a dog are in no sense inferential, for some unusual sense of the term 'infer' might be tailored to turn the trick. But we see that the sense in which such beliefs might be inferential does not come clear in the ordinary use of the term 'infer', and it is good counsel at this time that the defender of sense-data speak plain language.

Considerations regarding the inferential status or the dubiety of material object statements do not rescue the concept of sense-data from philosophic limbo. The type of perceptual misinformation against which Russell cautions us to be on our guard, however, can be interpreted in a less misleading way, and it will be helpful to do so in an attempt to preserve what is worthwhile in the concept of sense-data.

Imagine Jones seated at his desk, anticipating the visit of a friend. Presently he hears the sound of footsteps, and arises to let his visitor into the room. But if Jones should open the door onto an empty hallway, he would be no more than mildly surprised. For he has only tentative reasons for believing his friend has actually arrived. It is quite possible that he heard only the floor squeaking from an unknown structural strain, while the familiarity of the sound was contributed by his anticipation. Less probably, but possible nonetheless, Jones might have imagined the sound, or have been the victim of a hoax. The point of such consideration is not to advise Jones and others like him to be more cautious. Intelligent persons form habits early in life to guard them against being misled by their senses in ordinary circumstances. The point rather is that the sound of footsteps alone is not sufficient warrant for a firm belief that the friend has arrived.

But evidence from audition has a low confidence rating. Let us consider another example involving visual perception. Imagine Jones walking along a wooded path in the twilight, when suddenly he notices an ominous form a short way down the path. It looks very much as if a man is lying in ambush, partially concealed by a tree. But from where Jones stands it is hard to tell; perhaps it is only a large shrub which gives the appearance of a man in the twilight. Since there have been reports of robberies in this area, Jones is concerned to determine whether in fact it is a man or something else. There are several means by which to settle the problem; Jones could issue a challenge, throw a rock, or intrepidly continue along the path. Regardless of how the matter is settled, more evidence is needed than Jones has at the moment to tell what he is seeing. The point again is that Jones' *present* awareness does not furnish sufficient warrant for believing either that another man is present or that instead what he sees is only a bush or some other object.

Admittedly these examples are cases in which the average rational man would be skeptical about his evidence if he had compelling reasons to avoid mis-judgment. Consider, however, the case of a nearly complete illusion. Not long ago a popular magazine told of the return of a group of Arctic explorers to a bay they had visited before, but had explored only in part. The reason they had not previously explored further was that access to the inner part of the bay apparently was blocked by an enormous wall of ice. For some reason (perhaps air reconnaissance) they believed the obstructed part of the inlet has been cleared since their previous visit. Upon their return they were surprised to see the inlet completely blocked as before. They approached for a closer look at the blockade; and as they approached the wall of ice it began to change radically in appearance. Suddenly it was gone and the inlet opened clear before them. They had been victims of a rather costly illusion. Atmospheric conditions had caused the appearance of a huge block of ice, an appearance which has been convincing enough to cause them to turn back once before. According to their testimony, and photo graphs they took of the illusion, the mistaken appearance could not be distinguished from an appearance of the real thing.

Even when we are convinced without reservation of the evidence furnished by our senses, we *may* be mistaken. The moral is not that we should be generally distrustful of our senses. What is to be learned from these, and other more imaginative exercises in "philosophic skepticism", is that more evidence is needed for the adequate warrant of any belief about the material world than can be provided in a moment's sensory awareness. Regardless of the conviction which a moment's awareness might inspire in us, the test of veracity of any belief we might base on that awareness is in the accord of that belief with past and future experience. No sensory awareness of momentary duration, however clear, carries with it proof that it is not illusory. It is worth insisting again that this is not a call to general skepticism. Sensory awareness obviously is the basis of most of our beliefs about material objects, and some of these beliefs are highly warranted. I would want to argue, indeed, that some of these beliefs are warranted as completely as possible. But no momentary instance of sensory awareness in itself completely warrants any belief about a material object.

Awareness of this momentary character, however, does offer complete warrant for beliefs of a more limited sort. Any given sensory awareness, however described and under whatever circumstances, furnishes complete warrant for the belief that this awareness is occurring. The proposition that such an awareness is occurring is informative, since it might have been false, and is empirical since it is not decidable apart from the occurrence of the awareness which it reports.

The expression 'complete warrant' is central in these remarks, and may be explained with reference to a statement A which is claimed to introduce

474

complete warrant for a statement B. To say that A introduces complete warrant for B is to say that it is sufficient for the justification of B that A be true. More formally, it is to say that both A and B are true, and that there is no other statement C compatible with A such that if C were true then B would be false. If there were such a statement C and if B is true, then the negation of C would combine with A in the introduction of complete warrant for B. The character of the warrant introduced by A may be either empirical or theoretical, since this sense of 'warrant' includes not only empirical evidence but also evidence in the form of theoretical propositions which bear upon the truth of B.

The importance of this notion of complete warrant in theory of knowledge can be indicated by formulating a tautology:

> All assertions about material objects can be divided into two classes, 1) those which can be completely warranted by momentary sensory awareness, and 2) those which cannot.

This statement itself surely is unexceptionable. Yet one of the central problems of epistemology is how beliefs which fall into class 2) are warranted; and disagreements among epistemologists arise immediately with the attempt to determine what beliefs fall into class 1). Defenders of sense-data have often maintained that only statements about sense-data are properly classified under 1), and have given the impression that any disagreement regarding the propriety of this classification could be settled by careful observation. Russell, as we have seen, defined sense-data as those aspects of our awareness which are impervious to skeptical doubt, and then attempted to show that statements about these are the most highly warranted of empirical statements and hence alone belong in class 1). This procedure is open to two types of objection. First, it could be claimed that there are no elements of awareness which properly go by the name 'sense-data' thus defined, and hence that sense-data are non-empirical. Second, it could be objected that statements about sense-data, if such exist, are no more completely warranted than other statements which clearly are not about sense-data. Both objections have been ably developed, and I do not wish to quarrel with them.

Instead of arguing whether there are assertions which merit the name 'sense-datum statement' and which fall into class 1), I wish to leave the membership of class 1) an open question. This of course is not to leave the *character* of assertions in class 1) an open question, for by definition this class contains only assertions which are warrantable in a particular way. Further, I would like to provide a way of expressing assertions which are reasonable candidates for membership in class 1) without using the term 'sense-datum' or equivalent terminology. This should enable us to discuss the membership of class 1) without arousing suspicion of our having introduced an ontology of reified appearances. The expression 'sense-datum statement' then can be explicitly re-introduced as an optional but convenient generic name referring to all assertions which may in fact fall into class 1).

The expression 'sense-datum statement' will be used in this way during the remainder of this discussion. Philosophers who do not wish to use this expression may follow my argument by reading 'assertion of class 1)' wherever I write 'sense-datum statement'.

This procedure has the considerable advantage of avoiding the interminable problem of "whether sense-data exist". If there is any call to use the term 'sense-data' (as against 'sense-datum statement'), it can be understood as referring to whatever in sensory awareness warrants statements of class 1). Questions regarding "the nature of sense-data" may then be settled by the individual on the basis of his own experience, and no question regarding the degree of warrant of sense-datum statements will arise, for such statements will have been defined as those which are completely warranted by momentary sensory awareness.

How may beliefs, the statements of which fall into class 1), be expressed without use of 'sense-data', 'appearance', or other nouns which purport to have similar reference? Beliefs of this sort are those which are completely warranted on the basis of momentary awareness. Thus we may consider first what sort of belief can be correctly held without exceeding the warrant of momentary sensory awareness. The individual epistemologist has no more ultimate authority than his own experience in deciding this issue. In the next few paragraphs I describe relevant experience of my own, and assume that it is not radically different in important respects than that of other individuals interested in these problems.

Consider my awareness of the magnolia tree outside the window. I am firmly convinced that there is a magnolia tree there, and my belief that there is a magnolia tree there of which I am now aware, is based not only on my present awareness, but also (in a way difficult to explicate) upon memory and upon my general confidence that objects like trees do not suffer radical alterations from one moment to the next in the normal course of events. Although I have no reasonable doubt concerning the existence of that tree, I am not fully warranted in my belief by my current awareness alone. The statement that there is a magnolia tree outside the window falls into class 2).

What *is* warranted by my momentary awareness of the magnolia tree? I am warranted in believing, first, that this awareness is occurring *now* and, second, that *I* am having it. Third, I am warranted in believing that I do at least *seem* to see a magnolia tree. This belief is warranted simply because I *do* seem to see a magnolia tree, which is a matter admitting the relevance of no judgment other than my own. Even if I am the victim of some sort of illusion, which is perhaps remotely possible, I nonetheless do seem to see a magnolia tree. Moreover, no memory of past experience, nor any eventuality of future experience, can in any way influence the fact that now I seem to see such a tree. Since there is no possible additional information which would affect my present belief, and since I *do* seem to see a magnolia tree, my belief that this is so could not be more fully warranted. A statement of belief, then, which is completely warranted by my present awareness, can be expressed in these terms: 'It seems to me now as if I am seeing a magnolia tree'.[28] In the statement of this belief there is no occurrence of 'sense-data' nor of equivalent nouns of appearance.

It may be pointed out that it goes against the grain of language to say, in these circumstances: "It seems to me now as if I am seeing a magnolia tree". The reason this assertion seems out of place is that in fact a much stronger statement could be made. Counting on evidence accumulated from past experience, and from a closer inspection of the tree, if needed, I would indeed be justified in saying flatly: "I see a magnolia tree". As a convention of common use, the locution 'it seems as if. . .' is reserved for occasions on which evidence is obviously incomplete. When we wish to call attention to the fact that a belief we hold is mere opinion, or is held with admittedly incomplete evidence, a common way is to use 'it seems' or 'it appears'. Two points constitute my rejoinder. First, although I am indeed warranted in making a stronger statement than "It seems to me now as if I am seeing a magnolia tree", my warrant exceeds my awareness of the present moment. Second, whenever a statement of the form 'I see x' is warranted, a statement of the form 'It seems to me as if I am seeing x' also is warranted. Evidence for the former includes warrant for the latter. It may seem odd to use the latter locution when the former is justified, but at least one is not exceeding his warrant in doing so.

Another objection might be raised to the effect that even the statement 'It seems to me now as if I am seeing a magnolia tree' is not completely warranted, for it is not inconsistent to deny this statement in the face of the awareness which I have said furnishes its warrant. This is not a serious objection, for the relationships of consistency hold among statements, not between statements and sensory events. Moreover, although no sense-datum statement is *entailed* by any sensory occurrence, there is a sense in which a

---

[28] This is similar to expressions used for similar purposes by Ayer and Warnock. See *The Problem of Knowledge*, A. J. Ayer, London, 1953, p. 111; and *Berkeley*, G. J. Warnock, London, 1953, p. 169.

sense-datum statement is rendered logically incorrigible by the appropriate sensory awareness. By saying that a statement is logically incorrigible I mean that its function is such that no evidence which would tend to decrease the warrant of the statement is admissible. What I intend by the statement: "It seems to me now as if I am seeing a magnolia tree" is such that no added information (added now or at any other time) could possibly discredit that statement. The statement is meant to preclude from relevancy to its warrant all considerations other than the occurrence of the appropriate sensory awareness.

With respect to language usage, of course, the statement is not incorrigible. The language I use may be corrected; I might be informed for example, that such things are usually called "bushes" and not "trees". This correction would be admissible. But no proffered correction regarding my grounds for the sense-datum statement is acceptable. Not even if I were to glance away for a moment and look back to find, for some unknown reason, a large oak in place of my magnolia tree, would I admit any weakening of my previous statement about my seeming to see a magnolia tree. For at that time it did seem to me as if I were seeing a magnolia tree (although later I might not recall this with complete confidence, which is not to the point). Now, at this later moment, I would be warranted in saying that it seems to me as if I am seeing an oak tree, but this has no bearing on what I seemed to see before. Further, even though I were to have the most trustworthy information that there is no magnolia tree outside my window, this information would not bear upon the fact that I now seem to see one there. It would only tend to make me disbelieve that I would continue to seem to see a magnolia tree if I splashed cold water on my face, or advanced for a closer look.

Russell's criteria for the identification of sense data may be re-interpreted. A sense-datum statement may be called incorrigible in the sense that no added information could attest to its falsity, and non-inferential in the sense that no added information could bear upon its truth. But this is so only at the moment signified by the term 'now' occurring in the sense-datum statement when uttered. "It seems to me at t_0 that I am seeing a magnolia tree" is fully warranted and incorrigible only at t_0. At t_n, later than t_0, the statement is warranted primarily by my memory, and hence is neither incorrigible nor certain. And even if at t_n there were evidence against the statement "It seemed to me at t_0 as if I am seeing a magnolia tree", and if I had some sort of advance notice at t_0 that this evidence would be available at t_n, still this foreknowledge would have no bearing upon my warrant at t_0 for saying then "it seems to me now as if I am seeing a magnolia tree". Sensory warrant of a sense-datum statement might be thought of as an "all or nothing" affair. If such a statement has any warrant at all, it has complete warrant.

§4 *Difficulties with the Translatability Thesis*

The remarks of the previous section may not persuade everyone of the usefulness of the expression 'sense-datum statement', but they should suffice to preserve that expression in currency for those who do find it useful. The present section reviews the attempt of contemporary Phenomenalists to explicate the use of material object statements in terms of sense-datum statements.

Contemporary writers generally formulate Phenomenalism in a way which no longer suggests that it has anything to say about the actual composition of material objects. It is now customary instead to present Phenomenalism as a thesis about the meaning of material-object statements. Stout, for example, has defined Phenomenalism as the theory that any proposition about material objects can be *translated* into statements about actual and possible sense-data.[29] Ayer claims that every empirical statement about a material object is *reducible* to a statement or set of statements which refer exclusively to sense-data.[30] Firth defines Phenomenalism as the thesis that the meaning of any statement about the material world can be expressed, at least in theory, by a combination of hypothetical statements which refer only to sense-data.[31] A way of putting it which would perhaps be acceptable to each of these writers is that whatever one might wish to say of an empirical nature about material objects can be said in sense-datum statements. If this thesis is correct then all reference to material objects theoretically could be eliminated from our vocabulary and replaced by expressions which refer only to sense-data. In that case, *the concept of matter as distinct from our concept of the appearances of material objects would have been shown to be expendable.*

The best way for the Phenomenalist to support this thesis would be to produce a few examples and to give reasons for our thinking that these examples are typical. But in fact no sample translation has been given, and as far as I know no serious attempt has ever been made to produce one. The reason usually offered for this omission is the shortage of sense-datum terms in our working vocabulary. We do have a limited supply of terms for de-

---

[29] "Phenomenalism", p. 6.

[30] *Hume's Theory of the External World*, H. H. Price, Oxford, 1950, p. 177.

[31] "Phenomenalism", Roderick Firth, in *American Philosophical Association Eastern Division*, *1*, 1952, p. 5.

scribing colors, shapes, sounds, and the like, but it is not adequate to provide for the complete translation of even the simplest statement about material objects. Hence the Phenomenalist is constrained to use in his illustrations expressions like 'the sort of experience one gets when he is looking at a chair', or 'kinesthetic data typical of moving into the living room'. Translations which involve this sort of expression obviously have not been purified of all reference to material objects, but the fault is claimed to lie not with Phenomenalism but in the limitations of available language. If the critic is content to allow that the *de facto* failure of any attempt to produce an actual translation of any material object statement is attributable to a deficiency in language, then this failure cannot be construed as a disproof of Phenomenalism.

It is quite another thing, however, to claim that no Phenomenalistic translation could be completed *even* if adequate sense-datum terminology were available. This claim has been raised recently by a number of critics, and is intended to challenge the theoretical possibility of a sense-datum translation of material object statements.[32] The argument runs along the following lines: If the meaning of a material object statement can be expressed by a set of sense-datum statements, then those statements must be entailed by the object statement whose meaning they express. There are always circumstances, however, under which a given object statement would be true, but any sense-datum statement which might be taken to provide part of its meaning would be false. For example, part of the meaning of 'This is a telephone' might be expressed in terms of the tactual data one would expect to experience in picking up the receiver. But if one's fingers were numb, these data would not be obtained; nonetheless, 'This is a telephone' might convey a true statement. Similar conditions could be conceived which would prevent the sensing of any sense-datum one might refer to in the translation of any material object statement. From this it appears that no specific set of sense-datum statements can be entailed by any material object statement, and thus that Phenomenalism is incorrect.

This difficulty has been raised most forcibly in an argument by Chisholm, which may be paraphrased in our terminology.[33] Chisholm begins his argument by pointing out that before a material object statement could be translated into sense-datum statements, something would have to be known not

---

[32] Ayer in *The Problem of Knowledge*, pp. 138–39; Roderick Chisholm in "The Problem of Empiricism", *The Journal of Philosophy*, *45*, 1948, pp. 513–16; Paul Marhenke in "Phenomenalism", *Philosophical Analysis*, Max Black ed., Ithaca, 1950, p. 316; R. B. Braithwaite in "Propositions about Material Objects", *Proc. Aristotelian Society*, *38*, 1937–38, p. 275.
[33] "The Problem of Empiricism".

only about the object itself but also about the conditions under which it is perceived. Consider the material object statement P and the sense-datum statement R:

(*P*) This apple is red.
(*R*) It seems to me now as if I am seeing a red apple.

Since there is no contradiction in affirming P and denying R, P does not by itself entail R. In addition, a statement like Q is needed:

(*Q*) I am observing this apple under normal conditions; and if this apple is red and is observed under normal conditions, it seems to me now as if I am seeing a red apple.

The compound statement PQ does entail R. But another statement can be found which, in conjunction with P, entails not-R. Consider:

(*S*) I am observing this apple under conditions which are normal except for the presence of blue lights; and if this apple is observed by me now under conditions which are normal except for the presence of blue lights, it does not seem to me now as if I am seeing a red apple.

But if PS entails not-R, and if P and S are consistent, then it follows deductively that P does not entail R. Chisholm asserts generally that for every statement P' and every condition statement Q' there can be formulated another condition statement S' such that, if $P'Q'$ entails R', then $P'S'$ entails not-R'. It follows that there is no sense-datum statement R' which is entailed by any material object statement P', and hence that no material object statement can be translated into an equivalent set of sense-datum statements.

This argument is intended to constitute a disproof of Phenomenalism. In fact it does not have that force. The Phenomenalist may point out that a typical sense-datum statement entailed by P would be in conditional rather than categorical form. He could maintain that P entails, not R alone, but rather a conditional statement of the form: 'Q only if R', when Q is a statement like "It seems to me now as if my eyesight, and other conditions of observation, are normal, and that I am glancing at an object with the characteristics of an apple". The statement of entailment pertinent to his analysis, then, would be of the form 'P entails (Q only if R)'; and *this* statement contrary to what is the case with 'P entails R', *is* consistent with 'PS entails not-R (since 'PQ entails R' is consistent with 'PS entails not-R', and 'PQ entails R' entails 'P entails (Q only if R)'). Moreover, he could reject Chisholm's claim that there is a further statement S' which in conjunction with P entails that 'Q only if R' is false. Such a statement would either (i) be materially equivalent to Q, or else (ii) fail to be materially equivalent to Q. If (i), then the assertion that PS' entails not-(Q only if R) would be equivalent to the assertion that PS' entails $S'\overline{R}$, and obviously PS does not entail $S'\overline{R}$. If (ii), then Q could be false when S' is true, in which case PS' could be true when $Q\overline{R}$ is false. But if PS' could be true when $Q\overline{R}$ is false, then PS' could entail neither $Q\overline{R}$ nor its equivalent: not-(Q only if R). In neither case, then, does PS' entail the negation of (Q only if R).

The Phenomenalist who takes this line of reply would encounter difficulties of admitted severity in providing a statement like Q which would be entirely satisfactory for the purpose above. But his burden in this at least is not one of logical inconsistency. Thus Chisholm's argument is not conclusive against Phenomenalism in this form. It does, however, augment our reasons for being dissatisfied with the ordinary formulation of the Phenomenalistic thesis. But I think that most Phenomenalists would feel no more compunction in giving up this formulation of their thesis, if it seems to commit them to providing actual translations of particular material object statements, than they felt in giving up the earlier formulation which seemed to commit them to a thesis regarding the composition of material objects. In the remaining pages I wish to suggest a reformulation which allows the Phenomenalist to avoid problems of the nature of material objects and the actual translation of material object statements without giving the appearance of shifting his ground.

§5 *Phenomenalism and Empirical Warrant*

It is necessary first to secure a sense of the term 'observation' which can be used to refer to our ordinary sensory awareness of objects in the material world without theoretical overtones. In this sense of the term, for someone to say that he observes a chair or a magnolia tree is not to take a stand on the composition of a material object, on the relation of sensing to perceiving, or on any of the traditional problems of mind and matter. To observe a material object is something anyone can do whose senses are functioning normally and whose mind is not systematically disordered, and which he can do without benefit of the special training of the tea-taster or the special instruments and conceptual formation of the experimental scientist. It is on the basis of this non-technical sort of observation that we cross streets without mishap, recognize friends, and learn to apply the term 'material object'. It is also this sort of observation which furnishes whatever warrant we have for making statements of the ordinary variety about objects in the material world.

The main insight of the Phenomenalist tradition, I believe, regards the sort of statement for which warrant is provided by ordinary sensory observation. In order to bring this out more clearly, the Phenomenalist might ex-

plain the point of his thesis as follows: By asserting that material object statements theoretically can be expressed in sense-datum statements, he intends
to say something not about their "meaning" but about the sort of evidence
we normally have for the things we say about material objects. He intends
to say that the only warrant we have in ordinary observation is the sort of
warrant which backs up sense-datum statements, and that any material object statement which asserts more than can be expressed in sense-datum
statements cannot be warranted by ordinary sensory obervations alone. It is
apparent that Phenomenalists traditionally have meant to say this much at
least, and perhaps this is the main point of what they have tried to say.[34]

The Phenomenalist might continue to explain that the customary formulation of his thesis, which seems to concern the meaning of material object
statements generally, reflects the influence of the verifiability theory of
meaning. If the only warrant we have in ordinary sensory observation is the
sort of warrant which backs up sense-datum statements, then that warrant
can be reported in sense-datum statements. And if it is correct, as suggested
by the verifiability theory, that the meaning of any statement can be specified by specifying the sensory occurrences which tend to verify that statement, then it follows that the meaning of any material object statement can
be given in sense-datum statements. A variety of advantages are to be gained
by the Phenomenalist, however, if he explicitly dissociates his thesis from
the verifiability theory of meaning. He no longer gives the appearance of
having something of general significance to say in the area of semantics; he
is not bound to seek solutions for the nest of problems attached to the verifiability principle; and he need be embarrassed no longer by pointed requests
to provide actual translations of material object statements.

Thus, instead of trying to say something about the meaning of material
object statements generally, the Phenomenalist may reformulate his thesis
to assert that the only evidence available from ordinary observation is evidence which would count as warrant only for sense-datum statements, and
that any material object statement which can be wholly warranted on that
evidence is one which says no more than can be expressed in sense-datum
statements. It is compatible with this formulation of Phenomenalism that
some material object statements are not identical in meaning with any set of
sense-datum statements. It is compatible even that some material object
statements which are completely warranted are not warranted on the basis
of evidence expressible in sense-datum statements. In such cases, however,
the warrant could not come from ordinary sensory observation alone. The
thesis which the Phenomenalist has now to defend is weaker than the tra-

---

[34] Ayer agrees; see *The Problem of Knowledge*, London, 1956, pp. 147–48.

ditional formulation which makes an assertion about the meaning of all material object statements. He has only to maintain that all material object statements which are completely warrantable by sensory observation can be expressed in sense-datum statements.

Although it would be fruitless to attempt to establish this claim in a way which leaves no logical room for disagreement, the Phenomenalist can give cogent reasons for accepting rather than rejecting his thesis. Consider Jones observing a candle, which is situated on the mantel and burning normally. Jones is a normal observer in normal conditions, and no questions cross his mind regarding the actuality of the candle or its state of slow combustion. We assume that Jones has been observing the candle for some time, and has the best warrant imaginable for asserting that he is seeing a burning candle. Consider now that Jones is asked the philosophic question, "What do you now see?", and that he replies "It seems to me now as if I am seeing a candle". Jones would have been warranted in saying simply, "I am seeing a candle". But his warrant for that assertion would have exceeded the warrant provided by his observation the moment the question was asked. His response was calculated not to go beyond the warrant provided by that momentary observation. If Jones had only now entered the room, or had just noticed the candle for the first time, he would not have the warrant to claim that he actually is seeing a burning candle, although of course he would have complete warrant for claiming that it seemed to him then as if he were seeing a burning candle. Before he could assert confidently that there is a burning candle on the mantel, Jones would have to observe the candle from several points of view, and perhaps to check the space above the candle for convection currents and to touch the candle to make sure it is not a cardboard imitation. These further observations which would warrant Jones' assertion that there is a candle could be specified, along with the conditions under which the observations would have to be made to be relevant. The number of conditions necessary for further observation would be small, and certainly not infinite as some Phenomenalists have suggested. The point is that each of these additional conditions itself yields an observation which warrants completely only a sense-datum statement, for the expression 'sense-datum statement' has been taken to refer to all assertions completely warrantable on the basis of momentary sensory observation.

We have assumed that Jones has complete warrant for making the assertion that he is seeing a burning candle, and that his warrant comes entirely from these corroborating conditions. Since his observation in each of these conditions provides complete warrant only for what can be expressed in sense-datum statements, it follows that Jones' assertion that he sees a burning candle, which is completely warranted, can be expressed in sense-datum statements.

Similar remarks could be made for any statement about material objects which might be claimed to be warrantable strictly on the basis of sensory observation. Consider any material object statement P concerning which this claim is made, and designate the observations which contribute to its warrant by the series of symbols '$C_1 \ldots C_n$'. No one C_i taken alone offers complete warrant for P, but we assume that C_1 through C_n collectively offer complete warrant for P. As argued previously, each C_i offers warrant for a sense-datum statement of the form 'It seems to me now as if $\ldots$', and for that statement alone offers complete warrant. But since each C_i offers complete warrant only for sense-datum statements, the series of observations $C_1 \ldots C_n$ offers complete warrant only for a set of sense-datum statements Now if P asserts anything which cannot be expressed in sense-datum statements, then contrary to assumption it is not warranted completely by C_1 through C_n. It follows that P makes no assertion which cannot be expressed in sense-datum statements.

It might be objected that this argument involves what logic books call "the fallacy of composition". I have argued that since individual observations warrant only sense-datum statements, any statement completely warranted by a group of observations can be expressed in sense-datum statements. Although the argument does not involve that mistake, an explanation why it does not will help clarify the modest character of the Phenomenalist's claim. From the fact that the warrant provided for material object statements by each observation C_i of the observations C_1 through C_n warrants only sense-datum statements, it does not follow that *all* the evidence we might have for an assertion about material objects can be expressed in sense-datum statements. It follows only that assertions which cannot be expressed in sense-datum statements cannot be wholly warranted on the basis of ordinary sensory observation alone. The observations C_i and C_j might support each other in such a way that together they offer warrant for a material object statement which far exceeds the warrant offered by the set of observations C_i and C_j considered independently. But this would be the case only in the context of some *theory* which relates C_i and C_j in a way which makes them mutually corroborative. The added element which increases the warrant of C_i and C_j collectively beyond the set of sense-datum statements warranted by the observations separately considered is not another observation but rather a *theory*. It might be a theory of science or conceivably a philosophic theory. In either case, the statement P which would be warranted by C_i and C_j together in that context is not completely warranted by the observations C_i and C_j alone, but by the observations and that theory according to which these observations corroborate each other.

Phenomenalism as I have interpreted it thus does not deny that there are some assertions about material objects which cannot be expressed in sense-datum statements, for there may be statements about material objects which require warrant beyond that available in ordinary sensory observation. It is compatible with my thesis even that no assertions about material objects can be expressed in sense-datum statements. I think it would be incorrect to maintain this, however, for there are assertions which seem to me to be wholly warrantable on the basis on ordinary observation and which therefore I should say can be expressed in sense-datum statements. Among these are assertions about the way things appear in ordinary circumstances. According to the way I construe the assertions that my tea tastes bitter or that my toast feels hot, for example, what is asserted could be expressed by statements like "It seems to me now as if I am tasting bitter tea", and "It seems to me now as if I am touching hot toast". I would not insist upon these examples, however, for some people might not construe such assertions in the way I construe them. It might be even that some people never make assertions which, according to the way they construe them, can be expressed in sense-datum statements; and whether a person has made such an assertion on a given occasion is for him alone to decide. It should be clear from these remarks that my thesis is not strictly incompatible with any philosophic position in the context of which it is consistent to deny that any statement about material objects can be completely warranted in sensory observation.

This thesis has important consequences nonetheless for a variety of philosophic theories about the composition of material things. For if this thesis is correct, then any statement intended by its author to make an assertion which relies upon a fundamental distinction between that in a material object which can be given in appearance, and an underlying principle which cannot be given in appearance, is a statement which cannot be completely warranted on the basis of sensory observation.

A conclusion may be drawn in particular about any assertion to the effect that material objects are composed of two fundamentally distinct principles, matter and form. In asserting that matter and form are fundamentally distinct, one would be asserting, I think, that there are at least some statements about material objects which cannot be expressed solely in terms of the properties of these objects. And this assertion I take to entail that some things we say about material objects cannot be expressed in terms of the appearances we associate with material objects. In the terminology of this paper, the assertion that matter and form are fundamentally distinct principles in the composition of material things entails that some statements about material objects cannot be expressed in sense-datum statements. Any statement about the matter of an object apart from its form would serve as an example.

The conclusion of my paper which is directly relevant to the topic of the symposium is this: *no statement about matter which makes matter out to be a principle in material objects fundamentally distinct from appearances can be completely warranted by sensory observation.* If this conclusion is correct, it becomes the burden of a philosopher who would maintain such a distinction to explain how his statements about matter can be or could be warranted. It is sufficient here to point out that it is not enough for him to say that these statements can be warranted on the basis of a philosophic theory of matter and form, since statements in the theory of matter and form themselves are statements about matter, and surely these statements cannot be claimed to be self-authenticating.

My general conclusion, in behalf of what I take to be the only currently defensible form of Phenomenalism, is a conclusion about our evidence for material object statements. The term 'ordinary observation' has played a central role in this discussion, and in a sense my conclusion may be construed as a remark about the mode of observation by which we gain information about material objects. Concerning the ordinary sense of 'observation', I have argued that sensory observation provides complete warrant only for sense-datum statements. The central thesis of Phenomenalism follows directly from this: no statement which cannot be expressed in sense-datum statements can be completely warranted on the basis of our ordinary experience of material objects.

University of Notre Dame

COMMENT

MY CRITICISM OF MR. SAYRE'S PAPER IS THAT IF PHENOMENALISM IS WHAT HE says it is, then it seems non-controversial and trivial. Mr. Sayre wants to separate out the pure phenomenalist insight from the irrelevant metaphysical, semantical, and phenomenological theses which have been grafted onto it. I should hold that if the phenomenalist does *not* intend to make either a metaphysical, semantic, or phenomenological claim, then what he has to say is so obviously true as to be uninteresting.

Mr. Sayre says that "the central insight" of phenomenalism is that "the only warrant we have in ordinary observation is the sort of warrant which backs up a sense-datum statement". Now by 'sense-datum statement' here he presumably means what I shall call "seems"-statements—that is, statements of the form 'I now seem to be sensing . . . '. (I cannot accept Mr. Sayre's proposal that 'sense-datum statement' in his argument can be treated as synonymous with 'statement about the material world which can be completely warranted by momentary sensory awareness'. If this synonymy is granted, then his thesis: "any assertion about material objects which can be completely warranted on the basis of ordinary sensory experience can be expressed with reference exclusively to sense-data"—seems to become sheerly tautologous. The insight of phenomenalism, then, is that "seems"-statements are the only sort of statement which can be completely warranted by ordinary observation.)

Now if this insight were taken as a phenomenological thesis about what "ordinary experience" is and isn't like, then perhaps it might be non-trivial. But Mr. Sayre doesn't want us to take it this way. He wants us to take it as a remark which is directed toward the problem of "how what is given in sense-perception (however described) can furnish evidence for statements about the material world". But what sort of a problem is this?

Mr. Sayre does not, I take it, conceive it to be the traditional problem of how to get around Descartes' demon. It is not, in other words, the problem of whether the confidence we repose in momentary sensory awareness, if we do repose confidence, is *justified*. Apparently the problem is simply one of describing accurately how we do behave. So the phenomenalist's insight is presumably an answer to the question: "Under what circumstances do we dismiss objections to our statements on the ground that they are adequately backed up by our ordinary sensory experience?" Taken as an answer to this question, the phenomenalist's insight is unquestionably sound. The answer is that the only circumstances under which we dismiss such objections to our statements is when our statements are "seems"-statements. "Seems"-statements (suitably restricted to the specious present, as Mr. Sayre restricts them) are, indeed, the only variety of statements which, when uttered by other people, are not controverted by us except by an accusation of lying. Taken the other way, they are the only sort of statements we make which are not such as to require us to attend to possible correction by other people. This is because a "seems"-statement is, as Mr. Sayre says, "meant to preclude from relevancy to its warrant all considerations other than the occurrence of the appropriate sensory awareness".

Now if this is all phenomenalism comes to, it is hard to see why anybody should want to refute it. In order to find something more controversial, we may turn to the corollary which Mr. Sayre draws from phenomenalism at the end of his essay: "any statement intended by its author to make an assertion which relies upon a fundamental distinction between that in a material object which can be given in appearance, and an underlying principle which cannot be given in appearance, is a statement which cannot be completely warranted on the basis of sensory observation". Now suppose an opponent saying: "On the contrary, it seems to me that I am now seeing the difference between the appearance of that magnolia tree and an underlying principle of that magnolia tree which cannot be given in appearance". The opponent, having been careful to phrase his remark as a "seems"-statement, may now insist that "no added information could possibly discredit" it. Presumably Mr. Sayre would reply to such an opponent that it was a contradiction in terms for him to have claimed that the difference between what appears and what doesn't itself *appear*. But on what basis can Mr. Sayre make good the assertion that this is a contradiction? It seems to me that it can only be a phenomenological basis. Granted that although only "seems"-statements are warranted by momentary sensory experience, not *all* "seems"-statements are so warranted, it is hard to see how one can tell which such statements get warranted and which don't, except in terms of a phenomenological thesis about how momentary sensory awarenesses should be described.

This point may be put in another way by looking at a particular example of a statement which, according to Mr. Sayre, cannot be "completely" warranted by sensory observation: the assertion that "material objects are composed of two fundamentally distinct principles, matter and form". Mr. Sayre says that he takes such an assertion to entail "that some things we say about material objects cannot be expressed in terms of the appearances we associate with material objects"—because one of the things we say in this assertion is that it has matter as well as form. But why cannot the referent of the term 'matter' be expressed in terms of the appearances we associate with material objects? (If "matter" is leather, for example, it can be so described.) Presumably only because "matter", as Mr. Sayre is using the term, is by definition something that *cannot* be so expressed. But if this is the meaning that he gives to 'matter', his conclusion again seems trivial. If we define "matter" as that which we can't be aware of in momentary sensory awareness, then it is not surprising to be told that we can't warrant our remarks about matter by momentary sensory awarenesses.

It seems to me that in his thesis about statements referring to matter, as well as in his statement of the central insight of phenomenalism, Mr. Sayre is faced with a choice between phenomenology and triviality. In other words, I do not see how what he says in his paper, if it is not to belabor the obvious, can avoid commitment to a certain way of describing the immediately given.

In particular, I think that Mr. Sayre is implicitly committed to a way of describing momentary sensory awareness which precludes the occurrence of such predicates as 'form', 'matter', 'appears', 'awareness', and similar higher-level theoretic terms in such descriptions. I think his claims depend upon the assumption that such "seems"-statement as "It now seems to me that the matter and the form of the magnolia are distinct" can be dismissed as attempts to disguise theoretical speculation as unbiased reporting. I agree with his commitment, in that I find it pragmatically useless to attempt to defend a metaphysical thesis, such as the distinction between form and matter, by reporting what "seems to me". But I think that his argument in his paper depends upon this commitment, rather than providing reasons for it, and that in this sense his paper begs the question. I entirely agree with Mr. Sayre that it is "the burden of a philosopher who would maintain such a distinction to explain how his statements about matter can be or could be warranted". Shouldering this burden seems to me the most difficult meta-philosophical task which confronts anyone who employs the distinction between matter and form, or any similar distinction. But if a philosopher is unwilling to shoulder it, and prefers to just stand there pointing at magnolias and demanding that we divide them in the way in which he does, then I don't see that Mr. Sayre's version of phenomenalism can stop him.

Richard Rorty
Princeton University

DISCUSSION

Mc Mullin: I want to ask a question about the notion of warrant, principally in order to orient this paper towards the doctrine of matter. It seems to me that the paper is of relevance to the concept of matter primarily in raising the question of what sort of warrant we have for talking about matter. In other wards, the emphasis of the paper I take to be on the epistemological notion of warrant, rather than on the concept of matter itself. Now the two are obviously very closely connected, but I think perhaps they are not quite the same.

Sayre: I think the paper is both about the concept of matter and about warrant, in this respect. The theory of perception, of which Phenomenalism is an example, is primarily involved, I believe, in the analysis of the concept of matter, but in a particular context with a particular set of problems in focus. One problem is to determine how matter must be *conceived* in order that statements about material objects can be warranted in the way we usually think them to be warranted—on the basis of sensory observation. The Phenomenalist traditionally has responded by maintaining that the concept of matter must be so explicated as to enable statements about matter and material objects to be expressed in the sense-datum language. I have tried to expound this thesis in a way which throws the emphasis more on the question of warrant than upon the notion of sense-data or the particular way in which we chose to talk about our sensory experience.

Mc Mullin: This is where my difficulties begin. In effect, you drop the notion of sense-datum entirely and introduce that of a sense-datum statement. This notion is defined, not by reference to a theory of sense-data, but by making it a qualified statement of momentary awareness, such as 'I seem to see . . .'. The phrase 'sense-datum' could now be replaced by 'seems . . .', or 'incorrigible'; its retention is a gesture of piety to the older tradition, a gesture which could possibly mislead. The second step is to introduce the notion of "complete warrant", which is not clearly defined, but is ultimately presented as the sort of warrant that only a "seems-statement" has. A new version of Phenomenalism now follows: any statement which asserts more than can be expressed in "seems-statements" cannot be completely warranted by ordinary sensory observation alone.

Sayre: I had attempted in *Part 3* to show how the notion of sense-datum could be circumvented without removing our formulation of the Phenomenalist's thesis too far from its more traditional statements. To do this, I first provided a fairly explicit definition of what I understand in this context by 'complete warrant', and circumscribed a class of statements the defining characteristic of which is that they are completely warranted on the basis of momentary sensory awareness alone. I suggested then that the phrase 'sense-datum statement' could be used to refer to statements of this sort if convenient, but left this entirely optional. Finally, I offered the illustration of some statements beginning with 'It seems to me!' which I take to be members of this class but not necessarily the only members. I am beginning to fear now that this procedure was not sufficiently clear, since both Mr. Rorty and Fr. McMullin seem to have thought that I *define* 'sense-datum' in terms of the "seems-statement". In fact, I defined the class of statement which might, if one wishes, be taken to answer to the designation 'sense-datum statement' quite independently of any examples at all, and in a way which I had hoped would be beyond controversy. And *then* I suggested that, according to the way my sensory awareness is structured, a good example for me of a sense-datum statement would be a seems-statement. It is entirely an open question whether another person would choose an example like this. I am therefore not quite satisfied with the rendition of my thesis which makes it essential that material object statements be expressible in terms of seems-statements if they are to be warranted in a certain way. I have expounded instead the thesis that any statement which is completely warranted on the basis of sensory observation alone can be expressed in statements which are completely warranted on the basis of momentary sensory awareness.

Mc Mullin: There are two remarks I would like to make about this thesis. First, it is a tautology, since it is assumed to follow from the definition of 'complete warrant'. It would be a sad end, indeed, for Phenomenalism if it were to be withdrawn in this way from philosophical debate and promoted to the unassailable but uninteresting rank of tautology.

Second, the whole notion of *warrant* here needs further investigation. Your sense of 'complete warrant' is so strong that no statement of any philosophic or scientific interest seems to possess such a warrant. In that case, to say of some particular assertion (e.g., about a matter-form distinction) that is lacks complete warrant in this sense has little bite. It is not clear that this thesis has any specific negative implications for a doctrine of matter in the way that traditional Phenomenalism had. Moreover, your thesis seems equally to impugn statements in physics—for example, statements about electrons, which certainly are not given in appearances. If you would want to say that such statements could possibly be completely warranted, you would have to admit that a theoretical warrant might be sufficient. To be more concrete here, statements in electron theory, which we might take to back up statements about electrons, would themselves have to be translatable into statements which can be warranted on the basis of appearances if the theory is to have the type of warrant you are talking about. So you seem to be denying that there is a type of theoretical warrant which is ultimately different from your empirical warrant. If so, then you seem to be undercutting the ground of statements not only in metaphysics but in physics as well. I don't think you intend this, but that is the impression given by the end of the paper.

Sayre: I would like to clear my remarks from your charge of triviality or tautologousness which has been raised also by Mr. Rorty. There are various ways in which a philosophic thesis might be trivial, some but not all of which are probably bad. It would be trivial in a bad way to propound, with an air of being informative, a proposition which no one would contest. It is clear I have not done this. It would be objectionably trivial also to begin an argument with a set of premises and to conclude with a mere reformulation of these premises. I am sure my paper does not do this, although this may be the sense in which it has been accused of triviality. In my definition of what we have been calling the 'sense-datum statement' I use the expression 'momentary sensory awareness'. In my general thesis I use the expression 'sensory observation'. I tend to be convinced by Mr. Rorty that my thesis in some way commits me to an assertion of some sort about the constituency of sensory observation out of momentary sensory awarenesses, or momentary experiences. Such an assertion may be phenomenologically unfounded, but it clearly is not trivial. Neither, consequently, is the thesis which commits me to it. In another sense, a conclusion may be called trivial if it follows deductively from its premises. If my argument were trivial in this sense, I would be rather pleased. At any rate, I do not detect a bad sort of triviality in my thesis.

Your suggestion that I have made my sense of 'complete warrant' too strong to be of interest concerns me a bit more. According to my definition, the true statement A introduces complete warrant for B if there is no other statement C such that if C were true B would be false. If there were other statements of this sort, the truth of B would be contingent upon them since if any one of them is true B would be false. Complete warrant for B, in such a case, would include the falsehood of each of these statements. It follows from this definition that a statement which is not completely warranted may indeed be false. That is, for any statement B which is not completely warranted there is a statement C which may be true, and which is such that if it is true then B will be false. What I have in mind here most definitely is not Descartes' demon with his world of possible delusions, but rather the real world in which we do not always know whether our statements are true or false because we do not always have complete survey of all the conditions upon which their truth is contingent. And what I am saying about this world is that when we do not know whether there are conditions which in fact render one of our statements false, we do not know whether in fact our statement is true or false, and consequently we certainly cannot consider it to be completely warranted. We can consider it completely warranted only when we know that the conditions which could render it false do not obtain and can truly assert that this is so. The statements in which we assert this, then, provide complete warrant for our original statement, which without them is incompletely warranted or not warranted at all.

I do not believe that this definition, as I have used it, justifies our concluding that no philosophic or scientific statements are completely warranted. It would surprise me if this were so, and I would have to be persuaded to believe it. Some statements a scientist might make (reporting his observations) might be completely warranted by sensory observation, and others might be warranted by their theoretical context or by a combination of observation and theory. I am not sure whether there are any scientific statements quite like your example about electrons, which *are* completely warranted. But there very well might be

493

such statements, and if there are I think it is safe to say that their warrant is primarily of a theoretical rather than an observational sort. Nothing in my paper tends to deny this. I have not said much about electrons and their ilk, since electrons necessarily have properties different from those possessed by ordinary material objects which removes them from ordinary observation. About all I have said that bears upon the justification of statements about electrons is that insofar as their warrant cannot be exhibited entirely in sense-datum statements it depends upon their context in a theory, and that this theory itself cannot be *entirely* warranted on the basis of sensory observation. This should not disturb a scientist. The only person who might properly be disturbed by the consequences of my remarks, I believe, is one who advances a statement which he claims is based on ordinary sensory observation, but who cannot exhibit a set of statements, in his own chosen terminology, each of which is completely warranted, and which together express the same thing that his original statement expresses.

Eslick: I would like to suggest that, at least from your own point of view, pure sense-datum statements are not possible. I think that both Plato and Kant show clearly that unless you have access to categories that utterly transcend sense-data—sameness, difference, being, which are not really given in sense-data—you can't judge at all. If you are going to understand sense-data as one kind of flux of Humean impressions, I think you cannot, strictly speaking, understand how it is possible to make judgments.

Sayre: I certainly would not want to consider sense-data to be Humean impressions alone. In fact, I leave the question of the nature of sense-datum statements open. I would like to emphasize also that I think there are many statements which cannot be analyzed in terms of sense-datum statements. And among these surely are statements about the transcendent properties you mention. These statements would not be statements about material objects at all, and my thesis concerns only statements about physical objects.

Eslick: Nevertheless, it is crucial to know what you understand by 'sense-datum', because if you are going to limit it to what Whitehead calls "presentational immediacy", for example, it seems to me you have no real foundation for scientific endeavor, for predictions about the future, no real explanation of memory, of the way in which the past enters into your present experiences.

Sayre: You are asking me to do something I have deliberately avoided doing, to give a prefabricated definition of 'sense-datum'. I leave the question of the phenomenological character of his experiences entirely up to the person who finds it useful to use the phrase 'sense-datum statements' in reference to what I define as statements which can be completely warranted on the basis of momentary sensory awareness. It would lead to philosophic embarrassment if I were to attempt to tell you or anyone else how to describe his experience.

Hanson: I think the question of warrant and the question of just exactly how one is going to characterize a sense-datum are connected. It seems to me that sense-datum experiences have been on occasion treated as events, as things which take place. There are times at which an individual is said to be "having an experience" describable in a certain way. Common language often speaks this way. There is a whole class of literature having to do, in an oblique way, with the phenomenanalist's position—and I think that your paper falls in this class—where the sense-datum is really a kind of shadowy referent. It seems to serve as the limit of a series of decreasing empirical claims, such that each one becomes less and less vulnerable by the systematic removal of those vulnerable empirical contents. The question of how one would treat, for theoretical purposes, this limit of a series of decreasing empirical claims, of how one would relate this to the actual events that take place in people, is, to some extent, connected with the question of warrantability. And I felt that the way in which you resolved this (this might be a little unfair) was, in a sense, not to let it come up in too serious a way, namely, to stick where the paper belongs, with the logical-analytical issue. That's why I think Mr. Eslick's question ought to get in your side somewhere and bother you.

Sayre: It does get in my side to the extent that I try to exclude it. I have avoided using 'sense-datum' as an independent term. And if there is any call to introduce the term, I would want it to be taken as referring to whatever it is that warrants assertions that fall under my class of assertions which can be completely warranted on the basis of momentary sensory awareness.

Hanson: One further point about this. The question of whether or not any-one ever has a sense-datum experience seems to me thoroughly independent of the question of whether or not the claim that an individual did have a sense-datum experience makes sense. By analogy with physics, the question of whether or not anyone has discovered an ideal gas is independent of the question of whether descriptions of an ideal gas are sensible descriptions. It seems to me that you are talking about the second sort of thing and that Mr. Eslick is raising questions about the first. The issue of warrantability can't be resolved unless you are both talking about the same thing.

Sellars: I would like to return to the question raised about warrant, and to concentrate for the moment on the notion of an incomplete warrant. My suspicion is that if sense-datum statements are taken as you define them then *any* warranted statement about material objects would also involve incompletely warranted statements. In other words, you can only go from your completely warranted statements to an assertion that there is a material thing over there by adding *incompletely* warranted assertions about what other physical objects there are—good background perception, what the light is like, and so on. My suspicion is that incomplete warranty is an essential part of the very meaning of physical objects, and I think it is by an illegitimate twist that you have concluded that the meaning of physical objects must in some sense be expressible in terms of completely warrantable statements. This, I think, is the very crux of the matter, and this is where I would disagree with you. I think that any statement which is not about the appearances of physical objects, if it is to be warranted, will be incompletely warranted. Among the premises that we presuppose would also be other incompletely warranted statements, and this is part of the very logic of physical object statements. I think that what you show is that statements such as, 'There appears to be a physical object', can be completely warranted, but I do not think you show that any statement like,

'There is a horse in the corner', can be completely warranted. Now, I would argue that you must give an account of the warranting of the latter, and I would argue that any warrant of this statement is going to presuppose statements, which are not themselves completely warrantable, about the circumstances of perception.

I sympathize with the general drift of the paper, but I think that the Phenomenalism you are offering really consists in the tautology that the only completely warranted statements are those which are so set up that we do not challenge them. Nothing will take you from that to any conceptual analysis of physical objects in terms of such statements.

Sayre: Your comments are close to the mark, but I believe they add up to a clarification of rather than an objection to my thesis about the warrant of material object statements. It seems, however, that you may have overestimated my ambitions. I have not attempted to provide a conceptual analysis suitable for all types of material object statements. Phenomenalists traditionally have attempted something like this. But I have not aspired to join forces with them in this respect, and have in fact been rather critical of their attempts at such a conceptual analysis. I have been concerned only with what I take to be a dominant theme of traditional Phenomenalism, namely the claim that everything we say about material objects with a warrant of a certain type (*sensory* warrant) can be said in a certain type of statement (*completely* warrantable). To escape moot questions about the "nature of sense-data", I suggest a rather neutral definition of 'sense-datum statement' in terms of warrant, and in these terms expound the thesis that all statements which can be completely warranted on the basis of sensory observation can be expressed in sense-datum statements. You suggest that it is a consequence of this way of putting the matter than *any* statement about the existence of material objects involves incompletely warranted statements. You are probably right in this. To point this out is to give a reason for rejecting Phenomenalism as an analysis of material object statements generally. I would agree that it is inadequate generally, but would maintain that it is less obviously inadequate for some material object statements than for others of the sort you stress. Incidentally, to say that it is a consequence of my thesis that some (or all) statements about material objects cannot be completely warranted, assuming this is not a tautologous thing to say, is to give reason also for being very hesitant to consider my thesis a tautology. Tautologies do not have consequences which are not tautologous.

Cohen: I don't see how one can avoid sympathizing with the general drift of the paper. Its point is to try to persuade us not to believe that for which there is no reason to believe. Now, if you follow up the Sellars-McMullin qualification of this, however, I take the conclusion to be: that total phenomenalism is useful only insofar as any position which can be shown to reduce to that loses everything for us. It would be a good way, then, of refuting somebody to show that their position entails the demand for *complete* warrant in observation statements . . .

496

MATTER AND EVENT

Richard Rorty

§1 *Introduction*

Most fundamental controversies about the nature and status of matter are episodes in a struggle between Aristotelian realism and the tradition of subjectivist reductionism which stretches from Descartes through Berkeley and Hume to Russell and Goodman. This struggle has shifted ground many times, but there is a recognizable persistence in the sort of arguments employed, and the sort of distinctions invoked, on both sides. Realists hold that matter-vs.-form is going to have to be a basic distinction in any adequate cosmology, whereas reductionists hold that this distinction does more harm than good. If they give a place to matter, it is not matter-as-opposed-to-form, but matter in some meaning of the term which has little more than the name in common with what Aristotelians are talking about.

Whitehead viewed the grand opposition between these two schools as a reflection of the opposition between "two cosmologies which at different periods have dominated European thought, Plato's *Timaeus*, and the cosmology of the seventeenth century, whose chief authors were Galileo, Descartes, Newton and Locke".[1] He thought of Aristotle as having filled in and rounded out the *Timaeus* (*CN*, 24), and of the post-Kantian epistemological controversies between positivistic empiricists and idealists as the inevitable outcome of a search for the presuppositions and consequences of the Newtonian cosmology (*PR*, 76 ff., 123 ff.). He thought of "the philosophy of organism" as replacing *both* cosmologies, and as being as different from either as either was from the other.

Nevertheless, from the point of view of realistic philosophers, insisting

---

[1] *Process and Reality*, New York, 1929, p. ix. Future references to this book will be to *PR*, and will usually be inserted in the text. The following abbreviations will be used in occasional references to Whitehead's other books: *Adventures of Ideas*, New York, 1933 as *AI*; *Science and the Modern World*, New York, 1925 as *SMW*; *The Concept of Nature*, Cambridge, 1920 as *CN*; *Essays in Science and Philosophy*, New York, 1947 as *ESP*. William Christian's *An Interpretation of Whitehead's Metaphysics*, New Haven, 1959, which I have used heavily, will be cited as "Christian".

I very much regret that I had not read Ivor Leclerc's "Form and Actuality in Whitehead" (in *The Relevance of Whitehead,* ed. Leclerc, London, 1961) at the time this paper was written. Any future comparison of Aristotle and Whitehead should take its point of departure from Leclerc's essay.

upon the irreducibility of the distinction between substances and qualities, and between substances and relations, Whitehead's philosophy usually looks like one more variant of subjectivist reductionism. His cosmology, with its ingression of "eternal objects" into sub-microscopic "actual entities", seems one more attempt to blend hard-headed atomistic materialism with the elegance of Platonic logicism—a combination whose possibilities have fired the imagination of philosophers ever since the rise of modern mathematical physics (and have become dazzling since the invention of symbolic logic). To reduce substantial forms to "conceptual prehensions", and to reduce the particularity and concreteness of actualities to patterns of relatedness with other entities, as Whitehead seems to do, is apparently to abandon all hope of a *rapprochement* with Aristotelian realism. Whitehead's notion of "subjective aim" and his analysis of "concrescence" are, to be sure, reminiscent of some key Aristotelian terms and themes, but the resemblances do not seem to come to much. Whitehead's polemics against the quest for a "substratum", his assertion that "Creativity" should replace Aristotle's category of "primary substance" (*PR*, 32), as well as many of his historical allusions and judgements, suggest that Whitehead viewed his system as climaxing the revolt against the Aristotelian world-view which Descartes, Newton and Locke had begun. Further, the affinities of Whitehead's atomism of actual entities with the logical atomism of Russell and the nominalistic *Aufbauten* of Carnap and Goodman seem obvious.[2]

If one accepts these affinities at face value, however, one may lose sight of two other sets of affinities. In the first place, Whitehead's cosmology is at least as close to Bergson and James as it is to Russell and Goodman. One cannot ignore his Bergsonian insistence that taking time seriously—the substitution of process for stasis as the inclusive category—permits one to demolish Aristotelian substances in the *right* way, whereas everybody else (Russell and Goodman, as well as Descartes, Newton, Hume *et al.*) has been demolishing them in the *wrong* way. In the second place, one needs to notice that Whitehead's criticisms of these wrong-headed attempts draw on the same sort of arguments as those employed by Aristotle's defenders. Most of the usual points made by Aristotelian realists against nominalists, materialists, sceptics, and like, are strongly echoed by Whitehead. Whitehead stands be-

---

[2] Cf. Christian, 247, who points out that in 1919 Whitehead was still toying with the "class-theory of particulars" (cf. §3 below) characteristic of the Berkeley-Russell-Goodman tradition, but that by 1925 he had realized that he wanted to break with it. The Whitehead whom I shall be discussing in this paper is the Whitehead of *Process and Reality*, and I shall make no attempt to cover the shifts in Whitehead's views. (This, incidentally, is the reason why I refer throughout to "actual entities"—the term used in *PR*—rather than to "events", the term used in the earlier writings.)

tween two reductionistic philosophical movements—Bradley's and Bergson's (*ESP*, 116)—in the same way in which Aristotle stood between Plato and the materialist successors of Heraclitus. Both men find themselves insisting, against the simplistic analyses of such reductionisms, that a "critique of abstractions" is required. (Cf. *PR*, 253)

Contrariwise, Whitehead and Aristotle are attacked by reductionists for the same reasons. Both make heavy use of the distinction between potentiality and actuality to resolve cosmological dilemmas, and "potentiality", as all reductionists know, is merely an anthropomorphic vestige of pre-scientific picture-thinking. (As is teleological explanation, to which Aristotle and Whitehead are equally devoted.) Aristotle, in the distinction between matter and form, and Whitehead, in the distinction between actual entities and eternal objects, make heuristic use of the actuality-potentiality distinction to bifurcate the universe in (so the reductionists say) arbitrary, unempirical, and unnecessary ways. ("Aristotle without specific forms" and "Whitehead without eternal objects" are almost equally popular slogans.) Thus one might expect, on the principle that one's enemy's enemy is, at least temporarily, one's friend, that Aristotle and Whitehead would have interestingly similar aims and strategies.

In this paper, I shall try to spotlight some of the anti-reductionist features of Whitehead's cosmology, in order to show how Whitehead's critique of the Newtonian world-view, and the philosophical systems which presuppose this world-view, resembles the critique offered by Aristotelians. Then, on the basis of these similarities between Aristotle and Whitehead, I shall discuss some differences between them. On the basis of these differences, I hope to exhibit the significance of Whitehead's "taking time seriously" for a discussion of the concept of matter.

§2 *Reductionism and Distinctions of Level*

I have said that both Aristotle and Whitehead are realistic philosophers who build their respective cosmologies around distinctions which, in the eyes of reductionist philosophers, seem arbitrary. I now wish to define (dogmatically and curtly) "reductionism" and "realism" in terms of the presence or absence of a certain sort of distinction. These definitions are no more than rough hints, to be developed and given sense in what follows, but formulating them here will give us some pegs on which to hang the Whiteheadian doctrines which we need to extricate and examine.

Reductionism, as I shall use the term, is the position which adopts what Whitehead calls "the unreformed subjectivist principle"—the principle that "the datum in the act of experience can be analysed purely in terms of universals". (*PR*, 239) Holding to this principle, and defining a "universal" as "that which can enter into the description of many particulars" (*PR*, 76), leads to the dissolution of particularity itself. For any candidate for the status of an ultimate particular is confronted with the alternative of either disclosing itself as a congery of universals or condemning itself to unexperiencability. Making a virtue of necessity, reductionism then claims that particularity is either unknowable or unreal. The history of philosophy since Descartes, in Whitehead's eyes, is the history of the failure of reductionism—of the foredoomed attempt to develop an adequate cosmology with only one type of basic entity—*viz., repeatable* entities. The notion of an "unrepeatable entity" has, since Descartes, been taken to be an absurdity, and the admission that such entities exist has been taken as either a proof of scepticism or the mark of an "incomplete" analysis—which is why the Cartesian tradition can end only in Humean scepticism or Bradleyan idealism (cf. *PR*, 85).

Realism, as I shall use the term, is the position which holds that an adequate cosmological account can be achieved in terms of an irreducible distinction between two sorts of entities—entities of radically distinct categorical levels. The cash-value of the phrase 'distinct categorical levels' is that entities of these two sorts are such that any given arrangement of the first sort of entities is logically compatible with any given arrangement of entities of the other sort. That is, realism is the insistence that explanation must always be in terms of a correlation of *independent* arrangements,[3] and cannot consist in a reduction of entities on one level to entities on another.

These abstract and stark definitions may be given some initial relevance to the usual meanings of the terms defined by noting that the leading candidates for the position of irreducibly distinct levels of entities are "things" and "properties", and that the best efforts of three hundred years of reductionist thought have been devoted to breaking down this distinction. The view that the essence of realism lies in the refusal to reduce kinds of things to the sets of qualia which form the criteria for the application of thing-kind-names has become fairly familiar. The independence of the knower from the known, which forms the common-sense kernel of realism, becomes, in the light of philosophical analysis, the independence of the contexts and methods

---

[3] On this notion of independence of categoreal level as a prerequisite for realism, cf. W. Donald Oliver, *Theory of Order*, Yellow Springs, Ohio, 1951, chaps. 1–3, where the notion is developed in great detail and with a precision which I cannot attempt here. I have attempted to apply the arguments which Oliver presents to problems concerning the nature of philosophical controversy in "The Limits of Reductionism" (in *Experience, Existence and the Good: Essays in Honor of Paul Weiss*, ed. Irwin Lieb, Carbondale, Illinois, 1961) and to problems of epistemology in "Pragmatism, Categories, and Language", *Phil. Review, 70*, 197–223, esp. pp. 217 ff.

by which we *specify* things from those by which we *describe* them. Manley Thompson has argued (successfully, I believe) that the methodological analogue of the cosmological doctrine that "things are not collections of properties (nor, *a fortiori,* of sense-data, ideas, or the like)" is that the question "what *kind* of thing is it?" (which we answer by *specifying*) is not reducible to a series of questions of the form "which thing?" (which can be answered by *describing*).[4] Thompson suggests (and Whitehead would agree) that an attempt to perform the latter reduction can end only in a pragmatism which is indistinguishable from idealism.[5]

Thompson has further shown that specification can only be kept distinct from description if one erects an irreducible distinction between words which function as K-terms (members of a classificatory scheme which classifies things into kinds) and words which function as D-terms (names of properties), *even though* the same symbols may be used for both sorts of terms.[6] This distinction between two sets of terms, where the meanings of the members of one set are independent of the meanings of the other set, is the logical analogue of the distinction between thing and property. Whether the distinction is made metaphysically, methodologically, or logically, its import consists in the refusal to adopt, as it were, a "monism of explanation", in which to "explain" something is to reduce it to an instance of a class—a class definable in terms of universals.

The master argument which realists use against reductionists is that the reductionist position cannot be made intelligible without smuggling in a covert realism. If one attempts to take seriously the notion that all data can be analyzed in terms of universals, one finds oneself faced with the question "What *is* it that can be analyzed in terms of universals?" More spe-

---

[4] "On the Distinction Between Thing and Property" in *The Return to Reason: Essays in Realistic Philosophy,* ed. John Wild, Chicago, 1953, pp. 125–51, esp. pp. 129–33.

[5] Cf. Thompson, *loc. cit.,* pp. 148–51. See also, for a critique of the notion of a "method of pure description", Oliver, *op. cit.,* chap. 4. For the resemblance between pragmatism (as usually conceived) and idealism (as usually conceived), cf. J. A. Passmore, "The Meeting of Extremes in Contemporary Philosophy", *Phil. Review, 69,* pp. 363–75.

[6] Cf. Thompson, *loc. cit.,* pp. 130 ff. This last point suggests the way in which the distinction between independent levels of entities which is central to realism must take account of the fact that language communicates just to the degree that it avoids the use of token-reflexive terms. The strong point of reductionism (and the reason why reductionism came into its own only with the "linguistic turn" and the adoption of the "formal mode of speech") is that any singular terms are always replaceable by descriptions. But, as Strawson points out, the employment of a language in which such replacement is consistently carried out will make *all* reference to particulars impossible (cf. "Singular Terms, Ontology, and Identity", *Mind, 65,* p. 449).

cifically, if one adopts the view that all explanation is a matter of discovering which class a thing is a member of, then one sooner or later finds oneself faced with the problem "What is the analysis of the notion *member of a class*?" The "datum" or the "member" can only be a bare particular, a bare substrate. Just insofar as it is something more than this, it requires further analysis in terms of further universals. Just insofar as this analysis is *not* offered, a covert distinction between levels—the level of the repeatable universals and the level of the bare particulars—is being assumed. As soon as the challenge to reduce this distinction is accepted by the reductionist, however, a potentially infinite regress is generated. Each analysis of the level of particulars into a new pattern of universals calls forth the need for a new level of particulars in which the new pattern of universals can be exemplified. Awareness of this regress may lead the reductionist himself to question the notion of bare particularity. But if he does so, he is no longer able to give a clear meaning to the notion of "universal". Universals, as "repeatable", require something to distinguish their various repetitions.[7] The notion of repeatability is equivalent to the notion of "capable of entering into external relations"; if there are no particulars, there is no possibility of entering into such relationships. If objects are mere congeries of universals then, as idealists never tire of pointing out, all statements which attribute characters to objects are necessary truths, signifying internal relations. We thus wind up with a metaphysical monism as a consequence of our insistence upon a "monism of explanation". Given such a monism, the problem of "mere appearance" or "mere error" takes the place, for the reductionist, of the problem of "bare particular", or "mere substrate", and is equally baffling.[8] This is the *reductio ad absurdum* of the reductionist's attempt to simultaneously explain the datum and reduce it away, and the confirmation of the realist's contention that "order", "explanation", "knowledge", and "analysis" are only intelligible as long as we hold the entities *to be* ordered, explained, known, or analyzed apart from the entities *in terms of which* the ordering, explanation, knowing or analysis is to be performed.

In what follows, I shall try to show how Whitehead's awareness of the need to avoid this sequence of reductionist absurdities led him to adopt

---

[7] Cf. Charles Hartshorne, "The Compound Individual", in *Philosophical Essays for Alfred North Whitehead*, New York, 1936, p. 202: "Universal and individual are ideas that are clear only in relation to each other, and where either conception is neglected the other will suffer also."

[8] Cf. *PR*, 78, on how the misinterpretation of the doctrine of universals paves the way for Kant's "degradation of the world into mere appearance", and *PR*, 85, on Santayanian scepticism or Bradleyan idealism as the only possible outcomes of reductionism. Cf. also *PR*, 349–50.

certain key doctrines, and to show the analogies between these doctrines and certain key Aristotelian doctrines, adopted from the same motives. In the course of expounding these doctrines, I hope to put some flesh on the bare bones of the notion of "distinction of categoreal level" which I have introduced. Having done so, I shall be in a position to compare Aristotle's "form-matter" distinction with Whitehead's "eternal object-actual entity" distinction. Both distinctions are attempts to locate ultimate and irreducible categoreal distinctions whose discovery and exposition will provide a stable foundation for realism. I shall be arguing that Aristotle's hylomorphism was an attempt to establish such a distinction, and that this attempt failed because of Aristotle's identification of "definiteness" with "actuality". I shall try to show that Whitehead's substitution of "decisiveness" for "definiteness" as the criterion of actuality permits him to succeed where Aristotle fails.

Comparisons between Aristotelian and Whiteheadian concepts do not lend themselves to lucid exposition, for Whitehead's critique of alternative cosmologies is so radical as to systematically transform the meaning of almost every traditional philosophical term. This paper is intended as an attempt to plot these transformations.

§3 *Final Causality and Atomism*

Early in *Process and Reality*, Whitehead remarks that: "Final causality and atomism are interconnected philosophical principles." (*PR*, 29) The faintly paradoxical air of this remark is due to our habit of associating atomism (in its logical and psychological, as well as its physical, forms) with a doctrine of external relations. We associate teleology, on the other hand, with a doctrine of internal relations—a thing which is striving to realize its end constitutes itself by that striving, and would not be the same thing were it not so striving. Saying that atomism and final causality are interconnected, then, would seem to be saying that something can only sustain external relations if it also sustains internal relations, or the converse, or both. Now Whitehead does, in fact, want to say the former. He holds that only because actual entities sustain internal relations to goals—their "subjective aims"—are they capable of sustaining external relations to other actual entities.[9] What prevents an actual entity from being "reduced" to the sum

---

[9] As we shall see more clearly below, the external relations sustained by an actual entity A are not A's prehensions of other actual entities which are "objectified" by A; on the contrary, *these* relations are *internal* to A. The only external relations sustained by A are prehensions of A by "later" actual entities, for which A is objectified. The relation, X-prehending-Y, is always internal to X but external to Y.

of its physical prehensions of other actual entities (and thus what separates the "philosophy of organism" from Absolute Idealism) is the individuality and unrepeatability of its subjective aim. Whitehead holds that an actual entity cannot be analysed without remainder either into its physical prehensions of other actual entites (the domain of efficient causality; cf. *PR*, 134) or into its conceptual prehensions of eternal objects (the domain of final causality; cf. *PR*, 159). Nor can these two poles be disjoined in order to be interpreted as two independent actual entities in their own right.[10] An actual entity can retain its integrity only by being interpreted in terms of both levels of entities—the eternal objects and the other actual entities— *at once*. Particularity is safe, and the reductionist implications of the "subjectivist principle" are avoided, only if this distinction of level is maintained (Cf. *PR*, 128, 228).

This Whiteheadian doctrine should be compared with Aristotle's doctrine that a material substance cannot be reduced either to its form or to its matter, that it has matter only because it has form, and that "the actuality of a substance is its goal". (*Meta.* IX, 1050a 9)[11] Because a substance has a goal, a goal which is (in the case of "things which exist by nature") identical with its form, it cannot be analysed as "the sum of its qualities", in the sense of the sum of the properties which form the criteria for specifying it as a substance of such-and-such a species plus the sum of the properties which describe its accidents. To form the sum here involves a breakdown of categoreal level—a "category-confusion" in Ryle's sense of the term. The attempt to form such a sum is based upon the "unreformed subjectivist principle" and the ensuing myth of a "bare substratum"—a substratum which supports "essential" and "accidental" attributes in the same external way. The "formula of the definition" of which Aristotle speaks does not name a complex property; it names the substance, and names it directly.[12] "Each thing

---

[10] For Whitehead's critique of the attempt to thus disjoin them, cf. *PR*, 108.

[11] Compare also Aristotle's identification of *ergon* with both *telos* and *energeia*, Whitehead's identification of "decision" with "actuality" (*PR*, 68), and Leibniz's appeals to teleology against the mechanistic reductionisms of the Cartesians (in order to prevent the monads from dissolving into space-time points). For a comparison of these three philosophers on a related topic, cf. J. H. Randall, Jr., *Aristotle*, New York, 1960, p. 170.

[12] Cf. Thompson, *loc. cit.*, p. 136: "K-terms . . . signify but a single kind of entity and thus have *simple and direct signification* which is neither denotation nor connotation." Wilfrid Sellars arrives at the same conclusion in connection with an analysis of the forms of Aristotelian substances; cf. "Substance and Form in Aristotle", *J. of Phil.*, *54*, p. 695: ". . . thing-kind words are . . . common names of individuals, not proper names of universals".

itself and its essence are one and the same in no merely accidental way."
(*Meta.* VII, 1031b 19) The internal relation of the substance to the species
of which it is a member (and thus to its goal) is what permits the substance
to retain its independence (its atomic character)—an independence which
permits it to be externally related *to* its accidental properties, rather than
dissolving *into* them.[13]

Both Aristotle and Whitehead invoke teleology in order to explicate the
distinctions of level which save the primary actualities (the "atoms") of their
respective cosmologies from dissolution. However, this resemblance is obscured by, so to speak, a difference of scale. It is pointless to compare a
Whiteheadian "actual entity" with an "episode of accidental change" occurring in an Aristotelian substance. Although there is a sense in which
these two notions do explicate the same pre-analytic phenomenon, the radical
differences between Aristotle's and Whitehead's categoreal schemes make
such a comparison produce only paralogisms and misunderstandings. The
proper comparison is between an actual entity and an Aristotelian primary
substance—a substance which, however, is distinctive in being a species unto
itself (resembling, in this respect, angels as characterized by St. Thomas).
No two Whiteheadian occasions have the same subjective aim (cf. Christian,
310), and thus there is no distinction in Whitehead between specification
and individuation. There is, however, an analogue of the distinction between specification and description—namely the distinction between an
actual entity's description as "subjectively immediate" and as "objectively
immortal" (*PR*, 34). As we shall see in §§ 6 and 8 below, this analogue
preserves the requisite Aristotelian distinction of level, while dismissing the
Aristotelian problem of the relationship between the secondary substance
"*X*-hood" and the substantial forms of individual *X*'s. Thus, actual entities
are, as it were, miniature Aristotelian substances; they owe their unity and
their irreducibility (their "atomic" character) to their internal relationship
to a goal—a goal which is characterizable only in terms of entities of a different categoreal level than those which characterize their external relations
to other actualities.

---

[13] The problem of how the difference between the relation of a substance to its
form and its relation to its other attributes should be formulated is the major metaphysical problem which Aristotle willed to his heirs. (The trouble with taking seriously
the *identification* of substance and essence is, of course, that such an identification
seems to condemn the accidents, *à la* Plato, to the realm of "mere appearance".)
We have the record of Aristotle's own unsuccessful struggles with this problem in
Metaphysics VI–IX; see especially the discussion of the difference between τὶ σημαίνει
and τὸ τὶ ἦν εἶναι in VII, c. 4, and compare Thompson, *loc. cit.*, pp. 133 ff.

§4 *Unity as Requiring Categoreal Diversity*

A second crucial Whiteheadian doctrine is, to an adherent of the unreformed subjectivist principle, as paradoxical as the interconnection of teleology and atomism. This is the doctrine that the ultimate unit of actuality must be internally complex; a unit, in short, must be the *unity of* something. "Each ultimate unit of fact is a cell-complex, not analysable into components *with equivalent completeness of actuality*." (*PR*, 334, italics added) The implications of this doctrine are spelled out in an explication of the "category of objective diversity":

> The category of objective diversity expresses the inexorable condition—that a unity must provide for each of its components a real diversity of status, with a reality which bears the same sense as its own reality and is peculiar to itself. In other words, a real unity cannot provide sham diversities of status for its diverse components . . . The prohibition of sham diversities of status sweeps away the "class theory" of particular substances, which was waveringly suggested by Locke . . . was more emphatically endorsed by Hume . . . and has been adopted by Hume's followers. For the essence of a class is that it assigns no diversity of function to the members of its extension. . . . The "class", thus appealed to, is a mere multiplicity. (*PR*, 348; cf. Christian, 248)

The fundamental importance of this point for process philosophy is shown by Whitehead's statement that:

> This doctrine that a multiple contrast cannot be conceived as a mere disjunction of dual contrasts is the basis of the doctrine of emergent evolution. It is the doctrine of real unities being more than a mere collective disjunction of component elements. This doctrine has the same ground as the objection to the class-theory of particular substances. (*PR*, 349)

In this doctrine of internal diversity we have perhaps the clearest expression of Whitehead's rejection of the reductionist notion of explanation as "placing a datum within a class". As Christian says: "This principle of individuality [the subjective aim as defining a mode of togetherness of actual entities and eternal objects], in Whitehead's metaphysics, supersedes in importance the principle of classification" (Christian, 252). The "ontological principle" that "actual entities are the only reasons", (*PR*, 37) combined with the definition of "actuality" as "decision amid potentialities", (*PR*, 68) produces the most fundamental justification of Whitehead's insistence on the irreducibility of categoreal levels. The attempt to find an ultimate unit without internal complexity and without the teleology involved in the "decision" of an actual entity is simply one more form of the search for bare particulars—for "vacuous actuality". The impulse for such a search can only be the confusion of ease of classification with cosmological priority,[14] and its outcome can only be a tyranny of internal relations and the loss of real unity.

This protest against the confusion of the distinction between unity and plurality with the distinction between simplicity and complexity is also to be found in Aristotle, in his protests against both materialistic reductions of form to matter[15] and Platonic reductions of matter to form.[16] In both sets of protests, he is led to insist upon the irreducible complexity involved in the hylomorphic analysis of substance, and the loss of unity which occurs when it is proposed to replace this analysis with something simpler. However, in Whitehead's eyes, Aristotle betrayed his own better insight when, in *Metaphysics* XII, he made room for the Unmoved Mover—the perfect case of a "vacuous actuality". Aristotle's break with the realistic requirement of a distinction of level in the case of the Unmoved Mover gave fatal encouragement to the assumption that "satisfactory explanation" demands that "substances with undifferentiated endurance of essential attributes be produced" —an assumption which Whitehead calls "the basis of scientific materialism". (*PR*, 120: cf. *PR*, 241)[17]

However, if we put the Aristotelian notion of "immaterial substance" to one side for the moment, we can see that both Aristotle and Whitehead are, in their theories of the nature of real unity, conforming to the demands which we outlined in §2: the demand that recourse to bare particulars be avoided by establishing two categoreal levels, and that the unitary character of the ultimate cosmological unit should consist in its unification of those two levels—a unification which is possible, and is given meaning, only in virtue of their irreducible difference.

§5 *Potentiality and Actuality*

The paradox involved in the phrase 'unity which is internally complex' fairly cries out for resolution by means of a distinction between potentiality

---

[14] Cf. *PR*, 85, on "the assumption, unconscious and uncriticized, that logical simplicity can be identified with priority in the process of constituting an experient occasion". At *PR*, 202, Whitehead echoes Bergson in remarking that: "We may doubt whether 'simplicity' is ever more than a relative term, having regard to some definite procedure of analysis." For further polemics against reductionist notions of explanation, cf. *PR*, 246, 253, 120.

[15] Cf. *De Gen. et Corr.* I, c. 2, esp. 317a 19 ff.

[16] Cf., e.g., *Meta.* I.

[17] For an account of what Aristotle *should* have said about God in order to avoid abandoning his commitment to categoreal diversity (an account with which Whitehead would be in hearty accord), see Randall, *op. cit.*, p. 143 f.

and actuality, and both Aristotle and Whitehead do invoke this distinction for that purpose. Aristotle holds matter and form together in substantial unity by the formula: "the proximate matter and the form are one and the same thing, the one potentially and the other actually". (*Meta.* VIII, 1045b 18 f.) Whitehead's use of the distinction is summed up in the following passage:

> Just as *potentiality for process* is the meaning of the more general term 'entity' or 'thing', so *decision* is the additional meaning imported by the word 'actual' into the phrase 'actual entity'. "Actuality" is the decision amid "potentiality". (*PR*, 68)

Both Aristotle and Whitehead agree that the actuality-potentiality distinction is unavoidable, but their application of it is so drastically different as to have called forth the suggestion that their respective systems may be transformed into each other simply by following the rule: "What is potential for Aristotle is actual for Whitehead, and conversely".[18] In the previous two sections we have dwelt upon anti-reductionist doctrines on which Aristotle and Whitehead concur. Here, we begin to see how Whitehead separates himself off from both Aristotle and reductionism in the quest for a better reply to reductionism than Aristotle achieved, and thus for a more adequate formulation of realism.

Whitehead claims that

> Some chief notions of European thought were formed under the influence of a misapprehension only partially corrected by the scientific progress of the last century. This mistake consists in the confusion of mere potentiality with actuality. Continuity concerns what is potential; whereas actuality is incurably atomic. (*PR*, 95)

The immediate thrust of this remark is against Newtonian notions of space and time, but the extent of the confusion in question is much wider. The confused notion of the distinction of act and potency against which Whitehead is protesting here is the assumption that there are two equally atomic sorts of things: actual X's and potential X's. This notion, on reflection, drives one to the paradox that (1) "certain possible so-and-sos are not actual so-and-sos", yet (2) "the only possible entities are actual ones".[19] When the absurdity of an attempt to resolve this paradox by finding the "extra some-

---

[18] Cf. R. S. Brumbaugh, "A Preface to Cosmography", *Rev. Meta.*, 7, pp. 53–63. Cf. also Leo A. Foley, *A Critique of the Philosophy of Being of Alfred North Whitehead in the Light of Thomistic Philosophy*, Washington, 1946, p. 120.

[19] I borrow this formulation of the paradox from Nelson Goodman, *Fact, Fiction, and Forecast*, Cambridge, 1955, p. 55. Chapter Two of this book—"The Passing of the Possible"—is a good statement of what becomes of the actuality-potentiality distinction when it is considered under the aegis of the unreformed subjective principle.

thing" which transforms a potential X into an actual one becomes evident, we are tempted to give up the actuality-potentiality distinction altogether. When we do give it up, as reductionists do, we lose the ability to make intelligible the notion of "unity which is internally complex", and thus we have to fall back upon "bare particulars". Whitehead tells us that if we are going to keep and use this distinction, we must start all over again. We must get rid of the notion of potential X's, substitute the notion of "potentialities *for X"*, and abandon the assumption that "the only possible entities are actual ones". A possible entity, for Whitehead, is not a half-baked version of an actual entity; to think of it this way is like thinking of the datum about which one decides as itself a half-baked decision. The actuality-potentiality distinction is in danger, in Whitehead's eyes, whenever one attempts to use the vocabulary appropriate to atomic individuals in describing potentiality. The temptations exerted by language, a language built around pragmatically convenient abstractions,[20] will almost inevitably engender the reduction of the potential to the actual, and thus the loss of the distinction of categoreal levels upon which realism depends. The last person to really struggle with language in order to keep the distinction viable was Aristotle, who, Whitehead thinks, largely failed.[21] The key to his failure, and the reason for his acceptance of "vacuous actuality" in the doctrine of the Unmoved Mover, was the illicit transition from the doctrine of form-as-the-actuality-of-the-matter to the notion of form-as-the-actuality-of-the-composite-substance. This transition evolved into the notion of form-in-isolation contributing something called "actuality" to the composite substance, where-

---

[20] Cf. *PR*, 253. For Whitehead's views on the relation between language and philosophical speculation, cf. *PR*, 16 ff., esp. p. 18: "A precise language must await a completed metaphysical knowledge".

[21] Cf. fn. 12 above. Whitehead's attitude toward Aristotle is full of mixed feelings. Although he regards the subject-predicate model as largely responsible for the popularity of "vacuous actualities", he seems to feel that it is mediaeval philosophers, rather than Aristotle himself, who are chiefly blamable. "The exclusive dominance of the substance-quality metaphysics was enormously promoted by the logical bias of the mediaeval period. It was retarded by the study of Plato and Aristotle. These authors included the strains of thought which issued in this doctrine, but included them inconsistently blended with other notions. The substance-quality metaphysics triumphed with exclusive dominance in Descartes' doctrines." (*PR*, 209) Cf. also *PR*, 45, 81, 85, 122; *AI*, 356; A. H. Johnson, *Whitehead's Theory of Reality*, Boston, 1952, pp. 123–24. Foley (*op. cit.*, p. 109) says that Whitehead is arguing only against the "Lockian or Cartesian" notion of substance as inert substrate, and not the Thomistic-Aristotelian notion of substance as activity. This is largely true. Whitehead knows there is a difference between the two traditions, but he usually seems to think it not worthwhile to distinguish them, since he is convinced that the seeds of decay are already present in Aristotle's confusion of *energeia*-as-*ergon* with *energeia*-as-*morphē*.

as matter-in-isolation contributed the element of "potentiality". For White-head, the point of the contrast between actuality and potentiality is lost as soon as one begins to think of "actuality" as something other than "actual-ization *of the potential*".

This analysis permits us to formulate a first rough sketch (to be revised in §7 below) of the central contrast between Aristotle's and Whitehead's approach to the distinction between form and matter. For Aristotle, this distinction is a special case of the distinction between actuality and poten-tiality. For Whitehead, the form-matter distinction, when applied to the process of coming-to-be of an actuality, is the distinction between two sorts of potentiality. The criterion of actuality is found, for Whitehead, neither in pure form (eternal objects in themselves) nor in pure matter (the ex-tensive continuum of real potentiality), but in the unification—under the conditions of the "category of objective diversity" (cf. §4 above)—of both levels.[22] This unification is itself a member of neither level. In other words, Whitehead agrees with Aristotle that an irreducible distinction of level is requisite to realism, but for Whitehead such a distinction, in order to be irreducible, must be strictly correlative. By 'correlative' here I mean that each level must be essentially incomplete, and completable only by interpre-tation in terms of the other level—an interpretation which cannot be achieved wholesale and *a priori* by philosophical inquiry (or by God, for that matter), but only at retail and *pro tempore* by the concrescent activity of actual entities. (This latter point is illustrated by the fact that both 'order' (*PR*, 128) and 'actual world' (*PR*, 102) are, for Whitehead, token-reflexive terms.) Philosophy is thus not the study of "order" nor of "the structure of the actual world"—such a proposal would be analogous to a proposal to study "here" or "the structure of yesterday"—but rather, so to speak, of the grammar of token-reflexive terms and its relation to the grammar of non-token-reflexive terms.[23] "Philosophy is explanatory of abstraction, and not of concreteness". (*PR*, 30)

---

[22] It is perhaps useful to point out the analogy with Kant, who takes "concepts" as "form" and "intuitions" as "matter", and then devotes himself to showing that *neither* can count as "experience", that both are merely analytic components of (po-tentialities for, as it were) experience, and that scepticism (Hume) or idealism (Leibniz) are the result of speaking of either as if it could be, all by itself, a full-fledged experience. Whitehead, I think, conceives himself as having done cosmo-logically and completely what Kant did epistemologically and incompletely: namely, developing the implication of the "reformed" subjectivist principle that "the whole universe consists of elements disclosed in the analysis of the experiences of subjects". (*PR*, 252; on Kant, cf. *PR*, 234–37)

[23] On the importance of token-reflexivity, cf. Hartshorne, "Process as Inclusive Category: A Reply", *J. of Phil.* 52, pp. 95–96.

In place of Aristotle's contrast between form-as-actuality and matter-as-potency, Whitehead contrasts "pure" potentiality (the realm of eternal objects) with "real" potentiality (the extensive continuum: "one relational complex in which all potential objectifications find their niche" (*PR*, 103)). Both levels are required for the explanation of actualities, but neither level can do its job if the entities which compose it are thought of as quasi-atoms, as would-be actualities.[24] These two levels will be discussed in the next two sections, but first it will be useful to draw one more comparison between Whitehead and Aristotle. I have cited a suggestion that Whitehead attributes all the characteristics to actuality which Aristotle attributes to potentiality, and conversely. This suggestion cannot be explored in detail here, but there is much truth in it. The most signal instance of this inversion is, of course, that definiteness is for Aristotle a characteristic of form, and form is actuality, whereas for Whitehead definiteness is characteristic of eternal objects, which are pure potentialities. This identification of pure definiteness with pure potentiality seems paradoxical to Aristotelians because for Aristotle (in the *Metaphysics,* and thus in the "orthodox" Aristotelian tradition, though not in the scientific treatises) definiteness is the criterion of actuality. For Whitehead it is not. His criterion of actuality is *decisiveness,* which is not the same thing. This shift of the criterion of actuality is perhaps the most important feature of the difference between a realism built around the notion of *stasis* and one built around the notion of *process. Definiteness,* in Whitehead's eyes is primarily a *logical* notion—although, to be sure, one which needs to be grounded in cosmological notions. The seed of the reductionists' confusion of logical simplicity with "priority in the process of constituting an experient occasion" (cf. fn. 14 above) are already present in Aristotle's inability (despite desperate efforts[25]) to avoid the Platonic mastery of *logos, idea,* and *morphē* over *phusis*—of the terms which are necessary to discuss actualities over the actualities themselves. An actuality is a decision about *how to be* definite—a decision which, from the point of view of *other* actualities for which the first is a datum, looks like one more instance of definiteness. But if this exterior point of view is adopted as the point of view of philosophical analysis, then the interior decisiveness of the actuality will be analyzed away into patterns of definiteness. It will begin to seem, as it did to Aristotle, that

---

[24] The level of real potentiality is, of course, constituted by objectified actualities—past, but objectively immortal. But *as* past, and thus as potential, they lose their individuality. Having lost the power of decision, they become matter for decision. Because they *have been* actual, they are not would-be actualities, but simply suggestions to present actual entities about how to be actual.

[25] Cf. Randall, *op. cit.,* p. 116.

superior actuality consists not (as it does for Whitehead; cf. *PR*, 142) in making more and more important and far-reaching decisions, but in being so definite as no longer to have to make decisions at all. From here, it is but a step to the "unreformed subjectivist principle" that "the datum in the act of experience can be analyzed purely in terms of universals".[26] Aristotle shrank from this step, and his attempts to avoid taking it have been the foundation of anti-reductionist thinking ever since, but the "misunderstanding of the true analysis of 'presentational immediacy'" (*PR*, 43) which he shared with Plato left Aristotelianism too weak to withstand the assaults of the reductionist revolt of the seventeenth century.[27]

§6 *Real Potentiality: Matter as Objectified Actuality*

For Whitehead, there are two ways of describing any actual entity—as the culmination of process and as potential for process, as present and as past. The Eighth Category of Explanation tells us that:

> Two descriptions are required for an actual entity: (a) one which is analytical of its potentiality for "objectification" in the becoming of other actual entities, and (b) another which is analytical of the process which constitutes its own becoming. (*PR*, 34)

This distinction is, *prima facie,* the closest Whiteheadian parallel to the Aristotelian distinction between the-matter-in-a-substance and the form of that substance. If one calls the aspect described by (a) the "objective" reality of the actual entity and that described by (b) its "formal" reality (as Whitehead sometimes does[28]), then one can think of its objective reality as the entity considered *qua* matter and its formal reality as the entity considered

---

[26] Cf. Hartshorne, "The Compound Individual", p. 200: "Those who today defend Aristotelianism as the "commonsense philosophy" are simply inviting us to begin the foredoomed process all over again. Every new Aristotle can only usher in a new Berkeley . . ." Cf. also *PR,* 79.

[27] Whitehead's vision of the absurdities of modern reductionism as traceable to an initial misstep taken by Plato and Aristotle is very like Heidegger's. Cf. *Introduction to Metaphysics*, New Haven, 1959, pp. 180 ff., esp. p. 182: "The crux of the matter is not that *phusis* should have been characterized as *idea*, but that the *idea* should have become the sole and decisive interpretation of being." Heidegger's analysis, both in *Introduction to Metaphysics* and in *Sein und Zeit*, of Western ontology as dominated by the identification of "being" with "presence" (*parousia, Anwesenheit*)—cf. *Sein und Zeit*, sec. 6—should be compared with Whitehead's suspicion of the ultimacy of "presentational immediacy". Compare also Heidegger on *Zuhandensein-vs.-Vorhandensein* (*Sein und Zeit,* Secs. 15–17) with Whitehead on causal efficacy-vs.-presentational immediacy.

[28] Cf. *PR,* 118. William Alston ("Internal Relatedness in Whitehead", *Rev. Meta.* 5, pp. 535–58), equates "formal reality" with "existence" and "objective reality" with "actuality". The latter identification, I should want to argue, is very seriously misleading.

qua form. Differences appear, however, when one pursues the analogy. If one takes the general difficulty about "potentiality" to be summed up in the question "How can one ever talk about potentiality, since all we ever find are actualities?", then one is tempted to translate this into Whiteheadian terms as the question: "How can one speak of the objective reality of an actual entity, when all that it *really* is is a process of becoming?". On re-flection, however, one should realize that this question is wrong-headed. The *objective* reality of an actual entity is precisely what, ninety-nine times out of a hundred, we *do* speak of. The real problem for Whitehead is how to speak of the *formal* reality of an actual entity. The inversion of modality which, as we have noted, characterizes the contrast between Aristotle and Whitehead, is here marked by replacing the question "How can you talk about potentiality?" with the question "'How can you talk about anything else?" In place of the reductionist's paradox that "the only things that can possibly be encountered are actualities, but not all possibilities are actual", Whitehead asks us to reflect on the fact that everything that can be en-countered by an actuality is *objectively* real, and thus is merely a poten-tiality, yet actualities *do* influence other actualities.

This inversion is not a mere verbal twist, although it might seem so. Both Aristotle and Whitehead, after all, seem to identify actuality with im-mediacy, and it might seem obvious that the immediately encountered—the "given"—is actual, and that its function as a potentiality for further process is derivative, the product of reflection and analysis. But this is not obvious to Whitehead; on the contrary, viewing the situation in this way is as we shall see, a symptom of the failure to "take time seriously". For White-head, "immediacy" is of two sorts—the private subjective immediacy of present enjoyment, and the public objective immediacy of the given past. Although the former is a criterion of actuality, the latter is not. The ob-jective reality of an actual entity is "the actual entity as a definite, deter-minate, settled fact, stubborn and with unavoidable consequences" (*PR*, 336), but stubborn facticity is not the same as actuality, any more than is definiteness. The *decisiveness* which marks the *formal* reality of the actual entity is the *reason* for the objective reality of that entity being as stubborn as it is (cf. *PR*, 68-9), but stubbornness is not the same as decisiveness.[29] In

---

[29] On the derivative status of stubbornness, compare Heidegger, *Sein und Zeit*, s. 210: "Widerstandserfahrung, das heist strebensmässiges Entdecken von Widerständi-gem, ist ontologisch nur möglich auf dem Grunde der Erschlossenheit von Welt. Widerständigkeit, charakterisiert das Sein des innerweltlich, Seienden. Widerstand-serfahrungen bestimmen faktisch nur die Weite und Richtung des Entdeckens des innerweltlich begegnenden Seienden. Ihre Summierung leitet nicht erst die Erschliessung von Welt ein, sondern setzt sich voraus." The attempt to construct *Erschlossenheit* out of *Widerständigkeit* is a product of the attempt to make *Vorhan-*

a system in which "Creativity" is "The Category of the Ultimate", "stubbornness" is a mark of poteniality, not of actuality. The inversion of modalities here, far from being verbal, is part and parcel of Whitehead's campaign against the confusion of logical simplicity with ontological priority, and against the (pragmatically useful, but cosmologically disastrous) confusion of a thing's consequences with its nature.[30]

The importance of this inversion appears when we turn to the traditional dilemmas about the notion of matter. "Matter" has always been asked to play two distinct, and apparently incompatible, roles. On the one hand, matter is supposed to be cuddly, malleable, and receptive—it seeks form as the female seeks the male. On the other hand, it is resistant, obstreperous and stubborn—it needs, Aristotle tells us, to be "mastered".[31] In Aristotle, emphasis teeters back and forth between these two roles. The first appears when "matter" (as "material cause") is being used to make substantial change intelligible, and the second when "matter" is being invoked to explain accidents, individuation, and monstrosities. With the subsumption, in the cosmology of the seventeenth century, of substantial change under changes of quantity and quality, matter adopts the second role almost exclusively. Now when one focuses on this second role, one sees that matter is not resistant because of its indefiniteness, but precisely because of its definiteness. It is not because a lump of marble is "formless" that it resists the sculptor, but because it has the *wrong* form. Again, reflection from the seventeenth-century point of view on the malleability and feminine complaisance which Aristotle attributes to proximate matter makes one realize that these features are due not to the "materiality" of the material cause but simply to its possession of the "right" form. So, following the lead provided by the "unreformed subjectivist principle", it begins to look as if one could analyze both the cuddliness and the stubbornness of "matter" away into congeries of forms, and thus eliminate altogether the need to give indefiniteness an ontological status.

Thus, *if one identifies actuality with definiteness,* one finds it absurd to think of "potentiality" as anything but a name for the confusion among our ideas (which was how the seventeenth century philosophers did think of

---

densein prior to *Zuhandensein* (cf. fn. 27), as is the reductionism ensuing from an acceptance of the "unreformed subjectivist principle". (Compare also Peirce, on the impossibility of constructing "Thirds" out ، ᶠ "Seconds".)

[30] Cf. *PR*, 336: "The "formal" aspect is functional so far as that actual entity is concerned: by this it is meant that the process involved is immanent in it. But the objective consideration is pragmatic. It is the consideration of the actual entity in respect to its consequences."

[31] Cf. *De Gen. Anim.* IV, 769b 11 ff., 788a 5 f.

it). The actuality-potentiality distinction thus evaporates altogether. Without the heuristic aid provided by this distinction, all distinctions of categoreal level tend to evaporate. But if, with Whitehead, one distinguishes between definiteness and decisiveness, then one can unite the two roles played, in Aristotle, by "matter" by saying that matter ("objectified actual entities") is definite, stubborn, and resistant precisely because it *is* potential, and conversely. Only the definite and resistant is malleable—that is, only a perfectly definite feeling (cf. *PR,* 338) can be a datum for further feeling, but once a feeling *is* definite, it is over, past, and thus, though objectively immortal, *no longer* actual (cf. *PR,* 130). Instead of interpreting the distinction between matter and form as one between real indefiniteness and real definiteness, Whitehead interprets it as the distinction between the past and the present.

§7 *Pure Potentiality: Primary Matter as Abstract Multiplicity of Forms*

At this point, however, one may wish to raise questions of the following sort: is there then no place for the vague, the indefinite, and the muddled in Whitehead's system? Is there any point in using the notion of "potentiality" if all one means by it is "past actuality"? Doesn't a philosophy of creativity entail real indefiniteness as an ultimate categoreal level?

The answer to these questions, I shall argue, depends once again upon the contrast between "definiteness" and "decisiveness". There is no such thing in Whitehead's system as "real indefiniteness", but there distinctly *is* real indecisiveness, and this indecisiveness does form a distinct categoreal level. For it is here that the eternal objects come into the act. The Whiteheadian analogue of "primary matter" is the "barren inefficient disjunction of abstract potentialities" (*PR,* 64). Primary matter, in Aristotle, is the ultimate background against which substantial change—generation and destruction—takes place. In Whitehead, " 'Change' is the description of the adventures of eternal objects in the evolving universe of actual things" (*PR,* 92), and it is against this background of the bare unstructured multiplicity of eternal objects that actualities evolve. The concrescent processes which are the formal realities of actual entities order this multiplicity, and change it from a *mere* multiplicity into a pattern of *relevant* potentialities. The measure of an actual entity's actuality is the measure of the extent to which it succeeds in establishing such a pattern.[32] The analogue of the Great Chain

---

[32] Cf. Christian, 267: "This ordering of eternal objects is an actual occasion's contribution to its future," and *PR,* 132: ". . . "order" in the actual world introduces a derivative "order" among eternal objects". (But this does not mean that the eternal objects are "changed" by being thus ordered; cf. fn. 39 below.)

of Being which (for Aristotelians, if not for Aristotle[33]) stretches from Primary Matter to the Unmoved Mover(s) is an hierarchy stretching from "the-eternal-objects-as-mere-multiplicity" (an ultimate abstraction, which is precisely as inconceivable as "Primary Matter"[34]) to God (who *positively* prehends *all* the eternal objects, whereas all other actualities prehend positively only a tiny fraction of them). "Each occasion exhibits its measure of subjective intensity. The absolute standard of such intensity is that of the Primordial Nature of God, which is neither great nor small because it arises out of no actual world." (*PR*, 75) Each temporal actual entity inherits suggestions, as it were, about relevant patterns of form from past actual entities, and it rearranges these patterns in accordance with its own *telos*—its own subjective aim. The more inclusive its subjective aim, the more it will be able to do toward restructuring inherited patterns, and the more individuality, decisiveness, and actuality (three synonymous terms, for Whitehead) it will have. When we think in terms of "change" (that is, of the creative process in the large) rather than of "enjoyment" (the concrescence of an individual eternal object), we see the eternal objects as playing the role of that-which-becomes-arranged and the individual actual entities as doing the arranging. From this point of view, the whole creative process can be seen as the attempt to find the pattern of relevance among eternal objects which will produce the greatest subjective intensity of enjoyment.

Taking this conclusion together with the discussion of real potentiality in §6, we can now revise the description of the contrast between Aristotelian and Whiteheadian treatments of the form-matter distinction which we offered in §5. Our new set of analogies is as follows:

(1) the *specific form* of an individual material substance S has no Whiteheadian analogue, since (cf. §3) there is no distinction in Whitehead between specification and individuation;

(2) the *form* of S is analogous to the formal reality of an actual entity A;

(3) the *proximate matter* of S is analogous to A's past—the actual entities

---

[33] This parenthesis expresses my reservations about how seriously to take the (very rare) references to *protē hulē* in the Aristotelian corpus—reservations, however, which need not be discussed here. Cf. Hugh King, "Aristotle Without *Prima Materia*", *J. Hist. Ideas, 17*, pp. 370–89.

[34] Cf. Christian, p. 265 f., the references there cited, and *PR*, 42. As Christian points out, "multiplicity" is used in a highly technical sense by Whitehead, and must be sharply distinguished from "nexus" and "proposition". "Every statement about a multiplicity is a disjunctive statement about its individual members". (*PR*, 45)

(I should like to note that this section could not have been written without the help of Christian's discussion of the doctrine of eternal objects in Part Two of his book. The reader is urged to consult this discussion for a full account of the process of "establishing patterns of relevance"—a subtle topic which can only be sketched in the present space.)

from which A inherits, considered as objective realities (the "extensive continuum");

(4) the *matter-in-S* or *S-qua-matter* is analogous to A's objective reality—that is, A-as-prehended-by-later-actual-entities;

(5) primary matter is analogous to the bare multiplicity of eternal objects, by reference to which A and its ancestors may be described, and which A "orders" by reordering its inheritance from its ancestors.[35]

In §5, we treated the extensive continuum (3) as the analogue of *matter* and the multiplicity of eternal objects (5) as the analogue of *form,* while treating (2)—the formal reality of A—as the analogue of *composite substance.* That treatment expresses the way the situation looks from, as it were, "inside" A's concrescence: the real potentiality (3) is "matter" for the process of being felt under subjective forms dictated by a new "form" (the initial datum of A's subjective aim[36]) plucked out from (5). The table of analogies above, on the other hand, expresses how the situation appears when we step outside of A and look at the whole creative process: from this perspective, we can see both (3) and (5) as "matter" and (2) as "form", thus re-establishing the Aristotelian identification of form with actuality.

This table of analogies, however, should not mislead us into thinking that a concrescent actual entity's contact with primary matter is only by way of the traces of primary matter left in the proximate matter which it is prehending, as the Aristotelian analogues might suggest. A faces both ways—toward the level of real potentiality (3) and the level of pure potentiality (5) —and plays each off against the other in the interest of its own heightened enjoyment. It is in the space between these two levels, so to speak, that creation gets room to occur. Further (to repeat the conclusion of §3) it is by virtue of the independence of these two levels that actual entities can be genuine individuals. The irreducible individuality and novelty of each actual entity is made possible by the inexhaustible array of alternative subjective aims which its pure conceptual prehensions—its prehensions, that is, of eternal objects not yet exemplified among its ancestors—make available to it. Without such pure conceptual prehensions, the new actual entity would merely be the product of efficient causes (cf. *PR,* 75, 134). On the other hand, without the physical prehensions of the realm of real potentiality constituted by the objectified past actualities, it would be merely the product of idiosyncratic final causes, and the solidarity of the universe would be

---

[35] Whitehead himself was inclined to analogize "primary matter" to "Creativity" (*PR,* 46)—which, however, he also analogizes to primary substance (*PR,* 32). The former analogy is probably due to his reading Aristotle as saying that a thing's matter is its internal principle of change—the sort of reading suggested by, e.g., Santayana's "The Secret of Aristotle".

[36] On the notion of the initial datum of a subjective aim (about which Whitehead is rather vague), cf. Christian, 157 f., 215 f., 305 f.

lost:[37] such a cosmology would lead only to Heraclitean resignation. On neither alternative can time be taken seriously: on the first, there is no reason to transcend the past, since it can only be reiterated; on the second, there is no past to transcend.

There is, perhaps, a certain flavor of paradox in our claim that the multiplicity of eternal objects is the analogue of primary matter. For are not the eternal objects consciously modeled on the Platonic Forms? (Cf. *PR*, 69-70) "Forms of definiteness" seem, off-hand, about as far as one can get from primary matter, when the latter is viewed, as it usually is, as a sort of *Urschleim*. Here again, however, the appearance of paradox arises from our Aristotelian habit of identifying both form and actuality with definiteness. But definiteness doesn't decide anything; it is what gets decided *about*. Forms of definiteness are not forms of decisiveness, even though once a decision is taken is can be analyzed into forms of definiteness. We think of definiteness as a mark of actuality because we think that whenever there is something definite, there must have been an indefinite substratum, and a decision which formed that substratum into this definiteness. But this preconception, although it seems like hard-headed realism, in fact leads one down the reductionist path toward the notion of "bare particulars". It is no more arbitrary and irrational for Whitehead to postulate the non-temporal existence of an infinite and unstructured multiplicity of forms of definiteness than it is for Aristotle to presuppose the eternal structure of a finite number of specific forms. After all, *any* cosmology which declines the Hegelian challenge to "deduce", e.g., the colors of the visible spectrum, is going to have to start by letting forms of definiteness in on the ground floor of speculation—as an irreducible categoreal level. The only question is: how, once let in, can they be restrained from swallowing up any other sort of entity to which one wants to assign coeval ground-floor status? That is to say, how can one maintain a categoreal distinction between forms of definiteness and definite actualities?

The most dramatic version of this last question is the Platonic one: if the Forms are as definite as all *that,* what excuse can possibly be found for the sensible world? If actuality is identified with definiteness, then this problem is insoluble. Aristotle, tipped off by Plato to the existence of the problem,

---

[37] Cf. *PR*, 249: "The one eternal object in its two-way function, as a determinant of the datum [i.e., of the objectified past actual entity] and as a determinant of the subjective form [under which the present actual entity prehends the past actual entity], is thus relational. In this sense the solidarity of the universe is based on the relational functioning of eternal objects." (Cf. *AI*, 236) But if there is no datum other than the conceptually prehended eternal object itself, then there is nothing for this eternal object to relate.

but unwilling, in the end, to give up this identification, tried to solve the problem by letting just a *few* forms of definiteness in on the ground-floor —*viz.,* the thing-kind-names of common sense and of primitive science— while consigning all the others to a vague cosmological dustbin called "matter". In doing so, he paved the way for reductions, for when a more advanced science made it thoroughly unclear where substantial change left off and accidental change began, philosophers promptly endowed the forms of accidents with definiteness, and thus with actuality. They thereby (cf. §§5-6) made both the matter-form and the actuality-potentiality distinctions seem pointless.

Whitehead, abandoning the identification of actuality with definiteness, solves the problem by letting in *all* forms of definiteness at once, and by making the criterion of degree of actuality consist in the extent and complexity of the choice among those forms. Using this criterion, the only danger involved in postulating forms of definiteness is that the forms, might, all by themselves, exercise an influence upon the choices which are made concerning them. Insofar as such an influence *is* exercised, the totality of eternal objects would have to be counted as itself an actuality, and a dissolution of the distinction between categoreal levels would ensue. Whitehead was incautious about this danger in *Science and the Modern World*. In that book, he seems to think of each eternal object as being what it is by virtue of its place in a scheme of internal relations with all the other eternal objects. Such a scheme suggests that all the decisions have already been made, and that the concrescence of actual occasions must follow rigid guidelines, tiresomely reiterating pre-established patterns. (Cf. *SMW*, 299 ff.) In *Process and Reality,* he takes just the opposite tack and makes the eternal objects, by themselves, utterly unrelated to each other:[38] all "relationships" between eternal objects are now interpreted as derivative from choices ("valuations") made by actualities.[39] Since *every* possibility of order is itself an eternal object (and therefore incompatible possibilities of order are equally pos-

---

[38] As Christian (p. 262) has noted, Whitehead may be construed as speaking, in chap. 10 of *SMW*, of the eternal objects as they are related in the Primordial Nature of God. The latter—a "non-temporal actuality" which provides the primordial valuation of all eternal objects—raises many serious and complex problems for an analysis of Whitehead's cosmology. I shall make no attempt to go into these problems here, although a full defense of my argument in this paper would require that this Whiteheadian analogue of the Unmoved Mover (cf. *PR*, 522–23) be discussed. I am here treating the Primordial Nature as simply one more actuality which transmits suggestions about relevant eternal objects to the future, just as temporal actual entities do.

[39] I put "relationships" in quotes as a reminder that one should not think of eternal objects as in any way "changed" by being thus re-evaluated. Despite Whitehead's use of terms like 'ingression of eternal objects' and 'adventures of eternal objects', it is clear

sible) and since there can be no such eternal object as Order-in-general (corresponding to The Form of the Good),[40] the multiplicity of eternal objects remains as unstructured as ever Primary Matter was. To sum up, Whitehead's insight is that "pure potentiality" is to be found not in the *absence* of definiteness, but in piling definiteness on definiteness until no guidelines for decision between these alternative definitenesses remain.

§8 *Conclusions*

In this concluding section I shall try to tie what I have been saying together by answering the question: what does Whitehead's philosophy of process contribute to a discussion of the topic of matter? For this purpose, I shall return to my original distinction between realism and reductionism in §2, where I said that reductionism tries, and fails, to analyse experience exclusively in terms of *repeatable* entities. The contrast between the repeatable and the unrepeatable—between the universal and the particular—is traditionally explicated by both Aristotelianism and common sense in terms of the distinction between form and matter. When one attends to the macroscopic objects of common sense, it seems obvious that *man* for example, is a repeatable form, but that Socrates is unique and unrepeatable, and so we consider *man* as Socrates' form, and his unrepeatability as due to his matter.

The most obvious and dramatic difference between process philosophy and common sense is that the units of actuality, for process philosophy, are no longer such macroscopic objects. They are replaced by sub-microscopic unrepeatable entities. Taking time seriously means taking the break between past and present as the border between two different actualities.[41] If one does this, it becomes analytic that "only the non-actual is repeatable".

---

that nothing ever "happens" to an eternal object. The order which Whitehead says is introduced among them is not some sort of quasi-spatio-temporal reshuffling, but is simply the "suggestions" about which eternal objects are more relevant than others made to a concrescent actual entity by its predecessor-actualities or by the Primordial Nature of God. To speak of "an order among pure potentialities" is always an elliptical way of referring to real potentiality. To say that an eternal object has been made more relevant to the creative process is not to say that anything has been added to it, nor that its "position" in the multiplicity of eternal objects (in some unintelligible sense of "position") has changed, any more than to say that logarithms or ultrasonic vibrations have become relevant to human technology is to say that they have somehow suffered qualitative change or altered position.

[40] This is because of the paradoxes of self-inclusion. Cf. *PR*, 128, and Christian, pp. 271 ff.

[41] This is why time cannot be taken seriously until one ceases to think of the present as a knife-edge and begins to think of it as an extended duration.

Given this doctrine, it becomes clear that one must either (a) cease to use the matter-form distinction, or (b) deny that form is repeatable, or (c) deny that form is actual.

Aristotelians have fought against transferring the unit of actuality to this sub-microscopic level on the ground that, since such actualities do not change, one cannot preserve the distinction between matter and form. (This attitude has given Aristotelianism a bad name, since it has seemed to involve an unempirical insistence that science should always accommodate itself to philosophy, and never conversely.) Both the cosmology of the seventeenth century and Whitehead's process philosophy, on the other hand, accept this transference. But whereas the thinkers of the seventeenth century thought themselves well rid of the matter-form distinction, Whitehead is intent upon reinterpreting it so as to make it relevant to unchanging entities.

The way in which this reinterpretation proceeds will be clearer if we note the differences, within the cosmological tradition which we inherit from the seventeenth century, between rationalists and empiricists. Empiricists cling to the principle that only form is repeatable, but they deny that form is actual. They think of form as abstract, and of concreteness as inhering in an inexpressible and unintelligible "given". The "given" stands to form in the relation of "exemplification of", even as did Aristotelian matter, but unlike Aristotelian matter, (which was describable, even if not "knowable" in the honorific sense of the *Posterior Analytics*), it is undescribable, and thus its postulation involves the absurdities inherent in the notion of "bare particulars". Rationalists, on the other hand, clinging to the identification of form with both repeatability and actuality, interpret the form-matter distinction by reference to the Platonic distinction between reality and appearance—so that "givenness", like "time" and "individuality", are treated as illusions. They thus can reply that the "given" is not truly concrete, and that only the Concrete Universal is truly actual. Although avoiding the absurdities of the notion of "bare particulars", rationalists encounter analogous absurdities in their attempt to explain how Reality manages to disguise itself as Appearance. Rationalists and empiricists thus either gratefully abandon talk of matter-vs form altogether, or else (following up certain Aristotelian leads, but neglecting others), they speak of matter-as-the-unfortunately-indescribable-actual (in empiricism) or of matter-as-unfortunate-and-non-actual-illusion (in rationalism) .

Now Whitehead wants to say that:

(1) The seventeenth century was right, against Aristotle, in ceasing to regard middle-sized common-sense objects as paradigmatic of actuality.

(2) Rationalists are right, against empiricists, in saying that the "given" is not actual.

(3) Empiricists are right, against rationalists, in saying that what is repeatable is not actual.

(4) Aristotelian realists are right in insisting, against everybody, that the form-matter distinction, or some analogue thereof which will preserve the ability of actualities to sustain both external and internal relations, is needed.

Whitehead's treatment of the relations between actual entities and eternal objects—that is, his reinterpretation of the form-matter distinction—is dictated by the need to reconcile these four positions. His point of departure is (3): the repeatable is not actual. Empiricists, having grasped this, are misled by their acceptance of the unreformed subjectivist principle into inferring that the actual is indescribable. What is required in order to get around this principle, Whitehead says, is the recognition that actualities are describable in terms of other actualities. (Cf. *PR*, 76 ff.) Empiricists, however, are afraid that such description will lead to idealism, and thence to monism. They fear that admitting that actualities are "present in" (cf. *PR*, 79) other actualities will dissolve actualities into congeries of internal relations. Whitehead replies that a congeries of internal relations is not the same as a congeries of universals. Relations are as unrepeatable as anything can be (cf. *AI*, 296; *PR*, 349-50; Christian, 236), and an actuality which consists of internal relations to other entities is unrepeatable precisely by virtue of being a congeries of such relations. The idealist attempt to construe relations as universals is just another product of the unreformed subjectivist principle.

But this still leaves us without an account of external relations (without becoming involved in infinite regresses). Since entities which can sustain external relations must be repeatable, and since the repeatable is non-actual, we have to invoke repeatable potentialities to serve as "forms of definiteness" by which actualities, as terms of relations, may be characterized. But postulating such forms—the eternal objects—raises the traditional dilemma of the Platonic Forms: either (a) the forms postulated to characterize the actualities are so much like actualities as to make them indistinguishable from their actualizations, or (b) they are so different from actualities that they cannot do an adequate job of characterizing them. Now it is in the resolution of this dilemma that the significance of process philosophy emerges most clearly. The dilemma is resolved by distinguishing definiteness from decisiveness, a distinction which is unintelligible if one does not take time seriously. For if one does not, one will be unable to see a difference between the evaluative decision of a presently concrescent actual entity and the inheritance from that actual entity received by its successors between, in other words, formal and objective reality. The latter *is* indistinguishable from a form of definiteness, and if all actual entities were past (or, what comes to the same thing, if they could be viewed *sub specie aeternitatis*) there would be no difference between the actual world and the extremely complex eternal object which described it. If time is taken seriously, however, and it is thus recognized that 'actual world' and 'actuality' are token-reflexive terms, then one can escape the first horn of the above dilemma by distinguishing between the definiteness of an entity's characterization (its objective reality) and the decisiveness of its concrescence (its formal reality). The latter is actual, and therefore non-repeatable. The former is "repeatable", and therefore potential, in the sense that it is related (externally to it, although internally to each entity which prehends it) to a potentially infinite number of subsequent actual entities by being "present in" them. The apparent dilemma is now seen to rest upon a confusion between past and present—between characterization and entity characterized.[42] Its second horn is escaped by replying that the difference between the characterization of the actual and the actual entity is no greater, though no less great, than the difference between past and present—which, if one takes time seriously, is precisely the difference which one would expect.

We saw in §6 how the distinction between formal and objective reality resembles the traditional distinction between the form and the matter of a substance. In §7 we saw how the multiplicity of eternal objects resembles primary matter. We can now see that the crucial *difference* between Aristotle's and Whitehead's doctrines of matter is that Whitehead retains the advantages of the matter-form distinction while avoiding the disadvantages of the species-individual and essence-accident distinctions. Specifically, he (a) retains Aristotle's categoreal distinction of level while avoiding both (b) the "unscientific" character of Aristotle's distinction and (c) the latent tendency toward the subjectivist principle (cf. §5) inherent in Aristotle's use of teleology in regard to enduring and changing objects:

(a) The distinction between formal and objective reality permits one to save realism by (1) enabling the primary realities to bear both external and internal relations, (2) maintaining the independence of the level of pre-analytic (non-objectificatory) reference to an entity (the self-satisfaction of an actual entity in its subjective immediacy) and the level of its analysis (an actual entity as objectified, and thus as analyzable into a pattern of eternal objects); (3) uniting these two levels by the "two-way functioning

---

[42] Whitehead thus can be seen as replacing the distinction between "specification" and "description" (discussed in §2 above) with the distinction between reference-to-an-actual-entity-as-subjective-intensity and reference-to-an-object. The present-past distinction is thus substituted for the thing-property distinction.

of eternal objects" in conformal feeling (cf. *PR*, 249), so that despite the utter privacy of an actual entity's subjective intensity, it is genuinely "present in" later actualities.

(b) The ordinary seventeenth century objection to the Aristotelian form-matter distinction, interpreted as the distinction between the repeatable form of a species and the unrepeatable combination of accidents which individuate the species' members, was that since any given accident or congeries of accidents was as repeatable as a specific form, any distinction between the repeatable and the unrepeatable was arbitrary and unempirical. Whitehead's distinction between the decisiveness of formal reality and the definiteness of objective reality permits one to make sense of the notion of the ultimate unrepeatability of the actual, while his refusal of the gambit: "But how do they differ *sub specie aeternitatis?*" protects him against reductionist efforts to make the repeatable either unintelligible or illusory. He is thus able, as Aristotelians are not, to welcome the seventeenth century's substitution of a law-event framework of scientific explanation for the Aristotelian species-individual framework.

(c) The Aristotelian identification of actuality with definiteness was a result of Aristotle's unwillinginess to take time seriously. This unwillingness led him to postulate "immaterial substances", to identify form with actuality, and to lay the foundation for the tradition that satisfactory philosophical explanation must be in terms of "substances with undifferentiated endurance of essential attributes". (*PR*, 120) Process philosophy, by breaking with this latter tradition, is able to avoid the reductionisms which flow from an acceptance of the unreformed subjectivist principle while preserving the links with modern scientific results which make these reductionisms so plausible. Whitehead's willingness to accept the Heraclitean view that 'actual world' is a token-reflexive term, and his consequent refusal to identify "actuality" with the results of an ideally long or ideally "objective" analysis in terms of universals, radically transforms the Aristotelian notions of form and matter. The history of futile debate between philosophies which presuppose the Aristotelian cosmology and philosophies which presuppose the cosmology of the seventeenth century shows, I think, that they badly needed such transformation.

Princeton University

COMMENT

RORTY HAS GIVEN US A BRILLIANT PAPER THAT IS MUCH MORE THAN A DISCUSSION OF Whitehead. His general thesis, as I understand it, is two-fold: he argues (a) that Whitehead, like Aristotle, is a "realist", i.e. an anti-reductionist with respect to material things; and (b) that Whitehead's realism is stronger and more satisfactory than Aristotle's, for the reason that Whitehead "takes time seriously". I am not sure whether I think these general claims are true or not, but the questions I want to raise for discussion concern more particular points. There are three such points.

(1) Rorty says that Aristotle is a realist, that he is able to avoid the reduction of things to qualities (or relations or ideas or sense-data) because he regards things as composed of two irreducibly different elements, matter and form. But I do not see *how* the recognition of the matter-form distinction enables Aristotle to protect things from reduction; Rorty has not, I think, made this clear. Furthermore, I do not see that the matter-form distinction is *necessary* for this purpose. Things *are* not reducible to qualities; reductionism *is* a mistaken doctrine. But if a reason for this irreducibility of things is required, then it surely lies—as Rorty himself suggests—in the logical or grammatical difference between "specifying" and describing things, between referring and characterizing. Referring and characterizing are irreducibly different functions of language, irreducibly different things that people use words to do. It is this distinction that lies behind the distinction between things and qualities, and it is the irreducibility of referring to describing that accounts, ultimately, for the irreducibility of things to qualities. I do not claim that this is obvious or even very clear; that it is even *so* needs to be argued and the point itself needs to be explained, and I have no time here to do either. But I think it is true nonetheless, and hence that what Rorty says is not.

(2) Rorty says that Whitehead is a realist in the same sense as that in which Aristotle is, although on different grounds or in a different way. But I question this: I question whether Whitehead is even interested in protecting ordinary things (the individual man or horse) from reduction to qualities or the like. Aristotle's philosophical task is the explication and description of the scheme of concepts that is actually employed in our thinking about the world. Aristotle is trying to tell the truth about something already there, whose nature is fixed independently of his own inquiry. But Whitehead's task is quite different. He is not trying to describe a system of concepts that is already there for examination but rather to invent a new system that will be superior to the old in certain specific ways. Whitehead's philosophical task is that of construction or creation

525

—"imaginative generalization" as he himself calls it at one point in *Process and Reality*. This difference of philosophical procedure between Aristotle and Whitehead, this difference in what the two do *as* philosophy, has two consequences that are relevant here. First, Whitehead is a realist with respect, not to ordinary things (Aristotle's primary substances), but to actual entities, which are like things in being ontologically ultimate in the system in which they figure but in very little else. Hence that on behalf of which reductionism is being resisted, that which is being saved, is different in the two cases. Second, since actual entities are made and not found, Whitehead's realism is not so much a defense of the established order as a free, creative act or stipulation, one which can perhaps be supported or justified by citing reasons of a sort, but not the reason that this is how the world is. Whitehead is a realist because he wants to be (for certain reasons), not because he has to be, on pain of thinking what is false.

(3) Rorty says that Whitehead's realism has a different basis from that of Aristotle, that he is able to resist the reduction of actual entities to qualities or relations by some means different from that chosen by Aristotle, the matter-form distinction. But I do not think that Rorty has made clear in his paper what this means is, largely because he seems to say that it is different things at different times, and I cannot tell which of the apparently suggested alternatives is supposed to be the analogue of Aristotle's matter-form distinction, the device whereby the slough of reductionism is circumvented. I have just argued that Whitehead's task is different from Aristotle's and hence that the question: "What is the basis of philosophical realism?" has not the same sense when asked of Whitehead's actual entities that it has when asked of Aristotle's primary substances. So I would prefer to say that my present difficulty concerns not the basis of Whitehead's realism, as if there were some feature of actual entities that made it a mistake to reduce them to qualities, but rather the stipulated connections between the concept of an "actual entity" in Whitehead's system and other concepts in terms of which certain features of actual entities are explicated. The features in question are the individuality, particularity, and uniqueness or unrepeatability of actual entities. The question is: "What is it about Whitehead's system of concepts that guarantees or explains the presence in actual entities of these features?" Now sometimes Rorty answers that it is the fact that Whitehead distinguishes two sorts of elements or components of things, just as Aristotle distinguishes matter and form. But then to the further question: "What are the two sorts of element in question?" Rorty appears to give different answers. Sometimes he seems to say: actual entities and eternal objects; sometimes physical and conceptual prehensions; and sometimes the formal and the objective reality of an actual entity. At other times, however, Rorty seems to answer the question: "What is it that guarantees the individuality, etc. of actual entities?" by citing, not a distinction or pair of elements, but some single feature of actual entities. But here again he seems to give different answers to the question as to what this feature is. Sometimes he seems to say that it is the fact that each actual entity has a unique subjective aim provided

for it by God (but this is a mistake: a subjective aim is not unique for White-head, except accidentally, since it is composed entirely of eternal objects); some-times the fact that an actual entity is composed of unrepeatable physical pre-hensions (but the unrepeatability of physical prehensions is derivative and depends upon the unrepeatability of the prehending and prehended entities, hence cannot be used to explain the unrepeatability of the latter); and some-times the fact that actual entities enjoy "subjective immediacy" and exemplify "decisiveness" (but these are metaphors, whose sense needs to be made clear, besides which these features again presuppose and do not explain the individual-ity of actual entities). My reaction to this wealth of suggestions is mainly one of confusion (though some of them are untenable, as I have tried briefly to indicate in the foregoing parenthetical comments); I am just not clear as to what Rorty's view about the basis of Whitehead's realism is. Furthermore, I feel bound to add to the confusion by suggesting a further possibility of my own. Is it not the extensive continuum, an admittedly dark notion in White-head's philosophy, in terms of which the individuality of actual entities is to be explained? Is it not, i.e., rather this than any of the things that Rorty has mentioned?

V. C. Chappell
University of Chicago

MATTER AS ACT[1]

Robert O. Johann, S.J.

꘎ There is a growing desire among Catholic thinkers to follow White-head's advice and "take time seriously". They want to be able to see the world as temporally developing, with man, whatever his special preroga-tives, part and parcel of the temporal process. In implementing this desire, they are somewhat embarrassed by their Aristotelian heritage, whose cos-mology was elaborated against a completely different background and world-view, a "steady-state" view of the universe as opposed to an evolu-tionary one. The purpose of these pages is to suggest a possible alternative.

§1 *The Problem*

The very idea of evolution appears at first sight an affront to reason. It seems to suggest that you can have more at the end of a process than you had at the beginning, or more simply, that you can get something out of nothing. This apparent violation of the principle of causality is the general basis on which scholastic philosophers have normally rejected the idea in the past and refused even to consider the possibility of life arising from non-life, much less spirit from matter. Actually, however, philosophers holding for evolution have shown no less respect for causality. How else explain their tendency ei-ther to reduce the higher to the lower, as in the various forms of materialism, or to claim the presence of the higher in the lower from the outset, à la Teil-hard de Chardin, Whitehead and panpsychists in general? For if there are no essential differences between the different levels of perfection in the uni-verse, the problem of causality disappears—but so also, it would seem, does evolution. One may hold for variety in the world without progress, but it is at least difficult to speak of genuine progress if there is no genuine variety.

The problem, therefore, to be faced by any serious philosophy of evolution is how to be reasonable and evolutionary at the same time; how satisfy the exigencies of thought about process and still be true to the irreducible nov-elty of what supposedly has emerged through process. Life is something es-sentially new and more perfect in relation to brute matter; man is something

---

[1] This paper is a substantially revised version of the one presented at the Conference on the Concept of Matter. In making the revisions, I profited greatly from the dis-cussion and comments on the original version provided by the participants of the Conference, particularly Dr. L. J. Eslick of St. Louis University.

essentially new and more perfect in relation to other worldly forms of life. This much is certain and the Scholastics have been right in holding on to it. If an evolutionary theory denies it, not only does it become untrue to the clearest evidence of experience; it also deprives evolution itself of any real significance.

On the other hand, to maintain these differences in terms of traditional hylomorphic theory is to maintain them in a way that that would seem to rule out the possibility of evolution. For, according to hylomorphism,[2] essential differences between bodies are explained by the union of specifically distinct forms with a purely passive substrate, primary matter. It is this primary matter which provides the link of passage between one kind of body and another. Thus, an essential (substantial) change occurs when primary matter loses the form which it had and acquires a new one. Since, however, it is of itself pure potency, a bare and wholly indeterminate substrate, primary matter cannot "do" anything itself towards this acquisition. As regards any change it is wholly passive. Hence, the appearance of a new form in matter must necessarily be attributed to the influence of an efficient cause which is already in act, formally or eminently, with respect to that form and which is said to "educe" the same from the potency of matter. And here is the difficulty for any hylomorphic theory of an evolving universe. For the causes responsible for the transformation of matter will themselves be a part of this world, and then there can be no question of the emergence of new forms but merely a redistribution of old ones. Or the responsible cause will transcend the world—and this would have to be the case for the appearance of a spiritual soul which transcends the potency of matter—in which case the new perfections do not really arise by a process of development; they are inserted.

The question, therefore, arises: Is there possibly another way of interpreting the structure of bodies which, while allowing for essential differences— a necessary requirement, we have seen, for a genuine theory of evolution— does not at the same time exclude evolution? And since the difficulty with hylomorphism in this respect stems from its explanation of essential change as the transformation of a purely passive substrate, primary matter, we can narrow down the question to this: Does an understanding of the material world really require such a substrate? As an indication that it does not, we shall suggest in the following section a possible alternative.

---

[2] The theory of hylomorphism to which I refer is the one which has become traditional in manuals of Scholastic philosophy and which is centered on the idea of "primary matter" as pure subjective potency, completely lacking of itself in any formal determination. However, if one thing became clear in the discussions that led to this book, it is that not everyone who admits a doctrine of primary matter will subscribe to this interpretation of it.

§2 *The Scheme*

The basic element in our conceptual scheme for "thinking" evolution is the notion of "imperfect act". By "act" we mean here "source of action", and by "action" we mean "self-affirmation", "self-expression". An act is "perfect" insofar as it is in and by itself (i.e. as divided from the "other") an adequate and sufficient source of action, i.e. self-affirmation. And it will be in and by itself an adequate source of action when the other is in no sense an intrinsic component of its self-position. Perfect act is act that is capable of affirming itself precisely as divided from and opposed to the other. Insofar as it is perfect act, the term of its action is simply itself as affirmed. Perfect act is act that is actively one with itself. Concretely, it is an act that can say "I"; it is personal.

"Imperfect act", on the other hand, is act that in varying degrees falls short of the personal, that in varying degrees is divided from itself in its action. This is to say that the other will always be more or less an intrinsic component of its action. It may be a component only terminally, i.e. where the other is required not as co-principle of the action but as that at which it terminates, as in the case of animal act.[3] Or it may be a component initially, i.e. when act is active only as element in a complex, when it is really the complex of which the act in question is a "part" that initiates action, such that the other is co-principle with act of its action. This is the case with brute matter, and it represents the greatest division of act from itself and consequently the lowest level of act.

Now if what we say is true, viz. that the difference between the personal (spirit) and the impersonal (matter) can be explained in terms of the distinction between perfect and imperfect act, then we may have here a way of conceiving the evolutionary process. For if imperfect act is in a state of division from itself as act, then a progressive overcoming of this division would be at the same time a progressive emergence of spirit. In other words, although matter and spirit would still remain essentially distinct, they would nevertheless be in the same line of perfection, that namely of "act", and it might be possible to see the second as arising from the first through a process of development. Since the development would be precisely in terms of act's overcoming its initial division from itself, it would not demand the presence of spirit or personal act at the outset nor require the injection of such act from the outside.

How then would such development be explained? We have a clue to the

---

[3] See §3.

answer already in the notion of action. Traditionally, "action" has been divided into two kinds: transient and immanent, and both have been conceived in terms of motion. Transient action was the moving of another; immanent action was the moving of oneself. Transient action was a process of perfecting the other; immanent action a process of perfecting oneself. Now it has not always been noticed that this notion of action presupposes a more fundamental one, one more closely akin to our own. For the moving or perfecting of another can only be conceived as the self-affirmation of the act of an agent *in* a patient, whereas the perfecting of oneself requires a self-affirmation of oneself, which as a process abides *in oneself*. In other words, both transient and immanent action presuppose action as the self-affirmation of act. And in terms of action as self-affirmation or self-expression, the way is opened for conceiving evolutionary process. Let us examine how this is so.

Suppose at the outset a non-systematic manifold of imperfect acts. As imperfect, none of these acts is capable of action by itself but only in conjunction with the other elements of the manifold. Each, therefore, as act is essentially involved in a complex, in the manifold of the other. Such involvement, which implies a division of act from itself since each is act only in conjunction with what is not itself, is precisely what we mean by materiality.

Now it belongs to the nature of act to be active, to act. At this level, however, action can be conceived only as interaction, or perhaps better, as the union of imperfect acts in action. For since none of these acts is by itself a sufficient principle of action, what is really active is the complex. It is the plurality of elements taken precisely as a plurality, in which each element is as it were a function of the rest, that enjoys a true sufficiency as act. And it is to this sufficiency, the sufficiency of the complex, that the joint action of imperfect acts gives expression. In other words, the dynamic integration of imperfect acts in action terminates in themselves as integrated. The sufficiency in virtue of which they interacted and which initially existed only in a "fragmented" state, distributed as it were over the elements of the manifold, emerges now as that in virtue of which the imperfect acts form a whole or system. The term of interaction, therefore, includes not merely the original elements themselves, but the fruit of their active synthesis, *sc.* a formative act that integrates them into a unity and which, as their unification, enjoys itself the sufficiency of the original complex. Interaction is thus the way to synthesis, to the emergence of systems whose formative acts will be more and more sufficient as acts—or, to put it another way, less and less divided from themselves as acts.

Regarding this emergence of systems, several remarks are immediately in order. First of all, it should be noted, the new system is not strictly speaking the product of efficient causality. An efficient cause is a reality extrinsic to its effect and is therefore something complete in itself independent of the causal relationship. In the scheme we are proposing however, the dynamic source of the system enjoys no such extrinsic or independent status. For, as we have seen, the source of the system is the non-systematic complex of imperfect acts whose conjunction in action terminates in *themselves* as systematically integrated. In other words, if action is self-position, self-affirmation, then act-as-affirming-itself (source) and act-as-affirmed (term) do not constitute two independent realities. They are rather distinct states of a single reality, a reality whose processive character essentially involves both of them. The system which arises, therefore, is not a reality other than and extrinsic to the complex from which it has arisen; it is rather the complex itself *as other, sc.* as systematically integrated. It is not therefore efficiently caused by the complex. It *proceeds* from the complex. And it proceeds from the complex precisely because the complex proceeds to itself (affirms itself) as system.

This may be all very well, the reader will say, but does it really answer the problem? For a system cannot be reduced to the elements that make it up. The very idea of system implies not only a plurality of elements but also a principle of order and unity in which they participate, an act of a higher order which plays a formative role in relation to the elements it organizes and which is "higher" precisely because it is formative. The question is then: where does the formative act of the system come from? You seem to have more at the end of the process (elements plus formative act) than at its beginning (elements alone). Either this will have to be added from the outside by creation (therefore no evolution), or you are getting something from nothing (goodbye to causality and reasonableness).

Since this difficulty touches the heart of the matter, let us proceed slowly. When the complex is said to affirm itself, it does so in virtue of the collective sufficiency (as act) of its elements (imperfect acts). This collective sufficiency is not at the outset something over and above the elements themselves —it is precisely the sufficiency they enjoy, taken together, to initiate action. Now action is self-affirmation, self-expression. The action of the complex, therefore, is the expression of itself as a complex, i.e., the expression of the active sufficiency which the complex as a complex possesses. As expressed, this collective suffciency will now be an act over and above the bare elements: it is indeed the fruit of their action. However, as the terminal expression of their collective sufficiency, it is not something independent of them but is precisely *their* act, a single act in which they all participate. But such an act is what we mean by a formative act, and the participation of a plurality of elements in such an act is what makes them a system.

The formative act, therefore, cannot be conceived simply as added from the outside by creation.[4] Were it so, it would not be the terminal expression of the collective sufficiency of the complex of imperfect acts; it would not be *their* act. Neither, however, is it a question of getting something from nothing. For if it is the nature of act to be active, i.e., to assert and express itself, then act as terminally expressed belongs to the very reality of act. Unless act gives rise through action to itself as expressed, it would not be act. In like manner, apart from the terminal expression of their collective sufficiency, i.e., the formative act to which they give rise through their joint action, the imperfect acts of the complex would not be acts at all, even imperfectly. To speak, therefore, of a complex of imperfect acts is to speak of that whose nature it is to systematize itself through action, i.e., to give rise through action to an act that is formative of itself (the complex). Finally, precisely as formative of the complex itself and not something independent of it, it cannot, as we indicated above, be said to be caused by the complex. How then describe its origin? Its origin is one of procession; it proceeds from the complex of imperfect acts. And it does so because whatever enjoys the sufficiency of act (here, the complex) is by nature processive, i.e., active. Act is self-affirmative, self-expressive.

But here some further precisions are in order. If it is granted that the idea of "procession" involves no violation of the principle of causality, the question can then be asked whether we are not now back on the other horn of the dilemma. Is not our explanation in terms of the scheme: act-action-act, another example of panpsychism, i.e., of putting the "higher" in the "lower" to start with? If action is self-affirmation, self-expression, and if the various stages of evolution are explained in terms of the progressive self-affirmation of act, then the initial stage of evolution has to contain already whatever is going to "evolve" from it. Hence, once again the price of avoiding contradiction in evolutionary thinking is the apparent impossibility also of any real novelty—and the impossibility of any really significant evolution. In what sense, therefore, are the systems which emerge by action, or more precisely their formative acts, already contained in the manifold of imperfect acts? Or conversely, in what sense are they really new?

The formative act of an emergent system is, we have said, the terminal expression of the collective sufficiency (as act) of the complex of imperfect acts which are now the elements of the system. Prior to action, therefore, it can be said to be "contained" in the complex only tendentially, i.e., as the term of the natural tendency of any active sufficiency or act (here, the collec-

---

[4] It may, however, *also* be created (see §4, and the problem of the human soul).

tive sufficiency or, if one prefers, the collective act) to express itself. In other words, it is there only in the sense that what by nature is ordered to give rise to it is there, and therefore as ultimately pertaining to the complete intelligibility of what is there.

So far so good. But if it is really just an unfolding of what is there, in what sense is what unfolds really new? Is it like an acorn evolving into an oak, or an egg into a chicken? First of all, it is clear that the novelty cannot be absolute. It cannot be that what arises is completely new with respect to what was there, i.e., having no connection by way of origin with what was there—that would be contradictory. The newness can only be understood in terms of difference, "real novelty" being understood in terms of "essential difference". If we are to speak of significant evolution, it can only be because what arises is essentially different from that from which it arises. Is such the case here? And how can it be, if action is "self-expression"?

The answer to the first question is: yes. The answer to the second will require a little more ingenuity.

At the outset, let us remark that the disappearance of essential differences comes about when the various stages in the evolutionary process are interpreted ultimately in terms of one or other of them. Thus spirit will be reduced to a highly complex arrangement of particles of matter, or elementary matter will be seen as already endowed with a rudimentary form of life, consciousness, liberty, etc. The point, however, of our explanation has been to see the essentially different levels of perfection in the universe as successive stages in a single process. In other words, one level is not reduced to another, but all are included as separate and irreducible phases of a single, transcendent dynamism, the dynamism of act. Thus, for example, act as by itself an inadequate source of action, i.e., as divided from itself and a function of the other (*sc.* matter) is essentially distinct from act that is by itself an adequate source of action, i.e., that is divided from and opposed to the other and undivided from (actively one with) itself (*sc.* spirit). But they are likewise essentially inter-connected by their being separate phases in the single process of action by which act-as-divided-from-itself is enabled to overcome this division. And here, I think, we have the answer to our question.

The process of evolution is the process of act's overcoming its initial division from itself. It is therefore a process of progressive synthesis. The novelty then inherent in genuine evolution can be understood as the novelty of genuine synthesis. For a genuine synthesis of disparate elements, which is achieved through the emergence of a formative act that is the terminal expression of their collective sufficiency, will automatically differ essentially from the elements it synthesizes. Each step, therefore, in such a synthetizing process will be an advance, giving rise to an act that is more sufficient and comprehensive in itself as act[5] than anything that has preceded it. On the other hand, precisely because it arises as the term of action, it will look to what has gone before as its origin and the ground of its emergence. Thus, the fact that action is self-expression will not prevent the term of action from differing essentially from its principle so long as the principle is a collectivity of disparate elements and the term is their genuine synthesis. But the fact that action is self-expression will also assure that whatever emerges will belong to the same world as its predecessors and together with them go to make up one reality.

Summing up this section, therefore, we can say that all the real and essential variety in the world is a variety that is interior to an all-inclusive world-process. There are no higher unities that are not dynamically related to lower unities as the terminal expression of their collective sufficiency. Action (the process of act) thus becomes a sort of transcendent theme of which the variety in the world is the articulation. It will be a progressive articulation, one that takes time, since the higher and more complex syntheses will presuppose the existence of simpler syntheses for their own emergence and functioning. Perhaps more importantly, it will be a non-systematic articulation, proceeding not according to the rigid determinism of universal laws, but more or less at random, with false starts and dead-ends. For world-process, the process of act, is not to be understood as the pre-determined unfolding of a determinate nature or essence. Natures, essential structures, systems, all these are the emergent consequents of process (act's progressive overcoming of its initial division from itself), not its antecedents.

At the outset, as we have indicated, the active sufficiency of act is distributed non-systematically over a coincidental manifold (*sc.* of imperfect acts). Since the imperfect acts are not systematically related to one another, their conjunction in action (the way to synthesis) is likewise non-systematic. Each synthesis or system, therefore, that emerges will always have the character, not of a step in a logical process, but rather of a unique event. It will be a step forward in world history. And it will, moreover, be a tentative step. For the very fact that systems will arise non-systematically means also that they will find themselves non-systematically related to their environment. In other words, their success and survival as systems, as well as their ability to provide the bases for further syntheses, are not automatically guaranteed by their mere emergence but will depend on the host of coincidental factors outside themselves that constitutes their situation. Thus the only thing assured by the "nature" of act in its initial stage is that systems will emerge and that more complex systems (higher syntheses) will be preceded

---

[5] See §3.

by less complex ones. All that is assured is that the original abundance will strive in countless ways and by countless experiments towards its own synthesis. What these ways and experiments have actually been, which have succeeded and which failed, and what the future is likely to be, all these are elements in the unfinished story of the universe.

§3 *Steps in the Process*

So far we have concentrated on the broad outline of the scheme. Our purpose has been to show how it is possible to "think" evolution, to conceive of process in such a way that its giving rise to genuine novelty will not do violence to the principle of causality. For that reason, we have limited our attention to the general idea of a progressive synthesis of imperfect acts without detailing its stages. Now, however, that we have shown the theoretic possibility of such a process, we must try to fill in the main steps. Our aim, therefore, in this section will be to indicate how the actual and essential variety in the universe of our experience can be interpreted as a progressive articulation of the dynamism of act, i.e., as successive stages in the process by which act overcomes its initial division from itself and expresses itself in terms of ever increasing self-sufficiency and comprehensiveness.

The progressive sufficiency of act is measured according as the other is less and less intrinsically required for its being and exercise as act. In proportion as act becomes more and more "collected" in itself (less and less divided from itself), in the same measure it becomes more and more divided from the other in its activity, more and more self-sufficient. Now, the lowest level of sufficiency is that of wholly imperfect act, act in its greatest state of "uncollectedness" or division from itself, where it functions only and wholly as an element in a complex. Not itself a body, it is the root of bodiliness, that sheer multiplicity of which a body is the systematic unification. Next would come an act which while still radically insufficient and imperfect (i.e., while still needing the other precisely as co-principle of its action) would nevertheless have a certain role of its own independently of the other, namely, as formative of a system of wholly imperfect acts, or of a system of systems of such acts. Still unable to initiate an action attributable to itself as source, still brutely material, it is nevertheless a notch above the elements it organizes and of whose collective sufficiency it is the integration. Once, however, the threshold of life is passed, the radical insufficiency (as act) of brute matter is overcome. For it is the characteristic of living things that they act not only in conjunction with the other, but, in some sense, in opposition to the other. They are not merely subordinate elements in a larger complex; they begin to subordinate the other to themselves.

This can be seen, for example, on the level of vegetative life. In the vegetable, the formative act of the system of elements which is the vegetable does not look to what is outside the system for the completion of itself precisely as act, but for new elements to be integrated into the system and ultimately to be formed into new systems similarly organized. In other words, vegetative act looks to the other not as co-authoring its action but precisely as providing material in which to assert itself. Without such material, there can be no self-assertion. On the other hand, the assertion is of itself alone, not of itself plus the other. It must act *in* the other, but it authors the action by itself. Vegetative act, therefore, manifests a greater sufficiency as act than does act on the level of brute matter. But if its action is attributable to itself, as in the case of perfect act, nevertheless, unlike the latter, it still finds the other intrinsic to its action as its necessary matter. It is still, therefore, divided from itself in its activity and, in that sense, still "imperfect".

A higher level of sufficiency is found in the act which is the principle of animal life. The formative act of the system of elements called an animal does not look to the other to complete itself precisely as act; nor does it look to the other simply insofar as it is in the process of being integrated into its own system and supplies the matter for its own self-assertion. Rather it looks to the other precisely as distinct from the system which it itself informs and as that to which that system as a whole is referred in its action. Whereas vegetative act is related to the other only as the potential subject of its own formative influence, animal act is related to the other in its otherness. The other is not merely that in which it asserts itself, but that with which it deals in its action, that at which its action terminates, that which objectively specifies its self-affirmation. Since the animal is thus more clearly divided from the other than is the plant, it is correspondingly, to a greater extent than the plant, something in itself. Since, however, its act does not yet terminate at itself in its action but only at the other, so that the other is still an intrinsic complement of its action, it is still in a measure separated from itself in its activity; it still can affirm itself only outside itself; it is not yet actively one with itself, not yet perfect act.

Perfect act is reached for the first time in the human person. The formative act of the system of elements which is man does not look to the other merely as supplying potential elements for that system, nor again as the intrinsic term of its action. The action of this act is able to terminate at the very act which is its source, at itself. It is interior to itself, actively one with itself, aware of itself. In its ability to utter the electrifying "I am", it at last manifests an act that is no longer divided from itself in its action. And being no longer divided from itself, being at last complete in itself, it also manifests itself as perfectly divided from the other. It is an act for which the other is no longer, as it were, an aspect of itself, but for which the other exists precisely as other. Man, it should be noted, is not disjoined from the other on all the levels of his being. Insofar as he is a system of imperfect acts, of elements, he is wholly involved in the manifold of the other, a part of the world that surrounds him. Again, as sharing in the life of plant and animal, he is still more or less continuous with the other and divided from himself even as they are. It is only as person that he confronts the other as other. And even here, he still needs the other. A being that is in itself only as opposed to and facing the other, still needs the other in order to be itself. The human person defines himself and acquires his historical identity by freely relating himself to what is distinct from himself. His affirmation of himself can take place only in relation to the other. Without the other, in whose presence he is called to take his personal stand, there is no self-affirmation and no human person. In other words, the formative act which makes man a person is not Pure Act to which nothing is opposed and whose self-affirmation is wholly unconditioned. Since, on the other hand, what conditions personal act is the other *as other*, personal act manifests itself as wholly divided from the other and therefore as perfect act, complete and sufficient in itself as act.[6]

The interrelationship of the various levels of being in the universe, which we have described in terms of the progressive "sufficiency" of act as act, can likewise be seen in terms of the progressive "emergence" and "comprehensiveness" of act. The two ideas of *emergence* and *comprehensiveness* are connected. By "emergence" I mean the liberation of act from the state of being simply an element in a larger complex, simply a part included in (or comprehended by) the manifold of the other. Since, however, this liberation from being part of the other cannot be conceived as isolation from the other —we have seen, for example, how personal act, which is in no sense a mere element in a complex, is still not isolated from the manifold of the other— we are forced to say that in the measure that an act ceases to be subordinated and included as an element in the manifold of the other, to that extent it begins to subordinate the manifold to itself, to include it within the range of its activity, to be "comprehensive" of it. "Emergence" and "comprehensiveness", therefore, are two sides of the same coin and each is directly propor-

---

[6] This being the case, any further synthesis in which the person himself would be involved will have to take a different direction. Since personal act is complete in itself as act, it cannot be conceived as being further subsumed under some higher formative act. A further synthesis will have to be a synthesis of absolutes, one that maintains in their integrity and independence the realities it unites. As Teilhard de Chardin points out, there is one way that lies open, the way of love. If human experience is finally to fulfill its promise as being totally comprehensive, an active synthesis in which nothing at all is lost, this it will do only in so far as it becomes more and more an experience of communion.

tionate to the "self-sufficiency" that we considered above. A brief analysis will show how this works out.

Wholly imperfect act, act that is act only in conjunction with what is other than itself, is in no sense comprehensive of the manifold but is wholly comprehended by it. Imperfect act that is nonetheless the formative act of a system—such as you would have, for example, in the case of an atom—although still essentially an element in a larger complex, begins nevertheless to comprehend something of the manifold under itself, to include it within its proper range of influence. It is precisely formative of the elements within the system it unifies. What is thus comprehended, however, is not comprehended as other than itself, but only as its own matter. In the case of vital act, the range of comprehension is larger. Not only are the actual elements of the system it informs included under its scope, but the potential elements as well, i.e. those which, while actually other, are nevertheless in the process of being integrated as parts of the system. The activity proceeding from the formative act of the animal is more comprehensive still. Not only does this act assert itself in relation to what is actually or potentially a member of the system it unifies, but also to what is wholly outside the system. As we have seen, the act of the animal reaches the other in its otherness, although not precisely as other. Since the other is still an intrinsic complement of the animal's action, only that portion of the manifold of the other will be included within the active synthesis of animal life which is directly proportioned to the structure of the animal in question, i.e., only that portion which can be attained by its particular senses.

Coming at last to personal act, however, we have that which is totally comprehensive. In the active life of the person, the whole range of the other is included and included precisely as other. Human experience, as the active synthesis of the self and the other than self, is, as it were, all-inclusive and the whole of reality. For, to grasp the other as other, as distinct and independent of the self, is to grasp it as implicated in, and as itself implying, the self-sufficient totality that confronts the self and in relation to which the self is called upon actively to define itself. This totality, it is true, is only gradually discriminated by the self but right from the outset it is included in the self's experience as the "horizon" of whatever is explicitly attained in action. The range of personal act, therefore, is equal to the whole of the real. Instead of being comprehended as an element in the whole, it is itself comprehensive of the whole.

From what has been said it should be clear that the various levels of perfection in the universe constitute a veritable analogy of act. They are not related to one another simply as so many discrete structures or essences which only have this in common, namely, that each is proportionately related to existence. On the contrary, even in their very differences from one another they are rather just so many steps in the unfolding of the one perfection, the perfection of act. Each level is but a fuller articulation of the self-affirmation of act. Moreover, as we have seen, not only is there a progressive self-sufficiency of act as act; on each successive level of act, there is greater and greater comprehensiveness of the whole in which it is implicated. Looked at another way, since the various levels of perfection all pertain to the one universe, we might say that on each successive level the universe itself exists in a state of greater and greater synthesis, is less and less divided from itself. Instead, therefore, of seeing the various levels as constituted by successive differences added from the outside, we should rather look upon each level as a new step in the progressive possession of itself by the whole. Each level is but the universe itself coming more and more into its own.

§4 *Some Objections and Answers*

In the scheme we have proposed, evolution is explained in terms of the progressive self-affirmation of act. From this point of view, matter is not ultimately purely passive; matter itself is act, albeit imperfect act, or better, it is a manifold of imperfect acts. The active sufficiency which is initially distributed over this manifold asserts itself through the interaction of the original elements and progressively expresses itself more and more synthetically. Finally in man it completely overcomes its initial division from itself and we have the birth of self-presence and freedom. Henceforward the question of progress is placed in man's hands. He is called upon to master the universe and shape it into an abode of love.

Such is our proposed solution to the problem we started out with. Before we let our case rest, however, it may be well to forestall certain objections that can (and have been) raised against it.

The first has to do with the question of causality and concerns both the relationship of our theory of procession to the traditional doctrine of the creation of the human soul and, more generally, the effect of our position on the whole theory of secondary causality.

Concerning the creation of the soul, let me say at the outset that I do not intend the position I have outlined to be in any way a denial of that fact, nor do I think that there is any inconsistency between them. My whole point has simply been to indicate man's place in the universe as the natural term of a transcendental process, i.e., a process that includes not only man but all the other distinct grades of perfection present in the world and which is precisely the process of "act", the collective sufficiency of the universe, progressively affirming itself. The human soul belongs to the universe as a terminal expression of its collective sufficiency. Now since, as we have seen, its terminal expression belongs to the very intelligibility of act as source, it cannot be said to be produced by act but proceeds from it. For this reason the universe cannot be said to be the efficient cause of man nor to produce man, neither his body nor (much less) his soul. It is rather that whence the human composite arises as the highest individual synthesis of its collective sufficiency. This, however, is not to deny that the soul does have an efficient cause, i.e., that each soul is also the product of a divine creative act. The idea of creation comes into play (and must do so) when the soul is viewed not in terms of its position in world history (i.e., as a formative act that expresses the collective sufficiency of its antecedents and is the term of the process by which this sufficiency finally overcomes its initial division from itself) but simply in terms of its reality as a subsistent spiritual principle.

We might recall here the distinction which St. Thomas makes between the soul as *principium quod* and the soul as *principium quo*. For just as the assertion that the soul is a form (a *quo*) relationally integrated with the body does not preclude the fact that it is also a spiritual subsistent (a *quod*) and that as such it is causally dependent on a creative act, so neither does the assertion that the soul as formative act is the terminal expression of the collective sufficiency of the universe and as such is relationally integrated in the process of world history, preclude its also being created. To put together the idea of creation (which says nothing about how the soul is related to the other entities with which it finds itself in the world nor how, together with them, it goes to make up one world) and the idea of process or evolution, we might express it this way. The original creation of the universe as a manifold of imperfect acts automatically commits God to the eventual creation of perfect act (i.e., when and if that point is ever reached in the non-systematic process of progressive synthesis), since both imperfect act and perfect act are but separate stages in a single process of development, the progressive articulation of the transcendent dynamism of act. Thus our theory in no way precludes the creation of the human soul. It would merely insist that the doctrine of creation be complemented by one of procession if the soul's position in the world is to be understood.

Something similar, I think, must be said concerning the general doctrine of secondary causality. Our theory of the processive character of act does not exclude causality, secondary or otherwise. It merely insists that action is essentially self-affirmation and that consequently the relationship between act as source and act as term is not a causal one. This, however, does not prevent causality from being an aspect of certain instances of procession. On the contrary, I would maintain that the processive character of act is the ground of causality. Thus, for example, when act asserts itself in a pre-existent other (which is what happens on the level of secondary causality), such that the other is transformed into a likeness of the active entity, a causal relationship is set up. But this causal relationship is not between act as source and its self-expression in the other, but between act as source and the transformation of the other. As St. Thomas himself observes, secondary causes do not cause the form which the patient acquires but rather its acquisition by the patient; they do not cause the form as form but that this matter acquire this form. The form itself however, which now is newly present in the patient, is the terminal expression of the self-affirmation of the act of the agent. Thus, although action may in some circumstances involve motion, it is not primarily motion or transformation, but self-affirmation. And the point of our paper has been that only when it is seen in this more fundamental light, i.e., as grounding causality but not reducible to it, can it provide a clue to understanding evolution.

A second line of difficulties can arise from a misunderstanding of the unity of process. We have spoken of a single process of development that embraces all the variety in the world and have referred to it as a sort of transcendent theme that is progressively articulated, the theme of act's self-affirmation. From this it might be concluded that there is somehow "only a single Act of the whole universe, Reality with a capital 'R', of which finite acts are only the incomplete manifestations or appearances".[7] Evolution would then be merely the temporal unfolding on the level of appearance of this one eminent Reality which itself transcends time. Thus instead of taking time seriously, which was our stated purpose in this paper, we wind up relegating it to the order of mere Appearance, and since this order is completely dominated by that transcendent Reality of which it is the appearance, all honest contingency and genuine novelty disappear.

Needless to say, such an objection, for all its seriousness, completely misses the point of our explanation. For us, there is no single Act of the universe. There is indeed a total active sufficiency, but this, as we have insisted, is distributed over a non-systematic manifold. It is not something over and above the imperfect acts themselves, but is precisely their collective sufficiency. And this being the case, there is no such distinction as the one suggested between finite acts as Appearances and eminent Act as Reality, with all its baneful consequences. How contingency and novelty are genuine features of the world, we have already indicated (see §2). The only word to be added now is one about the unity of the process, and its transcendence with respect to the entities to which it gives rise. We speak of the process as one, as indeed a world process, because the original manifold of imperfect acts,

---

[7] From Dr. Eslick's "Comment" below.

due to the inter-dependence of the latter, constitutes a totality (the universe) which, through the union in action of its elements, is progressively systematized. There is nothing in it which is not related to all the rest or has not arisen as a terminal expression of the collective sufficiency of the original manifold. Moreover, since it is the nature of this collective (or total) sufficiency, precisely as active, to overcome its initial dividedness and since in the course of this it gives rise to entities essentially different from their antecedents, we may view the essential variety in the world as intrinsic to the process of self-affirmation of the original sufficiency and this process itself as transcending the different entities to which it gives rise.

There is one final difficulty. It concerns the idea of wholly imperfect act, and the sense that can be attached to a manifold of such acts. That the idea is obscure, I readily admit, for we are here at the lower limit of thought. As to whether or not it makes sense, I can only let the foregoing analyses stand on their own. One caution, however. Since imperfect act is act as divided from itself, it would be a mistake to try to understand it as a substance complete in itself. From the foregoing pages it should be clear that neither is imperfect act a substance, nor is the manifold of imperfect acts a substance. The coincidental complex of imperfect acts is rather a sort of matrix whence the substances we do encounter in our experience arise.

Fordham University (Shrub Oak, N.Y.)

COMMENT[1]

THE THEORY OF MATTER AS IMPERFECT ACT IS PROPOSED BY FATHER JOHANN IN THIS paper primarily as a philosophical explanation of evolution, if evolution be conceded as a fact. In commenting upon Father Johann's paper, there are three main lines of questioning I would like to develop. The first concerns problems arising from the distinction between causal production and procession of the higher from the lower. The second is about the unity and plurality of act. The third suggests certain difficulties which I, at least, feel about the doctrine of matter as wholly imperfect act, or acts.

The attempt to account for evolutionary progress by *causal* explanation, in the line of efficient causality, is regarded by Father Johann as precipitating dilemmas apparently defying solution. Explanation by efficient causes presupposes acceptance of the ancient maxim that out of nothing, nothing comes. Either the higher grades are reduced to the lower, at the cost of an essentially differentiated world, or the higher is regarded as present in the lower from the beginning, at the same cost. Explanation of evolutionary progress by efficient causality seems, according to Johann, possible only in either materialistic or panpsychic terms, and in either case there is nothing more at the end than at the beginning. The result is an un-dappled world, without real progress. A static dappled world is conceivable, but also at the cost of genuine evolutionary development—it would be a Porphyrian "tree", but not a living organism subject to true growth. Specifying perfections on the higher levels would be added from without, but such addition is either an unintelligible case of the universe lifting itself by its own bootstraps, or it is the result of divine intervention, but neither allows for real evolutionary advance.

In order to philosophically accommodate evolution, therefore, Father Johann moves from the level of efficient causality to that of "procession", and from the plane of *being* to that of *act*. The scholastic analogy of being cannot, according to Johann, provide the key which will allow for a dappled, *evolving* universe. (His conception of the analogy of being is, I think, simply wrong insofar as he regards it as the product of abstraction.) The analogy of being does not, Johann thinks, tell us anything about the dynamic relationship of essential structures to each other. The so-called analogy of "act", however, escapes this limitation. Evolutionary dynamism seems, for Johann, to be restricted to the

---

[1] This Comment is directed to the paper in the form in which it was originally given at the Conference. (The paper in this form was subsequently published in *Thought*, *36*, 1961, 595–612). In the final version of the paper printed here, the author has made some changes in the light of the Conference discussion. (Editorial Note)

essential order, and hence to formal causality of some sort, although a "formal causality" which appears to have much more affinity with Hegel and the post-Hegelians (or, perhaps, Plotinus) than with Aristotle. The "analogy of act", and the internal "procession" of act based upon it, is thus non-existential, concerned only with "progressive" specifications of act defined in terms of self assertion. "Act" is a "single formality underlying, running through, and finally embracing the whole hierarchy of forms".

The lower levels of self-affirmation cannot cause or produce the higher, ultimately personal levels. Rather, there is a *single reality,* of which the higher levels constitute the essential completion of the lower. The lower levels are insufficient and essentially deficient of themselves, and their essential or formal completion as acts requires the higher ones, which in this sense are said to "proceed" from the lower. This is all in the dimension of "immanent intelligibility", whereas efficient causality is said to pertain to extrinsic intelligibility. Nevertheless, the question of efficient causality with respect to evolutionary progression cannot, it seems to me, be simply shelved, so that *all* philosophical explanation is in terms of some kind of dialectical exigency or implication which the formally incomplete and partial has for the essentially complete whole, "the total act of the universe". Father Johann admits this with respect to the creation of soul as perfect act, which nevertheless is thought to "proceed" from the original manifold of imperfect acts in the sense that God, in creating the original manifold, is "automatically" committed to the creation of perfect acts. But must there not be a dimension of efficient causality immanent within the universe, secondary or caused efficient causes? Can a philosophical account of evolution completely ignore this dimension, howeved formidable the difficulties may be?

Secondly, there are crucial questions raised by Johann's theory bearing upon the ancient mystery of the One and the Many, here in the context of "act". The process of "act" is said to be the total act of the universe, progressively affirming itself. Even souls, or perfect acts, are relationally integrated in the dynamic structure of "total act". There seems clearly to be the assumption that there is an *essential* unity to the universe as a whole, and that it is something more than the unity of order which St. Thomas Aquinas ascribes to it. This is overwhelmingly reminiscent of the "Absolute" of Hegel, or of Bradley, Bosanquet and Royce, and it seems to me that Father Johann should unflinchingly face the classical difficulties of such a position. There is, it seems, only a single Act of the whole universe, Reality with a capital 'R', of which finite acts are only incomplete manifestations or *appearances.* Can the dialectical "procession" through appearances (imperfect acts) to the Absolute really be identified with evolution? How can there be *real* contingency, *real* novelty in such a world, in which every entity or act, no matter how trivial, *essentially* implies every other, and ultimately, a completed totality which must utterly transcend time and passage? It would seem that a satisfactory evolutionary philosophy must somehow manage to "take time seriously", as A. N. Whitehead was always urging. But on Father Johann's grounds, it would seem difficult not to relegate time, as in F. H. Bradley, to the side of Appearance, rather than Reality. Can a merely formal implication, whether Aristotelian, Hegelian, or any other kind, provide the dynamism which evolutionary development seems to demand? Nor is it clear, on the basis of Johann's· paper, why *procession* upwards out of the material matrix of wholly imperfect acts should be the preferred direction of dialectical movement rather than *emanation* downwards from an eminent, transcendent reality.

In either case, such an eminent reality, the total act of the whole universe, seems to be given and presupposed, and not really the term of an evolutionary progression. Indeed, in the metaphysical family to which Father Johann's theory seems to belong, the differentiation and multiplication of finite "acts" should be the function of the *negation* of primal act, of essential selfhood. I can only mention in passing two special difficulties which arise from this in Father Johann's theory. If, following Spinoza's famous law that all determination is negation, one also asserts a plurality of *perfect,* personal acts, is it possible to significantly differentiate them? And, finally, how can there be a significant *plurality* of wholly imperfect acts, on the level of matter?

The third line of questioning I would propose for Father Johann concerns the designation of matter as wholly imperfect *act*. Can the extension downward of the so-called analogy of "act" to this ultimate abyss and negation of all essential selfhood be justified? "Being active" is defined "as affirming or asserting oneself", but a wholly imperfect "act" cannot, as such, be self-assertive. It cannot, it would seem, be "act" in any significant sense whatsoever, and to speak .of the "interaction" of such non-acts (or even to regard them as somehow a manifold, and even a manifold which can form a unified whole, albeit non-systematic) is surely to beg the question. A hypothetical manifold of such "acts" cannot in any way be differentiated or articulated. Wholly imperfect "act" can "act" only by negating, like Plato's material principle, or Whitehead's Creativity. And even Whitehead's Creativity, regarded in complete abstraction from its conditioning by already constituted actual entities, is barren.

Leonard J. Eslick
Saint Louis University

PART FIVE

Modern Science: The "Dematerialization" of Matter

THE DEMATERIALIZATION
OF MATTER*

N. R. Hanson

§1 *Primary and Secondary Qualities*

William Whewell wrote in 1834:

> ... If we in our thoughts attempt to divest matter of its powers of resisting and moving, it ceases to be matter, according to our conceptions, and we can no longer reason upon it with any distinctness. And yet ... the properties of matter ... do not obtain by any absolute necessity ...[1]

Within the subsequent century the matter-concept underwent radical changes. Let us explore these changes and note how they relate to the distinction between primary and secondary properties.

Determining the essence of the matter-concept was a problem already familiar to Democritus:

> A thing merely appears to have color; it merely appears to be sweet or bitter. Only atoms and empty space have a real existence.[2]

Compare Plato:

> Properties such as hard, warm, and whatever their names may be, are nothing in themselves ...[3]

Galileo joined this chorus:

> White or red, bitter or sweet, noisy or silent, fragrant or malodorous, are names for certain effects upon the sense organs.[4]

Locke gives the distinction its classic shape:

> The qualities then that are in bodies, rightly considered, are ... : First, the bulk, figure, number, situation, and motion or rest of their solid parts.

---

* After this paper was delivered at the Symposium on the Concept of Matter, it was published in *The Philosophy of Science* journal. It appears here by permission of the editor of that journal.

[1] W. Whewell, *Astronomy and General Physics*, London, 1834, pp. 211–12.
[2] Diels, *Fragmente der Vorsokratiker*, A49, A1, section 45.
[3] *Theaetetus*, 156e.
[4] *Opere,* vol. IV, pp. 333 ff.

Those are in them, whether we perceive them or not; and when they are of that size that we can discover them, we have by these an idea of the thing as it is in itself; as is plain in artificial things. These I call *primary qualities.* Secondly, the power that is in any body, by reason of its insensible primary qualities, to operate after a peculiar manner any of our senses, and thereby produce in *us* the different ideas of several colors, sounds, smells, tastes, etc. These are usually called *sensible qualities* . . . The first of these . . . may be properly called real, original, or primary qualities; because they are in the things themselves, whether they are perceived or not: and upon their different modifications it is that the secondary qualities depend.[5]

Thus on the one hand there are the properties matter *really has*; these are geometrical, statical, and dynamical. Shape, mass, motion and impact—these are a body's primary properties. However, its apparent color in ultra-violet light—or daylight—its taste, its tone, its fragrance; these are the body's secondary properties. Our appreciation of these latter varies with the state of our senses; secondary properties result from interaction between percipient and perceived. The primary qualities, however, seem "in the bodies themselves". Hence, they are the very properties of matter itself.

As historians know, the primary-secondary distinction dissolved in George Berkeley's inkwell. Knowing a body's shape seemed to the Bishop as much the result of interaction as any secondary property. (18th-century psychologists knew that a given mass could generate variable perceptions in subjects differently conditioned.) Berkeley's epistemology, therefore, erased any distinction in principle between primary and secondary properties. Either the two were equally weak, or equally strong—depending on how one interprets Berkeley. Either secondary properties are just as basic to matter as the primaries, or the primaries give no more indication of matter "as it really is" than the secondaries. The latter seems more like Berkeley; hence I adopt it here.

Berkeley's analyses, however, seemed *merely* philosophical. Distinctions between primaries and secondaries may indeed fail under strict analysis. But Berkeley's scientific contemporaries still treated the distinction as fundamental, philosophers notwithstanding. Scientists were concerned with the physical properties of objects, not their "real" properties. We shall return to this distinction.

Consider now Heisenberg's insight into the history of atomism and the manner in which it reflects the primary-secondary contrast:

It is impossible to explain . . . qualities of matter except by tracing these back to the behavior of entities which themselves no longer possess these qualities. If atoms are really to explain the origin of color and smell of visible material bodies, then they cannot possess properties like color and

---

[5] *Essay*, London, 1726, Book II, chapter 8, section 23.

smell . . . Atomic theory consistently denies the atom and such perceptible qualities.[6]

Boyle is making a similar point:

Matter being in its own nature but one, the diversity we see in bodies must necessarily arise from somewhat else than the matter they consist of.[7]

Lucretius' atoms were colorless; an aggregate's color depended on the size, shape, and interrelations of its constituent atoms.[8] His atoms were without heat, sound, taste or smell.[9]

And Bacon wrote:

Bodies entirely even in the particles which affect vision are transparent, bodies simply uneven are white, bodies uneven and in a compound yet regular texture are all colors except black; while bodies uneven and in a compound, irregular, and confused texture are black.[10]

Birch writes of Newton:

The atoms . . . were themselves, he thought, transparent; opacity was caused by "the multitude of reflections caused in their internal parts".[11]

Thus the atomic hypothesis, and its intricate history, would crumble unless the ancient distinction between primary and secondary qualities braced it. No classical atomist thought atoms to be colored, fragrant, hot, or tasteable; the basic function of atoms was to explain away such properties as but the molar manifestations of the atom's primary properties and geometrical configurations.

Not every atomist stressed the same atomic primary properties, although all agreed that, whatever they were, the atom's properties were necessarily primary, an argument to which we shall return. The atom's primaries usually included things like position, shape, motions, etc.

Position was paramount for Democritus, but it was *shape* for Epicurus and Lucretius. Newton fixed on the *motions* of atoms. Gassendi remarked their *combinatory properties*; this already constitutes an extension of the Lockean notion. But doubtless combinatory capacity would have been accepted by all as a primary property, although not every atomist would have stressed it *à la* Gassendi. Henceforth, the term 'primary' will be used in this extended way. Atomic *irresolvability* attracted Boyle, but this is virtually

---

[6] Heisenberg, *Die Antike, 8.*
[7] Boyle, *Works,* London, 1744, *3,* p. 15.
[8] Lucretius, *On the Nature of Things,* Book II, lines 703 ff.
[9] *Op. cit.,* Book II, lines 842 ff.
[10] Bacon, *Works,* London, 1824, Aphorism xxiii; (*8,* p. 222).
[11] Birch, *History of the Royal Society,* London, 1756–7, 3, pp. 247 ff.

tautological, since '*atomos*' means just this. For Lavoisier, Richter, and Dalton, *mass* was basic. Berzelius stressed their *binding force* (again this falls within our extended class of primaries). Further properties were stressed by Faraday, Weber, Maxwell, Boltzmann, Clausius, Mayer, Loschmidt, and Hittorf. But, by all, the atoms were characterized by some cluster of primary properties, on a selected one of which further theoretical constructions were founded. The exception is Stumpf, who could not imagine atoms as spatial bodies lacking color.[12] But he is the exception proving the rule—by which is meant "probing the rule": we know what is generally true when we note how a counter-instance deviates.

The predominant sentiment of the Scientific Revolution was expressed by Newton:

> I . . . suspect that [the phenomena of nature] may all depend upon certain forces by which the particles of bodies . . . are either mutually impelled towards one another and cohere in regular figures, or are repelled and recede from one another.[13]

Here is a yet wider extension of Locke's use of 'primary'. But forces which impel and repel would surely be on the primary side of the ancient fence.

The degree to which the primary-secondary distinction remained scientifically fundamental, despite Berkeley's levelling analysis, is illustrated by Euler:

> The whole of natural science consists in showing in what state the bodies were when this or that change took place, and that . . . just that change had to take place which actually occurred.[14]

Helmholtz is as direct:

> The task of physical science is to reduce all phenomena of nature to forces of attraction and repulsion, the intensity of which is dependent only upon the mutual distance of material bodies. Only if this problem is solved are we sure that nature is conceivable.[15]

These sentiments reflect a spectrum of related attitudes: the mechanical philosophy, theoretical determinism, the reduction of all science to physics. These are generable only from an implicit atomism. Historically, this devolves into something resembling the classical distinction between primary and secondary properties.

---

[12] Stumpf, *Uber den Psychologischen Urstrung der Raumvorstellung*, Leipzig, 1873, p. 22.

[13] Newton, *Principia*, p. xviii.

[14] Euler, *Anleitung zur Naturlehre, Opere Posthumus, 2*, Leipzig, 1911; *6*, section 50.

[15] Helmholtz, *Uber die Erhaltung der Kraft*.

'Resembling' is the operative word. Berkeley speculated about the *real* properties of matter. He felt the classical primary-secondary distinction to be unsound. These properties were on the same epistemic level so far as knowing "reality" was concerned. One of the Bishop's scientific contemporaries could grant this, however, and yet preserve the same distinction at a different level—that concerned not with matter's *real* properties (a philosopher's inquiry at most), but with its *physical* properties. This latter is a scientist's inquiry at least.

Berkeley's "Thou shalt not speak of primary properties as philosophically real" is hence distinguishable from a prohibition heard in this century: "Thou shalt not speak of primary properties as physically real". In the 18th century, a scientist could have accepted the first and rejected the second. Now he may very well accept the second, whatever may be his attitude towards the first.

Hence, so far as one is concerned with distinguishing primary properties (which were real and in matter itself) from secondary properties (which were merely produced in us)—Berkeley's epistemic criticism was devastating. Still, the distinction remained viable in natural philosophy, the province not of philosophically real, but of physically real properties. Physically real properties contrast with mere appearances (intersubjectively understood). That a submerged stick is really straight contrasts with its bent appearance. and that the solidified CO_2 is really cold contrasts with our impression of it as blisteringly hot. But concern with the philosophically real undercuts these scientific inquiries altogether. The latter concern stable, permanent properties of objects as contrasted with those which are evanescent, contextually dependent, and accrue to them via special conditions of observation, e.g. ultraviolet illumination, intoxicated observers. Berkeley's inquiry is concerned with the philosophical extension of this scientific contrast, as signalled by the question: "And which of these kinds of properties does matter *really have?*" The scientist's use of the primary-secondary distinction is restricted to delineating the contrast 'observed under all conditions' vs. 'observed only under special conditions'. The philosopher asks the more pervasive question, which Berkeley answers by a denial: to wit, there are no better grounds for supposing matter really has properties we regularly observe it to have, than there are for thinking its properties are those we irregularly observe.

Within the class of physically real properties scientists did distinguish primaries from secondaries. They had to do so to sustain an intelligible atomism. But Berkeley's objectives were not scientific; he dismissed the distinction as philosophically untenable. Physical science is only now undergoing its Berkeleyan self-criticism. When Whewell wrote, it had not. He spoke of conceptual constraints against tinkering with our ideas of the primary physical properties of matter. These constraints are no longer as binding as in the 19th century. Indeed, our understanding of elementary matter, of electrons, cannot proceed within a classical conception of primary physical properties.

For a theory of electrons to succeed now, the electron-idea must be divested of its classical conceptions of resisting and moving. This is what Whewell claimed we could not do:

> Divest matter of its powers of resisting and moving . . . and we can no longer reason upon it with any distinctness.[16]

But electrons can be reasoned upon with distinctness, although, it may be granted, they remain unfamiliar material objects.

§2 *The Electron*

Consider the representative answers to "classical" questions about the electron, that most fundamental of particles.

What is the "diameter" of an electron? The usual theoretical answer is that it is of the order of 6×10^{-13} centimeters. Experimentally this is not determinable. Such a magnitude would be very difficult to detect because of pion and nucleon pair-creation phenomena at the required energies (80 Bev). The concept of electronic diameter is based on the formula:

$$d = 2a - 2e^2/m_0c^2 \approx 5.7 \times 10^{-13} \, \text{cm}; \text{or}, r \approx e^2/m_0c^2 \approx 2.81785 \times 10^{-13} \, \text{cm}.$$

No evidence contradicts this, but the fine determination is beyond current laboratory technique. Of course, some theoreticians put the diameter at zero, arguing that this is compatible with electron-proton scattering experiments at 1 Bev. Indeed, the quantum electrodynamics of small distances is already at stake in this question.

If theory allows the electron to have a diameter, it ought also to have a shape. What shape? Is it spherical? Punctiform? There is no experimental information enabling one now to form any consistent geometrical model of the electron. Of course, the electron's charge is assumed to have spherical distribution, as with its magnetic moment. Nonetheless, experimentalists are often prone to treat electrons as points. Again, this issue, like the "diametral" one above, awaits such tests as the very high energy electron-electron scattering experiments now in progress at Stanford.

What about the electron's "solidity"? Again, neither theory nor experiments help. Some theoreticians feel the concept to be meaningless. Others remark that the deeper electron penetration proceeds the more difficult a decision becomes because of the myriad new particles created by the probing particle and the target-electron. Still others think the particle may have a

---

[16] *Loc. cit.*

"solid" central core where some current theories break down (10^{-13} cm.) If this is not the case, then the electron can only be described as a cloud of virtual particles plus a central bare point charge.

Other magnitudes within electron physics are readily determinable. Collisions are understood: there are sound theories within quantum electrodynamics and myriad experiments on electron scattering properties. The electron's rest mass (after "renormalization") is determinable: $m_0 = 9.1083 \times 10^{-28}$ grams, a quantity confirmed in many divergent types of experiment. But again, the relation between electronic mass and charge is troublesome. (Attempts to understand mass in self-energy terms have been unsuccessful.) The spin-angular-momentum of the electron is always $\frac{1}{2}$, again well-established by the Zeeman effect, and other experiments. And quantal transformations of the electron (as theoretically represented in the Lorentz group) require just this spin. The rest-energy of the electron is m_0c^2, as disclosed in electron-positron pair production. This energy value determines the development of the electron's state in time. There are no *de facto* negative energies encountered in electron physics. However, negative frequencies make theoretical sense.

All this must be appreciated lest it seem that science's total knowledge of the electron is too slight to permit generalizations about today's matter-concept. A great deal is known about the particle. What is known, however, seems incompatible with classical ideas about matter. Thus, while one can always speak of the state of a classical particle, i.e., its simultaneous position and velocity, nothing like this can even be articulated in quantum theory, wherein the position and momentum operators are managed according to the rule: $PM - MP = (h/2\pi i)\psi$. This has implications. Is it that physics is just not yet in a position to determine electron states? No. Quantum mechanics is the only theory through which electrons can now be understood at all; that theory excludes the very possibility of forming a consistent concept of an electronic particle's state. Either we speak precisely of its position, or of its momentum. But one cannot speak precisely of both at once. Similarly, we can speak of a person then as a bachelor, and now as married. But we cannot speak of him as being at once married and a bachelor; the reason is analogous to that within microphysics. Conceptual tension results in either case. This is not to say that the tension in both cases is identical: it is not.

This has macrophysical consequences. It is often mooted that the conceptual pain of indeterminacy is restricted to the physics of very tiny and very brief phenomena. Not true. A Geiger counter intercepting particles from an unstable isotopic source will click in a wholly unpredictable way. Once a particle has been emitted, the counter's click is determined classically. But it remains conceptually untenable to predict when a particle will be emitted, and hence when the counter will next click. This is a logical feature of the only available means for understanding intra-atomic phenomena. Indeed, a Geiger counter so arranged constitutes the perfect randomizer. Its macrophysical clicks must be in principle unpredictable.

Still further classical properties of matter are jolted in electron theory. Electron solidity is a concept for which there is no relevant quantum theory or experiment. "Being in contact with an electron" has the same null status, although some theoreticians feel sympathetic to the possibility, especially when interpreted in field-theoretic terms. A spectacular departure from classical theory is the process of particle creation first described in the early 1930's. That particles could "materialize" out of radiation is an idea for which 20th-century physics had no preparation. Joliot and Curie, Millikan and Anderson, Blackett and Occhialini, Fermi and Uhlenbeck, noted oppositely curving cloud-chamber tracks of identical range emanating from a common point within a radiative source. This was a new phenomenon. The mass-energy equivalence had long been known; still, it remained implicit in molar physics that matter could be transformed from this shape to that, or from one state to another—but never could it become other than matter. Nor could it be created from other than matter. The discovery of the positron crushed this assumption. So matter (e.g., electrons) can be created out of energy alone. Yet, when electrons are created, one cannot speak of their states, shapes, or solidity in the familiar molar ways. Furthermore, the theoretical reason for supposing two electrons could not simultaneously occupy the same place is not overpoweringly strong, even though the Pauli exclusion principle has never been experimentally violated. And when an orbital electron is excited in the H-atom, it jumps out to a wider orbit; yet one has no way of speaking of it as having ever been between the orbits. There is no workable concept of an electron's age—unless it be taken as infinite—nor any intelligible conception of its density. Again, this is not ignorance comparable to science's limitations concerning Saturn. In the latter case, we lack facts; but we know what it would be like to have them. Within electron theory, the limitations referred to are built into the conceptual structure of the theory itself. We do not know now what it would be like to manage electrons as we do, save in terms of the theories and concepts we have actually got. Change the concepts and you change our current theories. But *until* the theories are changed, we must do as they now instruct us to do, abandon earlier notions of the properties of material particles.[17]

§3 *Dematerialization*

Matter has been dematerialized, not just as a concept of the philosophically real, but now as an idea of modern physics. Matter can be analyzed

---

[17] See Appendix for a fuller treatment of these points.

down to the level of fundamental particles. But at that depth the direction of the analysis changes, and this constitutes a major conceptual surprise in the history of science. The things which for Newton typified matter—e.g., an exactly determinable state, a point shape, absolute solidity—these are now the properties electrons do not, because theoretically they cannot, have.

Matter has been dematerialized, but now more radically than with Berkeley. He showed that, despite ancient epistemic dogmas, primary and secondary properties were in the same conceptual boat. One of his scientific contemporaries could have inferred from the Bishop's analyses that therefore primary properties were just as weak as were the secondaries as indicators of the real properties of matter. He could have concluded this and still continued to do consistent physics. For Berkeley's criticism was abstractly philosophical. It concerned our knowledge of the "real" properties of matter, as opposed to its physical properties. It left Newtonian mechanics intact and unscathed. Similarly, perplexities of contemporary epistemology have no effect on today's mechanical engineers.

The dematerialization of matter encountered in this century, however, has rocked mechanics at its foundations. As an intra-physical revolution in ideas, this compares with the intra-mathematical revolution initiated by Gödel. Some scientists still think of electrons as point-masses with most of the properties of minute billiard balls—just as some mathematicians still have formalist (i.e. Hilbertian) hankerings. But how unclear such physicists can be when questioned about the nature of things like β-beam interference patterns. Either they say nothing at all, or nothing at all intelligible (usually capped with some remark like "I am an empiricist"). In the 18th century one could have accepted Berkeley's demonstration of the inadequacy of primary properties as indicators of "real" matter, and still do consistent physics; much as today a psychologist can grant there are philosophical problems about other minds, and still rely on the verbal responses of his subjects. But the 20th century's dematerialization of matter has made it conceptually impossible to accept a Newtonian picture of the properties of matter and still do consistent physics.

Some will assent to much I have said here, and yet will qualify my conclusion. They may grant that the ancient distinction between primary and secondary properties, like philosophy itself, branched into the natural philosophy of the 17th century, and the pure philosophy of the 18th century—the latter as typified in Berkeley. And an intimate historical connection between the successful growth of atomism in science and the correlative dependence of scientists on some version of the primary-secondary distinction might also be granted. Perhaps it will even be conceded that Berkeley's challenge to this distinction affected only the epistemological branch of the conceptual tree, not its scientific branch. The latter has been affected only by *contemporary* matter theory, wherein any correspondence between the properties matter (e.g. electrons) is now known to have, and the classical "primary" properties, is at best analogical, and at worst non-existent.

These are my theses thus far. From them, however, some will not conclude, as I do, that modern physics has destroyed our intra-scientific version of the primary-secondary distinction just as Berkeley destroyed its intra-philosophical version. At least one critic will torment the body of my argument by hacking off its tail as follows:

> Granted, the properties electrons are now known to have, a, β . . . may be different from the properties classically termed "primary". *This* does not destroy the primary-secondary distinction. Quite the contrary. For if the electron has a, β . . . then, however dissimilar from the classical primaries of philosophy and natural philosophy, then a, β *are* . . . (along with the properties of other particles) the primary properties of matter, whatever they may be. And these primary electronic (protonic, neutronic) properties contrast with other manifestations of elementary particles and their aggregates, which disclose themselves only *via* interactions between observers and things observed, e.g. manifestations like the colors, tastes and odors of macrophysical objects (which are, after all, but constellations of fundamental particles). Granted, physics has changed the values appropriate for the property-variables a, β . . . still, the primary-secondary distinction remains viable so long as there are good reasons for claiming that fundamental particles *do* have a, β . . . This remains true so long as some properties of aggregates and some properties of components-of-aggregates are distinguishable in that the former result from observer-interaction whereas the latter, however unfamiliar, are such that we have good theoretical reasons for thinking them observer-independent. A theory of the electron is a theory about the properties electrons *have*, not a theory describing what bubbles up out of electron-observer interactions. The primary-secondary distinction of classical physics has now become a contrast between the objectifiable and the non-objectifiable properties of microparticles.

This specific criticism gets airborne only *via* a runway of concessions to my general thesis, to establish the plausibility of which has been my only objective here. I disagree with the entire spirit of this criticism and its tendency towards complete objectifiability within quantum theory. (I would indicate why, were there time). But since there is in this criticism no challenge to the historical point that *our* ideas about the primary properties of particles are different from those of the tradition concerned with primary properties (despite Whewell's contention that no such change could occur), nor any challenge to the further point that Berkeley's attack on the primary-secondary distinction left physicists free to exploit the distinction in their atomistic theories of the 18th and 19th centuries, whereas they are no longer free to do this in the old way—since these main points are unaffected by the contention that the objectifiability-non-objectifiability contrast *is* the same as primary-secondary contrast (with the property-values left unspecified), I will back off with only the grumble that even this contention could be demonstrated as indefensible. But the demonstration must await another occasion.[18]

APPENDIX

The important feature of our electron-positron theory is that it is a quantum-field theory. This means that the fields $\psi(x)$ are operators, rather than functions representing the state of the electron. E.g., $\psi(x)$ creates a positron or destroys an electron and $\psi^+(x)$ does the reverse. It is not feasible to describe this theory in detail, but the important physical fact is that in this theory electrons and positrons may be created and destroyed. A high energy γ-ray ($E > 2mc^2$) passing through the Coulomb field of a nucleus can create an electron-positron pair. Such a situation cannot be described by an ordinary wave function; rather it is described by a state vector in an abstract (non-separable) Hilbert space in which the basic states have different numbers of particles. Since the Hamiltonian of the system has matrix elements between these states of different particle number, transitions such as $\gamma \rightarrow e^+ + e^-$ are possible.

A few words about the non-relativistic limit where particle number is conserved and the ordinary wave function is a useful, though approximate, concept:

If the energies involved in a given physical situation are small compared to an electron's rest energy, one encounters this limit. This is the realm of most of atomic physics and chemistry (aside from small relativistic corrections which show up in fine structure, the Lamb shift, etc.). This is ordinary wave mechanics with wave-functions which obey the Pauli exclusion principle—odd under interchange of particle variables. In this realm, certain classical "primary" questions are simply answered: the electron is intrinsically a point particle with spin one-half and a definite mass. Here 'point' means that it is described by a wave function $u(\vec{x},t)$ in which there is no variable for internal structure (other than spin). Intrinsically the electron's charge is located at a point where it has an infinite density (δ-function). 'Age of an electron' has no meaning; solidity has no meaning (can a point be compressed?); 'shape' has no meaning (does a point have a shape?). Of course $u(\vec{x},t)$ gives a probability distribution for such quantities as position, momentum, energy. This is ordinary wave mechanics and is well confirmed by experiment (within its proper domain of applicability).

Perhaps an illustration will be helpful.

$P(\vec{x},t) = u(\vec{x},t)^2$ is probability distribution for x.

$\rho(x,t)$ is observable charge distribution

The theory says:

$$\rho(\vec{x},t) = e \qquad P(\vec{x},t) = e \iiint \delta(\vec{x} - \vec{x}') \; P(\vec{x}',t) \; d^3x'$$

The $\delta(\vec{x} - \vec{x})$ represents the intrinsic point charge nature of the electron. Conceivably,

---

[18] In *The Concept of the Positron* (Cambridge, Eng., 1963), this demonstration is presented in considerable detail.

a different connection could exist between ρ and P, with $\delta(\vec{x} - \vec{x}')$ replaced by $f(\vec{x} - \vec{x}')$, for example, with f a "spread-out" δ-function. Such an f would represent the intrinsic (or, if you like, internal) charge distribution of the electron. The remarkable agreement of atomic spectra with theoretical predictions of wave mechanics indicates that f is a δ-function, or at least has a very small spatial extension. (The Lamb shift, can, in some sense, be interpreted as due to a finite size of the electron).

Let us turn to the more complete theory. It should be emphasized that the word 'electron' is ambiguous; that is, the precise definition of what we mean by 'an electron' or 'a positron' cannot be given without taking into account the interactions of the particle with other fields, such as the electromagnetic field. To illustrate, we might try to write

$$\psi = \psi_{\mathrm{ce}+} + \psi_{\mathrm{de}-}$$

where $\psi_{\mathrm{ce}+}$ creates positrons and $\psi_{\mathrm{de}-}$ destroys electrons. It is easy to verify that this separation is not independent of the interaction. For instance, if there is no interaction, one obtains a separation $\psi'_{\mathrm{ce}+} + \psi'_{\mathrm{de}-}$, (free representation). But if one has a Coulomb potential there is a different separation $\psi''_{\mathrm{ce}+} + \psi''_{\mathrm{de}-}$, (bound representation). If we try to express the state of a bound electron (say the lowest state) in terms of the free representation, we find that it is a superposition of states of a free electron and various numbers of electron-positron pairs. However, in that case we would adopt the point of view that the bound representation is the proper one and gives the appropriate definition of an electron.

The situation is more complicated when we consider more realistic interactions such as that with the electromagnetic field, which is itself quantized (photons can be created and destroyed). Then we distinguish between "bare" electrons and "physical" electrons. The bare electrons correspond to the free representation in which interactions are neglected. These states form the starting point in perturbation treatments of the interaction. The physical electron state is supposed to contain all the effects of the interaction, and in some sense *is* the state which is produced from the bare electron state when the interactions are "turned on". It has definite mass and spin, but presumably has an intrinsic structure due to the interactions. This structure consists of a cloud of virtual bare photons and bare electron-positron pairs with one extra bare electron (this statement is more a characterization of the mathematical formalism than a meaningful physical statement). In space this structure is supposed to extend a distance of about h/mc^2. A physical electron has physical dimensions and other properties such as shape, charge density, and distribution of charge (the last three really mean about the same thing). The "age" of an electron plays no great role in the theory: i.e., the behavior of an electron is independent of its age.

This structure of the physical electron due to its interactions has been verified experimentally in many ways: Lamb shift, anomalous moment of electron, effect on hyperfine splitting, and effect on electron scattering from a Coulomb field. This structure comes from a theory in which the fields are local: that is, the intrinsic bare fields are points and the interactions take place at a point. Calculations using this theory give remarkably accurate predictions of the four types of experiments just mentioned —i.e., the internal structure produced by the interactions is well understood. It is conceivable that in addition to this the bare particles could themselves have an intrinsic non-point structure. There is at the moment no evidence for this. However, an important high-energy electron-electron scattering experiment is in progress at Stanford

University. With the present theory, the results of that experiment have been predicted in advance. If the experiment agrees with these predictions, it will mean that the electron has no internal structure other than that produced by interactions (I must emphasize that the physical electron has a known structure of dimensions $\sim 10^{-10}$ cm. which can be allowed for in the experiment); of course this statement would have been verified only for distances greater than $\sim 10^{-14}$ cm. Disagreement would mean that the laws of physics at distances less than 10^{-13} or 10^{-14} cm. may be different from our present conceptions. Future experiments will investigate this possible "breakdown of quantum electrodynamics" in even smaller regions of space-time.

To summarize:

(i) Intrinsically the non-interacting electron appears to have no structure at distances greater than 10^{-13} cm. The Stanford experiment will check whether this is true at smaller distances.

(ii) However, the interactions with the quantized electromagnetic field which lead to electron scattering, pair creation, etc. also give the physical electron an internal structure. This structure can (in principle) be computed accurately, and extends to distances of order h/mc.

(iii) On a larger scale one may find the uncertainties associated with the manner of formation of the electron's wave packet. The present point of view is that these do not represent the internal structure of the electron.

Indiana University

COMMENT: MATTER STILL LARGELY MATERIAL*

THE "DEMATERIALIZATION OF MATTER" IN RECENT PHYSICAL THEORY HAS BEEN WELcomed with enthusiasm in various philosophical quarters. Even tough-minded thinkers like Bertrand Russell have interpreted the new conceptions of matter as helpful in overcoming the traditional mind-body dualism. Others have sought comfort in the idea that the indeterminism of quantum physics provides a place for a genuinely free will in a world governed at least in part by statistical laws. The much emphasized quantum mechanical inseparability of observing subject (or measuring instrument) from the observed or measured object has been exploited in favor of a mystical union of the knowing subject and his world! Let me make it quite clear at the outset that I do not impute any of these views—which I consider seriously mistaken—to my esteemed friend and symposiast, Professor Hanson. But before I proceed to a discussion of his challenging presentation, I do wish to say a few words about those misinterpretations. My reason for doing this is simply that, just because I fully acknowledge the profound revolution in scientific thought regarding the nature of matter, I wish to warn against its (metaphysical) exploitation for the solution of philosophical problems.

If by "mind" or "mental life" we mean the immediate experiences and the thinking of persons, then no matter what we have learned from recent atomic and quantum physics, the puzzle of the relation between the mental and the physical remains one for logical and epistemological examination. To be sure, there are results of neurophysiology, as well as of its possible ultimate reduction to physical theory, which are relevant to the *scientific* components of the complex cluster of puzzles that constitutes the mind-body problem.[1] But as regards the typically *philosophical* components of the matter-mind problem, I don't find it makes any difference whether we conceive matter along the lines of 17th century or of 20th century physics. The contrasts of objective vs. subjective (public vs. private); spatial vs. non-spatial; quantitative vs. qualitative; nonintentional vs. intentional (in Brentano's sense) remain just as puzzling, even if matter is conceived along the lines of modern quantum mechanics. These con-

---

* This comment is reprinted with the kind permission of the author and the Editor of the *Philosophy of Science*.

[1] Cf. my essay, "The 'Mental' and the 'Physical' " in *Minnesota Studies in the Philosophy of Science, 2*, H. Fiegl, M. Scriven and G. Maxwell, eds., Minneapolis, 1958. Also: "Mind-Body not a Pseudoproblem" in S. Hook, ed., *Dimensions of Mind*, New York, 1960.

trasts demand a searching analysis if we are to arrive at a coherent account which goes beyond a mere psychophysiological parallelism. I am equally skeptical about the significance of the quantum-theoretical interpretation of matter and its indeterminism for the free will problem. In the first place, I am convinced that the philosophical issue of freewill vs. determinism is largely engendered by easily avoidable conceptual confusions (and is in this respect much less complex and difficult than the mind-body problem.)[2] Secondly I seriously doubt that the ideas of indeterminacy or of complementarity are helpful in establishing a physical basis for genuinely free choice. Among the philosophizing physicists A. S. Eddington and A. H. Compton[3] have in differing ways attempted to link human free choice with indeterminacy, but I think that their arguments are fallacious. However, I must not digress too far from our main topic.

Let me then turn to the notions of primary and secondary qualities. I think that, properly revised and reformulated, the distinction still makes perfectly good sense and is useful in an epistemological clarification of the concepts of modern physics. Locke's views, and the similar views of the scientists of the 17th century (Galileo, Newton, Boyle, Gassendi, etc.) can be restated in a form that is not open to Berkley's criticisms. Shape, size, duration, location, motion, mass, solidity, etc. as apprehended in direct perception are indeed just as well "subjective" as are the colors, sounds, odors, tastes, tactual and thermal qualities. Philosophically and scientifically unsophisticated perception ascribes *all* of these attributes to the "things as they are in themselves". This is the well known story of naïve realism. But corresponding to these perceptual properties there are the "objective" attributes which the physical sciences ascribe to matter-as-it-is-conceived on various levels of explanation. And it is the proper task of *psychophysics* to investigate the lawful dependencies of perceptual qualities on the features of physical reality. (If this be metaphysics, make the least of it! True, the stereotype of "logical positivist" no longer fits me—if it ever did. Even in the years of the Vienna Circle I was close to a critical realism. However, the *then* powerful position of Carnap and Schlick silenced me for a while. It must be remembered that the *pre-Vienna* Schlick was a critical realist; and Carnap, and even Ayer, have abandoned phenomenalistic positivism. In the case of Carnap I think that my continued arguments for more than twenty years contributed to the change in his point of view. My own position in many

---

[2] Cf. R. E. Hobart (pseudonym for D. S. Miller), "Freewill as involving Determination, and inconceivable without it", *Mind, 43*, 1934. "The Freedom of the Will", reprinted in H. Feigl and W. Sellars, eds., *Readings in Philosophical Analysis*, New York, 1949. A. Grünbaum, "Causality and the Science of Human Behavior", in H. Feigl and M. Brodbeck, eds., *Readings in the Philosophy of Science*, New York, 1953. Also: Arthur Pap, "Determinism, Freedom, Moral Responsibility, and Causal Talk" in: S. Hook, ed., *Determinism and Freedom*, New York, 1958.

[3] A. S. Eddington, *The Nature of the Physical World*, New York, 1932. A. H. Compton, *The Freedom of Man*, New Haven, 1935. Even the highly sophisticated and more recent views of Hans Reichenbach, "The Freedom of the Will" in: *Modern Philosophy of Science*, New York, 1950, do not seem to me to carry conviction.

respects agrees with the realistic views of Reichenbach, Popper, Mehlberg, Grünbaum and Feyerabend;—all of them scientific empiricists! Since I sense a streak of Berkeleyan phenomenalism in the Copenhagen interpretation of quantum mechanics, and, in accordance with it, in Professor Hanson's views, I feel impelled to argue for realism once more. Of course, I know only too well that the conceptual problems of quantum mechanics are extremely intricate and complex; and I admit there is no easy solution for them anywhere in sight).

For the sake of brevity let me assert somewhat dogmatically that it is epistemologically indispensable to distinguish between the qualities of appearance and the attributes ascribed to physical reality on the basis of measurement, experiment and theoretical interpretation. Psychophysically there are varying measures of correspondence between the qualities—sensed (or experienced) and the stimulus properties of physical objects. While agreeing with Berkeley that all sense qualties, be they spatio-temporal, or be they colors, sounds, tastes, odors, etc. are "in the same boat" (viz. in the "boat" of immediate experience), one may nevertheless agree with Locke in the (to be sure, highly qualified) sense that perceptually spatial, temporal, etc. qualities are by and large more reliable cues for the features of objective reality than are the perceptual qualities of color, sound, taste, odor or heat. This should be acceptable even to phenomenalistically oriented positivists who conceive of objective reality as a logical construction out of the data of direct experience. For it is clear that the spatial dimensions (length, breadth, height) of nearby, middle sized physical objects, as determined by measurement may often be fairly accurately judged on the basis of unimplemented sense-impressions. The case is different, however, for, e.g., stellar distances, where direct impressions are utterly unreliable, even topologically speaking. I maintain then that there is only a difference of *degree* in the reliability of experiential cues. The whistle of a passing locomotive sounds high in pitch first, and suddenly drops in pitch later. There was no change in the proper frequency of vibrations of the whistle; but there was a change in the frequency of the sound waves impinging on the ear drum. We have to know about the Doppler effect in order to make the proper ascriptions. A certain shade of green may be experienced under a great variety of stimulus conditions. It may be produced by monochromatic light, it may result from mixtures of radiation of differing wavelengths; it may be a negative after-image; it might even be produced by direct electric stimulation of a spot in the visual cortex of the brain. The qualities of warm or cold often depend largely on the condition of the experiencing subject. A full-fledged scientific account of perception—a *casual theory* of perception indeed—is needed for sorting out the respective contributions of the stimulus objects, the stimulus context, and of the perceiving organism. Experienced qualities or relations thus differ only in their degrees of reliability for the inference of objectively (or intersubjectively, scientifically) confirmable properties of physical reality. In sum, Locke's concession to Berkeley might well have to be: Allright, we don't perceive the "real", "primary" properties of things any more directly than we do the "secondary" ones. So, let us replace the old distinction by a graduation as to reliability. A Locke *redivivus* could also point out that the objective spatial order, at least in its topological structure (and in favorable cases in rough approximation, also in its metrical aspects) is often fairly reliably indicated by the impressions of both the visual and the tactual sense-modalities; and to a much lesser degree even the kinesthetic and the auditory data furnished some cues for the objective spatial order. In this respect the situation is different for the colors, sounds, tastes, odors, and thermal properties of physical objects. Only the eye discerns the colors, the ear, the sounds, etc. (That is, unless we are willing to say that Helen Keller appreciates music by feeling the vibrations of the piano with her sense of touch). Following W. E. Johnson and C. J. Ducasse we may call properties so discerned "physico-psychical" properties, and distinguish them from the "physico-physical" properties which are disclosed by experiment and/or measurement, i.e. by the observation of the interaction of bodies outside the observer's organism.—The so-called tertiary qualities, e.g. like the serenity of a landscape, or the attractiveness of a face, are even more unreliable indicators of objective properties. I repeat, one relevant distinction is one of degree only, that is, regarding the reliability of experiential cues for the indication or inference of objective properties or relations. But another distinction, which unfortunately has often been confused with the one just discussed, does need to be made, viz. the distinction between the attributes of perceptual appearance and the attributes of objective reality.

Now, the attributes of objective reality are different for different levels of scientific concept-formation and theory-construction. Distances, durations, and masses as conceived in ordinary life or by roadbuilders, architects, carpenters, beer brewers, etc., are essentially of the same logical structure as the distances, durations and masses of *experimental* classical mechanics. Characterizations of objective realities in terms of merely their physico-psychical properties, are at best only provisionally used, and for the sake of greater reliability and precision rapidly supplanted by characterizations in terms of their physico-physical properties.[4] Thus, e.g., we may first judge the acoustical properties of a violin string by the sounds-as-heard; but for an objective scientific characterization we adduce measurements of wave-frequencies and amplitudes. In the course of scientific investigation we come to form many (low-level) dispositional concepts of the physico-physical type. Surface colors initially characterized in terms of their effect on an observer, are replaced by the dispositional concept of selective reflectivity as determined spectroscopically.

There is no need here to go into an analysis of the logical structure of dispositional concepts. Whether we explicate them *à la* Carnap in terms of reduction sentences, or perhaps in terms of casual modalities, is not essential for our purposes. What is essential is the question concerning the logic of the concepts and principles with which we *explain* dispositional properties; or, what amounts to the same, how we explain the empirical regularities for which the dispositional concepts provide a short-hand formulation. It is in connection with these explan-

---

[4] Cf. C. J. Ducasse, *Nature, Mind and Death,* La Salle, Illinois, 1951; chapter 15.

atory concepts and principles that the issue of the "dematerialization of matter" arises.

On the level of experimental macro-physics and chemistry, matter clearly has its classical properties, ascribable in terms of the concepts of objective space, time, mass—and of the host of dispositional properties which are quantitatively expressed in the various material constants or parameters (e.g. density; specific heat; refraction index; modulus of elasticity; dielectric constant; magnetic permeability; compressibility; viscosity; electric or thermal conductivity, etc. etc.) It makes perfectly good sense to say, and it is even largely correct, that all these properties, though ultimately *known* by observation, are *existentially* independent of any acts of observation. (In this they clearly differ from sensory qualities whose *esse* is indeed *percipi*.) To be sure, there are some anomalies. The superfluidity (lack of viscosity) of liquid helium (below the alpha point); the strange behavior of electric "plasma"; the properties of matter under extreme conditions of pressure or temperature; the experimentally verified (relativistic) dependence of mass upon relative velocity; etc., all these require some emendations of the Newton-Boyle-Locke conception of matter even on a strictly experimental level. Nevertheless, matter remains still strikingly "material" despite these revisions.

The really incisive revolution with its attendant conceptual perplexities arose only in recent atomic and quantum physics. By way of a first impulse one might want to say: matter (macro-matter) is material allright, but the micro-constituents of matter are not material at all. But this will not quite do. The total mass of a macro-object is clearly the sum of the masses of the particles (neutrons, protons, electrons) of which it consists. Except for minor relativistic qualifications this is still correct. The rest mass of each of these fundamental particles is experimentally well determined. So, masses do consist of smaller masses. This much is clearly retained from classical atomistics. The diameters of atoms, the size of molecules, the spatial structure of the array of atoms in crystals are equally well established by experimental evidence. Conceptually a little more problematic is the spin of elementary particles. We are told that the spin is to be conceived as just one additional quantum-number, and that any question concerning the angular velocity of rotation of an electron around its axis is unanswerable, if not meaningless. And there are all the questions (raised by Professor Hanson) concerning the diameter of electrons; their genidentity; their precise simultaneous positions and velocities, and so forth. Now, of course, conservative (or should I say "reactionary"?) thinkers may hope for a restoration of something like the classical-mechanical-electrodynamic world picture on a deeper level of reality. Einstein, de Broglie, Bohm, Vigier, and others, have seriously pursued theoretical or speculative attempts in this direction. Unified field theories in which the particles are represented as singularities in the field understandably hold a great temptation. However, I would urge philosophers of science not to develop a physical ontology on the basis of what are currently only vague hopes and promissory notes. There is no a priori reason whatever (and hardly any a posteriori one either) to believe that a unified field theory of a strictly deterministic structure will ever be established. It is quite conceivable that wave mechanics in the statistical interpretation according to the Born rules is here to stay. It seems to me a much more fruitful task for the philosophers of science (unless they want to become creative theoretical physicists) to concern themselves with the logical analysis of the concepts and postulates of the currently fruitful theories. In connection with the "dematerialization of matter" I suggest, for example the following questions for thorough logical examination.

(1) How can we reconcile the usual realistic assumption of the independent existence of physical entities with the dependence of atomic and subatomic processes upon the intervention of measurements? It does seem odd to me to assume the occurrence of thermonuclear reactions in the unobserved interior of the sun or of other fixed stars, and at the same time to insist that these micro-processes occur only as a result of the interaction of measuring instruments and measured objects. And although I am decidedly not an "ordinary language philosopher", it does seem to me equally peculiar and objectionable to say that "measurements" are constantly going on in the vast and inaccessible interiors of the stars.

(2) Is it not possible to say that wave mechanics in its statistical interpretation presents us with *objective* probabilities—be they interpreted as propensities or as limits of relative frequency—of micro-events under specifiable macro- or micro-conditions? If so, we may well reconcile ourselves to the "popping into or out of existence" of micro-particles. But as long as they have definite rest-masses, electric charges, etc., is not even micro-matter still pretty material?

(3) Suppose one grants that the *some* of the concepts applicable to macro-objects are inapplicable to micro-objects; how are we to explicate this inapplicability? Is it a category mistake to apply, e.g. color predicates to electrons? But what precisely is a category mistake from a logical point of view? In the good old days of Carnap's *Logischer Aufbau der Welt,* category mistakes were exposed as violations of Russell's rule of types. But this is highly implausible after the abandonment of the phenomenalistic reconstruction. Does it make no sense to ascribe a temperature to a single micro-particle? Is it meaningless to speak of the simultaneous determination of precise position and momentum? If so, it should be possible to give a reconstruction of the language of micro-physics in which one could clearly see by what sort of rules this kind of nonsense is excluded. I don't insist on *one* unique reconstruction; but I should like to see at least a few plausible candidates. In the case of the transition from the Newtonian to the Einsteinian concept of simultaneity, it may well be said (and has been said) that a dyadic relation was supplanted by a triadic one. This is surely a change in the syntax of scientific language. I am tempted to speak of P-formation rules, if I may use some quasi-Carnapian jargon. Physical theories involve conceptual frameworks, and these determine what is, and what is not a well-formed sentence or formula. And although the choice of some formation rules (other than L-rules) is guided by certain pervasive features of experience, they differ from P-laws or P-postulates in that they are not confirmable or disconfirmable in the sense in which these factual laws or postulates are. The P-formation rules are *presupposed* in the confirmation of scientific hypotheses. (Perhaps this is a

slightly Kantian streak in my philosophy—but I submit it is the only one a scientific empiricist needs to allow for).

(4) Suggestive as this proposal may be, it seems to me to have difficulties too. It is perplexing (is it not?) that in the transition from macro- to micro-entities some predicates become inapplicable. How many molecules are needed for a sensible application of the macro-temperature concept? How large must an object be to ascribe to it definite size, shape and location? How large must a material object be in order to speak sensibly of its speed of rotation? Or is it silly to raise questions in this manner? Perhaps one way out is suggested by the formula of the indeterminacy principle itself: $\Delta x . \Delta v \approx \dfrac{h.}{m}$ With increasing m (the mass of the particle concerned) the statistical dispersions in the x-coordinate and the velocity v become smaller and smaller, and for any plainly visible or tangible macro-object, the indeterminacies are far below practical measurability. Shall we construe all this in terms of a graduation of meaningfulness? This would indeed be very odd, or at least extremely awkward. The applicability of such concepts as color, hardness, temperature, specific heat, electric conductivity would form a kind of slippery slope—clearly present in the upper range, but fading out more or less gradually as we go down the scale toward the micro-entities. In terms of an alternative reconstruction we might say that the language of quantum mechanics simply does not mesh with the language of classical physics; and that the progress of science consists (as far as logical structure is concerned), in the supplanting of one language by another. The older language is then, in principle, completely discarded, once the new language has been adopted. It is then only in the observational consequences that we find in certain areas practical agreement between the old and the new theory. This may be the germ of a solution.[5] Still it would be desirable to spell out in some detail the logical or empirical correspondence of classical and modern concepts wherever such correspondence exists. And it would be even more important to make fully explicit the logical syntax and semantics of microphysics. Do we use a *thing-attribute*, a *space-time-factor*, or an *event* language? What are the advantages, what the disadvantages of these various reconstructions? It seems to me imperative that we undertake this intriguing and no doubt difficult task in the logic of science. Perhaps I merely reveal my lack of comprehension, but I must confess I cannot make good clear sense out of Niels Bohr's assertions about the inseparability of measuring instrument and measured object in quantum mechanics. What is it then that micromeasurements can inform us about? If many attributes that we used to take as designated by one-place predicates have to be supplanted

---

[5] If I understand them correctly, R. Carnap in his work since his essay on "The methodological Character of Theoretical Concepts" (*Minn. Studies in The Philosophy of Science, 1*, 1956), P. K. Feyerabend, in many publications, culminating in "Explanation, Reduction, and Empiricism", in *Minn. Studies in the Philosophy of Science, 3*, 1962, and Wilfrid Sellars, "The Language of Theories", in H. Feigl and G. Maxwell, eds., *Current Issues in the Philosophy of Science*, New York, 1961, are tending in this direction.

by dyadic, triadic or polyadic relations, what are the terms of these relations, and what can we say about them except in the context of their relations? Holism is a highly unclarified notion. Do we really need it in physics (or for that matter in biology)? What I am pleading for is a consistent and coherent account that renders justice to what is to be retained of largely "material" matter concepts of 19th century and early 20th century atomic and electronic physics as it is absorbed in modern quantum and wave mechanics. It is no good to say that the most recent modern physics of Dirac, von Neumann, Schwinger et al. is a "purely abstract model", and that our mistake is picture-thinking. I don't hanker for pictures. I *grant* the abstract, unvisualizable character of most physical concepts, classical or modern. But I insist that physics deals with happenings in space-time, and that associated with those happenings there are aspects of mass, charge and motion which leave at least *some* characteristics of old-fashioned matter unaltered.

Herbert Feigl
University of Minnesota

DISCUSSION

McKeon: The history Mr. Hanson has given us is one in which primary, secondary, and tertiary qualities have gone through an evolution in which the primary have undergone a weakening. I think that this is one line of the history. But I would like to suggest that he should ask a broader question: what has happened to the attempt to separate out characteristics, properties that can be attributed to the thing objectively from those in which there is some meddling because of circumstances, the observers, and the rest? We would then have to take account of people like Whitehead who holds that the shape, the greenness and the pleasantness of a leaf all belong to the leaf, but denies that pleasantness is more removed than shape. Or Aristoteleans who would insist that there are certain primary characteristics—let's retain only his heavy and light— which they would still want to attribute to ultimate particles. The story would then become more complex and I think more interesting. What has happened in recent centuries is not that a group of people who used to make the distinction between primary and secondary qualities are beginning to get uneasy, but rather that Mr. Hanson has chosen the region in which almost the entire cast of characters who talk about the problem belong with Mr. Bridgman among the operationalists, and thus make their "primary qualities" dependent upon the measuring instruments used. Matter, at least, sub-atomic matter, has "dematerialized" for this reason and not because of the fate that has overcome one school of distinctions among basic qualities.

Hanson: Your main point can be put in the form of a rhetorical question: in the last four hundred years what tradition would call the primary properties have been weakened conceptually; what therefore has happened to what used to be known as "objectifiable" properties? Now, one of the answers that might be given to this might be that the subject-matter is never matter as such but rather this in inexorable conjunction with a *detector*. (I won't say an observer because this has an unfortunate subjective association.) This is a fundamental point involving contemporary physical principle in a way which would never have been predicted even as late as, say, 1910. It was just never thought that our theory of the degree to which the experimental detector was going to influence the claims which we could make about matter, was going to be as dominant as it has turned out to be. It was realized of course in the seventeenth century that in the absence of a controlled experiment or in the event of a failure to find some necessary piece of instrumentation, one couldn't get any quantitative determinations of the behavior of matter. But it was assumed that the degree to which the instrumentation was crude or the degree to which it actually interfered with the phenomenon was something which by successive approximations one could continually eliminate. Thus one could determine the degree to which this particular spring balance was defective by comparing it with a range of others and then smoothing out the ribbon of data. But one of the features of contemporary measurement theory is that there will always be an *incalculable* degree to which the detector will influence the entity or the process which is being dealt with. Consequently I think that one way of answering the question: "what has happened to objectifiability?" is that we have located objectifiability in the complex referent, matter-plus-detector, or perhaps better, physical-object-plus-detector. I think one can reach thoroughly objective determinations about this provided that one is careful to realize that the appropriate mode of characterization here is going to be rather unfamiliar in classical terms; it is going to be probabilistic, and it is going to have to do with gangs of phenomena and gangs of clusters of matter-plus-detectors rather than simply individual chunks of information about individual chunks of matter. I think that put in this way it might be possible then to run through the spectrum of what used to be called primary, secondary, and tertiary properties, and just to point out that there are still valid contrasts here. For example, let's take the "tertiaries" in which the role of the detector or the observer is so prominent that the degree to which it is influencing the complex is a controlling one. Whether or not an individual finds a particular object pleasant will to a considerable extent be a function of his training, where he has come from, etc. On the other hand, there will be a whole range of phenomena in the macrophysical world where the influence of the detector is quite minimal. Where, for example, you are dealing with planetary orbits, the brand name on your telescope or your having been educated in one school of astronomy rather than another will scarcely influence the results. In the region where the question of the nature of fundamental matter is the primary concern, namely, in elementary microphysics, the issue has become enormously complex because there the degree to which you are actually concerned at any one time with the properties of the detector or with the properties of that which is being detected is impossible to decide.

McKeon: I should agree with everything you've said but it leaves out the one question that I was trying to focus on, namely, is it the case that in this process there have been several *theoretical* screens which have determined among other things what it is that would constitute the inseparable qualities of matter, simply in terms of what constitutes the indivisible or the atoms? The "indivisible" or the "atom" might be (as the whole tradition behind this notion, *atom*, has emphasized—and it's out of this tradition that the primary-secondary quality distinction originally came) a determination of something like position, size, shape, motion, and so on. In *this* tradition, you would perhaps want to cross off one or other of these properties. There's no reason why two atomists should not in writing their equations have in mind totally different basic characteristics as the "primary" ones. There's another tradition in which "indivisibles" of the Platonic variety, the regular solids, are chosen because of their purely mathematical character. This has been a live tradition for much longer, and you're on safer ground because there are certain aspects of any material situation which would be more easily explained if the regularities that you are talking about have a mathematical basis. There's a third tradition which equates the "indivisible" with the metric measuring characteristic, including the measure. This is what I have been calling the "operational". This is much more nearly the phenomenal view of the indivisible. And in this connection, I would want to urge that the Aristotelian tradition has not gone into the ground completely; here the "indivisible" part is named by characteristics like *heavy, hot,* and *wet*. Take the group of men—philosophers or scientists—who have speculated about the "atomic" indivisible, or postulated beginning point. They have then said: there are modes of combination of these beginnings which will give us other properties. And what I'm arguing is that your story would gain a good deal more if you took into account the interchange among these *theoretic* possibilities as well as the developments within the field of physics.

Mc Mullin: When one talks about the "dematerialization" of matter, one is implying that the predicate 'material' is less applicable now to something or other than it was formerly. It seems to me that two different reasons for this are being suggested here. One reason is that the scientist originally took 'material' to be a predicate which could be used in a theory usefully in such a way as to provide predictions . . . The suggestion in your paper about the propositional function would be that the word 'material' cannot function in this way. It's a good rough denotative, not descriptive, term for what the scientist is talking about, but it is of no direct significance within the theory itself. Now, there's another component in the paper too. You seem to associate the predicate 'material' rather more with the corpuscular than with the field or continuous side of matter, and assume that a continuum theory is somehow less "material" than a particle theory would be. The dematerialization that has taken place in contemporary physics would in this case consist in the fact that contemporary theory has tended away from corpuscular theories to field theories, or at least to theories of an indeterminate kind that are both corpuscular and field. Now, the question I want to pose is this: Do you see these two notions of dematerialization to be connected, and which of them do you think to be the important one?

Hanson: Well, I would certainly take the first one to be the important one, that there's nothing in contemporary physical theory, and perhaps there never has been anything in any physical theory, which would correspond to what might be called a "matter variable". There are mass variables and there are dynamical variables but nothing which might be called a "matter variable", such that by substituting certain values for this complex variable you would get certain sorts of observation statements and by substituting other values, you would get other observation statements, and then you could check the two. Consequently, it begins to look like a kind of blank check, a way of referring in an elliptical way to what might be called the subject matter of a good deal of natural philosophy. As to the second point, I'm not inclined to agree that the

572

drift of contemporary physical theory is all that much away from corpuscular formulations. This is really in a sense a sociological issue and so we would have to address ourselves to it tangentially. Many of the phenomena seem simply incompatible with either one form of the interpretation of matter or the other. In other words, if you say; look here matter is fundamentally field-like (and this is, of course, the difficulty which sooner or later Mr. Misner is going to have, I think), then, of course, the whole discussion is going to turn on just how you are going to deal with the standard singularity phenomena, such as collisions, etc.

Mc Mullin: Do you take the field-theoretical approach to be in some sense a challenge to the "materiality" of matter?

Hanson: I think the point concerns rather the shifting toward new or different properties. It isn't so much a question of beginning with one preferred view of the nature of matter and then saying: look here, we thought it was all particles, but in point of fact we've discovered lots of reasons for supposing that there is an undulatory twist to the whole thing, or vice versa, but rather that although we had taken the fundamental particles to be point-masses, it now turns out that other properties, no less material, are perhaps more appropriate for describing what we had taken to be the behavior of fundamental particles. In other words, what looks to be unfamiliar here is the applying of certain sorts of predicates to subjects which we didn't think they would have a natural application to.

Mc Mullin: Is there a tension between this thesis and your earlier one? If 'material' has become a sort of blank term from the scientific point of view, then surely the developments in scientific theory you mention are irrelevant to the "materialization" or "dematerialization" of matter.

Hanson: No, I don't think so. I mean, the fact that one is able to mix up the properties in question as new phenomena require, suggest that you are not going to be able to fill in the blank in any particular way and make it stick. It may be that there are a finite number of properties which we will call "material", and it may be that this is the bag out of which we have to select. But the particular ones we are going to choose as "primary"—that is, "material"—properties might still be very much an open question and thoroughly contingent upon the current work in theoretical and in experimental physics. So, I think the blank check thing can still stand. It is blank in the sense that you don't know which values are going to go into which variables. If the "matter variable" goes into an equation, it doesn't make any difference because you still have to make the fundamental selection concerning which of the dynamical variables are going to count in the equations. And it's the selection of that, I think, which constitutes what I've been calling "dematerialization", namely, the selection now is unusual, and conceptually unusual not just psychologically unusual in the context of classical mechanics. That might be a way of putting it.

573

A NOTE ON

THREE CONCEPTS OF MASS

Cecil B. Mast

The term 'mass' is used in physics in three different ways. *Active gravitational mass* is a measure of the ability of a body to generate a gravitational field, whereas *passive gravitational mass* is a measure of the response of the body to an existing gravitational field. The term 'body' is used above, but it must be remembered that energy too possesses gravitational mass, both active and passive. Although defined differently, the active and passive gravitational masses of a given body are in fact numerically equal. This equality is not a result of the definitions, nor is it, as is sometimes claimed, a result of the law of action and reaction. It must be accepted as an empirical fact.

The third type of mass, namely *inertial mass*, refers to the resistance of an object to a change in motion. The concept of inertial mass has caused a considerable amount of argument since the time of Newton. For Newton, the mass (inertial mass) of a body was equal to the density of the body multiplied by its volume and was to be considered as a measure of the quantity of matter in the body. Now the term 'quantity of matter' was not otherwise defined in theory although, of course, it had intuitive meaning. As a consequence, the definition of mass as a measure of the quantity of matter in a body was not a usable definition. The definition of mass as a product of density and volume is likewise unusable until the term 'density' is defined. The difficulties inherent in Newton's definition were discussed at length by Mach in *The Science of Mechanics* and a scheme for defining mass (or rather the mass-ratio of two bodies) using the law of action and reaction was given by him. That Mach's definition was not free from defect has been pointed out by Pendse,[1] who showed that mass-ratios for the particles in a system containing more than seven particles were not determinable from observational data without recourse to the laws of inertia and gravitation, and that, in fact, the mass-ratio of two particles, as defined by Mach was dependent upon the choice of an observer.

We will not dwell further on the attempts to produce an acceptable defi-

---

[1] C. G. Pendse, *Phil. Mag. 24*, 1937, 1012–1022; 27, 1939, 51–61.

nition of inertial mass within the context of classical theory. Instead we turn our attention to the ideas of mass as they appear in modern physics.

The Einstein mass-energy relation is viewed by some scientists as a conceptual relationship between matter and energy. This must be so, otherwise how does one interpret the statement, sometimes made, that Einstein has shown that matter can be converted to energy? The relation is a numerical one and it indicates that mass is proportional to energy-content. To achieve a relationship between matter and energy, one would have to consider mass as a measure of the quantity of matter and yet such a definition has been attacked, as we have seen. Now the definition of mass as a measure of the quantity of matter is satisfactory from the psychological standpoint and should occasion no difficulty as long as it is not proposed as the definition to be used in science. It would, in fact, be reasonable to say that the matter in a body is defined to be that of which the mass is the quantity, the mass being then defined in some other way. The mass-energy relation, for example, could be used to define the mass in terms of energy.

Mass, as it appears in the mass-energy relation, means *inertial* mass. This is clear, since this relation is a product of special relativity theory, in which gravitational effects are presumed to be absent.

The equality of active and passive gravitational masses was pointed out above. It is a remarkable fact that the value of the inertial mass of a body can be made equal to that of the gravitational mass by a suitable choice of units. This again is a matter of experience rather than of definition. Einstein, finding it hard to believe that this equality was an accident, postulated an equality of inertial and gravitational mass as the basis of his famous principle of equivalence, from which he drew far-reaching consequences and from which ultimately grew the general theory of relativity.

In the general theory of relativity the physical aspects of a system are represented by the stress-energy tensor, whereas the geometric aspects of the space-time continuum are given by the Einstein tensor. The field equations, stating the proportionality of the components of these tensors, enable us to express physical quantities in terms of geometric quantities. Thus it is sometimes said that Einstein has "geometrized" physics. (This geometrization has been pushed even farther by Wheeler and his co-workers). An important point is this: If one is presented with a space-time continuum with a prescribed metric, then by the process of differentiation one can obtain the Einstein tensor and as a result infer the *physical* makeup of the given "world". In particular, the mass enclosed in a certain region can be computed from the components of the Einstein tensor, that is to say, entirely in terms of geometric quantities. On closer inspection, however, one sees that a quantity has been computed which is called the "mass", but it may be arguable whether the name has been correctly given. Let us examine this point a little further.

It is quite common in physics to retain the concepts and terminology of a theory even when it has been superseded. Certainly in the initial stages of development of the new theory this can hardly be avoided. It will be found, however, that as the new theory develops, the terms acquire meanings which may differ quite widely from the meanings assigned in the earlier theory or, what is more unfortunate, they may be only vaguely or not at all defined within the context of the new theory. This poses an enormous problem to an expositor when he wishes to present the theory to the layman and may cause confusion of ideas for those using the theory. This particular difficulty of language is quite pronounced in general relativity due to the fact that concepts adequately defined against the backdrop of a flat space-time are taken over into a theory using Riemannian geometry, the concepts of *position, relative velocity, acceleration* and *mass* being examples. *Mass* is a classical concept which has to be "forced" to get it into the structure of general relativity. Let us examine, then, some of the difficulties encountered in this attempt.

One important aspect of Newtonian gravitational theory is the superposability of the gravitational fields of several bodies. Only in the event that the mathematical approximation occasioned by the linearization of the field equations is valid, is such a thing possible in general relativity. The possibility of considering a body as "immersed" in a gravitational field which acts on the body is closely associated with such a linearization procedure, the validity of this procedure in turn depending upon the weakness of the field and the condition of low velocities. For the case of two bodies in close proximity and in rapid motion, the linearization procedure would not work. It would therefore be impossible (or at least exceedingly difficult) to assign either passive or active gravitational mass to either body, or even to give these concepts a satisfactory definition in this case. To the extent that the terms 'active' or 'passive gravitational mass' are used in the literature of general relativity, we may infer that the discussion concerns itself with weak fields and low velocities. It is, of course, just in this case that Newtonian theory is in approximate agreement with relativity.

Since the principle of equivalence underlies the theory of general relativity, the assignment of inertial mass is taken care of as soon as gravitational mass is assigned. But conceptually the problem is not quite so simple. If we regard inertial mass as a measure of the resistance of a body to change in motion then we must have at hand an adequate definition of acceleration. In classical physics or in the realm of observation there is thus no problem since acceleration may be defined as the vector rate of change of velocity. This cannot be done in any simple or straightforward way when the space-time possesses curvature, and, as a consequence, (relative) acceleration does not make an appearance in the theory except for those discussions relating theory to observation, in which case some conventional definition is adopted.

When relativists use the term 'acceleration', they frequently mean so-called "four-acceleration", which is just another name for the first curvature of the world-line of the particle under consideration. We might term this the "absolute" acceleration since it is a property intrinsic to the curve. There are a number of reasons for using the term 'acceleration' in this context but, it would not really be appropriate for use in defining inertial mass, since, for instance, spinning bodies which are free to move will have absolute accelerations.

In addition to the difficulties afforded by the vagueness of the term 'acceleration' in general relativity, the mathematical difficulties inherent in attempts to introduce constraints or to treat other than gravitational forces makes the definition of inertial mass conceptually very difficult. It might well be that the idea of mass should be considered as an irrevocably classical concept and of relevance in Einstein's theory only under the weak field approximation.

University of Notre Dame

THE ELEMENTARY PARTICLES

OF MATTER

A. E. Woodruff

⬛ Elementary particle physics is presently in a state of rapid development. Under these circumstances, to attempt to be definitive concerning what a particle is would be presumptuous, even if one is willing to accept an answer on the physicist's own terms. There simply is no fully elaborated and agreed-upon theory of the elementary particles, nor even agreement as to which particles are elementary. To be sure, we have theories which apply to the interactions and transformations of the particles. In some areas these theories work out very nicely, agreeing with the experimental results to within the small margins of error of the latter. But into these theories must be fed the empirical data concerning the particles *per se*; that is, their masses and symmetry properties. Therefore I will put forward in a brief fashion what we believe we *do* know about the elementary particles, what kinds of questions the physicist would desire to see answered by a "theory of the fundamental particles," and I will close with an indication of a few of the ways in which attempts are being made to construct such a theory.

The pervasive dualism of matter and field, of particle and wave properties, is a foundation-stone of modern physics. In 1905, Einstein postulated the existence of the photon, or quantum of light, to supplement the Maxwellian electromagnetic field theory so as to account for the photoelectric effect. In 1924, deBroglie predicted the wave nature of the electron on theoretical grounds, to supplement its corpuscular nature, which had been demonstrated by J. J. Thomson. DeBroglie's prediction was confirmed by an experiment of Davisson and Germer in 1927. These early advances were followed by efforts to incorporate this duality into a consistent and unified theory. Today every field presumably has its quanta, or particulate aspect, and to every type of particle there is associated a field of which it is a quantum. For example, just as the photon is the quantum of the electromagnetic field, the meson is the quantum of the nuclear force field.

Another property of the fundamental particles (as well as of more composite structures) is their lack of separate identity, in the sense which is manifested in the statistics proper to aggregates of large objects of the same kind. For example, if two coins are flipped at the same time there are four possible results. Both may come up heads, both tails, coin A may come up heads and B tails, or B may come up heads and A tails. The probability is ½ that one coin will come up heads and one tails, since this is the case in two of the four equally probable results. In the analogous case, when the polarizations of two photons of the same energy and momentum are observed, a different result is obtained. Let us suppose a situation in which each photon, observed separately, has an equal chance to be polarized in the right-hand or in the left-hand sense, so the probability that one will have right-hand and one left-hand polarization would be expected to be ½. Instead, it is found to be ⅓. The situation described does not represent the simple juxtaposition of two independent occurrences, as the flipping of two coins did. Photons do not have separate identities, not only in the sense that they are so alike that they cannot be distinguished from each other, but also in the sense that in a group they do not behave as separate objects. This follows from the fact that "photon A being right-handed and photon B left-handed" represents exactly the same state of affairs as "A being left-handed and B right-handed." This means there are only three possible states the two photons can be in if their polarizations are observed at the same time. Both are right-handed, or both left-handed, or one is left-handed and one is right-handed. The three states are equally probable so the probability of the third is ⅓, not ¼.

This intrinsic unidentifiability, a property of all the elementary particles, becomes masked in large scale structures but is amply confirmed on the nuclear level. This and other overall properties of the fundamental particles are neatly built into the quantum field theory. But the same is not true of most of those features of the particles which distinguish them from each other. A table of some of these properties may be found on the next page.

The particles are grouped into families, according to their spin (intrinsic angular momentum), mass, and the types of interactions they can enter into with each other. The individual species of particles appear in several electric charge states as for example the proton and neutron states of the nucleon. These states are symbolized by '+', '0', and '−' in the table, since the amount of charge is always +1, 0 or −1 times e, the magnitude of the charge of an electron. The different charge states of a species differ slightly in mass, as the table shows, but they are so much alike otherwise that it is natural to classify them as different charge states of the same particle. Aside from the electromagnetic interactions, into which all charged (and some neutral but magnetic) particles enter, the baryons and mesons undergo "strong" interactions (e.g. nuclear forces), while they and the leptons have in common "weak" interactions, such as beta decay. According to present theoretical considerations, every particle has its corresponding antiparticle,

PROPERTIES OF THE FUNDAMENTAL PARTICLES

Family	Name	Multiplicity	Rest Mass (in electron masses)
Baryons (massive spin ½ particles)	Ξ	2 (0 and −) + 2 antiparticles	charged 2580, neutral 2566
	Σ	3 (+, 0, −) + 3 a.p.	+:2327,7; 0:2340.5;−:2331.8
	Λ	1 (0) + 1 a.p.	2182.8
	nucleon N	2 (+ (proton), 0 (neutron)) + 2 a.p.	proton 1836.12, neutron 1838.65
Mesons (intermediate spin 0 particles)	K	2 (0 and −) + 2 a.p.	charged 966.6, neutral 974.2
	pion π	3 (+, 0, −) (+ and − are antiparticles to each other, 0 to itself)	charged 273.18, neutral 264.20
Leptons (light spin ½ particles)	muon μ	1 (+) + 1 a.p.	206.77
	electron e	1 (−) + 1 a.p. (positron)	1
	neutrino* ν	1 (0) + 1 a.p.	0
Photon (spin 1)	photon γ	1 (0) (its own a.p.)	0

(Spins are given in units of $h/2\pi$.)

---

* Recently evidence has been found for the existence of two kinds of neutrinos, one connected in its interactions with the muon and one with the electron. (Danby *et. al.*, *Phys. Rev. 9*, 1962, 36(L)).

with the same mass and opposite charge. Most of the particles (and antiparticles) are not stable when isolated, but decay into other species of particles in a short time as the result of weak or electromagnetic interactions. For example, a free neutron will decay spontaneously into a proton, electron and antineutrino. We have omitted from the table the newly discovered "resonances," or extremely short-lived particles which last for periods less than about 10^{-20} second and decay via the strong interactions, but there appears to be no reason in principle not to include these on an equal footing with the others. Furthermore, whether there exists a meaningful criterion for distinguishing between these "elementary" particles and what certainly appear to be composite structures such as nuclei and atoms is a moot point. To determine which are the elementary and which the composite particles, one needs a theory in which the terms are defined and the particles specified. Some of the present attempts at a theory of the elementary particles are inclined to drop the distinction between 'elementary' and 'composite' altogether.

Not only are most of the particles listed unstable, but any one of them may be created or annihilated in a collision. The only restriction is that various conservation laws must be satisfied, such as conservation of energy, momentum, charge, number of baryons minus number of antibaryons, etc. For example, if gamma-rays (photons) of high enough energy penetrate matter, electron-positron pairs are sometimes created. In this way, positrons, the first distinct antiparticles to be discovered, are created in cosmic ray showers. Other particle-antiparticle pairs can be created also, if enough energy is available in some form.

While the mutual transformability of the particles is subsumed in quantum field theory, there are other features of particles and their interactions for which we do not possess an adequate theoretical rationale at present. Four of these are: 1) the existence of different kinds of interactions of radically different strength (strong, electromagnetic, weak and—omitted from consideration here—gravitational); 2) the connection between this hierarchy of interactions and the existence of approximate conservation laws, as for instance the conservation of parity. This is an expression of the mirror-symmetry of physical laws, which does not hold for the weak interactions; 3) the symmetry properties of the particles, as manifested in part by their varying spins and charge multiplicities; and 4) the mass spectrum of these particles. We shall briefly consider the last of these mysteries here, although a satisfactory theory may have to comprehend all of them at once.[1]

Properties such as spin and multiplicity appear simple, because they are easily expressed in terms of integers or half-integers, and we may hope for a mathematical explanation of them which is simple in some sense too. The mass spectrum of the particles appears inherently more intractable in its seeming arbitrariness. There is not even a simple, semi-empirical formula, like Balmer's for the hydrogen spectral lines, that we can use to predict new resonances or particles. On the face of it, this intractability is not unreasonable. We expect that mass is, at least in part, a dynamical effect—something created in a complex way from the interaction energies of various fields. The energy of the electric field created by the electronic charge was regarded classically as the source of the electron's mass, and this assumption was used to compute the electron's radius. The field energy of a spherical charge distribution or radius r is of the order e^2/r, which is equivalently the amount of energy which must be expended to assemble the charge from an infinitely

---

[1] A more detailed survey of some theoretical attempts to cope with these problems was presented in the author's paper, "Philosophical Aspects of Quantum Field Theory", at section L of the AAAS meeting, Denver, December 1961 (to be published).

dispersed charge fluid. If this energy is equated by Einstein's relation to mc^2, where m is the electronic mass, r turns out to be of the order e^2/mc^2 or about 10^{-13} cm, which is a reasonable radius for an elementary particle.

Although quantum theory must handle this self-interaction problem in a more sophisticated way, the charge still should make a contribution to the mass. The mass difference between the charged and uncharged members of the same charge multiplet is always of the order of one or a few electron masses, suggesting that these differences do indeed originate from the different ways the particles interact with the electromagnetic field. Furthermore, the strongly interacting particles (baryons and mesons), for which one would expect the largest dynamical contributions to the masses, are in fact the most massive. These general indications may give rise to optimism even though the actual calculation of these contributions is beyond the scope of the prevalent theoretical ideas. But it would be difficult to explain certain anomalies on this basis, in particular the relatively large mass of the muon, which, in its ways of interacting, seems to be identical with the electron.

Many attempts are being made now to obtain the mass spectrum and other properties. The conventional treatment of quantum field theory gives infinite results for the contributions of interactions to the masses of particles. We remove these infinities by replacing them with the empirical values of the masses in question. In order to obtain an estimate of the actual contributions to the masses of particles of these self-interactions, we must resort to approximations of dubious validity. Using these methods, Feynman and Speisman were able to demonstrate that the proton-neutron mass difference was not unreasonable in terms of the electromagnetic self-interactions involved.[2] But the usual theory becomes far more intractable when the strong interaction contributions are to be calculated.

Another point of view treats some of the fundamental particles as composite (e.g. the pion as a metastable nucleon-antinucleon combination). Such schemes can be constructed in such a way that they correlate certain facts, such as the strengths with which particles interact with each other, but so far the masses of the presumed bound states are uncalculated. This is because the supposed binding forces are little known and too strong to be subjected to the usual methods of calculation, which apply only to weaker forces.

On the other hand, mass spectra may be forthcoming from theoretical attempts which abandon the traditional viewpoint. Heisenberg has proposed

---

[2] R. P. Feynman and G. Speisman, *Phys. Rev.* **94**, 1954, 500(L). More recently, using more sophisticated techniques, S. K. Bose and R. E. Marshak have given an account of the $\pi^+ - \pi^0$ mass difference (University of Rochester, NYO–10130 (1962)).

a quantized field theory involving only one field,[3] rather than a different field for each species of elementary particle as in the customary formalism. This field interacts with itself and appears capable of giving rise to a promising spectrum of particle masses and properties. While Heisenberg's approach is perhaps the most hopeful on the scene, the mathematics is difficult and various assumptions have to be made to fill in gaps in the argumentation. Another more tough-minded method receiving a good deal of attention drops the field idea completely as a fundamental notion and works directly with the so-called S-matrix instead.[4] In quantum theory any given state of a system of particles is represented by a vector in a Hilbert space. Information concerning the initial state, such as the number and species of particles, their energies, charges, and spins, etc., is given in the form of components of this vector. The S-matrix is an operator on the Hilbert space such that, when the vector representing the initial state is multiplied by the S-matrix, the resulting vector represents the final state of the system. The S-matrix is more immediately related to experience than the field idea in that the squares of elements of the matrix give the transition probabilities for various processes which occur among the strongly interacting fundamental particles. It is possible that the S-matrix approach will yield a mass spectrum for these strongly interacting particles, if one or more masses are fed in to supply the mass scale. However, this is still very much in the speculative stage.

Other radically different attacks exist, such as the "wormhole" theory of Misner and Wheeler.[5] No one of them can be considered more than a promising beginning. Although we are in possession of a good deal of knowledge of the properties of the particles, of which I have indicated only a part, it is quite clear that we do not yet understand the theoretical reasons for their existence in their particular species and with their particular properties. Physicists with different temperament disagree radically as to the length of time before we may expect clarity to come to this realm; some are sanguine, and think the problems will soon be "wrapped up"; others think in terms of several decades.

Nevertheless, we know much that is of interest to the philosopher. Clearly the "elementary" particles of today are a far cry from the Democrit-

[3] W. Heisenberg, *Rev. Mod Phys. 29*, 1957, 269; *Proceedings of the 1958 Annual International Conference on High Energy Physics,* CERN, pp. 119–26; *Proceedings of the 1960 Annual International Conference on High Energy Physics*, Rochester, pp. 851–58. H-P. Dürr, W. Heisenberg, H. Mitter, S. Schlieder and K. Yamakazi, *Zeit. fur Naturforschung 14a*, 1959, 441.

[4] See in particular G. F. Chew: *S-Matrix Theory of Strong Interactions*, New York, 1961.

[5] C. W. Misner and J. A. Wheeler, *Annals of Physics, 2*, 1957, 525; J. A. Wheeler, *Annals of Physics, 2*, 1957, 604.

ean atoms. The universe is not constructed of indestructible scaled-down bricks. The new "atoms" exhibit a behavior which is alien to our every-day experience; they are subject to the peculiar intrinsic indeterminism of quantum phenomena; they do not preserve their identity, and they are created and annihilated in the manifold transformations of the world.

I wish to acknowledge my gratitude to E. Gold for helping to make this presentation of a complex subject more nearly intelligible.

University of Chicago

MATTER AND ENERGY

IN SCIENTIFIC THEORY *

Cecil B. Mast

§1 *From Material Ether to Matter-Energy*

In his attempts to fashion a mechanical model for nature and, in particular, to provide for a mechanical interpretation of optical phenomena, Descartes found it expedient to introduce the concept of an "ether". This ether, composed of a type of "matter" imperceptible to the senses, but nonetheless possessing mechanical properties, was conceived to be granular in structure. The motions of the granules and the interactions between them was to provide not only the mechanism for transmission of light, but an explanation of light itself. While subsequent physical thought caused considerable modification in the concepts of the structure and function of the ether, the desire for a mechanical picture of nature was manifested in the continued use of the idea of space as a plenum. Today few scientists would desire a mechanical picture (and many would even discourage the asking for pictures at all), yet it may be asserted that in some senses the plenum is still with us.

The statement that Descartes' ether was "composed of matter" requires some clarification. First of all, it would be better to say that the ether, considered as an entity in Descartes' theory, was taken to represent a material medium actually pervading the universe. This material medium, perhaps because of its extreme tenuity, did not affect the senses, and its chief claim to the title "material" seems to lie in the fact that it was a carrier of mechanical variables, i.e. velocity, momentum, density, compressibility, etc.

The problem of an elastic solid ether having the vibrational properties required for a discussion of light was correctly solved by MacCullagh in 1839. This ether was not capable, however, of handling problems involving electric, magnetic or gravitational forces. In fact, no acceptable continuum model was ever constructed to discuss these problems. It would be out of place here to recount the many ether models proposed and discarded from

* This work was supported in part by a grant from the National Science Foundation. I would like to acknowledge the help of Dr. Ernan McMullin in formulating the problematic of the paper.

the time of Descartes to the end of the nineteenth century.[1] Suffice it to say that no model was ever constructed which was considered wholly satisfactory.

A new note was sounded in 1900 by Larmor urging that the attempts to consider all phenomena as mechanical consequences of some concealed structure of the ether be abandoned. The concept of the ether was retained, but the ether was to be considered as an "immaterial" medium. The term 'immaterial' here seems to mean that the elements or parts of the medium cannot be assigned a location. Insofar as scientists at the turn of the century conceived the ether to be representative of some entity in the real world, they postulated a "non-material" entity pervading the universe. The need for even this ghostly remnant of earlier ethers was obviated when Einstein, denying the physical meaningfulness of the term 'absolute rest', divested the ether of its status as a standard against which absolute velocity could be measured. This essay proposes to show that, as the ether was dematerialized and finally banished, energy underwent a sort of "materialization" until now it is not uncommon to hear the claim that matter and energy are merely different aspects of some more basic entity.

With the abandonment of attempts to found all physics on mechanics, energy, initially conceived as descriptive of matter in motion, has lost its purely mechanical interpretation. In physical theories utilizing a material ether, energy could always be thought of as a quantity describing the motion and interaction of material objects. However, the bizarre properties required of the ether by electromagnetic theory (and the fact that Maxwell's equations yielded correct results quite independently of any mechanical interpretation of the equations) caused a decline in interest on the part of the physicists in mechanical models of the ether. It was retained as a standard of absolute rest until the advent (and great success) of the special theory of relativity. The lumeniferous ether has now been replaced by the electromagnetic field, an entity which is conceived as "non-material" and which does not furnish a standard of absolute rest. One could, of course, say that the ether is still present in physics, but is described in terms of electromagnetic rather than of mechanical variables. This is a matter of taste; the fact is that the "material" ether of classical theory is absent in present-day physics.

If a "material" ether is abandoned, then how can one interpret the flux of energy in empty space predicted by electromagnetic theory? In the interim between emission of radiation from a source and its absorption by another body, we think of the energy as existing in otherwise empty space. Associated with this radiation is momentum, and interpretation of experiments

---

[1] See E. T. Whittaker, *History of the theories of aether and electricity*, vol. 1, London, 1953.

show that the radiation exhibits a particle-like nature in some circumstances. We are impelled by all this to abandon the older ideas and to consider energy as a sort of "stuff". It is interesting to note that if one could have logically retained a material ether in the theory, this change in the idea of energy need never have been made.

A further step toward what one might call the "materialization" of energy was taken when Einstein showed that the inertia of a body depends upon its energy content, thereby, in effect, ascribing inertial properties to energy. The truth of Einstein's assertion (abundantly verified in nuclear physics) can now be used to elevate energy to a higher status than that accorded to mass itself. Thus we can say that the inertial mass of a body can be computed from its energy content and the momentum from the energy flux.

Thus far we have discussed the evolution of the present day concept of energy. Let us turn now our attention to the concept of matter. Interpretation of experiments in atomic and nuclear spectroscopy and the scattering of beams by crystals shows that, if the term 'matter' is to be applied to electrons, protons etc., then matter has properties not envisioned in classical theory. The fact that the electron exhibits both wave and particle-like properties makes it difficult, if not impossible, to form a picture of it. The trend in physics, however, is away from such pictures and physicists are content with field-theoretical descriptions of the elementary particles and their interactions. The field (for instance, the electron field) is a mathematically-described entity from which the properties of matter can be deduced. It is "non-material" and need not represent any entity in the real world. The field variables may be taken as basic physical quantities with no "explanation" of the field in terms of other concepts required. In this way we may think of this new field as existing throughout space-time. This parallels, in spirit, the acceptance of the field variables in Maxwellian theory as basic entities with the consequent avoidance of mechanical interpretations of the electromagnetic field. Matter might now be thought to be a manifestation of the existence of a field permeating space-time and it is hoped that eventually a universal field theory will be obtained, from which the existence of the various elementary particles, their properties and their interactions might be deduced.

More recent work shows the attitude of some physicists toward the abandonment of field theories, at least in the realm of strong interactions. Chew[2] has expressed the opinion that conventional field theory is sterile with respect to strong interactions. It is proposed that all observed particles, their masses and mutual interactions can be predicted by use of symmetries and

---

[2] G. F. Chew, *S-Matrix Theory of Strong Interactions,* New York, 1961.

the analytically-continued S-Matrix. In this theory (which is by no means complete as yet), the microscopic detail of field-theoretic descriptions is absent and one might say that no model of the physical systems to be studied need be used. It is, in a sense, a sort of "black box" type of theory displaying no concern for what is happening inside the box.

No discussion of matter and energy would be complete without some mention of general relativity. In this theory, gravitation is a manifestation of space-time geometry, this geometry in turn being determined by the matter and energy present in the universe. The continuum is not itself thought to be material, but rather to be affected by matter and energy. In this way we see that energy possesses a new property in common with matter, namely active gravitational mass.

General relativity differs from the other field theories in the sense that space-time has been given a flexible structure. The field here is the metrical field itself. The theory gives the interactions of matter and energy (equations of motion), but offers no "explanation" for matter or energy themselves. Attempts have been made, however, to treat material objects as a manifestation of holes or kinks in the continuum, but until general relativity is connected with quantum theory, these models for matter cannot be considered as completely satisfactory.

§2 *The Theoretical and the Real*

It seems quite clear that science does not form a closed logical system. Certainly, at the present stage of development, science is not even a unified system, but rather is compartmentalized into various theories or branches which, however, have sufficient overlap to allow for consideration of science as a whole. (By 'overlap' here is meant not a common domain of applicability, but rather a community of language and concepts. In this sense general relativity and quantum field theory overlap, although at present there is no common domain of applicability). The language of science borrows rather heavily from the language of other disciplines and also from the language of everyday life. As a consequence, concepts and terms may appear in scientific discourse without being formally defined within the context of the particular theory, or without being completely defined by their usage, and yet much may be known about them. In particular, because a theory must be capable of interpretation and because the predictions of the theory must be set out in a manner comprehensible to the observer or experimentalist, terms and concepts may appear in a discussion of theoretical predictions, which are not themselves of scientific significance, but which are used in order to facilitate the comparison of the predictions with observation or to render the discussion more intelligible (or perhaps more palatable). We must consider the possibility that the term 'matter', when used by the scientist, is used in this way. If so, then the term could be eliminated from the scientist's vocabulary, as has been proposed by some members of the Vienna circle.

If a physical theory is to be capable of interpretation, it must contain entities which are conceived as analogues or representatives of entities in the real world. This is hardly surprising. If the physical theory purporting to discuss the game of billiards, say, had no entity which could be called a billiard ball, i.e. no entity which would represent the ball for theoretical purposes, then we would never be able to compare the predictions of the theory with observation. Since in establishing these analogies, we move from observation to theory, no difficulty is involved. We may say that if we wish to discuss the behaviour of any entity, a theory can be found that contains entities which may be called by the same name. This practice of calling the theoretical analogue by the same name as the real entity sometimes gives rise to confusion of thought and forgetfulness of the analogical nature of physical theory.

Perhaps the most primitive of these analogies is that between the mathematical space of theory and the space of our awareness. In classical physics, a Euclidean 3-space was adopted as the appropriate analogue, and points or point-sets in this space are taken as representative of perceived objects, insofar as they possess position, size, shape or orientation. Other properties of the objects could then be described in terms of functions defined in or over the space. The space of theory thus had existence apart from the objects considered as embedded in it, and could be thought of as a sort of backdrop against which objects moved. In classical theory, therefore, it is quite meaningful to speak of a single object in an otherwise empty space and to discuss the behaviour of the object when it undergoes acceleration. This provides a useful model, since it furnishes a good analogy for the situation in which a perceived object is considered as isolated. It is outside the province of the theory, however, to say what would actually happen in the case of a universe containing a single object. From this point of view, at least, the absolute character of the space of Newtonian theory is not necessarily a defect of the theory.

The extension to special relativity shifts attention from the objects themselves to the histories of the objects and the space of theory becomes a Minkowski space. This four-dimensional space-time manifold again serves as a backdrop and is absolute insofar as accelerated motion is concerned. In general relativity, the space-time is taken to be a Riemannian (or in more modern terminology a Lorentzian) manifold. It must again be kept in mind that the space or space-time of theory is only an analogue of the space or space-time of reality. The fact that Einstein utilized a curved space-time does not necessarily imply "curvature" in the space or space-time of our awareness. In fact, curvature of the space of our awareness is difficult, if not impossible to consider, since *curvature* is a mathematical concept applicable to mathematical spaces, whereas the space of our awareness is not mathematical.

§3 *Terminology*

The discussion in §1 showed that energy possesses many of the properties formerly ascribed to matter alone. The question then arises as to what actually distinguishes energy from matter. If matter were defined within the context of physical theory, this question could be readily answered. No such definition has been formulated however, so we must attempt to clarify the meaning of the terms 'matter' and 'material object' as used by the scientist before we can attempt to answer the question.

A basic requirement which an entity must satisfy before it will be considered as a candidate for the appellation 'material object', is that it be capable of physical existence in space-time. This stipulation will immediately remove concepts or ideas from consideration as material objects. Insofar as entities in a physical theory are considered as *concepts* of material objects, they are not themselves "material objects" in the strict sense of the term. Since, however, entities-in-theory are quite often *called* "material objects", and since questions such as: "Is the electron a material object?" are assumed to be non-trivial questions, we will understand that the assignation of the title 'material object' to an entity-in-theory will be an abbreviated way of saying that a material object is being indirectly referred to by this conceptual entity. The question of the "materiality of the election is really, therefore, a query about the existence of a material object of which the electron-concept is the concept. The electron, considered via a concept-in-theory, is commonly called a "material object" if it is taken to be the representative in theory of a material object conceived to exist in the external world. The expression 'theoretical material object' will be used in this context, where an ambiguity might otherwise arise.

It would be possible to define a material object as that about which physics purports to speak, or equivalently, as that whose properties form the domain of interest for science. A second definition would consider a material object as that which interacts with the scientist's equipment. These definitions admit all those entities in the external world which are ordinarily considered as material objects and, if used consistently, must be considered as valid definitions. The first definition is not adopted in this article, since it is felt that it does not furnish an adequate basis for distinguishing between entities-in-theory and entities in the world about us. The second definition would be acceptable if ambiguity could be removed from the words 'interact' and 'equipment'. As mentioned above, a theoretical entity is often called a "material object" if it *represents* a material object. However, there is no necessity for all entities in theory to be representative of entities in the external world and thus we would balk at the too-hasty application of the term 'material object' to all entities which, in the parlance of the physicist, "interact with the equipment", or whose "properties" are of interest to the scientist. Rather than attempt to remove the above-mentioned ambiguities we will proceed afresh with an alternative definition.

The concepts of *matter* and *material object* originally were applied to objects which directly affected the senses. These concepts are customarily extended in two rather different ways to situations in which the senses are not affected. The first way, which one might term a mere physical extrapolation of the concept, is exemplified by the assertion that if a stone were pulverized and the particles reduced to such a fineness as to elude our perception the particles would be "material objects". The second way, already discussed above, allows one to speak of the "materiality" of theoretical entities. The first category in effect refines the list of properties that objects must have in order to merit the title 'material'. In the example given, the attribute of a minimal size is eliminated from the list. Statements belonging to this category are essentially statements about the external world, whereas statements in the second category refer primarily to the realm of theory.

There is little doubt about the acceptability of the assertion that objects which are capable of directly affecting the senses are "material". Let us take this as our primary sense of the term 'material'. Since perception in man is relative to a particular group of organism-environment interactions, we can regard as "material" any object which would interact in such a way as to allow an organism to sense it. It should be noted that this does not necessarily include entities which in a *theoretical reconstruction* of an experiment are said to "interact" with the apparatus. One can also consider as a material object any object which, by virtue merely of a restriction on its spatial or temporal extension, falls below the threshold of sense-perception (keeping in mind of course our requirement that the object exist or be capable of existing physically in space-time). This completes our listing of entities falling in the category of *material object*, in the strict sense of that term. Any extension of this list will be via the inclusion of "theoretical" material objects. That is to say, the list may be extended by including as theoretical material objects those entities-in-theory which are representative of or analogues of material objects in the sense defined above. The inclusion of new entities in the category of material object must be justified, of course, and therefore we must try to set up criteria by which this may be accomplished. Ideally, we would like to have sufficient criteria to enable us to select any entity in any theory and decide whether it is the representative or analogue of a material object. The determination of these criteria is indeed a formidable problem and no pretence is made that it is solved in this article.

In common discourse and in scientific discussion, the terms 'matter' and 'material object' are quite often used interchangeably. We will not follow this practice, but rather will consider matter as "that which is common to all material objects" (these being defined as above). A material object is not simply matter, but matter under some particular form; while matter, *as such,* is not an individual object (and certainly not a material object). We might say that the term 'matter' is a "pervasive" term inasmuch as it is assumed to apply to all objects in the physical realm. With the distinction between the terms 'matter' and 'material object' in mind, we must differentiate between a theoretical entity which could be considered as the analogue of *matter* and one which could be considered as the analogue of a *material object.*

§4 *Matter and Energy*

If 'matter' is to have scientific significance, then there must be some entity in theory which would be the analogue of matter. Now it seems quite clear that in classical physics there existed no such entity, although there were, of course, many entities representative of material objects. In particular, the material ethers were analogues of material objects assumed to exist in reality. There was, in fact, no need for an analogue of matter since classical physics, was, by and large, a macroscopic theory. The connection with observation was via identification of the systems under discussion with perceived systems. The adjective 'material' really added nothing, since only material (i.e. perceivable) systems could be considered. This is evidenced in the attempts to explain electromagnetic phenomena in terms of an ether.

The introduction of the concept of the *field* in science signalled a change in philosophical outlook. Here was a theoretical entity of great importance, but one which was not in any obvious way, at least, the analogue of a material system. One may ask whether it is the analogue of anything in reality. While, as was pointed out above, it is clearly necessary that entities in the real world have analogues in the theory purporting to discuss them, there is no *a priori* reason that any one entity in theory, however important to that theory, be the analogue of something in reality. In fact, care must be taken to avoid such a viewpoint, since what is important in today's theory may be only vaguely or not at all defined in tomorrow's theory. A case in point is the concept of length which played an important part in classical physics, but which is seen in general relativity to have become a highly conventional concept.

Thus we might say that in classical physics the term 'matter' is borrowed from the language of everyday life and is itself not of scientific significance. The situation in modern physics is somewhat different. In general relativity, for instance, the field equations could be interpreted as defining *material* properties (stress-energy tensor) in terms of *geometrical* properties of the space-time (Einstein tensor). One might therefore consider the space-time continuum (or, rather, a 3-dimensional section of it) as the analogue of matter insofar as it serves as a substratum from which at least some properties of material objects could be deduced. The attempts to construct analogues of material objects in a Ricci flat space-time (vanishing Einstein tensor) by the use of multiple connectivity tend to bear out this analogy. The vanishing of the Einstein tensor, by virtue of the field equations, implies the vanishing of the stress-energy tensor. The vanishing of the stress-energy tensor is taken to mean that space-time is to be considered empty of matter or radiation. The field equations are partial differential equations satisfied by the components of the metric tensor. As a consequence, these equations refer to local phenomena and do not necessarily impose global features on the space-time manifold. In other words, these equations are compatible with many different topological structures. If it be assumed that the manifold is multiply-connected in the way described by Dr. Misner in his essay below, then the equations predict the existence of entities which behave somewhat like material particles.

In a manner of speaking one has thus "constructed" material objects from empty space (more properly space-time). A certain amount of care is required if a double usage of the adjective 'empty' is to be avoided. In one sense of the term, the space-time is just as "empty" after the calculations as before, since 'empty' only means that the stress-energy tensor vanishes. Since, however, there are entities in this space-time which behave *like* material objects (and therefore in our usage are theoretical material objects), one could say that the space-time is *not* empty in this sense of the term. These results, at first sight paradoxical, need only imply that the vanishing of the stress-energy tensor is not a *sufficient* condition for the absence of "material" objects. Following the procedure just outlined, one might then go on to claim that an analogue not only for material objects but also for matter could be found in a space-time of this sort, since we seem to be "manufacturing" material objects from the continuum. But the continuum is the *four*-dimensional space-time manifold, not the three-dimensional one required for the definition of an individual material object. There is no *unique* way of splitting the four-dimensional manifold into a separate space and time. Thus we must look with suspicion upon the claim that an analogue of matter exists in general relativity.

In quantum field theory, the field could not be considered as the analogue of a material object, but it would perhaps be possible to consider it as the analogue of matter. This brings to the fore the question of the correctness of the assertion that the "elementary particles" generated by the field are material objects. For those cases in which the "particles" are localized, it would seem that they are theoretical material objects. However, since the uncertainty relations might be considered to play some role here and since a discussion of this role would take us too far afield, we do not pursue this question further. It is, however, worthwhile to indicate the possibility of making the field in quantum field-theory an analogue of matter.

It seems doubtful whether scientists make the identifications mentioned in the last two paragraphs. While such proposals are of interest philosophically, they are of little use from the scientific standpoint. Ultimately the scientist is interested in material objects and their properties rather than in matter in any philosophical sense. In fact, the term 'matter' as used by the scientist can usually be taken to refer in an unspecified way to some material object. We have pointed out the possibility of analogues for matter in two areas of physics. Let us now propose another possibility.

The Newtonian definition of mass as the measure of the quantity of matter in a body is empty, since the quantity of matter is not otherwise defined in the theory. On the other hand, the definition has a certain appeal since the theory does purport to describe the real world. One can recover this definition in a disguised form by a consideration of the Einstein mass-energy relation. Let us see how this can be done. Einstein showed that if energy were to be added to a system, the inertia of the system would increase, that is to say, the inertial mass of the system would increase. He thereby showed that we could consistently ascribe an inertial mass to localized energy. The famous equation $E = mc^2$ shows the relation between the amount of energy and the value of the associated mass. It would not be correct to say that this equation shows that mass and energy are the same, since mass is a measure whereas 'energy', at least in modern terminology, seems to be a "stuff-term", so to speak. We can use the equation to define mass as the measure of the energy-content of a body. If we do so, then we are ascribing all the mass to the energy-content of a body; this seems to be in accord with modern practice. By virtue of this definition, the word 'energy' has taken the place of the word 'matter' in the Newtonian definition. This definition for mass could be a corrected form of Newton's definition if we were to consider energy as the analogue of matter. This then is the proposal: that energy, being an entity well-defined in theory, is or could be thought of as the analogue of matter.

The fact that energy in present-day science has many of the mechanical attributes of Newtonian "matter" tends to make this proposal not unreasonable.

Whenever we have energy severely localized, we find that it possesses many of the attributes of material objects. In particular, the localization allows for an assignment of position. An inertial mass can be assigned, as also an active and passive gravitational mass. Because we are proposing that energy be the theoretical *analogue* of matter rather than simply identifying the two, we need not expect that every aspect of energy mirror some aspect of matter. That they do not *exactly* correspond is already indicated in classical physics where, for instance, the flow of energy down a driveshaft need not be considered as representing the flow of some subtle type of material. The possibility of taking energy to be the scientist's analogue of matter is due to the fact that in modern physics energy is an independent theoretical entity rather than a simple measure-characteristic of material objects. The aptness of the analogy would be difficult, if not impossible, to defend if one remained within the realm of classical physics.

One final point in favor of relating the concepts of energy and matter in this way. In modern science, 'energy' is a pervasive or all-embracing term just as 'matter' is with reference to the physical world. If the philosophic matter-concept is to have an analogue in science, it is a concept such as this that would be required.

Let us return, then, to our initial questions. What does the scientist mean when he uses the term 'matter'? One can answer that he usually means "material objects in general". The term 'matter' in the philosophical sense is not of direct scientific importance and in purely scientific discussions could be dispensed with. There may exist analogues of matter in various branches of science, insofar as these theories utilize substrata from which analogues of material objects and their properties may be deduced. The question as to what distinguishes matter and energy can be answered only if a theoretical analogue for matter can be found in science (considered as a whole), or if energy can be shown to be the analogue of something in reality. Neither of these has, so far, been accomplished, but both goals might be achieved by considering energy as a theoretical analogue of matter.

University of Notre Dame

MASS AS A FORM OF VACUUM

Charles W. Misner

§1 *Introduction*

In other essays in this collection N. R. Hanson has introduced the idea of a "field" and C. Mast has shown how fields began to take on the properties of matter with Einstein's discovery of the equivalence of energy (which is carried by fields as well as matter in motion) and mass (which had been a characteristic of matter only). I will attempt to portray the present day status of the "field" concept. In brief, it has been found most fruitful to formulate *all* the known laws of physics exclusively as mathematical relationships among various fields, so that the physicist's concept of matter must be extracted from his idea of a "field theory".

The basic ideas of field theory are developed in §2. There a field is characterized as *any property of empty space*; that is, of a region of space containing no matter in the nineteenth century sense. A field theory is then an attempt to state physical laws in a way that makes all space empty in this sense. In recent decades physicists, essentially unanimously, have accepted as a working hypothesis that all of physical reality can be described by some field theory. This acceptance is based on two things: (1) the lack of any better idea, and (2) the very substantial insight into the properties of matter that field theory has given since 1930. Implied in the second point here is the fact that automobiles and cyclotrons and other everyday pieces of matter find a place in theories which view the universe as simply empty space with varying potentialities.

To define and describe what a field theory is is an unusual occupation for a physicist. He is familiar with many examples of field theories; he teaches these theories and works with them or on them in his research. He has no need for a definition of the generic term since he is ultimately interested only in one theory, the right one, and it needn't even be a field theory. Corresponding to the physicist's preoccupation with examples, I have decided to try to present the idea of a field theory by an example. The primary reason why this example, rather than some other, was chosen is that in this particular theory computational mathematics can be replaced by pictures. The pictures will be quite a strain on the imagination, but in whatever form it is presented, a field theoretic description of matter is far removed from common sense ideas.

It is not quite accurate to have implied that the idea of a field is the only basic concept that is used in constructing current physical theories. There is also one other idea, that of "the state of a physical system". In classical physics this was a relatively simple idea: the state of the system distinguished which of the possible motions of a particle (i.e., motions allowed by the theory) was actually taking place, and it served a similar purpose in classical field theory. This concept of the state of a system was drastically modified by quantum theory, and the quantum idea of "the state of a system" certainly reflects very fundamental properties of matter. I have not paid much attention to quantum ideas in this essay, since they only carry to greater extremes my principal contention, namely that matter as described by modern physics is on the verge of evaporating into nothingness. The classical field theory example will suggest that matter is merely some arrangement of properties which are so simple they can be thought of as properties of space-time itself (rather than as properties of stuff present within space-time). A quantum field theory makes these properties themselves rather ephemeral; a definite, predictable value of any given property need not exist, and one must be content to say that only the probability of each conceivable value is determinate in quantum theory.

§2 *Fields*

The most common "field" in everyday experience is the gravitational field, but gravity is not a good way to illustrate the idea of a field, because it is so expensive to make or notice changes in the gravitational field. However, magnetic fields are also within the range of everyone's experience, and a few experiments with them are within the budget of most small boys. So let us approach the idea of a field by imagining a magnet lying on a desk. If we place a boy scout pocket compass somewhere near the magnet it will point in a particular direction. The physicist prefers to think of this behaviour of the compass as due to a property of space at the point where the compass lies, rather than simply saying it is due to the magnet. He does not deny that the magnet is responsible for the compass' behaviour, but describes it as a two-step process: first the magnet does something to the space around it and, secondly, the compass responds to the structure of the space where it lies. I will explain why this seemingly artificial separation is meaningful and significant after a word about the "structure of space", called a "magnetic field", which we postulate as an intermediary between magnet and compass.

One aspect of the magnetic field is revealed by the direction in which the compass points, a second aspect is shown by the strength of the twist (torque) which the compass needle would feel if it were held in any other direction. (The mathematical physicist summarizes this information by three numbers: one is called the strength of the magnetic field, two others specify its direction as one might specify the bearing and angle of elevation of a cannon.) The most important feature of the magnetic field in the present discussion is that in describing what a magnetic field is, *nothing more* can be added to what I have already said. That is, the magnetic field at a point in space is that property of space which is sufficient to determine the strength of the twist a small magnet would feel (if placed there) and the direction to which it would be turned.

There are other physical ideas which can be defined in similar ways, but which I do not want to call fields in this essay. For instance, I could define "flow" at a point as a property sufficient to determine the strength of the twist which a weathervane would feel and the direction to which it would turn. But I know that this idea is not an elementary property of space at that point, but a partial description of the matter flowing past that point. The type of matter (air, water, etc.) and the positions and velocities of the molecules that make up this matter are more basic properties which completely determine the "flow". Why then do I want to call the magnetic field a "field", why think of it as a property of space? Briefly, because this is the picture to which the past 150 years developments in physics have led. But more informatively, because these magnetic properties can exist at a point without there being any "matter" there. It was irrelevant that the magnet and compass were lying on a desk in a room full of air. The same results would have been obtained if they had been held in position by glass wires inside a vacuum chamber. This argument, of course, merely says that the effect depends only on the magnet, the compass, and their relative positions, so we will have to look somewhat deeper to understand why the physicist also eliminates the magnet and compass from his thoughts and still finds something left to think about, the magnetic field. First let us focus on the compass and wish it away. Once we have used one compass to give a measure of the magnetic field, we can replace it by other compasses of different construction, and predict their behaviour, or we can shoot an electron through this region of space and predict its motion merely on the basis of the information the first compass gave (without having to know anything else about the magnet). We could replace the compass by a sodium vapor lamp and predict how its color would change (viewed through a spectroscope). Or we could predict how much a penny would heat up if it were spun around several times in the place where the compass had been. In brief, so many different effects can occur at one point in space, all determined by a few numbers which measure the magnetic field at that point, that we insist on speaking of the field there rather than attempting to discuss directly the interaction between each of these different instruments and the magnet. The magnet is, in a similar way, irrelevant, for many different magnets, located in appropriate different positions, could produce the identical series of effects at the point in question, or one could use coils of wire (again in many possible arrangements) with electric current flowing through them to get the effects. There still remains one way in which we could try to deny independent reality to magnetic fields, that is, we could propose that a magnetic field around a magnet is just a part of the piece of matter we call a magnet, a sort of aura surrounding the magnet which belongs to it, but has a different appearance from the iron itself. This point of view becomes difficult when we discover that if the magnet is shaken violently enough, little pieces of magnetic field break loose and go running away by themselves. (These bits of field are called radio waves, light, or gamma rays. Energetic ones can give quite violent displays when they hit a lead plate in a cloud chamber.)

The preceding discussion should give some impression of why physicists speak of fields, rather than of pieces of matter interacting with each other. In nineteenth century physics only two fields were known, the electromagnetic field and the gravitational field, and an idea of matter as "stuff" producing these fields was essential. Now, however, electrons, protons, and other "elementary" particles are described as manifestations of quantum mechanical fields. The theories which presently best describe the properties of matter, i.e., of crystals, gases, atoms, nuclei, etc., make no use of any concept of matter that does not enter the theory in the form of a field. The "stuff" is gone.

In the next section I shall describe a field theory (so that nothing but properties of empty space enter in the statement of the theory), and try to indicate how such a theory might serve as a model for a real universe containing matter. To a physicist it is not a good theory, that is, it does not agree with many experiments or observations. In particular, no quantum mechanical effects are taken into consideration, and there is nothing in the theory that can be called an electron or a proton. Its only purpose here is to indicate that it is possible to make a mathematical model using only the idea of a space with various properties, and end up with structures whose behaviour corresponds in some respects to that of pieces of matter. Whether it is possible to make a mathematical model which includes structures corresponding to every observable aspect of matter is the ultimate question in physics.

§3 *A Field Theory*

One aim of a discussion of field theory could be to show that physicists do not, at present, find it necessary to use any concept of matter beyond the idea of a field. But however much that discussion would teach about modern physics and about matter, it could not show that the concept of matter can in fact be reduced to the idea of interrelated properties of empty space. For no physicist believes he can safely predict in what terms the currently outstanding problems will be solved.

Therefore I will ignore the question of whether it appears more or less likely that matter can be described entirely in terms of fields, and with it the problem of how accurately and comprehensively matter is presently described purely by fields. Instead, I will merely try to suggest that it is not obviously inconsistent to imagine that the idea of matter can be replaced by that of a field. This will be done by giving an example of a field theory in which matter can be constructed out of fields. The theory is only an example, and the "matter" which arises in it cannot be found in nature. The reason I say matter arises in the theory is not that there appear various structures which behave respectively very much like protons, electrons, etc., but rather because there appear structures whose behaviour includes a few of the properties common to all pieces of matter, whether they be protons, baseballs, or planets. We will return later to this question of how we can claim matter arises out of fields, and begin now with an exposition of the example of a field theory.

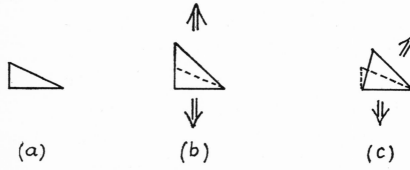

(a)   (b)   (c)

FIG. 1. The sides of a triangle drawn on a piece of rubber, as in (a), change their lengths when the rubber is stretched as in (b). A suitable combination of twisting and stretching as in (c) will change the length of only one side.

The first specification we make in setting up a field theory is the choice of the field or fields which will enter in the theory, that is, we decide what properties we are willing to imagine our empty space may possess. For the present example we decide to ignore any property space might possess except its geometry, and proceed to study what is meant here by 'geometry'. Since the imagination can more easily seize upon matter than upon empty space, we imagine a thin sheet of rubber as a model of two-dimensional space. Some aspects of the geometry are determined as soon as we say "two-dimensional," others are as yet unspecified, i.e. the rubber sheet may be stretched or bent into all kinds of shapes. As the space with which the theory is concerned is always four-dimensional, the shape aspect of geometry is the field of interest.

The concept of the shape of a space can be made more precise; and at the same time we will see that the "shape field" is not an entirely different category of thing from the magnetic field discussed in the previous section. (The "shape" of the space-time we live in is called the gravitational field, but I shall not try to make this statement plausible.) Two ways in which the shape field resembles the magnetic field are (1) it is determined by a local property of space, i.e. by a property that can be defined at each point of space, and (2) this local property can be described by giving a few numbers at each point. These statements are not obvious, and we pick up our sheet of rubber again in order to understand them. Imagine a small triangle marked in ink at some point on the rubber sheet as in Fig. (1a). Then if the rubber is stretched, the lengths of the sides of the triangle change (Fig. 1b), and in fact, a suitable combination of stretching and twisting will change the length of any one side of the triangle without affecting the others (Fig. 1c). Thus the three sides of the triangle may be independently changed in length, while no deformation at all is possible if the lengths are held fixed. (A parallelogram, in contrast, can be collapsed by a deformation which does not change the lengths of its sides.) We define the "metric field" as that property of space which determines the length of any line, and whose value at a given point may be specified by giving the lengths of the sides of a small triangle drawn at that point.[1] If one imagines a round rubber ball being stretched into the shape of a football, it should be obvious that the metric field changes its value at most points (i.e. small triangles drawn on the ball would have altered sizes or shapes when it became a football). This shows that the idea of the "metric field" and of the "shape (and size) of a space" are very closely related; that they are in fact equivalent ideas we accept as a theorem from mathematics.

It is the job of mathematicians to discover or invent abstractions, and then to analyze logical relations among them. What I really want when I say "space" is the mathematicians' idea, which is not a sheet of rubber but a

---

[1] In three-dimensional space, the triangle of this definition is replaced by a tetrahedron. It is the figure obtained by drawing all possible lines joining four points chosen as vertices. It has six edges (so the metric in three space requires six numbers to specify it) and its faces are four triangles. The corresponding figure in four dimensions is called a 4-simplex, and is obtained by fitting all possible edges, faces, etc. between five points chosen as vertices. It has ten edges whose lengths specify the metric field at a point in 4-space, and its "faces" are five tetrahedrons.

sheet without the rubber. It may be defined in terms of points and logical relations among these points sufficient to characterize ideas of "nearby points"
and "smooth" arrangements of points (topology and differentiable structure), which give meaning to words like 'two-dimensional'. Specifying the
distances between nearby points then adds further logical relations (metric
structure) among the points which I identify with the idea of the "shape" of
the space. Both the "two-dimensional" and the "shape" properties of the
rubber sheets can be defined as relationships among the points of the sheet
only, and require for their definition nothing analogous to the three-dimensional space which our imaginations will always show us surrounding the
two dimensional sheet. Thus the mathematical idea of the "shape" of space
can apply as well to three (or four) dimensional space without requiring us
to postulate a still higher dimensional space in which to measure the shape
of a three dimensional surface. (The simplest way to discover that the space
in which we live is curved would be to add up the angles in a (large) triangle and find a sum different from 180°. This has essentially been done, using light rays to define the straight edges of the triangle; the curvature of
space is found to be measurably different from zero. I am here thinking of
observations known as the "bending of light by the sun".)

The statement of our field theory has not yet gone beyond the injunction
to think only about geometry, i.e. we have specified what field we are considering. What is lacking yet is a statement about how this field is to behave,
that is, how the shapes of space at various different points are related and in-

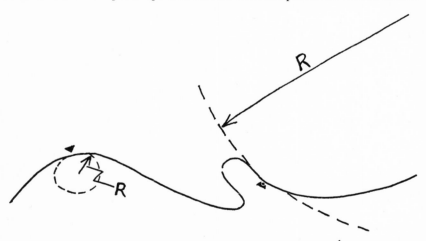

Fig. 2. The curvature of a curve at some point is the number $\frac{1}{R}$ where R is the
radius of that circle which best fits the curve at that point. If R is large, the curvature
is small.

teract with each other. Such a statement is called a "field equation", and I want to impose the Einstein equations on our four dimensional space-time. In order to get some idea of how these equations look, and how they determine the geometry, we need some idea of what curvature is.

The simplest situation in which curvature arises is when we consider just a curved line as in Fig. 2. By trying out what size of arc best matches the curving line at a point we determine a radius of curvature, R, at that point. So that a sharply bent line has a high curvature, while a straight line has zero curvature we define the curvature to be the number $\frac{1}{R}$. The next more complicated situation is when we imagine a two-dimensional surface sketched out in ordinary three dimensional-space, as in Fig. 3. Then if we try to choose a circle which can be held perpendicular to the surface and ad-

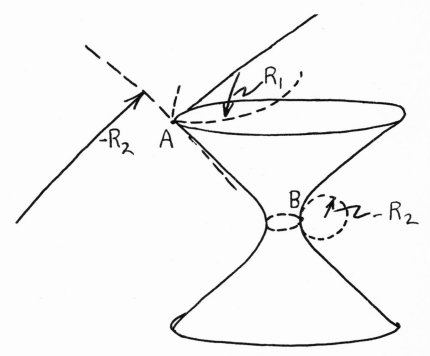

Fig. 3. The principal radii of curvature, R_1 and R_2, are shown for a surface which is shaped like the neck of an hour glass. These quantities are the radii of those two circles lying in planes perpendicular to the surface which most closely follow the curve of the surface at any given point. (The circles are shown for two different points, A, B.) Since the circles lie on opposite sides of the surface, one of the radii is considered negative.

justed to fit, we will find two different circles, perpendicular to each other, which best fit. Their radii, R_1 and R_2, determine the two "principal curvatures" of the surface, $\dfrac{1}{R_1}$ and $\dfrac{1}{R_2}$. A good way to get familiar with this idea is to compute the principal curvatures at various points on an inner tube by imagining the "best fit" circles. (One of the principal curvatures is constant, the other is both positive and negative at different points. Where is it zero?)

In many respects, the equation:

$$\frac{1}{R_1} + \frac{1}{R_2} = 0$$

which some (but rather few) two-dimensional surfaces satisfy, gives a good idea of what the Einstein equations require of a four-dimensional space. Its first point of resemblance is a formal resemblance; it requires, as does the Einstein equation, that some average of curvatures in various directions vanishes. Closely related to this formal resemblance is a similarity in content, namely that a "flat" space satisfies the equation, but not every space which satisfies the equation is "flat". For the equation I have just written it is quite easy to find non-flat solutions, due to the fact that an inexpensive analogue computer can be constructed to solve this equation. The procedure for constructing a solution is the following: take a closed loop of stiff wire and bend it into any desired shape, then dip it into a dish of soapy water and take it out gently. The soap film which spans the wire loop is a two dimensional surface satisfying our equation. (The reader is expected to accept this assertion as a matter of blind faith.) In addition to providing illlustrations of solutions of a field equation, this example illustrates an important property which is shared by all good field equations including the Einstein equation, namely that the value of the field throughout some region (shape of the soap film) is determined by its values on the boundary of that region (by shape of the wire), and that these boundary values are arbitrary, at least to some extent.

The preceding model of the Einstein equation also has some failings. The first is that it brings in the idea of three-dimensional space while discussing a two-dimensional surface. A sheet of paper satisfies the equation while it lies flat, but no longer does if rolled into a cylinder, yet the metric field (distances measured on the paper) do not change during this process, since paper cannot be stretched. A measure of the curvature which can be shown to depend *only* on the metric field is the product of the principal curvatures, $\dfrac{1}{R_1} \times \dfrac{1}{R_2}$, which may be called the "intrinsic" curvature of the surface. The Einstein equation involves only such intrinsic curvatures, so there is no need to think of curved space-time as a surface drawn in some higher-dimensional space. (In two dimensions, there is only one intrinsic curvature, but for a curved three-dimensional space we may, for instance, associate a different intrinsic curvature with each of three perpendicular two dimensional surfaces drawn through any point. Thus we recover the possibility of writing a field equation which sets some average of the curvatures to zero without making them all zero.) A second difficulty with the two-dimensional "soap film" equation is that any interesting wrinkles or bumps we specify on the boundary of the soap film always smooth out as we move away from the boundary. When we discuss how the four-dimensional theory provides a very crude model of mater, we will see that this "smoothing out" property of the soap film equation means that none of its solutions show structures which preserve themselves well enough to serve as models of pieces of matter.

Now, finally, let us try to discuss directly the theory of interest, namely four-dimensional spaces (space-times) satisfying the Einstein equation. We know from the soap film analogy that the Einstein equation says a particular average of the various (intrinsic) curvatures vanishes, and that as a consequence of this requirement, some properties of a three-dimensional boundary of a space-time region will determine the shape of the entire space-time. This last result, which gives us what is called a "boundary value problem", I want to discuss further since it is an essential point in any mathematical model of matter in motion. It is most convenient first to quickly be rid of four dimensions, and think instead of a curved three-dimensional space whose shape changes in time. Then this three-dimensional space at one fixed time can be regarded as the boundary of the four-dimensional region consisting of space at all later times (as I will illustrate presently). Then, just as the shape of the soap film boundary determines the shape of the soap film, one can discover that the shape of a space at a given time determines (as a consequence of the Einstein equations) the shape of space at all later times. Consequently, if we can interpret some aspects of the "shape of space" as representing matter at a given time, the theory completely determines the future behaviour of this "matter". The characteristic that the present "state of the system" completely determines its future state is found in all current physical theories. It is a very important characteristic of a physical theory because it means that the theory makes predictions, and can therefore be compared with experiments.

In order to speak more specifically about the sort of predictions this theory can make, we need a method of describing the shape of space-time, i.e. a means of drawing pictures of a curved four-dimensional space-time. Without considerable mathematical apparatus, it is impossible to describe such a space in any way that displays every detail of its structure. However, quite simple pictures can suggest all the main features. The whole trick in these pictures is to ignore a few dimensions and thus cut the space down to a manageable size. The first step in this direction is to think of a four-dimensional space as a curved three-dimensional space whose shape changes in time. To represent this three-dimensional space, we draw a picture of just one two-dimensional sheet of it. This sheet should be considered analogous to a single sheet of typewriter paper pulled out of the center of a full sheaf. (likewise, the entire three-dimensional space is to be thought of as a single sheet pulled from a four-dimensional sheaf; as time moves on we turn our attention successively to sheets lying higher and higher in the pack.) In Fig. 4, I have drawn a two-dimensional sheet taken from a three-space with two bumps in it, i.e. two regions where the curvature is high. The best way to imagine how this two-space lies in the curved three-space, is to notice how a single line (one-space) lies in the two-space we have drawn. One such line has been redrawn seperately, and we see that it is enough to suggest the entire two-space. It is in the same sense that the two-space is to suggest a curved three-space. But now, when a single line will suggest a simple sort of curved three-space to us, we have room on the paper to draw a four-

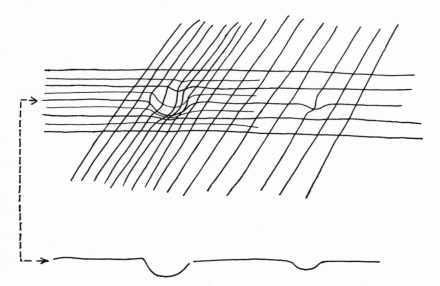

Fig. 4. The upper drawing shows a two-dimensional space with bumps in it (curved regions). By drawing only a single line from this space, but one that passes through the bumps, we can suggest the entire two-space (lower drawing). In the same way, the two-space shown here may be regarded as merely a single sheet taken from a three-space which has bumps in it.

space (Fig. 5). In this diagram each line marked with a particular time represents the shape of space at that time, and by stacking all these pictures of spaces together, we build a space-time of one higher dimension than space. The main point of this picture is to show that the "the shape of space-time" determines how the shape of space changes with time. It also helps to show how "space at a given time" may be regarded as the boundary of a space-time region. (The boundary in this case does not enclose the region completely, as it did in the soap film example.)

§4 *Matter and Space*

In what sense can "the shape of space" serve as a model of matter? This question, referring to the example of a field theory under discussion here, is to serve as a specific and simplified version of the question "What concept of matter do the field theories of modern physics suggest?" but I will be content to answer only the first question explicitly. A three-dimesional mathematical space with the shape shown in Fig. 4 can, I propose, be taken as a crude model of physical space containing two chunks of "matter". Whether this is a reasonable proposal depends on how the model behaves. The first important feature that this model has in common with matter is that there may or may not be matter in a given region of space, i.e. once we decide to compare bumps in space with matter we notice that we can equally well imagine spaces with many bumps or few, here or there, just as easily as arranging golf balls on a laboratory bench. The next feature is a very non-trivial mathematical theorem about the Einstein equations,

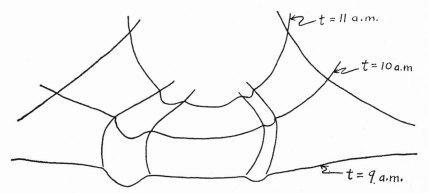

Fig. 5. When a single line, $t = constant$, is understood to represent all of space at a given time, a two-dimensional surface such as this can suggest an entire four-dimensional space-time. One can also see from this sketch that the way the shape of three-space changes with time is related to the shape of four-dimensional space-time.

namely that if the bumps in space are constructed properly at the start, then they change very little as time goes on.

Thus, when the bumps are interpreted as pieces of matter, these pieces of matter remain in existence for reasonable lengths of time; that is to say a given piece will exist for as long as we like if it is very carefully made and gently handled, while if two pieces collide violently they may disintegrate. My remarks here about "making" pieces of "matter" refer of course to how one might specify the shape of a mathematical three-space in such a way as to determine a unique space-time (mathematical four-space satisfying the Einstein equations). The question of whether two bumps will eventually collide is also determined by the initial conditions. For the properties of the initial three-space which must be specified in the boundary value problem actually include not only the intrinsic shape of this three-space, which shows what sort of bumps are where, but also some other geometrical information which includes the velocities with which the bumps are moving at this particular time. The third successful feature of this model it that those bumps which last for a long time actually move in rather reasonable ways. That is, a single bump left to itself moves in a straight line with constant velocity, while two bumps which are far apart attract each other according to Newton's laws of gravity. It is in fact possible to make a mathematical model (a curved space-time satisfying the Einstein "empty space" equations) which has several bumps corresponding respectively to the sun and each of the planets, in which the motion of these bumps agrees with the observed planetary orbits as well as these orbits are known. In contrast, the bumps themselves look *nothing* like the planets, and the one corresponding to the earth is only the size of a golf ball. Thus this particular simple theory has no place in it for any of the specific kinds of matter that actually exist in the world.

Princeton University

DISCUSSION

Hanson: I have two difficulties here. You point out that in principle there is nothing which forbids one to characterize singularity phenomena in field-theoretic terms. Suppose this is granted. Then perhaps you get more and more singularity-type phenomena which are less and less amenable to the field approach. But you will keep saying: I can explain them in field terms. But this is compatible with anything whatever that happens.

Misner: If things go this way for a while, I would almost certainly give up my preference for fields.

Hanson: Let me ask, then, what is it that motivates this attempt to eliminate particles in favor of a field approach? What advantage is expected from this? What makes you feel that there is a tension between the particle and the field pictures such that one of them should be eliminated? If certain phenomena are now being adequately explained in particle terms, why force them into the mold of field theory?

Misner: It is in the spirit of the times to try to unify in this way and the field approach seems to hold out the better possibilities. But a formal particle view would, in principle, be equally acceptable.

Mc Mullin: Your model is supposed to simulate the behavior of matter even though there "really" isn't any matter there. The geometrization is somehow supposed to have eliminated it. I am puzzled however to know just what *has* been eliminated. You speak of matter in different senses: matter is what cannot be modelled, that which resists formal treatment, a Platonic barrier to intelligibility; matter is something with properties that can be simulated by other presumably "non-material" entities; matter is what scientists talk about; matter is hard, massy, etc. Which of these "matters" is no longer there in your model?

Misner: The matter that isn't there never was. It was an illusion of a previous century of science.

Mc Mullin: This is the "matter" of 17th century science with certain properties you no longer find any need for. Yet you still retain the term 'matter' for any object of scientific concern.

Misner: Yes, I do think of matter as that which can be pointed at and theorized about.

Mc Mullin: But this leaves an ambiguity. Can space be pointed at, and properties assigned to it? If so, it is not strictly nothing; it is, in fact, "material" in this sense of 'matter'. Then what do you mean by the phrase 'empty space' that you frequently use? Classically, this meant space in which there was no "matter", but this sense is ruled out for you.

Misner: May we not decide that "empty" space has sufficiently many properties to be capable of being pointed at? 'Empty space' means an object which is capable of having the properties I require of it and which is defined as incapable of having any other properties. Is there such a thing as empty space? That is a question that as a physicist I would never discuss; as a mathematician, I say, yes there is a mathematical object which is capable of having these properties and no others. It is nothing but a web of mathematical relationships, and this is why I speak of "dematerialization".

Hanson: Dr. Misner's field-theoretic approach ought not to be simply contrasted with a particle approach as I at first thought; these two approaches are probably in the last analysis formally reducible to each other anyway. His point is to provide a general mathematical framework within terms of which one can deal with all the apparent experimental features of matter which come up. The issue is not field versus non-field, but *total* mathematical reduction versus partial. Is it the case that every feature of nature which is amenable to treatment by the physicist is in principle amenable also to a complete mathematical treatment in general terms? If someone says yes, then the onus of proof is on the person who objects: "You've got a mathematical formulation here but isn't there some difference between that and nature as it really stands". Dr. Misner's challenge seems to be: "Tell me what it is I'm lacking and I'll get a bit more mathematics".

Misner: I'm not sure that this *is* my challenge. I would rather allow that there may be something missing from the formal account. But there isn't as much missing as most Aristotelians I've ever heard think there is.

*   *   *   *   *

Misner: In the discussions of ether in the last century a distinction was made between the "field" which was a quality of the ether, and the "stuff" which was the ether itself. This distinction has been disappearing. Einstein could say: we have the ether back under another name. Space and fields are now considered to be just as corporeal as electrons. And matter is just the subject-matter of physics.

Mc Mullin: Why is ether no longer thought of in terms of stuff?

Misner: Because stuff implies mystery, something which is not yet completely described but which has as a partial description certain specified properties. But the new ether is defined *entirely* in terms of the properties specified.

McMullin: Are you suggesting that the ether-concept does in fact exhaustively describe the physical universe?

Misner: No, it's a developing concept. The physicist thinks only a very few properties will be needed to specify it.

Mc Mullin: If you are willing to make a distinction between the physicists' present model and that of which it is a model, could not one still ask whether the model is not a model *of* "stuff", that is, of something that in your terms has some predicates still undiscovered?

Misner: No, it's not. Stuff is something like the fluid studied in hydrodynamics; in the theory of fluid motions, one would focus entirely on density, temperature and so forth. But it would be understood that other adjectives which do not occur in this theory could be applied to any real fluid, for example, its electric polarizability. That's why it is a "stuff": an object of research which, understood in the light of present thought, is not an attempt to describe everything. On the other hand the new ether is the object of a discussion in which the explicit aim is to include everything. In mathematics, you can take a number of objects, like 1, 7, 10, and consider the set of them as a new object. As an object of thought, it is distinct from the three numbers, but it is entirely specified by them. In the same way, having listed all the properties you need to discuss, the set of these properties is in some logical sense the thing that possesses them. A statement of them defines the object and is thus exhaustive. Does one need any deeper idea of what they are properties of than that they are considered together as a unit?

McMullin: What you are saying is not so much that the present development challenges the notions of substance and substratum but rather that science *must* leave the substratum aside. It is, by definition, what science is for the moment not interested in; science says: let's forget about everything other than the properties presently being discussed. It does not deny their existence however.

Misner: Yes, I would agree up to a point. But this formulation implies that the rest which is being ignored has material properties of the same kind as those already being studied, properties which other sciences or other types of experiment could handle. This is what justifies us in saying that there *is* a "rest." But as you go deeper and deeper, the question is: By including so much, aren't you throwing light on what remains? What *does* remain?

Lobkowicz: It might help to think of your "properties" here not as accidents in the Aristotelean sense (thus needing a substratum) but simply as forms of an unspecified sort in terms of which the description is to be carried out. No hidden *Ding an sich* is meant to be implied.

McMullin: Would it be agreed, then, that the present development of field theories is irrelevant to the problem of a substratum?

Fisk: I would disagree . . . In a complete field theory, the properties would be "attached" to locations, but the locations themselves, so to speak, would not be fully characterizable by the properties. If someone wanted a structure similar to that of "pincushion plus properties," he could have it in the co-ordinate system plus the field-variables.

Taliaferro: What you're saying is that the physical space I am describing mathematically cannot be *fully* specified in this way . . .

Oesterle: The metaphor of a "blank check" which Dr. Hanson used to describe the role of matter in science might help at this point. If this isn't a return to prime matter, at least it indicates something purely potential in the background . . .

Manier: I don't think this is quite the common thread you are taking it to be. Dr. Misner seems to be talking about the possibility of indefinitely extended

611

research, and this is being taken as equivalent to the concept of prime matter, where the notion of the possibility of research has somehow replaced that of pure possibility. I find this a curious substitution. It is true that Leibniz's infinitely complex concept of the individual substance admitted a similar view of indefinitely continued research, but I do not think that it can play the same role in explaining *contingency* as prime matter did for Aristotle . . .

Lobkowicz: Would we say that the ether is an *X* which has certain specified properties and that there is no more to be known of it?

Misner: I regard that as acceptable. Your question is: Should the ether differ in *any* respect from its conception? My answer is: no.

Mc Mullin: Suppose the ether is not regarded as an *X* still ahead for science, an unknown. It is, on the contrary, completely known. But how about the unknown? Is it to be characterized as a reservoir of unexplored properties, whose "unlimited" character simply results from the infinite number or complexity of such properties? In that case, the matter *has* been reduced to a set of properties any one of which is in principle formally expressible. Or does its unlimit come from a constituent which is radically incapable of being formally expressed in the first place?

Misner: Why should the unknown be inexhaustible either? There may be only a few more properties, and these will be of the same general type as electric charge; individuality would not be a "property" in this sense . . . If everything not yet understood by science be listed as "matter", then the progress of physics is constantly shrinking it, and the question is: is there a non-zero limit to this shrinking? Is there a *scientific* way of answering this question? And if the answer is yes, is the "residue" to be identified with the primary matter of the philosopher? But if the answer be: no, as I have suggested, then what effect will this have upon the discussion of primary matter? . . .

Biographical Notes on the Authors

JOSEPH BOBIK, born July 21, 1927, Binghamton, N.Y. B.A., 1947, St. Bernard's College, Rochester; M.A., 1951; Ph.D., 1953, University of Notre Dame. Instructor in philosophy, Marymount College, Los Angeles, 1953-4; Marquette University, 1954-5; Assistant Professor, University of Notre Dame, 1955-61; Associate Professor, 1961—Recent articles include: "A note on the question: 'Is being a genus?'", *Philosophical Studies* (Maynooth, 1957); "A note on a problem about individuality", *Australasian Journal of Philosophy* (1958); "Some remarks on Father Owens' 'St. Thomas and the future of metaphysics'", *New Scholasticism* (1959).

A. ROBERT CAPONIGRI, born Nov. 16, 1915, Chicago, Illinois. A.B., Loyola University (Chicago), 1935; Ph.D., University of Chicago, 1942. Instructor, State University of Iowa, 1943-6; Assistant Professor in Philosophy, University of Notre Dame, 1946-52; Associate Professor, 1952-6; Professor, 1956- . Lecturer at Luigi Sturzo Institute, Rome, 1961. Author: *The Philosophy of Joseph de Maistre* (1945); *Time and Idea* (1953); *History and Liberty* (1955); editor: *Modern Catholic Thinkers* (1960); editor and translator: *The Prince of Machiavelli* (1963); *De Hominis Dignitate* of Pico della Mirandola (1959); *Church and State* of Luigi Sturzo (1962).

VERE CLAIBORNE CHAPPELL, born March 22, 1930, Rochester, N.Y. B.A., 1951; M.A., 1953; Ph.D., 1958, Yale University; Fulbright Fellow, Universität Heidelberg, 1953-4. Instructor, Yale University, 1954-7; Instructor, Assistant Professor and Associate Professor of Philosophy, University of Chicago, 1957—. Managing Editor, *Review of Metaphysics*, 1954-6; Assistant Editor, *Ethics*, 1958-61; Assistant Treasurer, *Philosophical Quarterly*, 1959—. Editor of *The Philosophy of Mind* (1962); *The Philosophy of David Hume*, in press; *Philosophy and Ordinary Language*, in press. Author of articles in *Analysis, Journal of Philosophy, Mind, Philosophical Quarterly, Philosophical Review*, etc.

LEONARD J. ESLICK, born November 8, 1914, Denver, Colorado. B.A., University of Chicago, 1934; M.A., Tulane University, 1936; Ph.D., University of Virginia, 1939. Instructor in Philosophy, Drake University, 1939-42; Tutor, St. John's College, Annapolis, 1943-8; Associate Professor, St. Louis University, 1948-57; Visiting Professor, University of Virginia, 1961; Professor of Philosophy, St. Louis University, 1957—. Associate Editor, *Modern Schoolman*. President, *Missouri Philosophical Association*, 1958-9. Recent articles include: "Dyadic character of being in Plato", *Modern Schoolman* (1953); "The Platonic dialectic of Non-Being", *New Scholasticism* (1955); "What is the starting point of Metaphysics?", *Modern Schoolman* (1957); "Substance, change and causality in Whitehead", *Philosophy and Phenomenological Research* (1958); "The two Cratyluses: the problem of identity of indiscernibles", *Atti del XII Congresso Internazionale de Filosofia* (1960); "Aristotle and the identity of indiscernibles", *Modern Schoolman* (1959).

HERBERT FEIGL, born December 14, 1902, Reichenberg (then Austria-Hungary), studied at Universities of Munich and Vienna, 1921-7; Ph.D., University of Vienna, 1927. Rockefeller Fellowship, Harvard, 1930; Rockefeller Fellowship, Columbia and Harvard, 1940; Guggenheim Fellowship, 1947; Fellow of the American

Association for the Advancement of Science, 1947. Taught at University of Iowa 1931-40; Professor of Philosophy, University of Minnesota, 1941. Director of newly-established Minnesota Center for Philosophy of Science, University of Minnesota, 1953; member of Governing Board, *Philosophy of Science,* 1961; President, American Philosophical Association (Western Division), 1962. Visiting professor, University of California, 1946-53; Columbia University, New York, 1950; University of Puerto Rico, 1957; University of Hawaii, 1958; Austrian College, International Forum, 1961. Co-editor of *Readings in Philosophical Analysis* with Wilfrid Sellars); *Readings in the Philosophy of Science* (with May Brodbeck), 1953; co-editor (with Wilfrid Sellars) of the journal, *Philosophical Studies;* co-editor of *Minnesota Studies in the Philosophy of Science,* (with Michael Scriven, 1956); (with Michael Scriven and Grover Maxwell, 1958); (with Grover Maxwell, 1961).

MILTON FISK, born February 15, 1932, Lexington, Kentucky. B.S., University of Notre Dame, 1953; Ph.D., Yale University, 1958. Instructor and Assistant Professor, University of Notre Dame, 1957-63. Recent articles include: "Contraries", *Methodos* (1959); "Language and the having of concepts", *Notre Dame Journal of Formal Logic* (1961); "Cause and time in physical theory", *Review of Metaphysics* (1963).

JOHN JAMES FITZGERALD, born April 12, 1912, Bristol, R.I. A.B., 1933, Boston College; Ph.D., 1937, University of Louvain. Special Fellow, C.R.B. Educational Foundation, 1935-7, University of Louvain. Advanced Fellow, Belgian American Educational Foundation, 1947-8, University of Louvain and Cambridge University. Instructor, Assistant Professor and Associate Professor, University of Notre Dame, 1937 to present. Articles include: "The nature of physical science and the objectives of the scientist", *Philosophy* (1952); "Philosophy for science students", *Physics Today* (1955); "The contemporary status of natural philosophy", *Proceedings American Catholic Philosophical Association* (1957); "Philosophy, science and the human situation", *Review of Politics* (1962).

MARIE BOAS HALL, born 1919, Springfield, Mass. A.B., 1940; M.A., 1942, Radcliffe College; Ph.D., Cornell University, 1949. Instructor and Assistant Professor of History, University of Massachusetts, 1949-52; Brandeis University, 1952-7 (on leave as Guggenheim Fellow, 1955-6); Assistant and Associate Professor of History of Science, University of California at Los Angeles, 1957-61; Professor of History and Logic of Science, Indiana University, 1961-3; Senior Lecturer in History of Science and Technology, Imperial College, London, 1963- . Author of "The Establishment of the mechanical philosophy", *Osiris* (1952); *Robert Boyle and XVIIth Century Chemistry* (1958); *The Scientific Renaissance 1450-1630* (1962); and (with A. Rupert Hall) *Unpublished Scientific Papers of Isaac Newton* (1962).

NORWOOD RUSSELL HANSON, born August 17, 1924, West New York, N.J.; B.A., University of Chicago, 1946; B.Sc., Columbia University, 1948; M.A., Columbia University, 1949; B.Phil., Oxford University, 1953; M.A. Cambridge University, 1953; D. Phil., Oxford University, 1955; Ph.D. Cambridge University, 1956. Lecturer and Tutor, Oxford, 1951-2; University Lecturer, Cambridge, 1952- . Fellow, St. John's College, Cambridge, 1956. Professor of Philosophy, Indiana University, 1957-63; Chairman, Department of Logic and History of Science, 1960-2; Vice-President, A.A.A.S., 1961; Distinguished Service Alumni Award, Columbia University, 1962; Professor of Philosophy, Yale University, 1963- . Author of *Patterns of Discovery* (1958); *The Concept of the Positron* (1963).

MARY B. HESSE, born 1924, Reigate, England. B.Sc., 1945; Ph.D., 1948, University of London; Lecturer in Mathematics, University of Leeds, 1951-5; Lecturer in History and Philosophy of Science, 1955-9, University College of London; Lecturer in Philosophy of Science, University of Cambridge, 1959- ; Visiting Professor, Yale University, 1962. Author of *Science and the Human Imagination* (1954); *Forces and Fields* (1961); *Models and Analogies in Science* (1963).

ROBERT O. JOHANN, S.J., born April 7, 1924; Jesuit since 1942 (ordained priest in 1954). A.B., 1947; M.A., 1948, St. Louis University; Ph.D., 1953, Louvain University; S.T.L., 1954, Woodstock College. Instructor and Assistant Professor of Philosophy, Fordham University (Shrub Oak), 1956- ; Visiting Lecturer in Philosophy, Loyola University (Chicago), summer 1962; Visiting Associate Professor of Philosophy, Yale University, 1963-4; Councillor of the Metaphysical Society of America for 1962-6. Author of *The Meaning of Love* (1955); "Subjectivity", *Review of Metaphysics* (1958); "Charity and Time", *Cross Currents* (1959); "Experience and Philosophy" in *Experience, Existence, and the Good* (ed. I.C.Lieb, 1961); "The Logic of Evolution", *Thought* (1961).

CZESLAW LEJEWSKI, born April 20, 1913, Minsk, now in Russia. Magister Filozofii in Classics, 1936, University of Warsaw; Ph.D. in Logic and Scientific Method, 1955, University of London; Assistant Lecturer in Philosophy, University of Manchester, 1956-8; Lecturer, 1958- ; Visiting Professor, University of Notre Dame, Indiana, 1960-1. Recent articles include: "Logic and Existence", *British Journal for the Philosophy of Science* (1954-5); "Proper Names", *Aristotelian Society* (Suppl. 1957); "On Lesniewski's ontology", *Ratio* (1957-8); "On implicational definitions", *Studia Logica* (1958); "A Re-examination of the Russellian theory of descriptions", *Philosophy* (1960); "Studies in the axiomatic foundations of Boolean algebra", *Notre Dame Journal of Formal Logic* (1960 and 1961); "On prosleptic syllogisms" (*ibid.* 1961).

NIKOLAUS LOBKOWICZ, born July 9, 1931, Prague, Czechoslovakia. Ph.D., University of Fribourg, Switzerland, 1958. First assistant at the Institute of East European Studies, University of Fribourg, 1958-60; Associate Professor of Philosophy, University of Notre Dame, 1960- . Consulting editor, *Studies in Soviet Thought,* 1962- ; Editor for Philosophy, *Entsiklopedichesky Slovar'* (Freiburg, Germany). Author of *Das Widerspruchsprinzip in der neuren sowjetischen philosophie* (1960); *Marxismus-Leninismus in der CSR* (1962); "Deduction of Sensibility", *International Philosophical Quarterly* (1963).

NORBERT ALFONS LUYTEN, born 1909 in Belgium. Ph.D., S.Th.L., Dominican House of Study; ordained priest, 1933. Philosophical studies, University of Louvain. Professor of Philosophy in Studium Sancti Thomae, Ghent. Ordinary Professor of cosmology and philosophical psychology, University of Fribourg, Switzerland since 1945. Visiting Professor at Montreal University, 1949-50 and 1950-1. Rector, University Fribourg, 1956-8. Dean of Philosophical Faculty, 1948-9 and 1961-3. President, Philosophical Society, Fribourg. Associate Member of Société Philosophique de Louvain. Founding Member of *Tijdschrift voor Philosophie*. Author of *Unsterblichkeit* (1956); *La condition corporelle de l'homme* (1957); *Universität und Weltanschaaung* (1959). Also articles in Dutch, French, German and American journals on problems of philosophy of nature and philosophical psychology.

A. EDWARD MANIER, born April 7, 1931, Versailles, Ohio. B.S., 1953, University of Notre Dame; M.A., 1956; Ph.D., 1961, St. Louis University. Lecturer in Philosophy and Chemistry, Webster College, Missouri, 1956-9; Instructor in Philosophy, 1959-62; Assistant Professor of Philosophy, 1962- , University of Notre Dame. Unpublished dissertation: *The Meaning of Nature in Leibniz.*

CECIL B. MAST, born February 21, 1927, Chicago. B.S., 1950, DePaul University; Ph.D. (Physics), University of Notre Dame, 1956. Scholar, Dublin Institute for Advanced Studies, 1957-9. Assistant Professor of Mathematics, University of Notre Dame, 1959-63; Associate Professor, 1963. Author of *Shell model calculations for the low energy nuclear photo effect in Be*[9] (unpublished doctoral dissertation, 1956); "The relativistic theory of astronomical observation" (with J. Strathdee), *Proceedings of Royal Society of London* (1959).

RICHARD P. MCKEON, born April 26, 1900, Union Hill, N.J. He was educated at Columbia University (1917-22, A.B., M.A., Ph.D.) and the University of Paris (1923-5). He has taught philosophy at Columbia University (1925-35) and the University of Chicago, where he is Distinguished Service Professor of Philosophy and Greek. He has been Visiting Professor of Philosophy at the University of Arkansas, Baroda University (India), and Yale University. He is author of *The Philosophy of Spinoza, Selections from Mediaeval Philosophers*, 2 vols., *The Basic Works of Aristotle, Introduction to Aristotle, Freedom and History, Thought, Action and Passion, The Freedom to Read* (with Robert K. Merton and Walter Gellhorn), and the *Edicts of Asoka* (with N. A. Nikam).

ERNAN MC MULLIN, born October 13, 1924, Donegal, Ireland. B.Sc., Maynooth College, 1945; B.D., 1948; ordained priest, 1949. Scholar in theoretical physics, Dublin Institute for Advanced Studies, 1949-50; Ph.D. in philosophy, University of Louvain, 1954. Instructor in Philosophy, University of Notre Dame, 1954. National Science Foundation grant for work in philosophy of science, Yale University, 1957-9; Assistant Professor of philosophy, University of Notre Dame, 1959- . Translator of *Contemporary European Thought and Christian Faith* (A. Dondeyne, 1958). Articles include: "Cosmology", *Philosophical Studies* (Maynooth, 1954); "The philosophy of nature", *ibid.* (1955); "Realism and modern cosmology", *Proc. Amer. Cath. Phil. Assoc.* (1955); "Critique of the temporality argument for hylomorphism" in *Readings in the Philosophy of Nature* (1957); "The analytic approach to philosophy", *Proc. Amer. Cath. Phil. Assoc.* (1960); "Cosmologia", *Philosophical Studies* (1961); "Galileo Galilei", *Collier's Encyclopedia* (1962).

CHARLES W. MISNER, born June 13, 1932, Jackson, Michigan. B.S., University of Notre Dame, 1952; Ph.D. (Physics), Princeton University, 1957. Instructor, Assistant Professor, Princeton University 1956-63; Associate Professor of Physics, University of Maryland, 1963- . Alfred P. Sloan Foundation Research Fellow, 1958-62. Recent articles include: "Geometrodynamics" (with J. A. Wheeler), *Annals of Physics* (1957), "The Dynamics of General Relativity" (with R. Arnowitt and S. Deser) in *Gravitation: An Introduction to Current Research* (ed. Witten, 1962).

HARRY A. NIELSEN, born 1924, Bridgeport, Conn. A.B., Rutgers, 1949; M.A., University of Connecticut, 1952; Ph.D., University of Nebraska, 1955. Taught at Pennsylvania State University, University of Illinois; Assistant Professor of Philosophy, University of Notre Dame, 1958; Associate Professor, 1963. Recent articles include: "Sampling and the problem of induction", *Mind* (1959); "Kant's mathematical antinomies", *New Scholasticism* (1960); "Language and the philosophy of nature", *Proc. Amer. Cath. Phil. Assoc.* (1960).

JOSEPH OWENS, C.Ss.R., born April 17, 1908, Saint John, N.B. M.S.D. (in philosophy) 1951, Pontifical Institute of Mediaeval Studies. Taught at St. Alphonsus Seminary, Woodstock, Ont.; Academia Alfonsiana, Rome; Assumption University of Windsor; and Pontifical Institute of Mediaeval Studies, Toronto. Author of *The Doctrine of Being in the Aristotelian Metaphysics* (1951); *St. Thomas and the*

Future of Metaphysics (1957); *A History of Ancient Western Philosophy* (1959);
An Elementary Christian Metaphysics (1963).

RICHARD RORTY, born October 4, 1931, New York, N.Y. B.A., University of Chicago,
1949; Ph.D., Yale University, 1956. Taught at Yale and at Wellesley. Presently
Assistant Professor of Philosophy at Princeton University. Recent articles include:
"The limits of reductionism" in *Experience, Existence and the Good* (ed. I. C.
Lieb, 1961); "Realism, categories, and the 'linguistic turn' ", *International Philo-
sophical Quarterly* (1962).

KENNETH M. SAYRE, born August 13, 1928, Scottsbluff, Nebraska. A.B., 1952, Grinnell
College, M.A., 1954; Ph.D. 1958, Harvard University. Staff member Lincoln
Laboratory 1956-8; Research Scientist, Sylvania Electric Co., Inc., 1959; Consultant,
Lincoln Laboratory, 1961; Instructor and Assistant Professor of Philosophy, University of Notre Dame, 1958- ; Director of National Science Foundation study of
mechanical simulation, 1962- . Author of articles in *Mind, Methodos, Révue
Philosophique de Louvain, Philosophical Studies* (Maynooth), and of publications
in the areas of Human Factors and Systems Analysis; co-editor of *The Modeling
of Mind* (forthcoming, 1963).

WILFRID SELLARS, born May 12, 1912, Ann Arbor, Michigan. Attended Lycée Louis
le Grand, 1929-30; B.A., 1933, University of Michigan; M.A., 1934, University of
Buffalo; 1937-8, Harvard University; M.A., 1940, Oxford University. Taught at
State University of Iowa, 1938-46 (on leave, 1943-6); University of Minnesota,
1946-58; Yale University, 1958-63; University of Pittsburgh, 1963-. Co-editor of
Readings in Philosophical Analysis (with Herbert Feigl), 1949; *Readings in Ethical
Theory* (with John Hospers), 1952; Author of *Perception, Science and Reality*
(1963). Founder and co-editor (with Herbert Feigl) of *Philosophical Studies*.

JOHN E. SMITH, born May 27, 1921, Brooklyn, New York. B.A., 1942, Columbia University; B.D., 1945, Union Theological Seminary, N.Y.; Ph.D., Columbia University, 1948. Instructor, Religion and Philosophy, Vassar College, 1945-6; Instructor
in Philosophy, Barnard College, Columbia University, 1946-8; Assistant Professor,
1948-52; Assistant Professor of Philosophy, Yale University, 1952-5; Morse Fellow,
Heidelberg University, 1955-6; Associate Professor, Yale, 1956-9; Professor of
Philosophy, 1959 . Also taught at University of Michigan, Union Theological
Seminary. Dudleian Lecturer, Harvard University, 1960; Research Associate, Ford
Humanities Project, Princeton University; Editorial Board, *The Monist.* Author of
Royce's Social Infinite (1950); *Value Convictions and Higher Education* (1958);
Reason and God (1961); *The Spirit of American Philosophy* (1963). Translation
R. Kroner, *Kant's Weltanschauung* (1956); Ed. J. Edwards, *Treatise Concerning
Religious Affections* (1959).

JAMES ATHANASIUS WEISHEIPL, O.P., born July 3, 1923, Oshkosh, Wisconsin. Ph.L.,
1947; S.T.Lr., 1950, River Forest, Ill.; Ph.D. in philosophy, Pont. Institute "Angeli-
cum", Rome, 1953; D.Phil. (Oxon.) in history, Oxford University, 1957. Lecturer
in natural philosophy, St. Thomas College, Hawkesyard, Staffs., England, 1950-2;
Instructor in theology, St. Xavier College, Chicago, 1949, 1953, 1957-62; Professor
of the History of Philosophy, Pont. Inst. of Philosophy, River Forest, 1957- .
Bursar-Archivist of the Albertus Magnus Lyceum, 1961- ; Secretary-General of
the Thomist Association, 1962- ; President of the American Catholic Philosophical
Association, 1963-4. Editor, *Reality,* 1960- ; *The Dignity of Science* (Festschrift),
1961. Author of *Nature and Gravitation* (1955), *Development of Physical Theory
in the Middle Ages* (London, 1959; New York, 1960); "The Sermo Epinicius

ascribed to Thomas Bradwardine" (with H. A. Oberman), *Archives d'hist. doctr. et lit. du M-A.* (1959); "The Place of John Dumbleton in the Merton School", *Isis* (1959); "The Problemata Determinata XLIII ascribed to Albertus Magnus", *Mediaeval Studies* (1960); "The Evolution of Scientific Method" (in press).

ALLAN B. WOLTER, O.F.M., born November 24, 1913, Peoria, Illinois. M.A., 1942; Ph.D., 1947, Catholic University of America; Lector Generalis, 1954, Franciscan Institute, St. Bonaventure University. Taught chemistry, biology and philosophy at Our Lady of Angels Seminary, Cleveland, 1943-5; ordinary associate professor of philosophy, *ibid.,* and visiting associate professor at Franciscan Institute, 1946-51; ordinary professor, Franciscan Institute, 1952-62; visiting professor at Catholic University of America, 1962-3. President of American Catholic Philosophical Association, 1957-8. Associate editor of *The New Scholasticism,* 1949-51; Editor of *Franciscan Studies,* 1949-52; Editor of *Franciscan Institute Publications,* Philosophy Series, 1946-62; Editorial board of *The Encyclopedia of Philosophy.* Author of *The Transcendentals and their Function in the Metaphysics of Duns Scotus* (1946); *The Book of Life* (1954); *Summula Metaphysicae* (1958); *Life in God's Love* (1958); *Duns Scotus: Philosophical Writings* (1962).

ARTHUR E. WOODRUFF, born August 18, 1928, New Haven, Conn. B.A., 1949; M.S., 1951, Yale University; Ph.D. in physics 1959, University of Rochester. Instructor, 1955-7; Assistant Professor, 1959- in Physical Sciences in the College, University of Chicago. National Science Foundation Faculty Fellow in the Department of the History of Science and Medicine, Yale University, 1962-3. Co-editor of the *Proceedings of the Fourth Annual Rochester Conference on High-Energy Physics, 1954.* Author of "Action at a Distance in Nineteenth Century Electrodynamics", *Isis,* to be published.

Index of Names